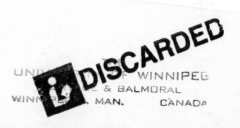

EXPERIMENTS IN PHYSIOLOGY AND BIOCHEMISTRY

Volume 3

EXPERIMENTS IN PHYSIOLOGY AND BIOCHEMISTRY

Edited by G. A. KERKUT

Department of Physiology and Biochemistry, University of Southampton, Southampton, England

Volume 3

ACADEMIC PRESS
London and New York
1970

ACADEMIC PRESS INC. (LONDON) LTD
Berkeley Square House
Berkeley Square,
London, W1X 6BA

U.S. edition published by
ACADEMIC PRESS INC.
111 Fifth Avenue,
New York, New York 10003

Library of Congress Catalog Card Number: 67–30765
SBN 12-404653-3

PRINTED IN GREAT BRITAIN BY
ADLARD & SON LIMITED, DORKING, SURREY

Contributors

M. H. APRISON, *The Institute of Psychiatric Research and Departments of Psychiatry and Biochemistry, Indiana University Medical Center, Indianapolis, Indiana, U.S.A.* (pp. 31 and 39)

JOHN CURLING, *Pharmacia Fine Chemicals AB, Uppsala, Sweden* (p. 417)

J. D. DUDAR, *Department of Physiology and Biophysics, Dalhousie University, Halifax, Nova Scotia, Canada* (p. 341)

BARBARA J. EXCELL, *Department of Physiology, Queen Elizabeth College, University of London, England* (p. 211)

MILTON FINGERMAN, *Department of Biology, Tulane University, New Orleans, Louisiana, U.S.A.* (p. 161)

ALAN R. FREEMAN, *Department of Physiology, Rutgers Medical School, New Brunswick, New Jersey, U.S.A.* (p. 161)

C. J. HANCOCK, *The Institute of Psychiatric Research and Departments of Psychiatry and Biochemistry, Indiana University Medical Center, Indianapolis, Indiana, U.S.A.* (p. 39)

ERNST G. HUF, *Departments of Medicine and Physiology, Medical College of Virginia, Health Sciences Division, Virginia Commonwealth University, Richmond, Virginia, U.S.A.* (p. 49)

DAVID R. JONES, *Department of Zoology, Bristol University, Bristol, England* (p. 233)*

R. H. LUMB, *Department of Biology, University of South Carolina, Columbia, South Carolina, U.S.A.* (p. 365)†

J. P. MONJARDINO, *Department of Molecular Virology, The Imperial Cancer Research Fund, London, England* (p. 333)

BARBARA MORELAND, *Department of Biochemistry, Guy's Hospital Medical School, London, England* (p. 1)

RALPH A. PAX, *Department of Zoology, Michigan State University, East Lansing, Michigan, U.S.A.* (p. 351)

JACK L. RATLIFF, *Naval Hospital, National Naval Medical Center, Bethesda, Maryland, U.S.A.* (p. 295)

PAUL O. SCHEIE, *Department of Biophysics, The Pennsylvania State University, University Park, Pennsylvania, U.S.A.* (p. 181)

* Present address: Department of Zoology, University of British Columbia, Vancouver, British Columbia, Canada.

† Present address: Western Carolina University, Cullowkee, North Carolina, U.S.A.

R. P. SHANK, *The Institute of Psychiatric Research and Departments of Psychiatry and Biochemistry, Indiana University Medical Center, Indianapolis, Indiana, U.S.A.* (p. 31)

ROBERT G. SHERMAN, *Department of Zoology, Michigan State University, East Lansing, Michigan, U.S.A.* (p. 351)

THOMAS C. SMITH, *Departments of Medicine and Physiology, Medical College of Virginia, Health Sciences Division, Virginia Commonwealth University, Richmond, Virginia, U.S.A.* (p. 49)

J. C. SZERB, *Department of Physiology and Biophysics, Dalhousie University, Halifax, Nova Scotia, Canada* (p. 341)

L. G. TATE, *Department of Biology, University of South Carolina, Columbia, South Carolina, U.S.A.* (p. 365)

CHARLES O. WATLINGTON, *Departments of Medicine and Physiology, Medical College of Virginia, Health Sciences Division, Virginia Commonwealth University, Richmond, Virginia, U.S.A.* (p. 49)

D. C. WATTS, *Department of Biochemistry, Guy's Hospital Medical School, London, England* (p. 1)

L. T. WIMER, *Department of Biology, University of South Carolina, Columbia, South Carolina, U.S.A.* (p. 365)

Preface to Volume 1

The easiest way of learning how to perform an experiment is to watch someone else demonstrating it and then, using the same equipment, to try to copy the procedure. If one fails the first time one can watch again then repeat the process; any further failures can be corrected by being shown precisely what has gone wrong. For most experiments this is the best method of learning; however, it is often impossible to follow this procedure because the specific methods are not easily available in the laboratory where one is working.

Another system is to read through a series of instructions and attempt to follow them out. This is more difficult because the writer often infers practical experience not possessed by the reader. Furthermore, there may be minor practical details that are not immediately appreciated either by the reader or the writer. Nevertheless, this is the most commonly used method of learning how to conduct an experiment, and the work published in the scientific journals provides the necessary information and stimulus.

However, it is often difficult to follow experimental procedure from the published account in a scientific paper. This is frequently the fault of an editorial system which considers the "materials and methods" to be less important than the "results and conclusion", and most authors are persuaded to present these sections in a very condensed form.

The present volume is the first of a series in which it is hoped to supply sufficient practical details to enable the reader to follow and carry out the experiments for himself. The information is presented in detail, though possibly there may be too much detail for some people and not enough for others. Initially, only those experiments that could be performed in three hours were selected for the present volume. However, it was felt that there were also many experiments that would take longer in time but which could be broken down into smaller periods and so fit in with a rather more liberal practical programme. It is intended that at a later date the three-hour class type of experiments will be collected from this and subsequent volumes and published separately.

I should welcome suggestions from authors for future contributions. A detailed scheme for the arrangement of material is presented on p. xi. Such a lay-out is only tentative and can be modified according to the particular needs of individual experiments.

It is hoped that the body of practical information to be presented in this series will help to spread skill and experience from one Laboratory to another.

DEPARTMENT OF PHYSIOLOGY AND BIOCHEMISTRY   G. A. KERKUT
UNIVERSITY OF SOUTHAMPTON
ENGLAND

March 1968

Note on Vivisection

All experimentalists should note that most countries have rules and regulations concerning that performance of experiments on living animals.

In England, Scotland and Wales it is necessary that any experiments carried out on vertebrate animals should be performed in a Government licensed laboratory, by persons licensed to carry out the experiments, under the supervision and guidance of licensed persons. Failure to do this may bring about legal proceedings against the experimentalists.

The exact legal situation differs according to the country where the experiments are being carried out, but in all cases students are advised to ask their instructors for specific information.

Guiding Principles in the Care and Use of Animals

Approved by the Council of the American
Physiological Society

Only animals that are lawfully acquired shall be used in this laboratory and their retention and use shall be in every case in strict compliance with state and local laws and regulations.

Animals in the laboratory must receive every consideration for their bodily comfort; they must be kindly treated, properly fed and their surroundings kept in a sanitary condition.

Appropriate anesthetics must be used to eliminate sensibility to pain during operative procedures. Where recovery from anesthesia is necessary during the study, acceptable technic to minimize pain must be followed. Curarizing agents are not anesthetics. Where the study does not require recovery from anesthesia, the animal must be killed in a humane manner at the conclusion of the observations.

The postoperative care of animals shall be such as to minimize discomfort and pain and in any case shall be equivalent to accepted practices in schools of Veterinary Medicine.

When animals are used by students for their education or the advancement of science such work shall be under the direct supervision of an experienced teacher or investigator. The rules for the care of such animals must be the same as for animals used for research.

Brand Names

Often in the experiment, a piece of equipment will be referred to by its trade, manufacturer's or supplier's name. It may be that you do not have this specific piece of *named* equipment in stock but that you have an equivalent or alternative make. In almost all cases there is nothing "magic" about the specified brand. It is mentioned because the author used it. When in doubt, it is advised that you carry out a trial experiment on your own equipment. This may be preferable to ordering the equipment BRAND X from your suppliers and finding when it is delivered some three months later that it is more expensive and worse than the model that you already have in the laboratory.

Suggestions for Future Contributors

These volumes will provide full details of methods and specific experiments on the biochemistry and physiology of animals. It is intended that they will fill the gap that has been made by the restricted amount of space that journals provide to the "Materials and Methods" section of papers.

Where possible each account should provide very full experimental details so that:

(1) Research workers and advanced students will be able to perform the experiments with the minimum of difficulty.

(2) Technicians will know what equipment to set out and which chemical solutions will be required.

It will help if the material can be presented as a series of separate but linked experiments so that the reader will realize the precise task involved in each experiment. In some cases it may be necessary to give details as to how to construct a piece of equipment and how to test it. This would then be equivalent to an "experiment".

A *suggested* plan of the account is as follows though the authors can, where necessary, alter the layout to suit the particular case.

(1) Title of experiments.

(2) General principles that the experiments and methods will illustrate.

(3) Title of specific experiment.

(4) Apparatus required.

(5) Animals required.

(6) Chemical solutions required. Please give solutions in terms of g/ml instead of molarity of solutions.

(7) Experimental details. These should be very full, in numbered paragraphs, with diagrams where this will help show specific equipment, dissections technique, manipulative methods, etc. The authors should not assume too much "know-how" on the part of the reader. The reader may be an expert, but in a slightly different field and these experiments are to help him extend his technique.

(8) Sample results. These should be edited labelled traces, titration readings, tables, graphs, etc., together with full calculation of the result. The worker should see from these records exactly the sort of result that he should be able to obtain for himself.

(9) Trouble shooting. Notes about what can go wrong with the experiment. What to check first if the experiment is unsuccessful.

(10) Further ideas about experiments that can be carried out with this equipment.

(11) Bibliography. Further reading with notes as to the significance of the selected references. Full titles to papers and books should be given together with first and last page references.

There is no strict limitation as to number of words or figures, though authors are asked to be as concise as is concomitant with clarity.

Contents

Exp. in Physiol. and Biochem. (1970). 3, 1–30.

1 | An Investigation of the Distribution and Properties of Some Phosphagen Phosphotransferases

D. C. WATTS and BARBARA MORELAND

Department of Biochemistry, Guy's Hospital Medical School, London, England

INTRODUCTION

The function of phosphagen phosphotransferases is thought to be to provide a store of readily available energy for cellular metabolism. They are found particularly in muscle, where they may form as much as 5% w/v of the water-soluble proteins, but also occur in other tissues such as brain and thyroid. Because it is easy to obtain from a wide variety of animals, the phosphagen phosphotransferase of muscle is particularly convenient for a comparative study. The general enzyme reaction, which requires magnesium ions is:

$$\text{guanidine} + \text{ATP/Mg} \underset{\text{pH 7·0}}{\overset{\text{pH 8·5}}{\rightleftharpoons}} \text{phosphagen} + \text{ADP/Mg}$$

Seven different guanidines may act as substrates and these, together with the corresponding phosphagens, are shown in Table I.

Of the phosphotransferases studied, those for arginine, creatine and glycocyamine are highly specific for their individual substrates. Those for taurocyamine, hypotaurocyamine, opheline and lombricine tend to be able to use all four of these substrates but show a particularly high activity with one of them. As only taurocyamine is readily obtainable, this property can be turned to advantage and taurocyamine used to test for general activity with the guanidinoethane group of enzymes (Table I).

The known distribution of phosphagen phosphotransferases together with their approximate molecular weights is shown in Table II. Individual animals have never been found to contain more than two (or in the annelids, three) different phosphotransferases. It is thought that the most evolutionarily primitive enzyme is the arginine kinase with a molecular weight of 40 000. In the course of evolution this dimerized to give an arginine kinase with a molecular weight of 80 000. At the same time it gave rise to an enzyme with

B

TABLE I

Natural substrates of the phosphagen phosphotransferases

GUANIDINE   PHOSPHAGEN

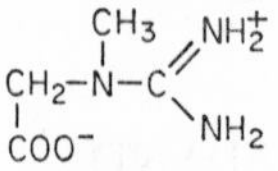

creatine   phosphocreatine

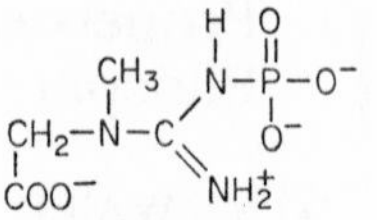

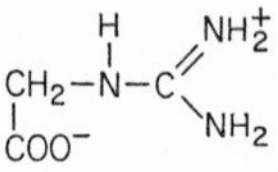

glycocyamine (guanidinoacetic acid)   phosphoglycocyamine

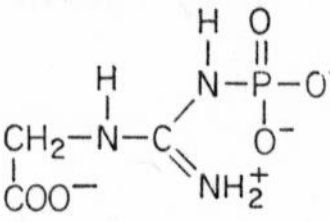

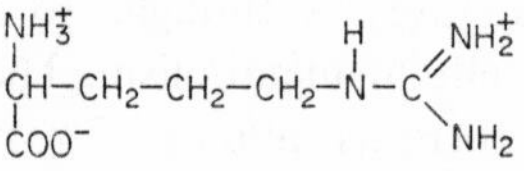

arginine   phosphoarginine

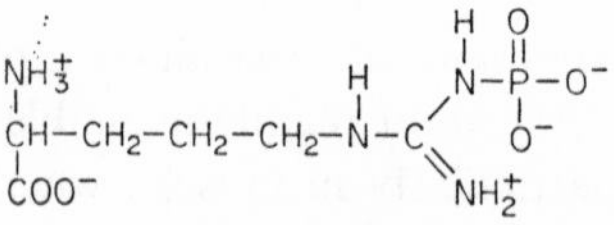

Substrates containing the guanidinoethane grouping

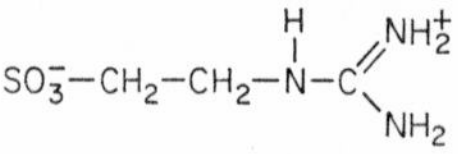

taurocyamine   phosphotaurocyamine

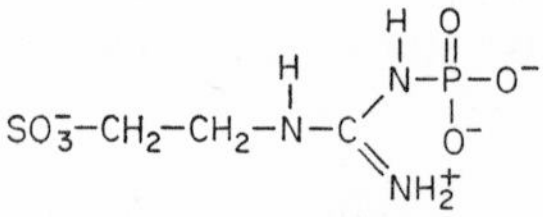

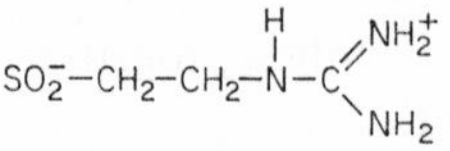

hypotaurocyamine   phosphohypotaurocyamine

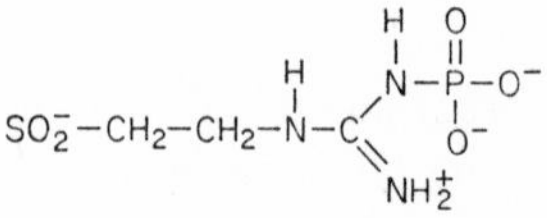

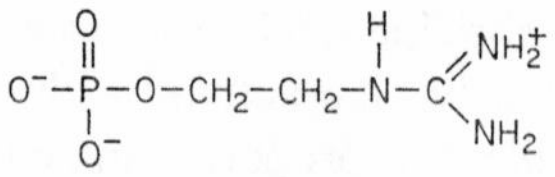

opheline   phospho-opheline

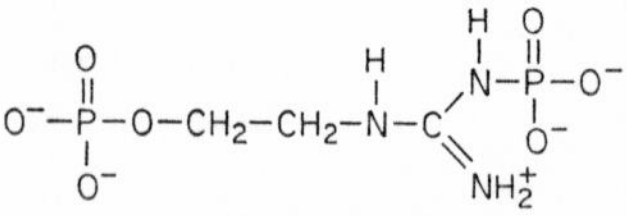

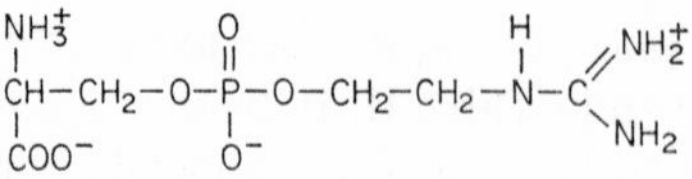

lombricine   phospholombricine

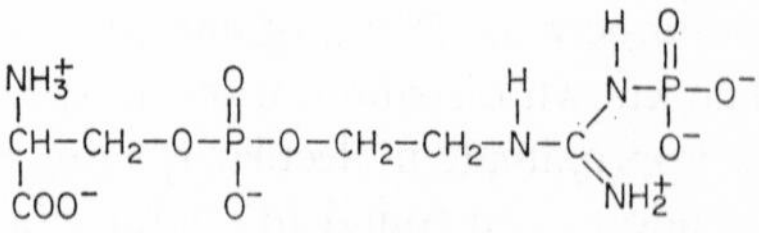

changed specificity—creatine phosphotransferase. So far a 40 000 molecular weight creatine kinase has not been found (Table II) so that evolution to form a dimer may have preceded the change in substrate specificity. In the marine annelids the specificity changes seem to have "gone wild" and all the phosphagens shown in Table I have been found. In contrast, in the terrestrial annelids only taurocyamine phosphotransferase has been found. However,

TABLE II

Distribution of the phosphagen phosphotransferases and their molecular weights

Group	Phosphotransferase	Approximate molecular weight
Protozoa	Arginine	80 000
Porifera	Arginine	?
Coelenterata	Arginine	?
Annelida		
Oligochaeta	Taurocyamine	80 000
Polychaeta	All seven enzymes	80 000 and 160 000
Platyhelminthes	Arginine	?
Arthropoda		
Crustacea	Arginine	40 000
Insecta	Arginine	40 000
Arachnida	Arginine	38 000
Myriapoda	?	?
Mollusca	Arginine	40 000*
Echinodermata		
Echinoidea	Arginine, Creatine	80 000
Ophiuroidea	Creatine	90–140 000?
Holothuroidea	Arginine	80 000
Asteroidea	Arginine	80 000
Crinoidea	Arginine	80 000
Tunicata	Arginine, Creatine	80 000
Protochordata	Arginine, Creatine?	?
Vertebrata	Creatine	80 000

* Eulamellibranchs and *Patella vulgata* also have an 80 000 mol. wt. enzyme.

only a handful of the living invertebrate species have so far been investigated and the suggested patterns of enzyme evolution may need to be revised when more information becomes readily available. The experiments described here are aimed to find out four things:

1. The type of phosphagen phosphotransferase the animal contains in its muscle.

2. If a particular extract contains more than one enzyme activity is this the product of one enzyme or more than one enzyme?

3. Its approximate molecular weight.

4. If the muscle contains two or more phosphotransferases, whether these can be distinguished by their electrophoretic mobility, or if there is only one enzyme, whether this has more than one electrophoretically distinct component (isoenzymes or multiple forms).

In this way it is possible to make a real contribution to our understanding of the distribution and evolution of an enzyme which appears to be essential for muscular activity.

MEASUREMENT OF PHOSPHOTRANSFERASE ACTIVITIES

Apparatus

1. Conical glass 15 ml centrifuge tubes (for assay).
2. Constriction pipettes, 0·25, 0·2, 0·1, 0·05 ml.
3. Graduated pipettes, 1·0 ml.
4. Bulb pipettes, 2·0, 1·0 ml.
5. Colorimeter with red (650 mμ) and yellow-green (540 mμ) filters.
6. Waterbath at 30°.
7. Crushed ice.
8. Small mortars and pestles.
9. Centrifuge, preferably medium speed refrigerated with 15 ml plastic centrifuge tubes (see item 10).
10. Ordinary low speed bench centrifuge (not always required or also use as an alternative to 9).
11. Balance, preferably three place.
12. Stop-clock or interval timer.
13. Boiling waterbath.
14. Rough balance for weighing muscle, 1–5 g (not essential).
15. Dialysis equipment (see Fig. 1).

Reagents

All solutions are made up in distilled or deionized water.

Buffers. (a) For extraction and assay. The best buffers for this purpose are glycylglycine or bicine (*N,N* bis(2-hydroxyethyl)glycine) but as these are expensive suitable alternatives are glycine or tris (*N*-tris-(hydroxymethyl)-methylamine). AnalaR grades should be used or the commercial grade first recrystallized from 1 mM EDTA.

(i) Glycine/NaOH, pH 8·8 and I = 0·1 at 25°. Dissolve 70·05 g of glycine in water, add 100 ml of 1·0N-NaOH and dilute to 1 litre.

(ii) Tris/HCl, pH 8·6 and I = 0·05 at 25°. Dissolve 23·49 g of Tris base in water, add 50 ml of 1·0 N-HCl and dilute to 1 litre.

In the following account it is assumed that Tris buffer is used. If glycine buffer is used make any pH adjustments necessary to 8·8.

(b) Stopping buffer for assay. Dissolve 9·32 g of sodium chloroacetate in approx. 400 ml of distilled water, adjust to pH 2·5 with AnalaR 60% perchloric acid and dilute to 500 ml.

Guanidine Solutions. Shelf life of solutions at least one month in the absence of bacterial contamination (may be sterilized by boiling). Arginine solution can be stored in the refrigerator but the others may crystallize out in the cold.

(a) Creatine (mol. wt. 131·14), 40 mM. Dissolve 0·525 g in 50 ml of Tris buffer and dilute to 100 ml.

(b) Glycocyamine (mol. wt. 117·09), 40 mM. Dissolve 0·468 g in 50 ml of Tris buffer and dilute to 100 ml.

(c) Arginine HCl (mol. wt. 210·68), 40 mM. Dissolve 0·834 g in 50 ml Tris buffer, adjust to pH 8·5 with approx. 1M-NaOH and dilute to 100 ml.

(d) Taurocyamine (mol. wt. 167·19), 40 mM. Dissolve 0·668 g in 50 ml Tris buffer and dilute to 100 ml.

Preparation of Taurocyamine. This guanidine is unfortunately still not available commercially but the synthesis, which is done in two steps, is quite easy.

(a) Preparation of S-ethylthiourea hydrobromide

$$S=C\begin{array}{c}NH_2\\NH_2\end{array} + C_2H_5Br \rightarrow C_2H_5-S-C\begin{array}{c}NH\\NH_2\end{array}.\,HBr$$

A mixture of powdered thiourea (150 g), ethyl bromide (250 g) and absolute ethanol (200 ml) is refluxed (efficient condenser) in a 1 litre round-bottom flask for 3 h at 55–65° (waterbath). Shake occasionally until all the thiourea dissolves.

Replace the reflux by a downward distillation condenser and remove the excess ethyl bromide and ethanol by heating under vacuum (water pump). During distillation raise the temperature of the waterbath to boiling.

Pour the residual oil into a beaker (500 ml) and allow to crystallize. Pulverize the cake and dry in a desiccator. Yield 340–360 g.

The product is stable for several months if kept cool and under vacuum.

(b) Preparation of taurocyamine

$$C_2H_5-S-C\begin{array}{c}NH\\NH_2\end{array}.\,HBr + HSO_3-CH_2-CH_2NH_2 \rightarrow$$

$$HSO_3^- - CH_2-CH_2-NH-C\begin{array}{c}NH.HBr\\NH_2\end{array} + C_2H_5SH$$

Since the smell of ethyl mercaptan (C_2H_5SH) is extremely unpleasant this reaction *must* be carried out in the fume cupboard.

In a 500 ml conical flask cooled in an ice-bath place ethylthiourea HBr (32 g) and add 2N-NaOH (87 ml) and stir until the solid has dissolved.

Dissolve taurine (24 g) in the minimum quantity of hot water (about 90 ml). The solution should be acid (about pH 3·0) to universal test paper. Add the taurine solution rapidly to the mixture in the conical flask with stirring and when the temperature reaches 25° (not critical) allow the mixture to stand at this temperature for 2 h.

Transfer the mixture to a 500 ml r.b. flask and concentrate under vacuum by warming in a waterbath at 45–50° to two-thirds of the original volume (about 120 ml).

The solution is then filtered, if necessary (still in the fume cupboard), and left overnight at 0° in a firmly stoppered vessel.

Filter off the crystals (fume cupboard) and wash with ice-cold distilled water (20 ml) and ice-cold ethanol (20 ml of 98%).

The solid is sucked dry and redissolved in the minimum quantity of warm water (about 40 ml), refiltered if necessary (warm filter) and cooled in an ice-bath when crystallization begins at once.

Recrystallize again from hot water. Yield 15 g, m.p. 265°.

ATP/Magnesium Sulphate Solution. (a) Stock ATP solution (mol. wt. for trihydrate, disodium salt, 605·0) 20 mM. Dissolve 1·210 g in 50 ml of Tris buffer and dilute to 100 ml. Store deep frozen in small batches.

(b) Stock magnesium sulphate solution (mol. wt. of septahydrate 246·5) 80 mM. Dissolve 1·972 g in water and make up to 100 ml.

To use mix 4 parts of solution (a) with 1 part of solution (b). The mixture should be kept on ice until required and used within 2 or 3 days.

Assay Reagents. (a) Acid molybdate reagent. Dissolve 10 g of finely powdered ammonium molybdate in warm water, cool, add 160 ml of AnalaR 60% perchloric acid and dilute to 1 litre.

(b) Reducing agent. Dissolve 12 g of sodium metabisulphite and 4·8 g of sodium sulphite ($7H_2O$) in about 50 ml of warm water. Add 0·2 g of 1-amino 2-naphthol 4-sulphonic acid (B.D.H. Chemicals Ltd., extra pure grade) and stir until dissolved before diluting to 100 ml. Filter twice through the same fine mesh filter paper and store in a black bottle in the refrigerator (storage life about 1 month).

(c) Standard potassium dihydrogen phosphate solution (mol. wt. 136·09). Dissolve 1·701 g in water and make up to 250 ml. Dilute 2 ml of this solution to 100 ml when 1 ml will contain 1 μ mole. The range of the phosphate assay is 0 to 0·5 μ mole per tube.

Biuret Reagent for Protein Determination. Place copper sulphate $5H_2O$ (1·5 g) and sodium potassium tartrate $4H_2O$ (6 g) in a *dry* 1 litre volumetric flask and dissolve *completely* in 500 ml of water. Add, with constant swirling, 300 ml of 10% w/v NaOH (this should preferentially be prepared from stock 65–70% w/v NaOH which has been allowed to stand in a container fitted with a CO_2 trap for about 3 weeks so that any carbonate is precipitated. Alternatively use freshly distilled water and work as rapidly as possible.) Make up to the mark and store in well-stoppered polythene or wax-lined bottles. Discard the reagent if a red or blackish precipitate occurs.

Preparation of Muscle Extracts

A list of animals suitable for investigation is given in Table III. Since these are all invertebrates, a simple way of killing is to cool the animal to 0° and then freeze by immersing for about 30 min in the deep freeze (-18 to $-20°$) or in an ice-salt mixture. A suitable piece of muscle (0·5–2·0 g) is dissected out, rapidly weighed and then pulverized (still in the frozen state) with acid-washed sand in a cold pestle and mortar. As the tissue begins to thaw, 5 volumes of cold Tris buffer, diluted $\times 50$ and made approx. 1 mM with mercaptoethanol (0·1 ml/litre), are slowly added and the grinding continued to give a smooth cream. The homogenate is then centrifuged at 25 000 g for 20 min at 5° in an M.S.E. High Speed 18 centrifuge (see note 2).

The supernatant is concentrated overnight by vacuum dialysis (Fig. 1) against 50–100 ml of the $50 \times$ diluted Tris buffer containing mercaptoethanol.

For subsequent analysis by starch gel electrophoresis a concentration of at least tenfold should be achieved. For enzyme assay, concentration is less important but if the extracts are very dilute difficulty may be experienced in determining the protein concentration. With some animal extracts a protein precipitate forms during dialysis. Since the volume is generally too small to centrifuge, if the supernatant cannot be withdrawn from above the precipitate then the precipitate should simply be ignored.

Notes on Pitfalls and Advice

1. Although homogenizing the muscle with sand is simple, it is relatively inefficient. The same job can be done more effectively using a sonic disintegrating homogenizer such as the Polytron ST 10 (obtainable from Northern Media Supply Ltd., 12 Blanket Row, Hull, England). Homogenization should be carried out for about 30 sec at half maximum speed in a 15 or 50 ml polypropylene centrifuge tube, according to the size of the sample, but with only 2 volumes of buffer. The homogenate can then be centrifuged without the need for transfer from one vessel to another.

2. Although a high speed refrigerated centrifuge is desirable, it is by no means essential and satisfactory results have been obtained using an ordinary

TABLE III *Suggestions for animals and assay conditions for the study of the distribution of phosphagen phosphotransferases*

Animal	Tissue	ATPase	Assay conditions Protein conc./tube (μg)	Incubation time (min)	*Keeping properties of dialysed extract at 4°
Crustacea					
1. *Homarus vulgaris* (lobster)	Tail or Claw muscle	Nil	0·5	10	Good
2. *Palaemon* spp. (prawn)	Tail muscle	Nil	0·4	10	Good
3. *Cancer pagurus* (edible crab)	Claw muscle	Nil	0·4	10	Good
4. *Carcinus maenas* (common shore crab)	Claw muscle	Nil	0·4	10	Good
Insecta					
5. *Blatta orientalis* (locust)	Thoracic muscle	Present	25·0	10	Good
Mollusca					
6. *Pecten maximus* (scallop)	Striated adductor	Present	5·0	10	Fair
7. *Patella vulgata* (limpet)	Foot	Present	8·0	10	Unreliable
8. *Cardium edule* (cockle)	Foot, Adductors	Present	10·0	10	Fair
Echinodermata					
9. *Echinus esculentus* (sea urchin)	Lantern muscle	Present	4·0	10	Fair
10. *Holothuria forskali* (sea cucumber)	Longitudinal muscle	Nil	4·0	10	Good
11. *Asterias rubens* (common starfish)	Tube feet	Nil	10·0	30	Good
Tunicata					
12. *Ciona intestinalis* (sea squirt)	Atrial muscle	Present	15·0	60	Fair
13. *Styella mammiculata* (sea squirt)	Atrial muscle	Present	17·5	60	Fair
Annelida					
14. *Myxicola infundibulum* (jelly tube worm)	Body wall	Present	100·0	30	Unreliable
15. *Nereis fucata* (commensal ragworm)	Body wall	Present	100·0	30	Unreliable
16. *Aphrodite aculeata* (sea mouse)	Body wall	Present	200·0	60	Unreliable
17. *Branchiomma vesiculosum* (fanworm)	Body wall	Present	100·0	30	Unreliable
18. *Nereis diversicolor* (oligochaeta)	Body wall	Present	100·0	30	Unreliable
19. *Lumbricus terrestris* (earthworm)	Body wall	Present	100·0	30	Unreliable

* Good means that a reasonable enzyme activity can still be measured after 1 week; fair means 2 or 3 days; unreliable means that activity may be lost within 36 hours (usually due to contamination by digestive juices) or may last several days. Animal No. 1–8, APT; 9, APT, CPT; 10–12, APT; 13, APT, CPT; 14, APT, GPT, Key to the phosphotransferases in the animals listed.

bench centrifuge for 20–30 min. However, as these tend to run hot it is advisable to spin for 5 min, cool the tube for 3 min in ice and then spin for another 5 min and so on until a reasonably clear solution is obtained. Fine comminuting devices such as the Polytron should not be used unless a high speed centrifuge is also available.

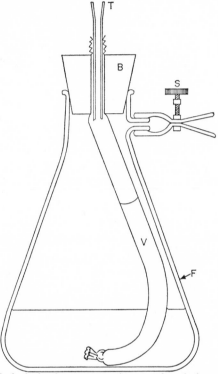

Fig. 1. Vacuum dialysis device for concentrating protein solutions. About 10 in. of 9/32 Visking dialysis tubing, V, is boiled for 5 min in 1mM EDTA, pH 7·0 (to remove heavy metals) and then rinsed in distilled water. One end is then twisted like a rope and a thumb knot tied in it and pulled tight. Test for watertightness by filling the sac with water and squeezing. There should be no leaks. Empty sac and thread the open end through a hole in a rubber bung, B (made with a no. 3 cork borer) which fits a 250 ml buchner flask, F. The tubing is sealed in the bung with a short length of glass tubing, T, about 7 mm external diameter, slightly tapered at one end and flared at the other. The dialysis sac is drawn over the glass tubing which is then pushed through the hole in the bung until the tapered end just protrudes. Connect a short length of pressure tubing to the side-arm of the flask which can be sealed with a screw clip, S. Put about 100 ml of cold buffer in the flask and firmly insert the bung carrying the dialysis sac. Connect the side-arm of the flask to a water-pump and evacuate to about 550 mm Hg or until the dialysis sac has swollen to nearly twice its normal diameter. Rapidly close the screw clip and detach from the pump. Invert the flask and check that there are no air bubbles coming in round the stopper or where the dialysis sac enters the bung. Introduce the protein solution into the dialysis sac with a hypodermic syringe which has a short length of fine bore polythene tubing attached to the needle. A 5 ml sample of extract should concentrate to about 0·5 ml in 15–18 h in the cold.

Determination of Protein Concentration

A sample of the concentrated protein extract, usually 0·05 ml, is added to 2 ml of Biuret reagent, mixed and the optical density (at 540 mμ or with a yellow-green filter, Ilford No. 625) measured after 5 min. Set the colorimeter

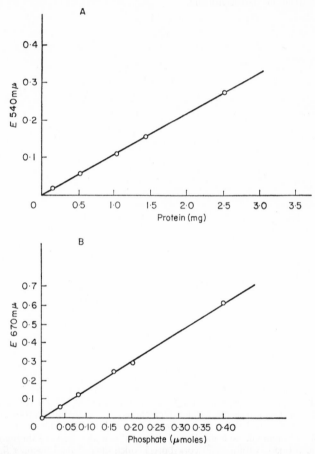

FIG. 2. Calibration curves showing the variation in optical density with the concentration in the appropriate assay of (A) Protein, and (B) Phosphate. Details of the assay procedures are given in the text. The curves shown here were obtained with a Gallenkamp Mk III colorimeter and a test tube cell of 1 cm pathlength.

to zero optical density using distilled water and measure the protein-Biuret solutions and a blank in which the protein is replaced by 0·05 ml of the dialysis buffer. Subtract the blank reading from each protein reading and determine the protein concentration from your calibration curve prepared with a protein solution of known concentration (Fig. 2). This gives the protein concentration in the 0·05 ml sample which you took originally. Multiply this value by 20 to get the protein concentration of the extract in mg/ml.

Notes on Pitfalls and Advice

1. If the total volume of 2·05 ml is too small to read in the colorimeter, this may be scaled up by taking double or treble the volumes. The solution must not be diluted.
2. If the protein concentration is low, it may be necessary to add more than 0·05 ml of muscle extract in order to obtain a reasonable reading on the colorimeter. Up to 0·25 ml of extract may be added but the measured optical density must be corrected for the change in total volume of the solution before subtracting the blank value.

    e.g.   0·2 ml of extract added to 2·0 ml of Biuret reagent
           Total volume = 2·2 ml
           Measured optical density = 0·18
           Optical density corrected for a volume of 2·05 ml

$$= \frac{0·18 \times 2·2}{2·05} = 0·193.$$

Assay for Enzyme Activities

An 0·05 ml sample of the suitably diluted extract (see Table III) is incubated in a 15 ml conical centrifuge tube with 0·25 ml of 0·04M guanidine base, pH 8·6–8·8, for 5 min at 30°. The reaction is started by the addition of 0·1 ml of ATP/MgSO$_4$ solution. After incubation for the appropriate time (see Table III), the reaction is stopped by the addition of 0·5 ml of ice-cold stopping buffer and the tube transferred to an ice bath. When assaying a number of tubes it is easiest to start the reaction of each tube in turn at half- or one-minute intervals (depending on your skill with the pipette) and, after the appropriate incubation time, stop the reaction and transfer the tubes to an ice-bath in the same order and at the same time intervals used in starting the reaction.

The phosphoguanidine is hydrolysed by heating the tube for exactly 1 min in a boiling waterbath and then returning the tube to the ice-bath. After 5 min, for temperature re-equilibration, the phosphate liberated is determined by the addition of 1 ml of acid molybdate reagent immediately followed by 0·1 ml of reducing agent. The phosphate colour is allowed to develop for 15 min at room temperature and optical density (650 mμ or red filter) determined. The reading obtained is converted to μ mole of phosphagen using the calibration curve obtained with standard phosphate solution (Fig. 2).

Controls should be set up with water instead of guanidine to determine the amount of ATPase in the extract (see note 3), and with water instead of

TABLE IV

Pipetting schedule for the determination of ATPase and phosphagen phosphotransferase activities in a crude muscle extract

Tube Number	Water	Muscle extract	Creatine	Glycocyamine	Arginine	Taurocyamine	ATP/Mg
1	—	0·05	0·25	—	—	—	0·1
2	—	0·05	—	0·25	—	—	0·1
3	—	0·05	—	—	0·25	—	0·1
4	—	0·05	—	—	—	0·25	0·1
5	0·25	0·05	—	—	—	—	0·1
6	0·25	—	0·25	—	—	—	0·1

Volumes should be pipetted with constriction pipettes, taking care to wipe the outside of the filled pipette before transferring the solution to a numbered tube.

enzyme (or using boiled enzyme) to determine the amount of inorganic phosphate in the ATP plus that released from the ATP by boiling.

A typical pipetting schedule is shown in Table IV.

Notes on Pitfalls and Advice

1. The procedure is described for an assay volume of 0·4 ml and a final volume for the colorimeter reading of 2·0 ml. These may be scaled up if necessary by simply multiplying all volumes by the appropriate factor. The only difficulty which may arise is that the hydrolysis time of the phosphagen may need to be increased, say to 1·25 min. If necessary, this can be checked by setting up a number of identical assay tubes and hydrolysing them at 100° for different periods of time. The hydrolysis time must not be prolonged unnecessarily or breakdown of ATP to ADP and inorganic phosphate will also occur.

2. If only a small increase in the final colorimeter volume is required (say from 2·0 to 2·5 ml), this can be achieved by simply adding 0·5 ml of water to the coloured solution in each tube just before reading in the colorimeter. This is possible because the phosphate colour closely obeys Beer's law and optical density is proportional to concentration. Excessive dilution may result in the colour being too weak to measure.

3. The hydrolysis of phosphocreatine is catalysed by acid molybdate so that boiling at 100° is not strictly necessary for creatine kinase assays. However, for acid molybdate catalysed hydrolysis the time between adding the reducing agent and reading in the colorimeter should be increased to 30 min. Hydrolysis of phosphoarginine, on the other hand, is not catalysed by acid molybdate. This provides an additional useful criterion by which these two phosphagens can be distinguished. A full account of the effect of acid molybdate on phosphagens can be found in Ennor and Morrison (1958).

4. If very high protein concentrations are used, a protein haze may form when the stopping buffer is added. If the haze is faint it can be ignored as a suitable control will be provided by the tube without guanidine. If the haze is pronounced the tube should be spun for 10 min in a bench centrifuge after the phosphagen has been hydrolysed and cooled. If conical centrifuge tubes have been used for the assay then the protein pellet can be ignored and it is not necessary to transfer the supernatant to a clean tube. Simply return the tube to the ice-bath and proceed with the assay but be careful not to shake the tube too vigorously when mixing in the acid molybdate and reducing agent.

Calculation of Specific Activity

The following worked calculation is based on results typical of those obtained in crustacean muscle extracts.

0·05 ml of the concentrated dialysed muscle extract gave an O.D. reading at 540 mμ of 0·13 in the Biuret protein estimation.

Reading the value off the protein calibration curve

O.D. of 0·13 $\equiv$ 1·2 mg of protein in the 0·05 ml sample

Protein concentration expressed per ml of extract

$$= 1·2 \times 20 = 24 \text{ mg/ml}$$

The amount of protein required in the assay for estimation of arginine phosphotransferase activity in crustacea is approximately 0·5 μg of protein for a 10 min incubation time. The volume of extract added to the reaction medium is 0·05 ml, therefore for 0·05 ml to contain 0·5 μg of protein, the concentrated extract was diluted 2400-fold.

0·01 ml of extract was diluted to 1 ml with Tris buffer and then 0·1 ml of this diluted again to 2·4 ml. 0·05 ml of this final diluted extract was incubated for 10 min at 30°C with 0·25 ml of arginine and 0·1 ml of ATP/Mg solution. At the end of the assay, the O.D. at 670 mμ was 0·38. Reading this value off the phosphate calibration curve

O.D. of 0·38 $\equiv$ 0·25 μ moles of phosphate

Under these conditions of assay, 0·25 μ moles of phosphate are transferred from ATP to arginine in 10 min at 30°C by 0·5 μg of protein. The value expressed as μ moles of phosphate transferred per minute per mg of protein

$$= 0·25 \times \frac{1}{10} \times \frac{1000}{0·5} = 50$$

This value is known as the specific activity of the muscle extract and is a useful way of comparing the relative enzyme activities of different extracts per 1 mg of protein as the unit of protein concentration.

Does an Extract with More than One Phosphotransferase Activity Contain More than One Enzyme?

This question can readily be resolved when it is realized that for one enzyme with more than one phosphotransferase activity the different guanidine substrates must all compete for the same substrate binding site on the enzyme. If there are two (or more) different enzymes then each will have its own specific binding site and the guanidine substrates will not compete. Hence if we test the activity of a muscle extract with two substrates added together, in the first case the measured activity will be no greater than that of the most active single substrate added alone while in the second case the measured activity will be approximately the sum of the activities found when the two substrates are added separately.

A pipetting schedule for an extract containing glycocyamine and tauro-cyamine phosphotransferase activities is shown in Table V. If the extract has three activities then it is necessary to test all the possible combinations in pairs. Thus for arginine, creatine and glycocyamine, it would be necessary to test arginine with creatine, creatine with glycocyamine and glycocyamine

TABLE V

Pipetting schedule and procedure for determining whether the presence of more than one phosphotransferase activity in an extract is caused by more than one enzyme

Tube number	Water	Muscle Extract	Glycocyamine	Taurocyamine	ATP/Mg
1	0·25	0·1	0·25	—	0·2
2	0·25	0·1	—	0·25	0·2
3	—	0·1	0·25	0·25	0·2
4	0·5	0·1	—	—	0·2

After incubation for the appropriate time the enzyme reaction is stopped with 1·0 ml of stopping buffer and the tube cooled in ice. The phosphagen is then hydrolysed for 75 sec in a boiling waterbath and the tube returned to the ice-bath. After 5 min the phosphate colour is developed by adding 2 ml of acid molybdate reagent immediately followed by 0·2 ml of reducing agent. The colour is allowed to develop for 15 min at room temperature before reading in the colorimeter. Details of the procedure are given in the section "Assay for Enzyme Activities" (page 11).

with arginine as well as controls containing each substrate separately and an ATPase blank with no guanidine.

The assay volumes given in Table V are twice the normal assay volume. However, the same phosphate calibration curve can be used and the resultant value multiplied by two to get the μ moles of phosphagen synthesized per assay tube.

DETERMINATION OF MOLECULAR WEIGHTS

Apparatus for Sephadex Gel Filtration

1. Fraction collector and tubes.
2. Peristaltic pump (optional see Methods section).
3. Column approx. 2·4 × 70 cm preferably with sinter disc with accessories shown in Fig. 3.
4. Aspirators, 2 l.
5. 2 ml hypodermic syringe and needle extended with fine polythene tube.
6. Equipment for assay procedure (p. 4).
7. Spectrophotometer measuring 280 mμ for determining the protein content of fractions. Alternatively the Biuret method can be used (p. 10).

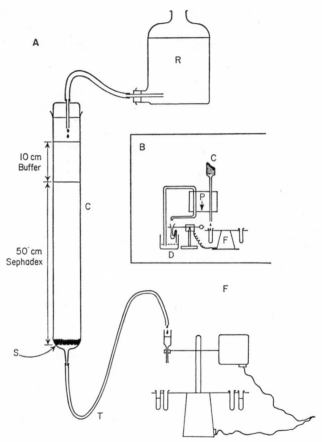

Fig. 3(A). Equipment for molecular weight determination by Sephadex gel filtration. Buffer from the reservoir, R, flows through the column, C, and then via a thin polythene tube, T, into the fraction collector, F. The Sephadex is retained in the column by a layer of fine glass beads resting on a sinter, S. Details of the method are given in the text. (B) Arrangement for collecting small fractions containing a high protein concentration. Effluent from the column, C, is pumped at a constant rate through the peristaltic pump, P, directly into the fraction collector, F. The fraction collector is operated by a separate line of dilute detergent, D, which is pumped from a beaker through the peristaltic pump into a siphon. The siphon discharges back into the beaker and simultaneously operates the fraction collector. In this way very small fractions can be collected without any risk of siphon blockage.

Reagents

1. Tris/KCl buffer. Dilute the Tris buffer, I 0·05 (see p. 4) 20-fold and add 7·4 g of KCl/litre (0·1M in KCl).
2. Standard proteins.
   (a) Cytochrome c (horse heart), mol. wt. 12 400.
Myoglobin (horse or sperm whale), mol. wt. 17 800.
   (b) β-lactoglobulin A, mol. wt. 36 500.
Ovalbumin, mol. wt. 45 000.
   (c) Serum albumin (bovine) mol. wt. 67 000 (this also contains about 10% of the dimer mol. wt. 134 000).
Creatine kinase (or rabbit muscle extract), mol. wt. 81 000.
γ-Globulins (human), mol. wt. 160 000.
One each of groups (a), (b) and (c) are required together with Blue Dextran (Pharmacia) mol. wt. approx. 2 000 000.

SEPHADEX GEL FILTRATION FOR THE ESTIMATION OF MOLECULAR WEIGHTS

For a full theoretical description of gel filtration, students should read Andrews (1964) or Andrews (1967).

Briefly, a mixture of proteins is applied to the top of a column packed with porous granules of cross-linked dextrans (Sephadex), fully equilibrated with buffer. The proteins are washed through the column with a steady flow of buffer and separation of the protein molecules depends on the extent to which they can penetrate into the pores of the Sephadex. The proteins emerge from the column in decreasing order of molecular size. The larger molecules, being unable to penetrate into the granules, will be washed straight through the column by the buffer stream and smaller molecules capable of entering right into the matrix of the granules will take proportionately longer to be flushed right out of the column. The technique can be used to determine molecular weights of proteins if the column is calibrated first by measuring the volume of buffer required to elute proteins of known molecular weight. A calibration curve can be drawn of the elution volume against the logarithm of the molecular weight of each protein. For Sephadex G-100, the calibration curve is linear for proteins of molecular weights in the range 10 000–150 000 (Fig. 5).

Method for Gel Filtration

A glass column, approx. 2·4 cm internal diameter and 60–70 cm in length, fitted at the lower end with a fine gauze or sintered glass disc, covered with a 1 cm layer of washed small glass beads is connected by a suitable length of thin polythene tubing (0·2 cm diameter) to a fraction collector as shown in Fig. 3A.

Fraction Collectors. (a) Those which measure 3 ml fractions by weight of solution or by drop-counting are more reliable for obtaining reproducible fraction sizes than those employing a siphon. The latter can frequently clog or overflow during separation runs with solutions containing viscous muscle proteins.

(b) If a 3 ml siphon has to be used, and a peristaltic pump with twin channels is available, the double flow system drawn diagrammatically in Fig. 3B overcomes this complication. The 3 ml siphon device which operates the fraction collector turntable is repeatedly filled by a closed flow system of dilute detergent which flows back into its own reservoir and the elution buffer from the column drips directly into the tubes on the fraction collector.

(c) If only a siphon fraction collector is available the siphon should be siliconized by pouring through it a solution of I.C.I. silicone M441 diluted 5-fold with petroleum ether (b.p. 60–80°). The silicone fluid is corrosive and rubber gloves should be worn for this operation. The siphon is then washed several times in distilled water and dried overnight in an oven at about 110–120°. This silicone coat greatly minimizes protein denaturation on the glass surface. The siphon can usually be used twice before recoating becomes necessary. To do this put the siphon in 5% w/v KOH in ethanol and bring just to the boil (take care, inflammable!). Allow to cool, remove the siphon and wash with tap and distilled water, finally drying before recoating with silicone solution.

Preparing the Sephadex Column. About 20 g of Sephadex G-100 is allowed to swell for two days in about 1 litre of the Tris buffer diluted 1 in 10, and made to 0·1M with KCl (7·4 g/litre). The slurry of Sephadex is then poured into the column while the buffer flows slowly out of the bottom so that the Sephadex settles to a depth of 50 cm, with a good horizontal surface on the top of the gel. The column is filled with buffer to 10–15 cm above the surface of the gel and a constant stream of Tris/KCl buffer of about 1 ml/min is then maintained through the column to keep the bed volume constant.

For calibration of the column, the buffer flow is temporarily stopped and 2 ml of Tris buffer containing 10 mg of horse myoglobin, 10 mg of ovalbumin and 0·1 ml of a 0·1% solution of Blue Dextran (Pharmacia Ltd.), or 10 mg of myoglobin and 10 mg of bovine serum albumen, is carefully layered on to the surface of the Sephadex column using a syringe with a length of thin polythene tubing attached to the needle so that it reaches to within 2–3 mm of the surface of the Sephadex. Avoiding the introduction of air bubbles, press the syringe gently so that a slow steady stream of protein runs on to the surface of the gel and forms a clean even layer. When all the sample has been loaded as a horizontal band on the surface of the gel the buffer flow is restarted and about 80 fractions are collected.

The highest molecular weight component, the Blue Dextran, will emerge with an elution volume of about 70–100 ml, equal to the void volume of the column used. For 3 ml fractions, this means that only fractions 28 onwards need be considered. The optical density of fractions 24–70 are measured at 280 mμ for protein estimation, or by the Biuret method (see p. 10) using 0·25 ml per assay, and the optical density value of the solution plotted against the fraction number (Fig. 4). The mid-point of each peak is taken as the elution volume for that protein and a calibration curve can be drawn of the elution volume plotted against the logarithm of the protein molecular weight (Fig. 5).

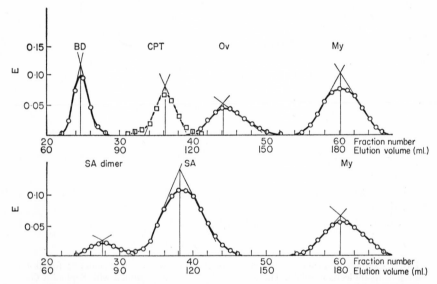

Fig. 4. Typical protein elution patterns from a Sephadex G-100 column set up as in Fig. 3. Ordinate; ○, protein concentration measured by absorption at 280 mμ, □, phosphotransferase activity. The standards used were: BD, Blue Dextran; CPT, creatine phosphotransferase (rabbit muscle extract); Ov, ovalbumin; My, myoglobin; SA, serum albumin; SA dimer, serum albumin dimer.

To determine the molecular weight of the phosphotransferases, a sample of the muscle extract containing about 5 mg of muscle protein is diluted to 2 ml with Tris/KCl buffer and 2 or 3 grains of sucrose added to increase the density of the sample. The elution characteristics of the Sephadex column can vary slightly between runs. For this reason, it is useful to include 5–10 mg of horse myoglobin with each sample of muscle extract loaded to check that the myoglobin peak emerges at the normal elution volume or to find the value of the small correction which may have to be applied to the elution volume to fit the calibration curve.

As before, about 80 fractions are collected from the time of restarting the buffer flow after loading the sample.

Samples are removed from each of the fractions numbered 30–45 for phosphotransferases of molecular weights thought to be in the 80 000 range and fractions 45–65 for 40 000 molecular weight phosphotransferases. For estimation of enzyme activity in the phosphate assay, 0·05 ml aliquots are

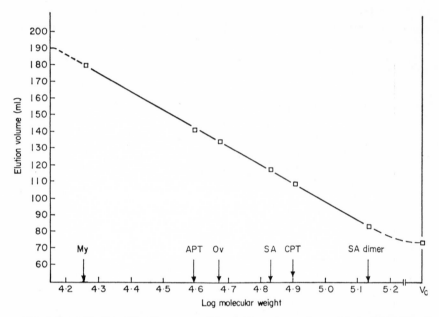

FIG. 5. Example of a calibration curve of the elution volume of a protein as a function of the log of its molecular weight. The curve shown here was obtained with Sephadex G-100 using the equipment shown in Fig. 3. APT, arginine phosphotransferase; V_0, void volume of BD. Other abbreviations as Fig. 4.

convenient with 10-min incubations for extracts with high enzyme specific activity, over 5 μ moles P/min/mg of protein and 30-min incubations for extracts with lower specific activities.

The value obtained for the enzyme activity in each fraction is plotted against the fraction tube number to obtain a diagram for the elution pattern of the enzyme activity. The elution volume is taken as the midpoint of the peak of activity and the molecular weight for the kinase enzyme can be estimated by reading the appropriate value for that elution volume off the calibration curve.

It will be found that any ATPase present in the extract usually emerges near the void volume and may be accompanied by some phosphotransferase activity. The explanation of this finding is thought to be that the extract contains some myosin which has a high ATPase activity and is also capable of binding the phosphagen phosphotransferase. The molecular weight of the myosin-phosphotransferase complex is about 600 000. An example of the sort of results that are obtained with various molluscan muscles is given by Moreland and Watts (1967).

STARCH GEL ELECTROPHORESIS OF PHOSPHOTRANSFERASES

Electrophoresis at pH 8·6 on starch gels has been found to be an extremely useful technique for examining phosphotransferase in both whole muscle extracts and also in purified protein preparations.

At pH 8·6 the majority of muscle proteins, including the phosphotransferases, bear a net negative charge and migrate towards the anode. Starch gel is particularly useful as a supporting medium for electrophoresis because not only are proteins separated in proportion to their charge and mass but also the matrix of the gel is sufficiently fine to have a sieving effect, slowing down the movement of large or asymmetrical molecules more than those which are small or globular. After electrophoresis, the gel can be stained either with a specific histochemical stain to find the position of enzyme activity, or with a general protein staining dye to indicate the positions of all the different protein components present.

Equipment

1. DC power pack. 0–40 mA constant current, 0–400 V plus connector wires.
2. Use of cold room or space in large refrigerator.
3. Perspex gel tray 24 × 12 × 0·5 cm (see Fig. 8A).
4. Buffer and electrode compartments, capacity 400 ml.
5. Gel cutter (see Fig. 8C).
6. Long necked round bottomed glass flask plus bung and glass tubing.
7. Water pump and thick walled rubber tubing.
8. Whatman 3MM filter paper.
9. Blotting paper sheets, and thin polythene sheet.
10. Fine tungsten resistance wire (about 0·003 in. diameter).

Chemicals and Reagents

Buffers. 1. Tris/citrate pH 8·6. Dissolve 10·5 g Tris and 2·1 g citric acid in 500 ml water and dilute to 2 litres.
2. Borate pH 8·6. Dissolve 46·7 g boric acid in 1·5 litres of hot water. Cool to room temperature. Adjust the pH to 8·6 with saturated NaOH solution and dilute to 2 litres.

3. Connaught hydrolysed starch (Connaught Medical Research Labs., Toronto).
4. α-Naphthol.
5. Diacetyl.
6. n-Propanol.
7. Naphthalene black 12B.
8. 1N-NaOH solution.
9. Phosphotransferase assay solutions.

Terminology and Theory

Bands of protein on the gel which have the same enzyme activity but different electrophoretic mobilities are known as isoenzymes (isozymes) or multiple forms and the overall pattern of distribution as a zymogram. However, these terms only apply to the comparison of enzyme patterns in tissues from the same individual or species. For example, the arginine phosphotransferases of lobster and scallop have different electrophoretic mobilities but they are *not* isoenzymes. This is called species variation.

The causes of isoenzymes are now understood but, so far, there are no universally accepted terms to describe the different effects.

Enzymes Composed of a Single Polypeptide Chain. (a) "Functional" isoenzymes. These are coded in the chromosome by different structural genes. They may be located in different cell organelles or in different organs or associated with a more specific reaction than is located by the staining procedure. For example, a general stain for proteolytic activity would not distinguish trypsin and chymotrypsin and, although this might be readily appreciated for vertebrates, the proteases of invertebrates have been so little studied that such a confusion could easily arise.

(b) Enzyme variants. These have the same structural gene but the two alleles have slightly different structures; that is, the organism is heterozygous for that particular gene. This means that if a population is studied, three types of individual will be found corresponding to the two homozygous and the heterozygous states (Fig. 6A).*

Enzymes composed of identical subunits. (a) Functional isoenzymes corresponding to (a) above.

(b) Enzyme variants. The presence of subunits simply increases the possible number of electrophoretically distinct forms. Thus for an enzyme composed of two subunits the normal and variant homozygous forms can be described as AA and aa. The heterozygous animal will contain alleles for both A and a

---

* It is here assumed that the variant has a different electrophoretic mobility from the normal. If the variant has the same electrophoretic mobility as the normal then, of course, no difference will be observed.

but, because the subunits combine randomly three forms of the enzyme will be produced AA, aa and a new hybrid Aa which has an electrophoretic mobility intermediate between that of the two homozygous forms. This is illustrated in Fig. 6B. Hence, in the absence of other complicating factors,

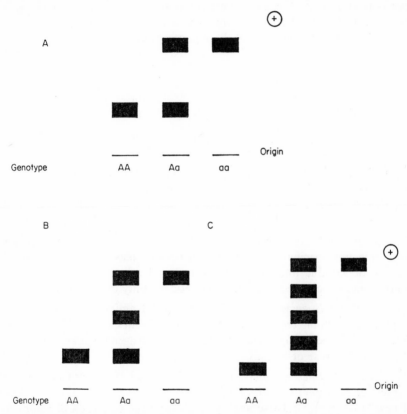

FIG. 6. Theoretical starch gel zymograms of enzymes composed of (A) single proteins; (B) two subunits; (C) four subunits; with the genotypes, AA, homozygous normal; aa, homozygous mutant form or variant; Aa, heterozygous.

a population study of enzyme variants will also reveal that the enzyme has at least a dimeric structure.

An enzyme composed of four identical subunits with a variant will have five bands in the heterozygote

$$A_4 \qquad A_3a \qquad A_2a_2 \qquad Aa_3 \qquad a_4$$

where the subscripts indicate the number of subunits in the molecule (Fig. 6C).

Enzymes Composed of Two Different Subunits. This implies that the two types of subunit are each coded by separate genes.

(a) If the subunits combine in a fixed ratio, like the subunits of human haemoglobin, then only a single band will be found if the gene for each subunit is homozygous. For an enzyme composed of $2 + 2$ subunits a variant allele for 1 subunit will give a zymogram like the dimer shown in Fig. 6B. An organism heterozygous for both subunits would have nine different forms.*

AA	Aa	aa
bb	bb	bb
AA	Aa	aa
bB	bB	bB
AA	Aa	aa
BB	BB	BB

(b) If the subunits combine randomly a doubly homozygous two subunit enzyme will have three forms and a four subunit enzyme five forms, while a doubly heterozygous enzyme will have ten and thirty-five forms, respectively. The student may work the combinations out for himself.

Binding by Small Molecules. In some enzymes, such as alkaline phosphatase and some non-specific esterases, multiple forms may be produced by the binding of variable numbers of sialic acid molecules which are themselves charged and hence affect the electrophoretic mobility of the enzyme.

Conformational Isoenzymes. An enzyme of fixed amino acid sequence has two (or more) stable tertiary structures with different electrophoretic properties. This has been suggested for lactate dehydrogenase and the creatine phosphotransferase of birds.

Oxidation and Other Artifacts. It has been found that storage of muscle extracts or even pure enzymes for long periods may result in the production of new "isoenzymes". These usually result from the oxidation of sulphydryl groups on the enzyme and can sometimes be reversed by dialyzing against buffer containing 1 mM mercaptoethanol.

Apparent isoenzymes may also arise by partial digestion of the enzyme by proteolytic enzymes in the tissue (cathepsins) which are released by homogenizing. This can be tested for by the use of specific proteolytic enzyme inhibitors but is outside the scope of these experiments.

Both vertebrates and invertebrates show phosphotransferase zymograms. In vertebrates two types of creatine phosphotransferase subunit have been found giving rise to three electrophoretically distinct forms. One, called MM,

---

* With haemoglobin, pairing of a variant subunit with a normal subunit cannot be detected by electrophoresis. Thus subunits A, a, B, and b, would only combine to give A_2B_2, A_2b_2, a_2B_2 and a_2b_2.

is characteristic of skeletal muscle; the second BB is characteristic of brain, while the third is a hybrid BM (or MB) consisting of one brain and one muscle type subunit (Eppenberger, Eppenberger, Richterich and Aebi, 1964). Analogous forms have not so far been recognized in invertebrates but in some molluscs there are two arginine phosphotransferases with different electrophoretic mobilities which are thought to be associated with different muscle functions (see Moreland and Watts, 1967). There is also thought to be a creatine kinase specifically associated with mitochondria.

Method

The conventional horizontal starch gel electrophoresis system of Smithies (1955) (see Fig. 7) is used with the discontinuous buffer system slightly adapted from that of Poulik (1957)

The gels are made by thoroughly suspending 36 g of Connaught hydrolysed starch in 300 ml of Tris/citrate buffer, in a round bottomed long-necked flask, fitted with a rubber bung through which a short length of glass tubing is inserted. Holding the flask with a cloth, the suspension of starch is slowly brought almost to boiling over a bunsen flame with constant swirling to prevent any charring at the bottom of the flask. The suspension first becomes viscous and then starts to thin again; at this point the flask is removed from the heat, the glass tubing is connected by rubber tubing to a water pump and the contents of the flask degassed for 30 sec.

The gel is then poured gently into the perspex forming tray in one smooth motion, allowed to set at room temperature (10 min), and then cooled to about 4°C in a refrigerator. This takes about 1 h.

A gel of this size will take about 5 or 6 inserts, 1·5 cm wide and 0·5 cm deep in the gel on a line about 8 cm from one of the shorter ends of the gel tray. With the gel insert cutter (Fig. 8B, C) resting horizontally on the gel surface, the razor blade edge will cut into the gel to form the slots 0·5 cm deep. With the cutter still in position, a filter paper insert (Whatman 3MM paper cut to the size of the slots) is soaked in the protein solution to be examined and inserted with forceps into the slots by sliding it down in front of the blade which is simultaneously pulled gently back to create a small gap in the gel. Make sure no air bubbles are trapped between the paper and the sides of the gel. The blade is then withdrawn and the next slot cut and the insert put into place. When all the inserts are in position, the gel is transferred to a cold-room or fridge (0–5°C) and arranged as shown in Fig. 8A on the edges of the two electrode vessels which each contain 400 ml of cold borate buffer. Folded sheets of blotting paper soaked in borate buffer are placed over the edges of the gel with the other end dipping in the buffer to act as wicks providing electrical contact between the two. A thin sheet of polythene placed over the top surface of the gel and wicks prevents evaporation of water from the gel which can cause distortion of protein bands. The electrodes are connected to a constant current DC power supply set with the proteins at the inserts to run towards the anode (positive). The gels are run for 4–5 h at 36 mA for the size of gel slab described above (3 mA/cm width of gel). Do not touch the apparatus once the power has been swtiched on.

Side View

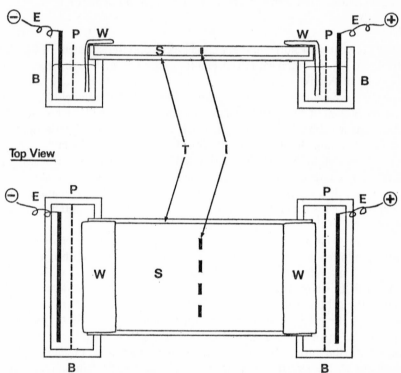

Top View

FIG. 7. Equipment for the analysis of enzymes by electrophoresis on a starch gel. The gel, S, is formed in the perspex tray, T. Pieces of filter paper soaked in the enzyme solution, I, are inserted vertically in the starch gel. Electrical contact between the gel and tanks of buffer, B, is obtained by means of filter paper wicks, W, soaked in buffer. The perforated partitions, P, are to minimize the change in pH caused by electrolysis at the platinum electrodes, E. After electrophoresis the gel is cut horizontally along its length and the cut faces stained for protein or for enzyme activity.

At the completion of the run, when the buffer front, seen as a faint yellow line, has travelled about 10 cm from the inserts, the power supply is disconnected and the gel tray removed for staining. The upper half of the perspex forming tray is unscrewed and removed and also the filter paper inserts facilitating the slicing of the gel into two halves horizontally by running a taut length of thin tungsten wire through the entire length of the gel like cutting a cheese. Careful removal of the top layer of the gel gives two cut surfaces, one of which can be stained for phosphotransferase activity, the other for protein or a second enzyme stain.

For the estimation of kinase activity the following Sakaguchi stain has been found to be fairly reliable as well as inexpensive.

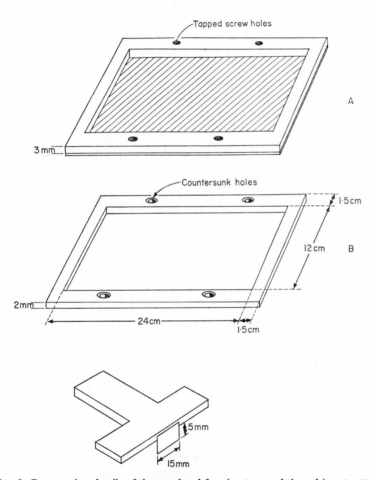

FIG. 8. Construction details of the starch gel forming tray and the gel insert cutter. The starch gel forming tray consists of two cut-out rectangles of perspex, one of which, A, has a sheet of thin perspex cemented to it to form a base. The detachable top section, B, is fastened to the bottom section by four countersunk screws which locate into tapped holes in the bottom section. The dimensions of the gel insert cutter, C, are not important and a simple T-shape should be cut from $\frac{1}{4}$ or $\frac{1}{2}$ in. perspex to carry the piece of safety razor blade which is cemented in position as shown. The arms of the perspex "T" are to aid in making a straight row of cuts across the gel.

Two pieces of Whatman 3MM filter paper are cut to fit the area of the gel to be stained. The first piece is soaked in 10 ml of a mixture of the appropriate substrates for the kinase. For arginine, glycocyamine and taurocyamine kinase, this is made up from 5·5 ml of the ATP/Mg mixture and 4·5 ml of the 40 mM solutions of the appropriate guanidine substrate. For creatine kinase, the 10 ml is made up from 5·5 ml of the ATP/Mg mixture, 1·25 ml of 40 mM creatine and 3·25 ml of Tris buffer. The soaked piece of filter paper is placed over the cut surface of the gel (making sure no air bubbles are trapped) and left in contact with the gel for 30 min at 30°C. The paper is removed and carefully replaced with the second piece soaked in a solution of 20 ml of 1N-sodium hydroxide containing 0·4 g of α-naphthol, plus 1 drop of n-propanol and 1 drop of diacetyl made up *immediately* before use. This staining mixture develops a red or brown colour on the gel in the presence of guanidine compounds after about 5 min. The presence of enzyme activity in the gel is indicated by colourless zones on the gel against a red background in the areas where the free guanidine has been converted to its corresponding phosphagen.* ATPase activity can be located by applying to the other gel surface a piece of filter paper soaked in 10 ml of a solution containing 5 ml of the ATP/Mg mixture and 5 ml of Tris buffer. After 30 min incubation at 30°C the inorganic phosphate liberated at the positions of enzyme activity can be detected as blue zones by applying a second piece of filter paper soaked in a solution of 10 ml of acid molybdate and 1 ml of reducing agent and incubating at 30°C for 20 min.

As phosphotransferase stain fades after about 30 min, the positions of enzyme activity should be marked on the gel with a needle and the gels then stained for general protein. The gels are left overnight in a 0·05% solution of naphthalene black 12B in a solution of methanol 40%, acetic acid 10% and water 50%. The colour may continue to develop for several days. Excess stain is removed by subsequently soaking the gel in several washes of the methanol, acid, water mixture. Different protein components stain up as dark blue bands and these can then be compared with the marked positions of enzyme activity.

DISCUSSION

Figure 9 shows the sort of results that are obtained. The phosphotransferases are usually associated with a major protein band. This is not the case for all enzymes because the enzyme stain is usually much more sensitive than the protein stain. *Pecten*, the scallop, has a pronounced ATPase that appears to be associated with the phosphotransferase activity. The hermit crab, *Eupagurus*, has no ATPase but at least two bands of arginine phosphotransferase activity and up to five bands may be observed. *Nereis fucata* is a

* A more sensitive but expensive stain is described by Blethen and Kaplan (1968).

commensal worm that lives in the upper whorls of the shell inhabited by *Eupagurus*. The glycocyamine and creatine phosphotransferases have identical electrophoretic mobilities but additivity experiments show that they are two different enzymes. The phosphotransferases from *Pecten* and *Eupagurus* have

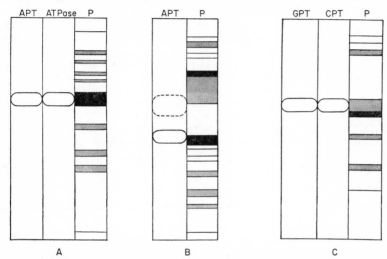

Fig. 9. Starch gel zymograms and the related protein bands of muscle extracts from, A, *Pecten maximus*; B, *Eupagurus bernhardus*; C, *Nereis fucata*. APT, GPT, and CPT are the phosphotransferases of arginine, glycocyamine and creatine, respectively; ATPase is adenosine 5′ triphosphatase and P is the same extract stained for protein.

molecular weights of 40 000 but those from *Nereis* are 80 000. These examples illustrate how the complementary information from the different types of investigation is necessary for an understanding of the nature of the phosphagen phosphotransferases.

REFERENCES

Andrews, P. (1964). Estimation of the molecular weights of proteins by Sephadex gel filtration. *Biochem. J.*, **91**, 222–233.
Andrews, P. (1967). Molecular sieve chromatography. Reprinted from *Lab. Prac.*, 851 [A general and theoretical account of the use of Sephadex.]
Blethen, S. L. and Kaplan, N. O. (1968). Characteristics of arthropod arginine kinases. *Biochemistry*, **7**, 2123–2135.
Eppenberger, H. M., Eppenberger, M., Richterich, R. and Aebi, H. (1964). The ontogeny of creatine kinase isoenzymes. *Devel Biol.*, **10**, 1–16.
Ennor, A. H. and Morrison, J. F. (1958). Biochemistry of the phosphagens and related guanidines. *Physiol Rev.*, **38**, 631–674. [Hydrolysis of phosphagens; distribution and some properties of phosphotransferases.]
Moreland, B. and Watts, D. C. (1967). Molecular weight isoenzymes of arginine kinase in the Mollusca and their association with muscle function. *Nature, Lond.*, **215**, 1092–1094.

Moreland, B., Watts, D. C. and Virden, R. (1967). Phosphagen kinases and evolution in the Echinodermata. *Nature, Lond.*, **214**, 458–462. [Molecular weight determination of phosphotransferases using Sephadex; enzyme distribution and evolution.]

Poulik, M. D. (1957). Starch gel electrophoresis in a discontinuous sytem of buffers. *Nature, Lond.*, **180**, 1477–1479.

Smithies, O. (1955). Zone electrophoresis in starch gels: group variations in the serum proteins of normal human adults. *Biochem. J.*, **61**, 629–641. [Original description of the method.]

Virden, R. and Watts, D. C. (1964) The distribution of guanidine adenosine triphosphate phosphotransferases and adenosine triphosphatase in animals from several phyla. *Comp. Biochem. Physiol.*, **13**, 161–177. [Assay procedure; starch gel electrophoresis procedure; distribution of some enzymes and a general discussion about them.]

Watts, D. C. (1968). Variation in enzyme structure and function: the guidelines of evolution. *In* "Advances in Comparative Biochemistry and Physiology", (O. E. Lowenstein, ed.), pp. 1–108 Academic Press, New York and London. [General review.]

Exp. in Physiol. and Biochem. (1970). 3, 31–38.

2 | Estimation of the Glycine Concentration in Small Tissue Samples from the Central Nervous System*

M. H. APRISON and R. P. SHANK

*The Institute of Psychiatric Research and Departments of
Psychiatry and Biochemistry,
Indiana University Medical Center, Indianapolis,
Indiana, U.S.A.*

INTRODUCTION

In 1820, Braconnot found glycine as a naturally occurring constituent in a gelatine hydrolysate. Glycine has since been shown to occur in most proteins and natural peptides. Although glycine is the simplest amino acid, its intermediary metabolism is rather complex. Thus glycine is incorporated into purines, creatine, glycocholate and porphyrins; it is also involved in the formation of active one carbon units. In most organisms glycine is readily interconverted with serine, and in some organisms with threonine. Aprison and Werman (1965) postulated on the basis of neurochemical and neuroanatomical considerations that glycine has an additional and unexpected function in the cat nervous system—that of an inhibitory transmitter in lumbar spinal cord. These investigators with their collaborators published neurochemical and neurophysiological studies to substantiate the above hypothesis (Aprison and Werman, 1965; Graham *et al.*, 1967; Davidoff *et al.*, 1967a; Davidoff *et al.*, 1967b; Werman *et al.*, 1967; Werman *et al.*, 1968) and recently summarized their data (Aprison and Werman, 1968; Werman and Aprison, 1968). Confirmatory data has now appeared from another laboratory (Curtis *et al.*, 1967; Curtis *et al.*, 1968). Although a number of glycine assay methods are described in the literature, most of these methods are not readily adaptable to measuring glycine concentrations found in mg quantities of tissue. The method described in this paper is based on a macromethod published by Giroux and Puech (1963). The present specific microchemical method is sensitive to 10^{-9} moles of glycine in the presence of other free amino acids. The method has also been used to measure the glycine concentration in cerebral spinal fluid and blood and is probably applicable to non-nervous tissue.

* These experiments were supported in part by Grant MH-03225 from N.I.M.H. and Grant NB-07301 from N.I.H., U.S.P.H.S.

PRINCIPLES

1. In the presence of nitrous acid, glycine is the only amino acid converted into glycolic acid.
2. Glycolic acid forms formaldehyde in the presence of concentrated hot H_2SO_4.
3. Formaldehyde reacts with chromotropic acid in the presence of sulfuric acid to give a purple colored product.
4. The optical density of the purple colored compound at 580 mμ is directly proportional to the concentration of glycine over a large range.

EQUIPMENT

1. Beckman DU spectrophotometer equipped with microcells.
2. Small glass tubes (5 × 50, 6 × 50, 7 × 70, 10 × 75 mm); also small cellulose nitrate centrifuge tubes.
3. Sorvall RC-2B centrifuge.
4. Small glass homogenizers.
5. Water bath with capacity to maintain 100°C water.
6. Test tube mixer or "buzzer" (Lowry et al., 1954).
7. Various sizes of lambda pipettes (i.e., 1 μl, 3 μl, 10 μl, 20 μl, 25 μl and 300 μl).

ANIMALS AND TISSUES

1. Central nervous system tissues from the following animals have been used in this assay (Aprison et al., 1968a, b): cat (*Felix domesticus*), rat (*Rattus norvegicus*), pigeon (*Columbia livia domestica*), bullfrog (*Rana catesbeiana*), caiman (*Caiman latirostris*), catfish (*Ictalurus punctatus*) and snake (*Constrictor constrictor*).
2. The following brain areas have been assayed: telencephalon (cerebral hemispheres including the basal ganglia), diencephalon, midbrain (including tectum), medulla oblongata and cerebellum (Aprison et al., 1968a, b).
3. Spinal cord tissue such as cervical enlargement, mid-thoracic spinal cord and lumbar enlargement, as well as six subdivisions of cervical and lumbar enlargement such as dorsal and ventral grey, dorsal lateral and dorsal medial white, and ventral lateral and ventral medial white have been analyzed for their glycine concentration (Graham et al., 1967; Aprison et al., 1968a, b).
4. Dorsal and ventral spinal roots from the upper sacral and lower lumbar spine (Graham et al., 1967) as well as cat blood serum and cerebrospinal fluid (Aprison and Werman, 1965) have also been used in the glycine assay.

CHEMICAL SOLUTIONS

1. 5% trichloroacetic acid (TCA). Dissolve 5 g TCA in 100 ml of double distilled water* (volumetric flask).
2. 7% sodium nitrite. Dissolve 0·7 g sodium nitrite in 10 ml distilled water (volumetric flask; prepare weekly).
3. Concentrated sulfuric acid.
4. 1N sulfuric acid.
5. Aqueous stannous chloride solution. Dissolve 2 g $SnCl_2.2H_2O$ in 1·0 ml H_2O.
6. 5% chromotropic acid. Prepare freshly from recrystallized chromotropic acid or the disodium salt of chromotropic acid. Dissolve 50 mg chromotropic acid in 1 ml water (warm gently).
7. Standard glycine solutions. A standard solution of glycine is made by dissolving 75·1 mg in 100 ml of distilled water (volumetric flask). This solution (sol. A) is stable for several weeks at 4°C. More dilute standards are made daily or weekly from solution A. Solution B is prepared by diluting 0·4 ml (400 μl) of solution A to 10 ml with 5% TCA (volumetric flask). Three ml of solution B are diluted to 5 ml (volumetric flask) with 5% TCA to make solution C. Two ml of solution C are diluted to 4 ml with 2 ml 5% TCA to make solution D, and 2 ml of solution D are then diluted to 4 ml with 2 ml 5% TCA to make solution E. Solutions B, C, D, and E are the working standards and the 5% TCA is used as the standard blank solution.

EXPERIMENTAL DETAILS

TISSUE EXTRACTION

The tissue is weighed and placed in ground glass homogenizers containing some cold 5% TCA; a volume equal to 10 to 20 times the tissue weight is used. If the glycine concentration in tissue is expected to be 1·0 μmole/g or less, the TCA volume should not greatly exceed 10 times the tissue weight. If the glycine concentration is expected to exceed 5·0 μmoles/g, the TCA volume should approach 20 times the tissue weight. After homogenization the samples are centrifuged at 23 000 g for 20 min in a refrigerated centrifuge.

NITROUS ACID REACTION PROCEDURE

Duplicate 25 μl portions of each standard or 25 μl 5% TCA (blank) are placed into small glass tubes (6 × 50 mm).† The same volume of each tissue sample supernatant is placed into 4 tubes, 2 of which are used as tissue blanks.

* Hereafter, distilled water refers to double distilled water.
† Internal standards (standards added to tissue before extraction) yield a standard curve with the same slope as that obtained with external standards (as described here).

C

The glass tubes should be uniform with an *inside* diameter 4 mm or less to reduce evaporation. It is important to exclude particulate material from the tissue samples. Ten μl of 1N-sulfuric acid are then added to all standards and samples. Ten μl of 7% sodium nitrite are next added to all standards and samples except those tubes used as the tissue blanks. To these, 10 μl of water are added. Each tube is buzzed after each addition. All tubes are capped with parafilm; a pin hole is introduced to allow for expansion and escape of nitrogen gas. Next the tubes are placed into a boiling water bath for 45 min. After allowing the tubes to cool, condensed moisture adhering to the inside of the parafilm is tapped into the tubes. The parafilm is removed and the tubes are centrifuged at 3000 *g* for 5 min to drive all liquid to the bottom.

CHROMOTROPIC ACID REACTION PROCEDURE

Two 20 μl portions are removed from each tube and placed into larger glass tubes (7–10 × 70 mm). This procedure results in a total of 4 tubes for each standard, tissue sample and tissue blank. Three μl of freshly prepared stannous chloride solution are added to each standard and tissue sample tube, while 1 μl is added to each tissue blank tube. The addition of 2 μl H_2O to each tissue blank tube does not affect the results. Each tube is buzzed after the addition of the stannous chloride. Concentrated sulfuric acid (300 μl) is added next and each tube is buzzed until the white precipitate disappears. The sulfuric acid may be added with a micro burette, pipette or a commercially available "jet pipette". If a micro pipette is used it should have a large opening and care must be exercised to ensure consistent delivery. Ten μl of freshly prepared 5% chromotropic acid are added and each tube is buzzed again. The chromotropic acid solution should be prepared and stored in the dark; it should be added to the tubes in a room containing subdued lighting to provide minimal visibility. The time required for the chromotropic acid addition should not exceed 15 min. The tubes are then placed in a boiling ($> 95°C$) water bath for 20 min. The tubes are not exposed to any light during this period. The tubes are removed, stored in a cool, dark place for at least 30 min and then the optical density of each is measured.

OPTICAL DENSITY MEASUREMENTS

The samples are placed in microcells and read in a spectrophotometer at 580 mμ. The spectrophotometer is kept in a room containing only enough lighting to ensure enough visibility for the operator to read the samples. Samples are read in groups of two or three. Each group is removed in turn from a dark cabinet and read.

SUMMARY OF PROCEDURE

1. 25 μl of glycine solution (6 mm $\times$ 50 mm tubes) or tissue sample.
2. 10 μl of 1·0N H_2SO_4.
3. 10 μl of 7% $NaNO_2$ (10 μl H_2O for tissue blank). Buzz, cap with parafilm and make a hole in parafilm with needle. Boil 45 min. Cool, centrifuge at 3000 rev/min for 5 min.
4. Transfer 20 μl portions into (7–10 mm $\times$ 50 mm) tubes.
5. Add 3 μl $SnCl_2$ solution (1 μl for tissue blanks). Buzz immediately.
6. Add 300 μl conc. H_2SO_4. Buzz immediately.
7. Add 10 μl 5% chromotropic acid (in dark). Boil 20 min in dark and leave to cool in dark for 30 min.
8. Using microcells, read optical density at 580 mμ in spectrophotometer.

ADDITIONAL EXPERIMENTAL SUGGESTIONS

If the glycine concentration in any sample is less than 1·0 μmole/g, or if it contains substances which char in the presence of concentrated sulfuric acid, the investigator may find it advantageous or necessary to concentrate and/or purify the tissue samples. This may be done by passing a known amount of the supernatant (minus protein) through a charcoal column. The column may be prepared in the following manner: Mix together equal parts of Norite -A and Celite, slurry with water and pour into a column (0·8 $\times$ 10 cm) containing a thin layer (1 mm) of Celite in the bottom. The column should be packed to a height of about 7 cm and rinsed twice with 5N HCl followed by 2 rinses with water. After the sample is passed through the column, it is rinsed twice with 2 volumes of water. The eluate is then dried and redissolved in an appropriate amount of water. A suction flask will facilitate the passage of the sample and water rinses through the column.

SAMPLE CALCULATIONS

The concentration of glycine in a particular tissue sample may be calculated from the following results:

Optical Density Measurements

A. Standards	Mean of 4 readings	Delta
Std Blank	0·022	—
Std 1 (1·5 $\times$ 10^{-9} moles)	0·054	0·032
Std 2 (3·0 $\times$ 10^{-9} moles)	0·088	0·066
Std 3 (6·0 $\times$ 10^{-9} moles)	0·152	0·130
Std 4 (10·0 $\times$ 10^{-9} moles)	0·254	0·232

Optical Density Measurements

B. Tissue Sample (Rat Medulla-Pons)   Mean of 4 readings   Delta

Tissue blank   0·042   —

Tissue sample   0·165   0·123

$$\text{Standard curve slope} = \frac{0\cdot225 \text{ O.D. units}}{10\cdot0 \times 10^{-9} \text{ moles}}$$

$$\text{Amt. of glycine in tissue sample} = \frac{0\cdot123 \text{ O.D. units}}{\dfrac{0\cdot225 \text{ O.D. units}}{10\cdot0 \times 10^{-9} \text{ moles}}} = 4\cdot92 \times 10^{-9} \text{ moles}$$

Tissue weight in sample   175·3 mg of tissue were homogenized in 3·0 ml TCA

$$\text{Wt. in 25 } \mu\text{l} = \frac{175\cdot3 \text{ mg} \times 25 \text{ }\mu\text{l}}{3000 \text{ }\mu\text{l} + 175 \text{ }\mu\text{l}^*} = 1\cdot38 \text{ mg}$$

$$\text{Calculated glycine concentration} = \frac{4\cdot92 \times 10^{-9} \text{ moles}}{1\cdot38 \times 10^{-3} \text{ g}} = 3\cdot56 \frac{\mu\text{moles}}{\text{g}}$$

TROUBLE SHOOTING

(a) The test tubes must be clean, detergent free and lint free. These contaminants result in formation of a light brown color in the presence of the hot concentrated sulfuric acid. Particulate tissue matter when present also causes the formation of a brown color.

(b) Sufficient stannous chloride must be added to destroy all the unreacted sodium nitrite or a deep yellow color will form when the chromotropic acid is added. If too much stannous chloride is added, the white precipitate formed upon the addition of sulfuric acid will not disappear.

(c) Chromotropic acid decomposes over a period of time resulting in higher blank readings. It must, therefore, be periodically recrystallized. The disodium salt is more stable than the acid and is commercially available in a form pure enough to use without recrystallization.

(d) The concentrated sulfuric acid must be reagent grade and its concentration must exceed 95% to obtain maximum color formation.

(e) Any tube, including blanks, when exposed for a period of time to bright light after the addition of chromotropic acid will form a purple color. A purple color may also be formed if the chromotropic acid is greatly decomposed or if the samples have been exposed to formaldehyde.

* It is assumed that 1 g of tissue equals a volume of 1 ml.

Further Comments

This assay was developed to do a large number of very small central nervous system tissue samples. It is easily adaptable to large tissue samples. In our experience eight to ten samples with appropriate standards (80 to 100 readings) can be assayed in a normal working day. This method is readily adaptable to other studies requiring the measurement of glycine in the presence of different amino acids.

References

Aprison, M. H. and Werman, R. (1965). The distribution of glycine in cat spinal cord and roots. *Life Sci.*, **4**, 2075–2083.

Aprison, M. H. and Werman, R. (1968). A combined neurochemical and neurophysiological approach to identification of central nervous system transmitters. In "Neurosciences Research" (S. Ehrenpreis and O. C. Solnitzky, eds), Vol. 1, pp. 143–174, Academic Press, New York and London.

Aprison, M. H., Shank, R. P. and Davidoff, R. A. (1968a). A comparison of the concentration of glycine, a transmitter suspect, in different areas of the brain and spinal cord in seven different vertebrates. *Comp. Biochem. Physiol.* **24**, 1345–1355.

Aprison, M. H., Shank, R. P., Davidoff, R. A. and Werman, R. (1968b). The distribution of glycine, a neurotransmitter suspect in the central nervous system of several vertebrate species. *Life Sci.*, **7**, 583–590.

Curtis, D. R., Hosli, L., Johnston, G. A. R. and Johnston, I. H. (1967). Glycine and spinal inhibition. *Brain Res.*, **5**, 112–114.

Curtis, D. R., Hosli, L., Johnston, G. A. R. and Johnston, I. H. (1968). The hyperpolarization of spinal motoneurones by glycine and related amino acids. *Exp. Brain Res.*, **5**, 235–258.

Davidoff, R. A., Graham, L. T. Jr., Shank, R. P., Werman, R. and Aprison, M. H. (1967a). Changes in amino acid concentrations associated with loss of spinal interneurons. *J. Neurochem.*, **14**, 1025–1031.

Davidoff, R. A., Shank, R. P., Graham, L. T. Jr., Aprison, M. H. and Werman, R. (1967b). Association of glycine with spinal interneurons. *Nature, Lond.*, **214**, 680–681.

Giroux, J. and Puech, A. (1963). Nouvelle methods de dosage du glycocolle. *Annls pharm. fr.*, **21**, 469–476.

Graham, L. T., Jr., Shank, R. P., Werman, R. and Aprison, M. H. (1967). Distribution of some synaptic transmitter suspects in cat spinal cord: glutamic acid, aspartic acid, γ-aminobutyric acid, glycine and glutamine. *J. Neurochem.*, **14**, 465–472.

Lowry, O. H., Roberts, N. R., Leiner, K., Wu, M. L. and Farr, A. L. (1954). The quantitative histochemistry of the brain. I. Chemical methods. *J. biol. Chem.*, **207**, 1–17.

Werman, R., Davidoff, R. A. and Aprison, M. H. (1967). Inhibition of motoneurons by iontophoresis of glycine. *Nature, Lond.*, **214**, 681–683.

Werman, R. and Aprison, M. H. (1968). Glycine: The search for a spinal cord inhibitory transmitter. *In* "Structure and Functions of Inhibitory Neuronal Mechanisms" (C. von Euler, S. Skogland and U. Soderbert, eds), pp. 473–486, Pergamon Press, New York.

Werman, R., Davidoff, R. A. and Aprison, M. H. (1968). Inhibitory action of glycine on spinal neurons in the cat. *J. Neurophysiol.*, **31**, 81–95.

Exp. in Physiol. and Biochem. (1970).ʻ3, 39–48.

3 | A Controlled Humidity Constant Temperature Cold Box for Dissection of Small Frozen Tissue Sections*

M. H. APRISON and C. J. HANCOCK

The Institute of Psychiatric Research and Departments of Psychiatry and Biochemistry

Indiana University Medical Center, Indianapolis, Indiana, U.S.A.

INTRODUCTION

The trend in biochemistry and especially in neurobiology is to analyse smaller and smaller tissue samples. Analyses of specific biochemical constituents have already been done in single cells. Although most investigators have not geared their biochemical analyses to single cells, many are interested in making measurements on small, discrete areas in tissues taken from animals or plants. Such tissues are almost always frozen to prevent biochemical changes from occurring. Consider the problem of fine dissection of 0·5–1 mm thick transverse sections of frozen spinal cord of the cat or rat. Such small frozen tissue samples (at dry ice or liquid nitrogen temperatures) can be easily dissected into 6 or more discrete areas if the sample temperature is raised to $-20°C$ in a temperature–humidity controlled environment. At $-20°C$, anabolic and catabolic processes which normally might change the concentration of a substance from that present in the tissue taken at the time of death are prevented from occurring (Takahashi and Aprison, 1964).

The need for such an environment is apparent when such frozen tissue must be dissected into specific areas and then weighed on an analytical balance. Dissection of such small frozen tissue areas leads to difficulties because of two reasons: (a) dissection of frozen tissue at dry ice (or liquid nitrogen) temperatures into samples of 2–30 mg are difficult since it is hard, brittle and cleavage planes are not always predictable (causing some tissue fragments to be deflected or bounce away from the working area during dissection); (b) frost collects on the frozen samples resulting in errors in weighing. Arbitrarily raising the tissue temperature under uncontrolled conditions is risky. In order to accurately dissect frozen tissue into 2–30 mg

* This work was supported in part by Grant MH-03225 from N.I.M.H. and Grant NB-07301 from N.I.H., U.S.P.H.S.

samples and also to prevent frost or minute ice crystals from forming on them during the dissection, a special temperature–humidity cold box can be easily built and is described below. In addition, a method for weighing such frozen samples is also given.

PRINCIPLES

1. Frozen tissue at −20°C is easier to dissect into small discrete areas than at dry ice temperatures.
2. Fresh frozen tissue in mg quantities will not accumulate frost in a cold nitrogen atmosphere.
3. Usual metabolic processes do not occur in excized tissue dissected at −20°C.

APPARATUS REQUIRED

1. Cryostat with temperature control unit (both made in laboratory shop, see below).
2. Balance to weigh frozen samples accurately (see below).
3. Dissection instruments.
4. Surface thermometer in −50 to +50°C range or its equivalent.

CHEMICAL REQUIREMENTS

1. Quantities of dry ice (frozen CO_2); slabs 1 in. × 9 in. × 9 in. and 2 in. × 9 in. × 9 in.
2. Liquid nitrogen (when needed).
3. Anhydrous calcium sulphate (Drierite).
4. Aluminum foil.

EXPERIMENTAL

Excised tissue is quickly frozen either in liquid nitrogen or on dry ice. Each sample is wrapped in aluminum foil and while frozen (keep on dry ice or in liquid nitrogen) is taken to the room where the dissections are done. The dissection problem was solved by using a temperature–humidity controlled shop-made cryostat whereas the weighing problem was solved by an inexpensive modification* of a Cahn microbalance which allowed the tissue to be weighed in a chest-type freezer while manipulating the balance chamber remotely from outside the freezer. A commercial unit (Cahn Instrument Co., Paramount, California, U.S.A.) is also available for this step.

The device used for dissecting frozen tissue (for example cat spinal cord

---

* Personal communication of D. Clapp and M. J. Joseph, Krannert Heart Research Institute, Indiana University Medical Center, Indianapolis, Indiana, U.S.A.

segments) while maintaining a temperature of $-20°C$ and a minimal humidity to prevent moisture formation can be easily made in a laboratory shop. It is essentially a small cryostat (about 1 foot on a side) made in the form of a stainless steel box with a plastic top for viewing and a plastic front with handports (covered with $\frac{1}{8}$ in. thick slitted rubber sheets for manipulation of dissecting instruments) (see Fig. 1B and Fig. 2). These dimensions are not critical. The handport front, and the front one-half of the top, are made in

FIG. 1. (A) Cold box shown on side inside plywood box. Note raised work surface on underside to allow slab of dry ice to fit snugly. Also note heating unit and flat wire cable to remote control unit. (B) Complete earlier model. Magnifier-fluorescent light in place inside cryostat with nitrogen source coupled to cold box for normal use. Control box for heater unit at left (Richardson and Aprison, 1969). (C) Dissection microscope in place on special plastic front for closer inspection of very small pieces of tissue.

one piece to allow the arm of a fluorescent light with a 4 in. magnifying lens to be placed through a notch in the top so that the light and lens are inside the cold box (see Fig. 1B and Fig. 2). An additional handport front was made to accommodate a binocular dissecting microscope for very close inspection of dissected sections when necessary to determine if the segments of gray matter contained adhering pieces of white matter and vice versa (see Fig. 1C). An improvement over the front used in Fig. 1B is shown in Fig. 2 and the dimensions of the plastic handport front are shown in Fig. 3. Note that corners have been cut to provide a more natural position for the investigator doing his dissection work. Plastic gloves are worn while dissecting the tissue in order to prevent moisture escaping from the hands to form ice crystals on the frozen tissue. A manifold to disperse a stream of nitrogen gas at several levels was placed inside the cold box on the back side to displace the moisture laden air from the box and to prevent entrance of any air from the outside. The stainless steel box was placed inside a three-sided plywood box (Fig. 1). The nitrogen gas was first passed from the source (tank) through a large drying tube containing Drierite and then through a coil of copper tubing attached to the back of the stainless steel box and consequently next to the dry ice (Fig. 2). The latter cooled the nitrogen gas before entering the manifold for dispersion inside the cold box. The nitrogen gas was turned on before the box became cold (i.e., before the dry ice was put in place) in order to displace the moisture ladened air inside; less ice crystals formed on the inside of the stainless steel box after it was cooled with the dry ice. This procedure also helped prevent ice crystal formation on frozen tissue during the dissection.

Fig. 2. Complete unit as now in use in author's laboratory (see text). Modification of handport allows wrists and lower arms to enter cryostat at an angle more natural to operator. Note surface thermometer in position on usual work area (directly over automatic heating unit attached to undersurface of work area). The vacuum desiccator on left (when in use dry ice is placed directly on desiccator plate with vacuum port left open) is used to transfer frozen samples to balance.

Four slabs of dry ice (2 in. × 9 in. × 9 in.) were fitted between the stainless steel box and the wooden box: one on the left and right sides, one at the back and one under the bottom. The interior of the enclosed stainless steel box was thus cooled rapidly to the dry ice temperature. Crushed dry ice was inserted where needed to fill spaces on the sides. A polystyrene cover cut to fit on top of the dry ice was put in place to prevent rapid evaporation (see Fig. 1B, C and Fig. 2). The bottom inside of the stainless steel box was used for the working surface. When in place, the lower work surface of the stainless steel box was raised above the wood box (see Fig. 1A). This allowed a slab of dry ice to fit underneath the working surface and still provide space between the dry ice and the bottom of the stainless steel box for an automatic heating and sensing unit. A heating coil (described below) in a circular metal case enclosing a temperature sensing thermistor (Richardson and Aprison, 1969) was permanently attached to the underside of the bottom of the stainless steel box (Fig. 1A).

Since the dry ice cooled the stainless steel working surface to about −50°C which in turn made the tissue too brittle to dissect easily and precisely, the

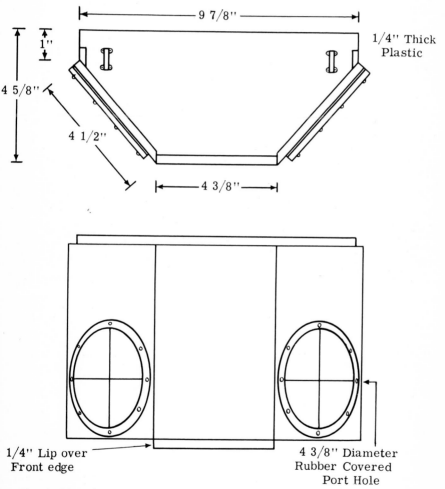

FIG. 3. Dimensions of modified plastic handport front for cryostat. Fronts are interchangeable to allow replacement with special dissecting microscope front.

temperature regulating heating coil (placed between the work surface and the bottom piece of dry ice) was adjusted to add just enough heat to maintain the work surface and hence the tissue at a constant −20°C temperature. A surface temperature thermometer (A. H. Thomas No. 9548–A) was used

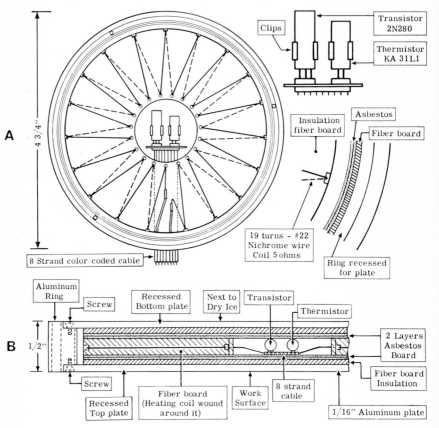

FIG. 4. Diagrammatic view of temperature sensing and heating coil unit. View shows bottom next to dry ice since the top plate is attached to underside of work surface of cold box. Note temperature sensing thermistor is in center of unit (with permission of *J. appl. Physiol.*).

to monitor the temperature of the working surface. The heater coil (see Fig. 1A and Fig. 4) was manufactured in our machine shop and was electronically controlled by a slight modification of an automatic DC operating temperature-control device (Richardson and Aprison, 1969; Richardson *et al.*, 1965). The surface area just above the circular ($4\frac{3}{4}$ in. diameter) metal heating unit (which contains the nichrome wire heating coil, Fig. 4) can be maintained at a constant temperature below zero as long as the slab of dry ice has not totally evaporated. Whenever the temperature of the stainless steel surface area cools below the preset temperature (i.e., $-20°C$), the sensing element located in the circular heating unit detects this change and automatically activates the electronic circuits which permit current to flow (12 V battery source is used) through the nichrome wire (see Fig. 4). The heat added is just enough to compensate for the heat loss. The settings on the unit are made to provide minimum overshoot of the heating system (Richardson *et al.*, 1965).

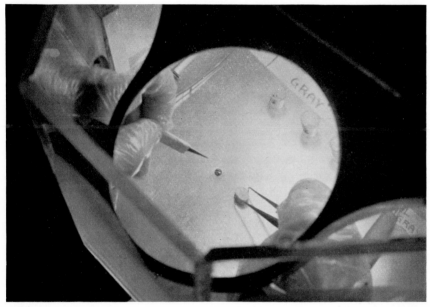

FIG. 5. Investigator's view through magnifying lens inside cryostat. Note transverse section of cat cord between forceps.

As the tissue was dissected, the parts were placed in small cups made from aluminum foil. In some early experiments small plastic cups were used (Fig. 5). The latter were labelled and placed to the rear of the cryostat prior to the dissection. The aluminum foil cups (or plastic cups) were then placed on a piece of dry ice in a glass vacuum desiccator. The desiccator had been previously prepared with desiccant and dry ice was placed on the plate. The hole for the vacuum was left open at all times for the release of displaced air and CO_2. The desiccator with the frozen tissue was carried to the microbalance chamber in the freezer and the transfer of tissue was thus effected without thawing or incurring a weight increase from condensed moisture (Fig. 6). The tissue samples were then weighed while still frozen. In Fig. 6A

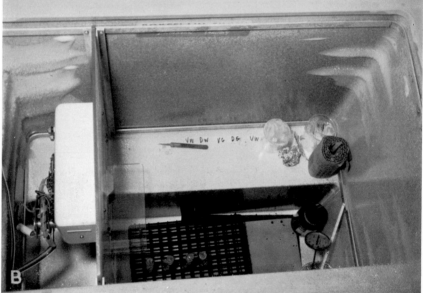

FIG. 6. (A) Balance unit. Remote use of Cahn balance chamber attached to vertical support (plastic sheet) inside freezer unit. Note flat wire cable to null meter (square meter) on external control panel indicating when beam is in balance. (B) Modification of Cahn balance chamber showing some electronic circuitry and light source for easier replacement of bulb. Vacuum desiccator with tissue sample on dry ice is placed on ledge inside freezer. Tissue samples are then individually weighed.

the Cahn electrobalance, adapted as previously described, is shown; the freezer door is open. Note the position of the weighing chamber inside. A closer view is shown in Fig. 6B.

FURTHER IDEAS

Using the apparatus described in this paper, an investigator can accurately dissect from frozen materials extremely small but specific tissue areas. He then is limited only by the sensitivity of his methods and his imagination. In the senior author's laboratories, a research project on the "Identification of Central Nervous System Transmitters" has been in progress for over six years. Aprison and Werman (1968) reviewed some of this work. Crucial to the approach has been the need to measure the concentration of a number of amino acids in specific areas of the cat spinal cord. Fine dissection of tissue with the controlled humidity constant temperature cold box facilitated this work. From these studies, neurochemical as well as neurophysiological evidence has appeared to implicate glycine as an inhibitory transmitter. The further implication of this result is that glycine may be present in cells in compartments or pools: metabolic and functional. Aprison *et al.* (1969) have shown that glycine has a unique distribution in other areas of the neuraxis of a number of vertebrates. The neurochemical work was possible because of the development of the equipment described above. Similar studies (assaying for other amino acids and other important compounds) are now more easily done since the equipment is relatively inexpensive and can be made in a laboratory shop.

ACKNOWLEDGEMENT

The authors wish to thank Mr. T. W. Richardson, electronic engineer in our Institute, for helping set up the heating device in our dissection cold box; thanks are also due to Mr. Robert Leckrone of our Institute machine shop.

REFERENCES

Aprison, M. H. and Werman, R. (1968). A combined Neurochemical and Neurophysiological Approach to Identification of Central Nervous System Transmitters. *In* "Neurosciences Research", (S. Ehrenpreis and O. C. Solnitsky, eds) Vol. 1, pp. 143–174, Academic Press, New York and London.

Aprison, M. H., Shank, R. P. and Davidoff, R. A. (1969). A Comparison of the Concentration of Glycine, A Transmitter Suspect, in Different Areas of the Brain and Spinal Cord in Seven Different Vertebrates. *Comp. Biochem. Physiol.*, **24**, 1345–1355.

Richardson, T. W. and Aprison, M. H. (1969). An Automatic Control Device to Regulate at Subzero Temperatures. *J. appl. Physiol.* (In Press).

Richardson, T. W., Aprison, M. H. and Werman, R. (1965). An Automatic Direct-Current Operating Temperature-Control Device. *J. appl. Physiol.*, **20**, 1355–1356.

Takahashi, R. and Aprison, M. H. (1964). The Acetylcholine Content of Discrete Areas of the Brain Obtained by a Near-Freezing Method. *J. Neurochem.*, **11**, 887–898.

Exp. in Physiol. and Biochem. (1970). 3, 49–159.

4 | Direct Electrical Currents in Metabolizing Epithelial Membranes

CHARLES O. WATLINGTON, THOMAS C. SMITH and
ERNST G. HUF

*Departments of Medicine and Physiology, Medical College of Virginia,
Health Sciences Division, Virginia Commonwealth University,
Richmond, Virginia, U.S.A.*

INTRODUCTION

An electrical potential difference (PD) can be measured across the surfaces of most resting cells and membraneous tissues. The PD may be as low as a few millivolts or, as in the case of the electric organs in certain fishes, as high as 600 V. Cell surfaces and tissue membranes behave as if they contained batteries which convert chemical energy into an electromotive force. The existence of PDs within metabolizing biological structures, or between a given tissue and its environment has intrigued physiologists for decades. These investigators have been concerned with the origin of the electromotive force (EMF) and its dependence on cellular metabolism. They have attempted to uncover relationships which may exist between the EMF resulting from tissue-environment interactions and the specific physiological function of a tissue or organ. The short-circuiting of tissues is one method used in the search for answers to these questions. This can be done by shunting the electrical potential barriers by an external conductor of low electrical resistance. A more effective approach is to send a direct current through the tissues so as to reversibly annul the "spontaneous" tissue PD. It is the purpose of this article to describe in detail these techniques. The presentation will be restricted to certain animal epithelial tissues which have been studied; the stomach, frog skin, toad bladder, turtle bladder and intestine. For the non-expert who is desirous to enter this field of experimental research, 20 typical experiments will be described from the extensive literature available. Efforts were made to select experiments from different groups of investigators. It is hoped that in this way scientists representing various biological specialities may find it easier to become acquainted with the vast field of "membrane transport" research, which frequently includes measurements of direct electrical currents in biological membranes. For most theoretical aspects and details of interpretations of results the reader is referred to the original literature quoted.

D

In studies on the electrophysiology of the membranes mentioned above, simple physical concepts and laws are applied using *fundamental* physical quantities (length, mass, time, degree absolute temperature and electrical charge) and several *derived* physical quantities (potential, current, resistance, conductance, energy and flux). The definitions for some of the relevant quantities and the units in which they are measured are given below.

DEFINITIONS OF PHYSICAL QUANTITIES AND THEIR UNITS

1. *Electromotive force* (EMF, or simply E). Such a force results from the operation of a "charge pump", which separates electrical charges (in chemical systems, ions) across a given barrier. The EMF is measured by the maximal potential difference (in volts) across the barrier.

2. *Electrical potential difference* (PD, ΔV, or simply V) between two points is measured by the work necessary to carry a unit of positive charge from one point to the other against the potential gradient. A distinction is made in using the symbols EMF and PD. The former refers to the physical or chemical source that gives rise to the potential difference and the latter to the potential difference measurable at two points along the path of a conductor, when the source is shunted.

It is customary to give a ($-$) sign to the point of greater electron density and a ($+$) sign to the point of lesser density in a metallic conductor. Electrical current is said to flow from ($+$) to ($-$). Likewise, in an electrochemical system one gives a ($-$) sign to the point or area where the anion concentration minutely exceeds the cation concentration and a ($+$) sign to the area where the reverse is true. When a membrane separates two solutions, one frequently speaks of an "outside" and an "inside" potential, Ψ_o and Ψ_i, respectively. The potential difference across the membrane may then be expressed as: $PD = \Delta V = V = (\Psi_o - \Psi_i)$; or $-(\Psi_i - \Psi_o)$. The equality $(\Psi_o - \Psi_i) = +40$ mV states that the outside potential (Ψ_o) is more positive (or less negative) relative to the inside potential (Ψ_i) which is less positive (or more negative). This may be also expressed as $(\Psi_i - \Psi_o) = -40$ mV.

3. *Volt* (V). One volt is that potential difference against which one joule of work is done in the transfer of one coulomb of electrical charge. 1 volt $= 1$ joule $\times 1$ coulomb^{-1}.

4. *Electrical current* (I). This is the rate of transfer of electrical charge.

5. *Ampere* (A). One ampere is a current or charge transfer of one coulomb per second. 1 ampere $= 1$ coulomb $\times$ sec^{-1}.

6. *Electrical resistance* (R; r). This is the property of conductors which determines the current produced by a given potential difference. The reciprocal of resistance is called *conductance* ($G = 1/R$).

7. *Ohm* (Ω). One ohm is the resistance of a conductor in which a potential difference of one volt causes a flow of current of one ampere. One mho (Ω^{-1}) is the unit of conductance.

8. *Specific resistance.* The resistance of a conductor (e.g. electrolyte solution) is proportional to its length (L) and inversely proportional to its cross sectional area (A): $R = \rho L/A$. The proportionality constant (ρ) is the specific resistance. Its reciprocal is the specific conductance (κ). A conductor of 1 cm length and 1 cm^2 cross sectional area has a specific resistance of ρ ohms $\times$ cm, and a specific conductance of κ ohms^{-1} $\times$ cm^{-1}.

For membranes, L is equivalent to the thickness (d) of the membrane. Assuming that d does not change in short term experiments specific membrane resistances may be expressed as $R_M = \rho \times d = R \times A$ in units of ohms $\times$ cm^2. Similarly, specific membrane conductance may be expressed $1/R_M = G_M$ in units of ohms^{-1} $\times$ cm^{-2} or mhos/cm^2. Occasionally one finds in the older literature data on specific membrane resistances expressed in units of ohms/cm^2 which is incorrect and should read ohms $\times$ cm^2.

9. *Equivalence conductance* (Λ). This is defined by the expression $\Lambda = 1\,000\,\kappa/c$, in which c is the ion concentration in gram equivalents/1. Hence, Λ has the dimensions ohm^{-1} $\times$ cm^2/Eq. Since $\kappa = 1/\rho$, then $\rho = 1000/(\Lambda \times c)$. For a 0·1N NaCl solution (approximately equivalent to frog Ringer's), Λ(at 25°C) = 106·7 ohm^{-1} $\times$ cm^2/Eq. Thus, $\rho = 94\ \Omega \times$ cm. This says that the resistance, $R = \rho d/A$, of a 0·1N NaCl solution between two plates 1 cm^2 in area and 1 cm apart is 94 Ω. Therefore, for two plates of the same area, but only 0·1 cm (1 mm) apart, the resistance is $\simeq$10 Ω. This is equivalent to the statement that a 0·1N NaCl "fluid membrane" of 1 cm^2 area and 0·1 cm thickness has a specific membrane resistance,

$$R_M = \rho \times d = 94 \times 0·1 \simeq 10 \text{ ohms} \times \text{cm}^2$$

For a 0·01N NaCl solution (25°C), $R = 86\ \Omega$. Other R values needed in experimental work with various electrolyte solutions may be calculated from the ionic conductances given in Table I (Netter, 1959). The total conductance of a salt solution is the sum of the ion conductances listed. ($\Lambda = \lambda_{\text{cation}} + \lambda_{\text{anion}}$.) Except for weak electrolytes, the temperature coefficient at ordinary temperatures is approximately 2% per degree centigrade (Glasstone, 1946). The importance of the conductance (or resistance) values of salt solutions used in membrane studies will be further discussed on pages 65 and 75.

10. *Power.* This is the rate at which work is done.

11. *Watt.* One watt is the power of a device that delivers work at a rate of one joule per second. 1 watt = 1 joule $\times$ sec^{-1}.

12. *Power of a direct current.* To maintain a current of I ampere, an EMF

source of E volts must produce power at the rate of $E \times I$ ($= V \times I$ along the external conductor) expressed in units of joules $\times$ sec^{-1}, or watts).

13. *Electrical energy* (work, W). This is the power delivered in a given period of time, e.g. in one minute, or one hour. $W =$ power $\times$ time.

14. *Short-circuit current* (I_{sc}). This is defined as $-I_{sc} = \text{EMF}/R_i$. It is the current that flows through an EMF source, with an internal "cell" resistance

TABLE I

Equivalent ion conductances (λ) at 18°C, in ohms$^{-1} \times$ cm^2/Eq
Within the limits of physiological interest a temperature coeffi-
cient of 2% increase in λ per degree centrigrade increase in
temperature should be applied

Ion	Dilution ∞	0·001	Concentration 0·01	0·05	0·1
			g–Eq/1		
H$^+$	315	311	307	301	294
Li$^+$	33·4	32·5	30·8	28·8	27·5
Na$^+$	43·5	42·4	40·5	37·9	36·4
K$^+$	64·6	63·3	60·7	57·2	55·1
NH$_4^+$	65·8	64·7	62·5	59·1	57·4
1/2 Mg^{2+}	45	42	37	31	28
1/2 Ca^{2+}	51	48	41·9	35·2	32
OH$^-$	174	171	167	161	157
Cl$^-$	65·5	64	61·5	57·9	55·8
1/2 SO$_4^{2-}$	68·3	63·8	55·5	45	40
NO$_3^-$	61·7	60·4	57·6	53·3	50·8
HCO$_3^-$	39·0	37·8	35·9	—	30·4

of R_i Ω, when the poles are connected by a conductor of zero Ω. The negative sign indicates that I_{sc} flows from ($-$) to ($+$) within the EMF source, i.e., in a direction opposite to what is conventionally taken as the direction of current flow in the external circuit, i.e. from ($+$) to ($-$).

15. *Flux* (J). In the context of this article this expression is used to describe transport of substance, especially of ions. To be consistent with common practice the expression influx ($\vec{J}$, or J_i) and outflux ($\overleftarrow{J}$, or J_o) are used to describe unidirectional transport in the "forward" and "backward" direction across a membrane. Net flux, J_n, is the algebraic sum of influx and outflux ($J_n = \vec{J} + \overleftarrow{J}$). A convenient unit for flux is (μ Eq $\times$ cm$^{-2} \times$ h^{-1}).

16. *Current-flux equivalent* (CFE). This expression gives the quantitative relationship between flow of electrical current (in amperes) and ion flux (in Eq $\times$ sec^{-1}). Since 1 ampere is the flow of 1 coulomb/sec, and 1 Eq ion

carries (or lacks) 96 500 coulombs, the conversion of electrical current into ion flux equivalents is as follows:

$$1 \ \mu A = 1{\cdot}036 \times 10^{-5} \ \mu Eq \times sec^{-1} = 6{\cdot}22 \times 10^{-4} \ \mu Eq \times min^{-1}$$
$$= 3{\cdot}73 \times 10^{-2} \ \mu Eq \times h^{-1}$$

By convention, flow of electrical current is considered as occurring in the direction from $+$ to $-$ in the external circuit. Therefore, the above mentioned relationship states that when a positive current of 1 μA flows across a membrane of a given area, a net flux of $6{\cdot}22 \times 10^{-4}$ $\mu Eq/min$ of positive ions

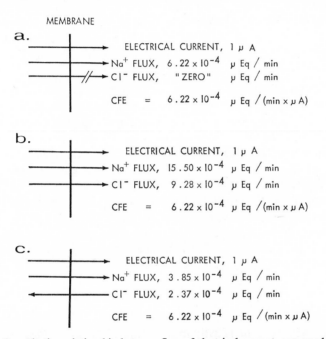

FIG. 1. Quantitative relationship between flow of electrical current, expressed in μA, and net cation (Na^+) and anion (Cl^-) fluxes. This illustration emphasizes the point, that flow of electrical current in a given direction can be accounted for by movements of cations and anions in the direction indicated. The driving forces may be active (metabolic) or passive (diffusion). For each experimental situation, ion flux measurements are needed to "explain" the chemical basis for the electrical current. (a) The membrane is considered as permeable to Na^+ and impermeable to Cl^- ions. (b) and (c) The membrane is permeable to Na^+ ions and to some degree to Cl^- ions.

(cations) occurs in the direction of the current flow, or a flow of $6{\cdot}22 \times 10^{-4}$ $\mu Eq/min$ of negative ions (anions) occurs in the direction opposite to the positive current. In other words, the CFE is $6{\cdot}22 \times 10^{-4}$ $\mu Eq/(min \times \mu A)$. The extent to which the several ions present in the system contribute to the current must be experimentally determined with isotopes. Several factors which must be considered are as follows: active ion transport; ion permeability of the membrane and ion concentrations, as well as the presence of osmotically active substances in the solutions on the two sides of the membrane. This is further explained diagrammatically in Fig. 1. Generally speaking,

$$[\Sigma J_n \overrightarrow{(\text{cations})} - \Sigma J_n \overrightarrow{(\text{anions})}] \; \mu\text{Eq/min}$$

$$= 6{\cdot}22 \times 10^{-4} \; \mu\text{Eq/(min} \times \mu\text{A)} \times \overrightarrow{I} \; \mu\text{A}$$

in the case that both ions species flow in the direction of the positive current. Or,

$$[\Sigma J_n \overrightarrow{(\text{cations})} + \Sigma J_n \overleftarrow{(\text{anions})}] = 6{\cdot}22 \times 10^{-4} \times \overrightarrow{I}$$

in the case that cations flow in the direction of the positive current and anions flow in the opposite direction. Thus, an investigation to establish the chemical basis for an electric current flowing across a membrane with solutions of different ionic composition (or activity) on the two sides can become a tedious experimental task. This is especially true if the membrane engaged in active ion transport is also permeable in varying degrees to passively moving ions, for net ion flux of passively moving ions of the species i can take place if the electrochemical potentials of the ion at the sides A and B of the membrane are unequal ($\bar{\mu}_i^A \neq \bar{\mu}_i^B$).

The electrochemical potential is given by the sum of the chemical and electrochemical potentials. Thermodynamic ion equilibrium across the membrane permeable to a particular ion species is reached if

$$RT \ln a_i^A + zF\Psi_i^A = RT \ln a_i^B + zF\Psi_i^B \tag{1}$$

In this equation a_i is the activity of the ion species i, present at a given concentration, relative to its activity in the so called "standard state" (a_i^0) which is taken as unity for a unimolar solution. Hence the expression behind the ln sign has no dimension (Ives and Janz, 1961). The internal electrical potential of the solution containing the ions is Ψ_i. Its absolute value is not determinable. However, a difference between the Ψ_i values of the solutions at the two sides of the membrane, $\Psi_i^A - \Psi_i^B = \Delta\Psi_i$, is observed across membranes which have preferential ion permeabilities. This PD is called membrane diffusion potential. It is equal to the EMF of a cell which consists of: calomel half cell/ saturated KCl bridge/solution A/membrane/solution B/saturated KCl bridge/calomel half cell. In equation (1) R, T, z, and F have conventional thermodynamic meaning.

The existence of a membrane diffusion potential obscures the study of an electrogenic active ion transport mechanism. Therefore, in order to avoid the generation of membrane diffusion potentials, and to circumvent the drawing of a current derived from this source when short-circuiting the membrane, one must place identical solutions at the two sides of the membrane. If this is not possible, the analysis of the current/flux relationship is complicated by the fact that net ion diffusion produced by concentration gradients must also be taken into account. This is relatively simple in short-circuited membranes if the permeability coefficients for the participating ions (Pi) are known. Net ion flux, and the rate of electrical charge transfer across the membrane can be calculated by applying Fick's law : $J_n^i = P_i(a_i^A - a_i^B)$.

The current-flux equivalent relationship discussed above is valid for any current flowing across a membrane of varying permeability for cations and anions. It also holds for a very special case of great interest in membrane transport studies, i.e., when the current is adjusted in such a manner as to keep an existing PD across the membrane (regardless of the origin of PD) at "zero". This is accomplished by reducing all external resistances (those not arising in the membrane system) to zero. The current that is then drawn from the system is the apparent maximal, or the "short-circuit current" (see pages 58–68). Several experiments to be described utilize this approach.

It is also quite important to realize that when a current flows across the membrane (closed circuit) cations and anions need not travel in equivalent amounts across the membranes. Chemical reactions occur at the electrodes and release into or remove ions from the solutions at the two sides of the membrane. For instance, if calomel electrodes are used to establish a closed circuit and if the membrane is only permeable to Na^+ (diffusing along a gradient), or actively transports Na^+ ions (in the absence of a gradient), Cl^- ions are generated from Hg_2Cl_2 into the compartment into which Na^+ moves. Simultaneously, Cl^- ions are removed as Hg_2Cl_2 from the compartment from which Nay disappears (see page 71). Thus, the total current flowing across membrane is carried by Na^+ ions.

LAWS AND RULES APPLICABLE TO DIRECT CURRENT ELECTRICITY

1. *Ohm's law.* The current flowing in a conductor is proportional to the potential difference at the ends of the conductor and inversely proportional to its resistance. $I = V/R$.

2. *Kirchhoff's rules. First rule* : The algebraic sum of the currents which meet at any point of a network is zero. *Second rule* : The algebraic sum of the IR products in any loop of the network is equal to the algebraic sum of the EMFs in the loop.

3. *Current in a simple circuit.* $I = E/(R + r)$, in which R is the external resistance, and r is the resistance of the source of the EMF.

4. *Total resistance of n conductors in series* : $R = R_1 + R_2 + R_3 \ldots + R_n$.

5. *Total resistance of n conductors in parallel*:

$$\frac{1}{R} = \frac{1}{R_1} + \frac{1}{R_2} \cdots + \frac{1}{R_n}$$

Constants, Coefficients, Conversion of Units

1. The prefixes kilo (K)-, milli (m)-, micro (μ)-, nano (n)-, and pico (p)- are used to express 10^3, 10^{-3}, 10^{-6}, 10^{-9}, and 10^{-12} times a given unit (e.g. meter, moles, watts, Ω, etc.).

2. Gas constant, $R = 8\cdot314$ joules $\times$ degree^{-1} $\times$ mole^{-1}.
$$= 1\cdot987 \text{ cal.} \times \text{degree}^{-1} \times \text{mole}^{-1}.$$

3. One joule $= 1 \times 10^7$ ergs.
One gram calorie (20°C) $= 4\cdot184$ joules.
One joule $= 0\cdot239$ cal. (20°C).

4. One Faraday (F) $= 96\ 500$ coulombs $\times$ gram-equivalent^{-1} $= 23\ 064$ cal. $\times$ volt^{-1} $\times$ gram-equivalent^{-1}.

5. $RT/F = 2\cdot52 \times 10^{-2}$ V $= 25\cdot2$ mV (20°C)
$\qquad = 2\cdot57 \times 10^{-2}$ V $= 25\cdot7$ mV (25°C)
$F/RT = 39\cdot7$ V^{-1} $= 0\cdot0397$ mV^{-1} (20°C)
$\qquad = 38\cdot9$ V^{-1} $= 0\cdot0389$ mV^{-1} (25°C).

6. Conversion of logarithms; $\ln a = 2\cdot302 \log a$; $\log a = 0\cdot434 \ln a$.

Radioisotope Data

In addition to measurement of the flow of electrical current, several experiments to be described utilize measurement of ion fluxes. Details concerning radioisotope methodology are beyond the scope of this article. The investigator is referred to books dealing with these matters (see, e.g., Chase and Rabinowitz, 1965). Some commonly used isotope data are given here to facilitate the conductance of the experiments that will be described below and the calculations of results.

1. One millicurie (mc) $= 3\cdot7 \times 10^7$ distintegrations $\times$ sec^{-1}.
One microcurie (μc) $= 2\cdot22 \times 10^6$ disintegrations $\times$ min^{-1}.

2. Physical half-life (t_h) of isotopes: Na^{22} (strong γ ray emitter), 2·6 years. Na^{24} (β and γ ray emitter), 14·9 h. K^{42} (β and γ ray emitter), 12·4 h. Cl^{36} (β ray emitter), 2×10^6 yr.

3. In experiments with short-lived isotopes, one frequently has to apply corrections to a count rate of a given sample because of decay of radioactivity. Radioactive elements decay according to the law: $A_t = A_0 e^{-0\cdot693t/t_h}$. A_t is the count rate, often expressed as counts per min (CPM), at the time t. A_0 is the count rate at "zero" time (t_0), and t_h is the so-called half-life of the element in question. It follows from this that after a time $t = 3\times$, or $10\times$ the half-life

of the element, A_t, the radioactivity of the sample at the time t is 12·5%, and 0·1%, respectively, of the activity at zero time (A_0).

Application of a correction for decay of a given sample which is counted t hours after t_0, can be done in two ways. In the context of the type of experiments under discussion, t_0 is the time when the radioactive element is added to one side of the membrane system. First method for correction: since the half-life of the element is known, calculate $A_0 = A_t e^{0·693t/t_h}$. The necessary calculations are most conveniently carried out by using mathematical tables for exponential values of e. Second method for correction: count a standard solution containing the radioactive element at zero time and again at the time t, when the experimental sample in question is counted. The sample count must be multiplied by the ratio A_0/A_t to give the "corrected count rate". A convenient standard is obtained by appropriate dilution of a small amount of fluid from the membrane compartment to which the isotope is added. Recounting this standard at various times to obtain the correction factor must always be done under identical geometric counting conditions. Often it is not necessary to calculate the numerical value of the correction factor since the results are used in calculations which express the activity of a sample relative to the activity of a source (see equation 2). Therefore, if sample and source are counted at the same time, the correction factor cancels out.

4. Specific activity (s) of a solution is defined as the count rate per ml sample containing an isotope substance (ion), divided by the equivalent concentration of the material using the same unit volume:

$$s = \frac{CPM/ml}{\mu Eq/ml} = \frac{CPM}{\mu Eq}$$

In calculations of chemical flux based on isotope flux measurements the assumption is generally made that the membrane (or membrane components) do not distinguish between the radioactive and the non-radioactive species. Hence, unidirectional flux rates ($\overrightarrow{J}$ or $\overleftarrow{J}$) for the non-radioactive species which are present in great excess over the radioactive species with flux rates of $\overrightarrow{J^*}$ (or $\overleftarrow{J^*}$), are calculated as:

$$\overrightarrow{J} = \overrightarrow{J^*}/s; \quad \text{or} \quad \overleftarrow{J} = \overleftarrow{J^*}/s \tag{2}$$

The identity of the terms on the left and right side (if not immediately obvious) is attested by the following dimensional analysis:

$$J(\mu Eq/min) = \frac{CPM/min}{CPM/\mu Eq}$$

5. In recent years the use of radio isotopes (e.g. Na[22]) and equation (2) to calculate unidirectional fluxes of non radioisotopic species (e.g. Na[23]) has

been subjected to considerable scrutiny with regard to several assumptions. Obviously, radioactive ions are physically different from their non-radioactive form. The possibility exists that metabolizing membranes of considerable structural complexity act on isotopic species of a given ion in a different manner. The frictional interactions between all ions and molecules present in the membrane and the two or more isotopic species may be significantly different. This would have important bearing on all types of studies where tracer ions are used, including experiments analysing ion flux–electrical current relationships. The enthusiastic experimenter should be aware of this problem and is referred to the literature for details (Kedem and Essig, 1965; Curran *et al.*, 1967). Fortunately, in the opinion of Curran *et al.* (1967) the "suggestion that the tracer technique is invalid because of interactions is unwarranted". These authors have calculated that "tracer flow can be used to predict flow of the bulk substance to an accuracy of a few per cent".

PHYSICAL PRINCIPLES OF "SHORT-CIRCUITING"

METHOD OF APPLYING A LOW EXTERNAL RESISTANCE

If a cell or battery with an internal resistance of R_i Ω producing an EMF of E volts is shunted by an external conductor of R_e Ω, the current I_e, in amperes, in the external conductor is given by:

$$I_e = \frac{E}{R_i + R_e} \tag{3}$$

A current, I_i, of the same magnitude flows through the EMF source from $-$ to $+$. Hence,

$$-I_i = \frac{E}{R_i + R_e} \tag{4}$$

For $R_e = $ zero Ω,

$$-I_i = -I_{sc} = \frac{E}{R_i} \tag{5}$$

What is said here for a simple cell may also be applied to a membrane, which generates an EMF of E_a volts because of "active ion transport". One can then write:

$$-I_{sc} = \frac{E_a}{R_a} \tag{6}$$

I_{sc} is given the minus sign to indicate that the short circuit current flows across the membrane from its negatively charged to its positive charged side. This is the situation if a cation is actively transported ("pumped") across the membrane generating an EMF, making the membrane side from which the cation is transported negative, and the side to which the cation is transported positive. Once this is recognized, one may omit the minus sign and deal with the magnitude of the current only.

It must be stressed that for the case $R_e =$ zero (equation 5) it is immaterial whether or not a shunt resistance R_s exists within the membrane since all the current will follow the path of zero resistance. In other words, $I_{sc} = E_a/R_a$ for $R_e = 0$, regardless of the existence of R_s. In reality R_e will never be zero, and it becomes important to ascertain the value of the current flowing via the EMF source for the case of $R' \neq 0$, in the presence of a shunt resistance (R_s) of a certain value. The network one has to consider is as follows: an EMF source (E_a) in series with a source resistance R_a, shorted by two resistances, R_s and R_e, in parallel. The shunt resistance in the membrane is R_s, and R_e is the resistance of the external circuit, containing the current measuring instrument and leads. If the laws and rules mentioned on pages 55 and 56 are applied to this network and the sign of the current is neglected, one finds for the current flowing via the EMF source (I'_{sc}),

$$I'_{sc} = (I_s + I_e) = E_a \cdot \frac{(R_s + R_e)}{R_a(R_s + R_e) + R_s R_e} \tag{7}$$

I_s is the current flowing across the internal shunt and I_e is the measurable external current at the meter. Its value is

$$I_e = E_a \cdot \frac{R_s}{R_a(R_s + R_e) + R_s R_e} \tag{8}$$

A similar expression can be obtained for I_s, except that in the numerator of equation (8) R_e appears instead of R_s.

Considering the case of $R_s \gg R_e$, equation (7) reduces to:

$$I'_{sc} \cong \frac{E_a}{R_a + R_e}$$

This is the analogue to equation (3). If $R_e =$ zero, one obtains $I'_{sc} = I_{sc} = E_a/R_a$ as the maximal current value. This value, however, will never be quite realized in practice.

METHOD OF APPLYING AN EXTERNAL CURRENT

Karger's Analysis

An electric current is sent through the membrane of such strength and in such a direction as to abolish the "spontaneous" tissue membrane potential which exists across the two faces of the membrane. This is best explained by the circuit diagram, Fig. 2, which is the one used by Karger (1959) to analyse this system for frog skin. However, in Fig. 2 an additional resistance (R_R) has been added to Karger's circuit diagram to make it more generally applicable to biological membranes. R_R stands for the resistance of the thin layers of salt solution between the anatomical surfaces of the membrane and the points near to the membranes where the electrodes for measuring the spontaneous

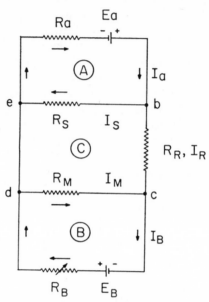

FIG. 2. Electric circuit diagram, slightly modified, to explain the physical principle involved in "short-circuiting" a membrane using an external EMF source and measuring the short-circuit current. (a), (b), (c) are three circuit loops in which the current flow is in the directions indicated. (a) is the "membrane loop" with EMF source E_a, and resistances R_a (active transport path) and R_s (passive shunt path). (b) is the "analogue loop" with EMF source E_B, variable resistance R_B, and resistance R_M of a volt meter. (c) is the loop resulting from connecting (a) and (b) as shown. This loop has R_R as a component which is the resistance of the two thin layers of Ringer's solution on either side of the membrane and the membrane potential probes, the tips of which are located at points c and d (or e). Points d (or e) and b are points at the membrane surfaces. The currents flowing in the loops are I_a, I_s, I_m, and I_B. The "short-circuit current" flowing in the outer frame of the circuit diagram is I_R. (From Fig. 4, W. Karger, Z. Naturf., **14b**, 118–124, 1959.)

membrane potential are placed. It will be shown that R_R may be neglected in some but not in all biological tissue membranes. The symbols used are defined in the legend of Fig. 2.

The net work shown consists of 3 loops, A, B, and C, A represents the membrane, B, the external circuit with the measuring instrument, the millivolt meter, and C is the loop which results from connecting A with B. One may apply Kirchhoff's rules (page 55) and proceed arbitrarily in the clockwise direction.

Applying the first rule:
At point "b"

$$I_a + (-I_S) + (-I_R) = 0; \quad \text{or} \quad I_a = (I_S + I_R) \tag{9}$$

I_S and I_R are given $(-)$ signs with reference to I_a, assuming conditions are such that I_S and I_R are currents that flow away from "b".
At point "c".

$$I_M + I_R + (-I_B) = 0; \quad \text{or} \quad I_B = I_M + I_R \tag{10}$$

Applying the second rule:

$$\text{(A):} \qquad R_a I_a + R_S I_S - E_a = 0 \tag{11}$$

$$\text{(B):} \qquad R_M I_M + R_B I_B - E_B = 0 \tag{12}$$

$$\text{(C):} \quad -R_S I_S + R_R I_R - R_M I_M = 0 \tag{13}$$

Let us now consider two special cases where $R_R = 0$ and where $R_R \neq 0$.

First case, $R_R = 0$. Applying equation (13),

$$-R_S I_S = R_M I_M \tag{14}$$

By varying R_B one achieves the condition for $I_M = 0$. It follows from (14) that I_S is also zero, i.e., the membrane has been completely short-circuited. There is no flow of current via the shunt pathway in the membrane. A current flows only through the outer circuit, and one has

$$I_a = I_B = I_{sc} \quad \text{("true" short-circuit current)} \tag{15}$$

Thus by placing a micro-ammeter in the B loop, e.g., between point c and E_B (Fig. 2) one can measure I_{sc}. We shall refer to this as the "true" short-circuit current.

Second case, $R_R \neq 0$. If R_R cannot be neglected, the simple relationship expressed by (15) no longer holds. Referring again to (13) it will be seen that for $I_M = 0$ there is flow of current, I_S, equal to $I_R R_R / R_S$. Figure 3 facilitates analysis of this situation (Asano, 1964).

Asano's Analysis

Using the relationship given on page 56 one can write for the voltage–current (V, I_B) relationship:

$$V = \left(\frac{R_a R_S}{R_a + R_S}\right) . I_B = \left(\frac{R_S}{R_a + R_S}\right) . E_a + R_R I_B \tag{16}$$

or

$$V = I_B \left(R_R + \frac{R_a R_S}{R_a + R_S}\right) + E_a \left(\frac{R_S}{R_a + R_S}\right) \tag{17}$$

Introducing into (17)

$$E'_a = E_a \cdot \frac{R_S}{R_a + R_S} \qquad \text{(Resting potential)}$$

and

$$R_M = \frac{R_a R_S}{R_a + R_S} \qquad \text{(Membrane resistance)}$$

recognizing that the total resistance (Ringer's solution + membrane) is

$$R_T = R_R + R_M$$

one can simplify equation (17) and write

$$V = I_B R_T + E'_a \tag{18}$$

Comparing the result expressed by equation (17) with what has been previously stated, equation (17) can be solved for I_B for the case of $R_R = 0$, and $V = 0$ (short-circuit conditions). One finds

$$-I_B = - I_{sc} = \frac{E'_a}{R_M} = \frac{E_a}{R_a} \tag{19}$$

It is clear from (17) that if R_R cannot be neglected, the current I_B which flows in the external circuit is not the "true" short-circuit current. It may be referred to as the "apparent" short-circuit current, I'_{sc}. The relationship between I_{sc} and I'_{sc} is then important and can be obtained by again making use of equation (17). For $V = 0$.

$$-I'_{sc} \left(R_R + \frac{R_a R_S}{R_a + R_S} \right) = E_a \cdot \frac{R_S}{R_a + R_S} \tag{20}$$

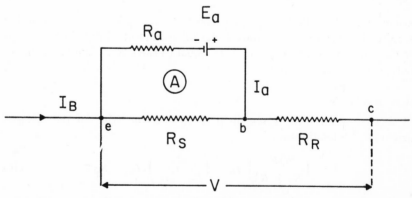

FIG. 3. Electric circuit diagram (after Asano, 1964). This circuit is identical with loop (A) and R_R (Fig. 2). I_B is the depolarizing current. Symbols and lettering are the same used in Fig. 2. (From Fig. 7, T. Asano, *Am. J. Physiol.*, **207**, 415–422, 1964.)

Introducing for the sum of the resistance terms on the left side the total resistance R_T, which is equal to $(R_R + R_M)$ and multiplying both numerator and denominator on the right side by R_a, one obtains

$$I'_{sc}R_T = -\frac{E_a}{R_a}(R_T - R_R) \tag{21}$$

Since $E_a/R_a = -I_{sc}$ ("true" short-circuit current) the relationship between I_{sc} and I'_a is given by

$$I_{sc} = I'_{sc} \cdot \frac{R_T}{R_T - R_R} \tag{22}$$

True Short-circuit Current, Calculated by Applying a Correction Factor

Equation (22) states that when R_R cannot be neglected the "true" short-circuit current can be obtained by calculation, provided one also takes a measurement of the total resistance. It is worth mentioning that (22) holds true regardless of area since both R_T and R_R increase or decrease by the same factor when the area decreases or increases, respectively.

When R_R cannot be neglected, equation (22) can be used to calculate to what degree the "true" short-circuit current (I_{sc}) is underestimated. Table II gives the result of such calculations. From a practical viewpoint when R_R is 5% or less of the total membrane resistance (R_T) the current measured in the external circuit (for $V = 0$) may be taken as the "true" short-circuit current. In agreement with what has been said previously, equation (22) also shows that for $R_R = 0$, $I_{sc} = I'_{sc}$.

TABLE II

Degree of underestimation of the "true" short circuit current (I_{sc}).
R_R = resistance of Ringer's solution
R_T = total membrane resistance

Fraction of R_R relative to R_T	Underestimation of I_{sc}
%	%
2·0	2·0
5·0	5·3
10·0	11·1
20·0	25·0
30·0	42·8
40·0	66·6
50·0	100·0

It is clear that some caution is necessary in short-circuit current measurements. Only if $R_T \gg R_R$ can the current which is measured in the external circuit be taken as the "true" short-circuit current, the parameter which is often related to simultaneously conducted ion flux measurements. As mentioned on page 51 a $0 \cdot 1 \text{N}$ NaCl solution of 1 cm² area and 1 mm thickness has a specific "membrane" resistance of approximately 10 Ω × cm². A thickness of 1 mm is used, because the distances of 0·5 mm on the two sides of a membrane approach the practical limit for close positioning of the two electrical leads at the membrane surfaces to measure (or abolish, in the case of short-circuiting) the membrane potential. In Table III are listed the average specific resistances, R_M, of the biological membranes with which this article is concerned. When using the data given in Table III, it is important to realize that the relationship between R_R and R_T may change during an experiment. For instance, metabolic inhibitors and hormones often change R_T and it must be determined whether the current measured under varying conditions is the "true" or the "apparent" short circuit. If the latter is the case, equation (22) must be applied. To accomplish this, R_R must be obtained by calculations

TABLE III

Average specific "resting" resistance, R_M, and conductances, G_M, under physiological conditions, applicable to the animal species referred to in the Table. It must be noted that the effective surface area in some tissues (stomach; gut) is difficult to assess, but is larger than that calculated from simple geometric measurements, applicable to structures with a sheet-like eqidermis (skin; bladder)

Tissue	R_M	G_M	References
	Ω × cm²	$k\Omega^{-1} \times$ cm^{-2}	
Frog skin (*Rana temporaria*)	1000	1·0	Gerstner (1939a; 1939b)
			Linderholm (1950)
Frog skin (*Rana pipiens*)	800	1·3	Myers *et al.* (1961)
Toad Bladder (*Bufo marinus*)	3500	0·3	Leaf *et al.* (1958)
Fresh-water turtle bladder			
(*Pseudemys scripta*)	2500	0·4	Klahr and Bricker (1964)
Frog stomach mucosa			
(*Rana temporaria*)	500	2·0	Hogben (1955)
Frog stomach mucosa			
(*Rana pipiens*)	200	5·0*	Durbin and Heinz (1958)
Frog large intestine			
(*Rana catesbiana*)	400	2·5*	Cooperstein and Hogben (1959)
Dog stomach	200	5·0	Rehm (1939; 1953)
Rat small intestine	50	20·0	Asano (1964)
Rabbit ileum	60	16·7*	Schultz and Zalusky (1964a)

* In the literature these values are expressed as 5·0, 2·5, and 16·7 mmhos/cm².

or actual measurements under a given set of conditions, excluding the membrane from the system. Also, R_R may be considerably greater than 10 Ω if one uses salt solutions of a concentration less than 0·1 N. This would be the case for a diluted NaCl–sugar solution with a total osmolarity equal to a 0·1 NaCl solution placed on one side of the membrane. Also, it should be noted that the data on R_M (Table III) are based on the readily measurable surface area, i.e. the one obtained either from simple geometric calculations, or from planimetric measurements at the end of experimentation. These methods are correct in practice if the effective "membrane" is in the overall geometric plane which is used for establishing the membrane area. This may be acceptable for such tissue membranes as frog skin or bladder from the toad or turtle because the epithelium, the tissue of interest, constitutes a nearly plane surface. However, this is not true for stomach and intestine.

True Short-circuit Current Obtained by Over Short-circuiting

It was pointed out in the previous section that under short-circuit conditions ($V = 0$), I_B is the "apparent" short-circuit current (I'_{sc}) if R_R in equation 17 is not zero. Recognizing that $I'_{sc}R_R = V_R$, i.e., the voltage drop across the resistance R_R, one can rewrite equation (17) as:

$$(V - V_R) = I'_{sc} \left(\frac{R_a R_S}{R_a + R_S} \right) + E_a \left(\frac{R_S}{R_a + R_S} \right) \tag{23}$$

From Fig. 3 it is apparent that if one brings ($V - V_R$) equal to zero (rather than $V = 0$), the current required to accomplish this is the "true" short-circuit current, $-I_{sc} = E_a/R_a$. This is obtained if one inserts I_{sc} for I'_{sc} in equation (23) and solves for I_{sc}, for the condition ($V - V_R$) = 0. To achieve this experimentally V is made equal to $V_R = I'_{sc} \times R_R$, i.e., one over short-circuits the system.

The following example will illustrate the procedure. Consider 6·5 cm² of frog skin in a chamber containing 0·1N NaCl solution on both sides of the skin. The epidermis will be electrically negative relative to the corium before short-circuiting. Let us assume that the skin potential electrodes are placed 0·5 mm away from the surfaces of the skin. This is the same as saying that a "salt solution membrane" of 0·1 cm thickness is in series with the skin membrane. The resistance of the salt solution membrane is $R_R = \rho \times d/A$, or $94 \times 0·1/6·5 = 1·4$ Ω (see page 51). Furthermore, assume that the apparent short-circuit current $I'_{sc} = 600$ μA (0·6 mA) per 6·5 cm². Therefore, $I'_{sc} \cdot R_R = 0·9$ mV. In other words, if one makes the skin at the epithelial side 0·9 mV positive relative to the corium, one draws the "true" short-circuit current. This seems to be little different from the condition of completely cancelling the PD between the skin potential electrodes. As has been pointed out on page 64, the need to consider this difference in PD settings becomes increasingly important with solutions of low conductance, or with tissue membranes of low spontaneous PD and low resistance.

Significance of Liquid Junction Potentials in Short-circuit Current and PD Measurements

As pointed out on page 59 the method of short-circuiting a membrane by applying an external current requires measurements of the membrane potential. The aim is to cancel this potential. Therefore, two "potential probes" must be placed near the outer and inner face of the membrane. These probes are connected to a millivolt meter via calomel half cells or Ag/AgCl electrodes. Two types of "potential probes" are used, Ringer-agar probes or saturated KCl agar probes. If the solutions on the two sides of the membrane are identical in ionic composition and concentration, both types of probes are equally satisfactory to obtain the true short-circuit if correction is applied for the resistance of the fluid layers between probes and membrane surfaces (see pages 63–65). However, if the solutions on the two sides of the membrane are not identical in ionic composition or concentration, the question arises whether a difference in liquid junction potentials (ΔE_J) leads to false short-circuit current readings. It can be shown that this is not the case, for the liquid junction potentials are in series with a high input impedance millivolt meter and this resistance approaches infinite value at the point of null balancing. Hence, no current is drawn from this source.

However, the existence of a difference in liquid junction potentials must be taken into account in "open" membrane potential measurements. The polarity of ΔE_J may be the same or opposite of the membrane potential and is dependent on the composition and the concentration of the solution on the two sides of the membrane. Values of a few mV to 10 mV may be encountered in experiments of interest to physiologists. Frequently in ion flux and short circuiting experiments, the "open" membrane potential is measured at intervals. The measured potential may or may not be the "true" membrane potential depending on whether the system is or is not free of a difference in liquid junction potentials at the level of the potential probes. The best method to avoid errors is to use saturated KCl-agar bridges. It is well known that liquid junction potentials between saturated KCl solution and salt solutions of varying composition are negligible. If one decides against use of saturated KCl probes and prefers use of Ringer-agar probes, one can calculate approximate values for liquid junction potentials and use these data to apply corrections to the measured potential readings.

For calculations of liquid junction potentials, one may use the Henderson equation (Henderson, 1907, 1908) which in its most general form is as follows:

$$E_J = \frac{RT}{F} \cdot \frac{(U_I - V_I) - (U_{II} - V_{II})}{(U_I' + V_I') - (U_{II}' + V_{II}')} \ln \frac{U_I' + V_I'}{U_{II}' + V_{II}'} \tag{24}$$

E_J is positive if the current flow via the junction is from solution "one" to solution "two". In other words, in the external circuit current flows from solution "two" to solution "one", or $E_J = (\Psi_2 - \Psi_1)$. The potentials of solution "one" and solution "two" are Ψ_1 and Ψ_2, respectively. In equation (24) R, T, and F have their usual thermodynamic meaning. The other symbols are defined by Henderson as follows:

$$U_I = u_1 c_1 + u_2 c_2 + u_3 c_3 + \ldots$$
$$V_I = v_1 \bar{c}_1 + v_2 \bar{c}_2 + v_3 \bar{c}_3 + \ldots$$
$$U'_I = u_1 c_1 w_1 + u_2 c_2 w_2 + u_3 c_3 w_3 + \ldots$$
$$V'_I = v_1 \bar{c}_1 \bar{w}_1 + v_2 \bar{c}_2 \bar{w}_2 + v_3 \bar{c}_3 \bar{w}_3 + \ldots$$

The symbols U_{II}, V_{II}, U'_{II}, V'_{II} are analog sums. The equivalent concentration of the ions is denoted by c, the mobilities of cations and anions by u and v and the valency (without sign) of the ions of the species 1, 2, 3 . . . by w. Bars over the symbols are used to identify values for the anions. For incompletely dissociated electrolytes, the equivalent concentrations must be multiplied by the degree of dissociation, α. Values for α can be obtained from physicochemical tables. Ion mobilities are calculated as: u (or v) $= \lambda/96\,500$. The necessary λ data are given in Table I. Interpolated λ values must be used for concentrations not listed in Table I. This is justified on the basis that exact values for liquid junction potentials are difficult to obtain. Mention should also be made that several simpler equations for the calculation of liquid junction potentials have been derived from equation (24) for cases where the electrolytes on the two sides of the junction have some common characteristic. The reader is referred to standard textbooks on Physical Chemistry and Electrochemistry.

Practical Conclusions Drawn from the Principles Discussed in this Section

On pages 59–67 the physical principles of "short-circuiting" tissue membranes have been discussed. Attention has also been called to factors which, if neglected, may lead to false interpretation of the actually measured current. Whether this current is or is not the true short-circuit current (I_{sc}) depends upon the electrical resistance of the salt solution between the membrane potential probes, relative to the electrical resistance of the membrane. Only if the resistance of the salt solution is much smaller than the membrane resistance can the measured current be taken as practically identical with I_{sc}. If this is not the case, one of two procedures must be applied to obtain I_{sc} as follows: (1) The specific resistance of the salt solution must be calculated or measured and a correction applied to the values of the measured current (see pages 63–65); (2) The membrane must be over short-circuited, in which case the measured current is I_{sc} (see page 65). If the salt solutions on the two sides of the membrane are not identical and Ringer-agar potential probes are used, a difference in liquid junction potentials (ΔE_J) on the two sides of the membrane may be a significant source of error in "open" membrane potential measurements, but not in short-circuit current measurements. Hence, a correction must be applied to the PD measurements as explained on pages 66–67. Approximate values for liquid junction potentials can be calculated. In situations like these, saturated KCl-agar membrane potential probes rather than Ringer-agar probes are generally recommended since KCl probes are nearly free of liquid junction potentials. However the degree of KCl leakage should be estimated.

CALCULATION OF MEMBRANE RESISTANCE

It is customary in membrane studies to calculate a membrane resistance (R_M) by dividing the "open" membrane potential by the short-circuit current (I_{sc}). By "open" membrane potential is meant the PD that can be measured between the two surfaces of the membrane. This measurement is performed by placing two electrical leads (Ringer-agar leads) into the solutions at the two sides of the membrane and connecting them (usually via calomel half cells) to a millivolt meter of high impedance. Since under these conditions little if any current flows in the external measuring circuit, the measured PD may be designated by $V_{I_B=0}$. However, there is current flowing within the membrane and if one applies the "equivalent circuit" depicted by loop A (Fig. 2; loop B and C are considered disconnected) one has for $V_{I_B=0}$ between points b and e:

$$V_{I_B=0} = \left(\frac{R_S}{R_a + R_S}\right) E_a \tag{25}$$

By definition (neglecting the sign):

$$I_{sc} = \frac{E_a}{R_a} \tag{26}$$

Combining (25) and (26) gives:

$$V_{I_B=0} = \left(\frac{R_a R_S}{R_a + R_S}\right) I_{sc} \tag{27}$$

The resistance term in (27) is the membrane resistance, R_M, according to page 56(5). Hence,

$$R_M = \left(\frac{V_{I_B=0}}{I_{sc}}\right) \tag{28}$$

If the resistance in the measuring circuit includes a resistance of Ringer's solution between potential probes and membrane surfaces (R_R) which is not negligible, one may again resort to equation (22) which may be written as:

$$I_{sc} = I'_{sc}\left(\frac{R_M + R_R}{R_M}\right) \tag{29}$$

since $R_T = R_M + R_R$.

Introducing I_{sc} from (29) into (28) yields:

$$R_M = \frac{V_{I_B=0}}{I'_{sc}} - R_R$$

I'_{sc} is the apparent short-circuit current which is actually measured under the condition that R_R cannot be neglected.

If the membrane behaves like a simple ohmic conductor (i.e. follows Ohm's law), measurement of R_M can also be made by sending a polarizing current, i (the short-circuit is a depolarizing current) through the membrane and calculate R_M from:

$$R_M = \left(\frac{V_{I_B=i} - V_{I_B=0}}{i}\right) - R_R \tag{30}$$

This method has been used by Heinz and Durbin (1957) and Durbin and Heinz (1958) to measure the conductance of frog gastric mucosa but it also may be applied to other tissue membranes.

It should be stressed that the assumption is tacitly made that the membrane behaves like a simple wire conductor to which Ohm's law can be applied. If the density of the current which flows through the membrane is of the order of 10 to 20 μA/cm^2, the assumption seems tenable. It must be realized, however, that the modes of current conduction in biological membranes and in metallic conductors are physically different. The interested reader is referred to the vast literature on "membrane impedance", which is beyond the aims of this article. (See e.g., Gerstner, 1939a, b; Fukuda, 1944; Linderholm, 1950; Brown and Kastella, 1965). Even at the low current densities, stable currents are generally not attained immediately upon application of the external current because of polarization effects occurring within the membrane. In practice an arbitrary fixed time (1 to 2 min) is chosen before the "final" current reading is made (Heinz and Durbin, 1957).

Electrical Equipment

For measurement of potentials and currents across biological membranes of the type considered here, several pieces of general equipment are needed. They are as follows: millivolt meter; microampere meter; variable resistance; reversible reference electrodes, especially calomel, silver-silver chloride, zinc-zinc acetate and lead-lead chloride (or acetate) electrodes;

salt-bridges; dry-cells and, if desired, constant temperature water bath. The latter is usually not needed, since many experiments are of relatively short duration and room temperature may not fluctuate sufficiently to affect the results.

METERS

Potential measurements are in the range from 0 to 100 mV, current measurements in the range from 0 to 1000 μA. Occasionally higher readings are encountered. The precision of readings should be within 0·5% of full scale reading. It is an advantage to use meters which give the experimenter a choice of ranges; e.g., the same microampere meter may be set for 100 or for 1000 μA full scale. It is imperative that the millivolt meter is of the high impedance type, i.e., with an internal resistance of at least 100 KΩ. No particular models of instruments will be mentioned, here, because the choice will largely depend on the location of the experimenter. There are today many excellent direct reading and recording instruments commercially available in most locations. In addition to those mentioned, possession of a general purpose Volt–Ampere–Ohm meter (multimeter), with a wide choice of ranges, is a necessity for quick tests of battery voltages, checking broken leads, etc. Since most of the modern meters mentioned employ either vacuum tubes or solid state transistors, the experimenter should have access to electronic specialists so that problems arising from failures in components of these systems can be solved.

VARIABLE RESISTORS

Some of the experiments which will be described below call for a decade "resistance box" which permits selection of resistance, varying from 1–1000 Ω. For the short-circuit current experiments a 10-turn precision potentiometer is recommended. It can be obtained from most electronic supply houses.

REVERSIBLE REFERENCE ELECTRODES

Great care must be given to selection and use of the reference electrodes. They are used both for the measurement and control of the membrane potential, and for the application of the short-circuit current. It will be pointed out below that for the current application, other non-reversible electrodes may be used, if special precautions are taken. Reversible electrodes are electrodes which do not generate a polarization potential when current is passed through them. They maintain, within limits, the same reference potential. The chemical make-up determines the electro-chemical properties of these electrodes.

Theory and practical matters concerning reference electrodes are fully discussed in the book by Ives and Janz (1961) which the reader is urged to consult.

Calomel Half Cell

The electro-chemical system involved in the so called "saturated KCl" ($4 \cdot 81$N) calomel half cell is as follows:

$$\underbrace{\text{Hg} \quad | \quad \text{Hg}_2\text{Cl}_2 \quad | \quad \text{KCl (sat)}}_{E_{\text{calomel}} \,=\, 0 \cdot 2412 \text{ V } (25^\circ\text{C})} \quad | \quad \text{salt bridge} \quad | \quad \text{Ringer's solution}$$

$$E_{\text{calomel}} + E_{\text{liquid junction}} = 0 \cdot 2445 \text{ V } (25^\circ\text{C})$$

The potential of $+0 \cdot 2445$ V for the calomel cell is with reference to the Pt-H$_2$ electrode which, by convention, has "zero" potential. Essentially, the electrode reaction when passing a current through this system is:

$$\text{Hg} \,|\, \text{Hg}_2\text{Cl}_2 \rightleftarrows \text{Hg}_2^{2+} + 2\text{Cl}^- + 2\text{e} \rightleftarrows 2\text{Hg} + 2\text{Cl}^-$$

This shows that regardless whether the Hg is connected to the negative or the positive pole of an external battery, the interphase Hg $|$ Hg$_2$Cl$_2$ $-$ KCl remains chemically the same since the system is saturated for each component. Thus, the equilibrium potential (the reference potential) characteristic for this system does not change. However, this may not be true when the current density becomes very high, although this is not the condition of the experiments described on later pages.

Most experimenters will find it more convenient to construct their own calomel half cells rather than depend on the geometric forms commercially available. This does not present particular difficulties, but certain precautions must be taken, which are well described by Hills and Ives (1961). The following points need attention: the mercury must be clean or cleaned, if necessary. Coarse crystalline calomel is unsatisfactory. Only calomel prepared by chemical precipitation or by an electrolytic process should be used. Such a preparation, labelled "for use in calomel cells", can be purchased. A sample of calomel should be mixed with mercury and saturated KCl solution, using mortar and pestle. A thin layer of the wet paste should then be transferred with a non-metallic spatula to the surface of the mercury in the desired electrode vessel. Preferably, the glass electrode vessel should be siliconized to render it hydrophobic. A heavy layer of the mercury–calomel paste on the mercury surface never yields a "good" electrode. Connection between the mercury and an external lead is made via a piece of platinum wire which must be well sealed into a glass tube. A copper wire fused to the portion of the Pt-wire inside the glass tube is the connection to the outside circuit. An electrode designed as shown in Fig. 4 has been used for years in this laboratory and found both rigid and otherwise satisfactory in performance. It should not be assumed that such electrodes are stable for indefinite periods of time. The experimenter should start out each experiment by checking electrodes against each other (one usually has a large number of electrodes available in a laboratory) to make sure that they are "isoelectric". In practice we accept an electrode pair if the P.D. is below 1 mV.

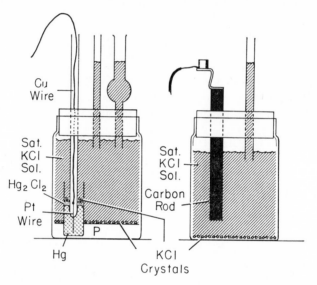

FIG. 4. Cross section of a calomel half cell (left hand side) and a carbon rod electrode (right hand side). These cells can easily be constructed from common laboratory equipment and the chemicals mentioned. P = Paraffin.

Silver-Silver Chloride Electrode

Occasionally this type of reversible electrode is used. Consult Ives and Janz (1961) for a detailed description and preparation of these electrodes. A platinum wire may be used as the electrode base. Silver is electrolytically deposited onto the platinum which is then chloridized to convert it into a Ag/AgCl electrode. It is simpler to use a cleaned silver wire and chloridize it by an electrolytic process making the Ag-wire the anode and a Pt-wire the cathode. This may be done in a beaker containing $0 \cdot 1N$ HCl. Electrolysis is done at a current density of about 1 mA/cm² for 1 or 2 h. The electrodes must then be thoroughly washed out with distilled water and then be sealed into a glass tube with plastic materials.

Zinc-Zinc Acetate Electrode

The use of this type of electrode in studies of living tissue is open to question because of the known toxic effects of zinc ions. However, this disadvantage can be circumvented by the interposition of Ringer-Agar, and full advantage taken of their low polarizability compared to calomel and silver-silver chloride electrodes. The explanation for the low polarizability is that zinc acetate (sulfate is also in use) is much more soluble than mercury and silver chloride. The same applies to lead electrodes described below.

A saturated zinc acetate solution contains 30 g $Zn(Ac)_2$ in 100 ml solution (25°C). If such a solution is prepared with 2% agar, it may be used as a semisolid "solution" which can be well contained in an electrode vessel of the form and shape desired (see Exp. No. 3; 4). A zinc plate (or rod), joined to a copper wire for connection to the external circuit, is inserted (or embedded) in the salt solution to complete the preparation. The zinc metal is usually "amalgamized". This may be done by rubbing the surface of the zinc with metallic mercury on a cotton swab until a perfectly silverish appearance of the surface is obtained. This produces a better defined electrode reference potential. The surface zinc in the amalgam behaves more like a "pure" zinc surface because of impurities contained in the bulk of the zinc.

Lead-Lead Chloride Electrode

Lund (1947) found this electrode superior to zinc-zinc sulfate electrodes. He prepared lead-amalgam electrodes as follows: chemically pure sheet-lead was added to redistilled mercury until a solid amalgam was formed which did not easily crumble. The exact lead concentration was irrelevant for the behavior of the electrode. Amalgam and electrode vessel (glass) were then heated to about 180°C and the amalgam poured into the bottom of the vessel with a sealed-in Pt wire to give a depth of about 1 cm amalgam. After cooling, the amalgam adhered well to the wall of the vessel. The top layer of the amalgam was scraped slightly and was then covered with layer of a lead chloride, 1 mm thick (see Exp. 2). Currents up to 50 $\mu A/cm^2$ for 20 h did not polarize the electrodes when exposed to Ringer's solution. Lead-lead acetate electrodes are employed in Exp. 20.

POLARIZABLE ELECTRODES

Carbon Electrode

A rod of carbon in a salt solution does not constitute a "non-polarizable" electrode. However, we have found it useful to apply short-circuit current to a membrane if care is taken that the products of electrolysis (chiefly Cl_2) do not reach tissue. Under many circumstances this can be accomplished by providing salt bridges of sufficient length. A simple way of accomplishing this is shown in Fig. 4. Such electrodes do polarize and thereby increase their resistance to flow of current. However, in practice no more adjustments in the external variable resistance (R_B, Fig. 2) are needed for constancy of the short-circuit current than are needed when using calomel half cells. Carbon electrodes are easy to prepare and easier to maintain than calomel electrodes. It is recommended that carbon rod electrodes are kept shorted when not in use, a procedure which should also be applied to non-polarizable electrodes. All cells containing saturated KCl must be kept scrupulously clean and free of "creeping" KCl crystals. Otherwise, rather erratic current loops can occur and frustrate the experimenter to no end!

Platinized Platinum Electrode

In electrical conductivity measurements the platinized platinum electrode is generally used. This electrode consists of a sheet of platinum (with Pt-wire welded onto it) which is coated with a layer of finely divided platinum black. This coating minimizes polarization effects. Deposition of platinum black is done electrolytically. The metallic platinum must be thoroughly cleaned with warm, concentrated sulfuric acid. The electrode to be coated is used as cathode and an auxiliary Pt-electrode serves as anode. The electrodes are dipped into a solution of 2% commercial platinic chloride in 2N HCl to which 0·02% lead acetate is added. This promotes the deposition of an even coat of platinum black. Electrolysis is carried out for 10–20 min using a 4 V battery and a current density of approximately 10–20 mA/cm². Several washings with distilled water are needed to remove the reagents from the platinized electrode. When such electrodes are carefully handled by their wire leads, they can be inserted or built into any shape of vessel or chamber used in a particular type of study. Like the carbon electrode mentioned above, the platinized platinum electrode when used as an anode will produce Cl_2 and hypochlorite that might be harmful to living tissue. However, under most conditions the harmful effects of these agents are insignificant. Application of this type of electrode is made in Experiment 8.

SALT BRIDGES

Connections between the solution in the membrane vessel and the measuring devices via electrodes as described on pages 70–74 are commonly made with salt bridges. Two kinds of bridges are needed, saturated KCl and Ringer bridges. Their use will be indicated in the presentation of the experiments. Both kinds of bridges may be "fluid" or semi-solid, agar supported, depending on design of apparatus and preference of the experimenter. If fluid bridges are used, one may decide to use a U-tube with outlet at the top of the angular portion through which the solution can be aspirated, free of air bubbles, to electrically complete the circuit. Agar leads have the advantage that they can be prepared in advance, stored in the appropriate solution and inserted into openings in the electrode vessel and the membrane vessel to complete the circuit. In either case, great care must be taken to avoid air bubbles, since they interrupt electrical continuity. If it appears that this might be the case, a quick test with a general purpose ohm meter (multimeter) usually reveals the source of trouble.

Agar bridges are prepared by gently heating KCl or Ringer's solution with finely granulated agar (3 %) until all agar is "dissolved". This is a slow process. Boiling of the mixture must be avoided. When a perfectly clear, transparent fluid is obtained, pieces of flexible plastic tubing are dipped into the fluid which is then aspirated into the tubing. A clamp can be attached to the free end of the tubing until the agar solution has hardened. Ten to 15 cm sections of filled tubing are then cut and placed for storage in covered vessels with saturated KCl or Ringer's solution, as the case may be. The cutting is best done with a razor blade, avoiding undue pressure. These bridges should be used only once since they change composition or may become contaminated by radioisotopic materials which are used in flux experiments. The electrical resistance of the bridges described above can be calculated by applying the equation: $R = \rho L/A$ (see page 51). Thus, each cm of a Ringer-agar bridge of 2 mm i.d. has a resistance of approximately 23000 Ω. Saturated (4·81M) KCl bridges of the dimensions given above have a considerably smaller resistance. The specific resistance of a 1M KCl solution at 25°C is given as $\rho = 8·98\ \Omega \times$ cm (Clark, 1952). For a 4·81M KCl solution, ρ must be close to $8·98/4·81 = 2\ \Omega \times$ cm. Thus, the saturated KCl-agar bridge (2 mm i.d.) has a resistance of approximately 65 Ω/cm length.

Salt bridges are used in PD measurements on membranes because some non-metallic connection must be established between the membrane, or the solutions bathing it, and the calomel cells which are connected to the measuring instrument. KCl-bridges are characterized by near absence of "diffusion potentials" because the ion mobilities for K^+ and Cl^- are very nearly the same. Under special conditions, e.g. in short term experiments, such bridges may be used directly as the link between membrane solutions and calomel cells. The difficulty with this simple method is that KCl slowly leaks out of the agar bridge into the salt solutions bathing the membrane and this may have effects on the membrane. To avoid this, one establishes the following connections: membrane solution—Ringer-agar bridge—saturated KCl solution (in beaker)— saturated KCl agar bridge—calomel cell. In this manner, possible K^+ effects on the membrane are minimized but the total resistance of the system is increased. Two Ringer-agar bridges, 2 mm i.d. and each 10 cm long, represent a resistance of approximately 60 000 Ω. This is irrelevant for PD recordings if one uses a high input impedance meter, but is a factor to consider when sending currents through membranes.

DRY CELLS

Depending on the total resistance of the electrode-membrane bridge system, several dry cells in series are usually required for short-circuiting the membrane. Large cells should be employed because they have a greater working capacity. These cells are commercially available and have a voltage of 1·56 V. When using calomel half cells to feed current into the membrane system, it must be remembered that at the cathode Hg_2Cl_2 disappears, whereas Hg_2Cl_2 is formed and deposited at the anode (see page 71). When the calomel cells are used for many hours and all Hg_2Cl_2 has disappeared from the cathode, it will no longer function as an ideal reversible cell. It is not recommended to supply a heavy layer of Hg_2Cl_2 which would overcome the problem discussed. Therefore, if one uses calomel half cells for feeding the current into the system, it is advisable to rotate them, using them as cathode and anode in alternating experiments. Because of polarization effects at carbon electrodes (page 73) voltages of 30 to 40 V are needed (occasionally higher) to short-circuit the tissue membrane. For convenience, one may resort to a DC power supply rather than batteries.

CHEMICALS AND SOLUTIONS

The chemicals needed in the experiments described on pages 80–154 should be of CP grade and distilled or demineralized water should be used to prepare the required solutions. Adjustments in pH are done with diluted (1N and 0·1N) NaOH and HCl, using a pH meter. Unless the experimental procedure demands special attention to gas tensions, a recommended procedure to assure sufficient oxygen supply to the living membrane is to bubble O_2 through the salt solution for 10 to 15 min prior to pH adjustment. Details concerning the composition of the salt media used will be given in connection with a full description of the experiments. However, it might be useful for the experimenter to tabulate chemical data on the most commonly needed salts for preparation of the salt media, see Table IV. Metabolic inhibitors, drugs and several hormones will be mentioned later in the text.

In this text, *concentrations* are most frequently given in units of M, mM, or (for ions) $\mu Eq/ml$. For instance, if it is stated that the final concentration of an inhibitor was $5 \times 10^{-5}M$, it means that the concentration was 5×10^{-5} mols/1.

Studies on the effects of chemicals on flow of current and ions in membranes are usually conducted in such a way that materials are added to the solutions bathing the tissue membrane some time (e.g. one hour) after the beginning of the experiment. This waiting period is necessary because the physical-chemical properties of the tissue are usually unstable in the beginning. For instance, one observes that the short-circuit current falls (or rises) during the first hour but thereafter reaches a steady-state level, at which time the effects of a chemical agent may be tested. Since the addition of the substance must be done with as little interference as possible, one may adopt one of two methods.

TABLE IV

Molecular weights (MW) of some common chemicals

Chemical	MW	Chemical	MW
NaCl	58·45	K_2SO_4	174·25
$NaHCO_3$	84·02	$CaCl_2$	110·99
Na_2HPO_4	142·05	$MgCl_2$	95·23
NaH_2PO_4	120·05	$MgSO_4$	120·38
Na_2SO_4	142·05	Choline chloride	139·63
KCl	74·55	Choline bicarbonate	165·18
$KHCO_3$	100·11	Glucose	180·00
KH_2PO_4	136·13	Sucrose	342·30
*Tris	121·14	Mannitol	182·17

* Tris(hydroxymethyl)-aminomethan (Tham), used as a buffer.

If the chemical very easily dissolves in water, one may add the calculated amount of substance (e.g. 10 mg) directly to the solution in the experimental chamber. If the amounts that have to be weighed out are too small to assure accuracy, or if the material is not too readily soluble, a stock solution of this substance is prepared and a small volume of it is added to the salt solution in the membrane chamber. To do this one uses "lambda pipettes" $(1\lambda = 1 \mu l = 1/1\,000$ ml). The material is dissolved in salt solution of the same composition as used in the membrane experiment. Controls must also be carried out in which an equal volume of vehicle without the chemical is added to the fluid in the chamber. For example, if one wishes to test the effect of $2 \times 10^{-5}M$ dinitrophenol (MW = 184) on the membrane, prepare a stock solution 100 times as strong i.e., $2 \times 10^{-3}M$. By dissolving 9·2 mg of dinitrophenol in 25 ml of salt solution the desired stock solution is obtained. Addition of 10 λ for each ml of salt solution in the membrane chamber gives nearly the desired final concentration of 2×10^{-5} M. Chamber sizes will vary according to the aims and needs of the investigator. Thus, if by calibration the chamber size is found to be 11·5 ml, one must add 115 λ (0·115 ml) of dinitrophenol stock solution to the fluid in the chamber.

In practice one can apply the following relationships:

$$C_{stock} = C_{final} \times \frac{1000}{n}$$

Where n is the number of λs (e.g., $\lambda \leq 10$) that are added to each ml of salt solution in the transport chamber. Limitations are imposed upon the experimenter because chemicals have limitations in their solubilities. If the chemical agents (enzyme inhibitors, drugs, hormones) are rather insoluble in water, one may choose an organic solvent, such as alcohol. If very low final concentration (10^{-6}, 10^{-7}M or lower values) are to be applied it may be practical and more economical to prepare a small volume of a concentrated stock solution, and obtain the working stock solution by further dilution in one or two steps.

SURGICAL PROCEDURES AND HANDLING OF TISSUES

Where surgical procedures on warm blooded animals are required the experimenter is referred to standard laboratory manuals and to the original literature cited in the following text.

PREPARATION OF TISSUE MEMBRANES

Tissue membranes obtained from cold blooded animals are technically simple but do require care. Preparation of abdominal frog skin usually begins with pithing or decapitation of the animal in the manner described in most Physiology Laboratory Manuals. After death, the frog is then placed on his back and the abdominal skin is excised, avoiding a strong pulling force in attempting to separate it from the underlying tissue. The skin is then placed on a clean glass or porcelain plate, epidermis downward; loose connective tissue, if present, is cautiously cut away. The skin is then quickly washed in the appropriate salt solution and is ready for mounting.

The urinary bladder of the toad and turtle is a bilobate organ which can readily be reached after pithing the animals and, in the case of the turtle, removal of the plastron. The fact that there are two half bladders available from the same animal suggests the use of one half for a particular experiment, the other half for a control study. After dissection of the bladders, they are opened and rinsed with the appropriate salt solutions before suspending them as diaphragms between two half cells. This will be described in the following text.

CHAMBER EDGE DAMAGE

Dobson and Kidder (1968) have investigated how much tissue damage occurs as a result of clamping the frog skin between two chamber halves. They found a zone, extending 0·066 mm from the clamped edge, in which the intercellular spaces are enlarged. It must be assumed that other tissue membranes also show edge damage, although the extent of the damage is not known. The edge/surface area (E/S) ratio has been used by Dobson and Kidder (1968) to relate the edge damage to short-circuit current and "open" membrane potential. The smaller the area of the tissue used, the greater is the percentage of damaged tissue. For cylindrical chamber apertures, the E/S ratio is calculated as $2\pi r/\pi r^2$. For tissue areas of 1 cm^2 and 7 cm^2 the E/S ratios are 3·54 cm^{-1}, and 1·34 cm^{-1}, respectively. For frog skin, 22% of a 1 cm^2 membrane area and 9% of a 7 cm^2 skin area show signs of tissue edge damage. Wherever possible, the use of large membrane areas is recommended to minimize edge damage effects on measurements on electrical and permeability characteristics of the membrane under investigation. Dobson and Kidder (1968) found that edge damage has no effect on short-circuit measurements in frog skin. However, open skin potentials decreased with increasing E/S ratios, up to a value of approximately 16 cm^{-1}. The damaged tissue apparently represents, in electrical terms, a shunt across the skin. Hence, only a fraction of the maximal potential generated by an electrogenic mechanism within the skin is actually measured by placing PD probes across the skin and as near as possible to the anatomical surfaces. On the other hand no effect of edge damage on the short-circuit current is expected since the current which is measured is the current which flows in the EMF source, and not via the shunt (see equation 19).

HYPOPHYSECTOMY IN FROGS

A detailed description of the procedures for removal of the anterior lobe of the pituitary gland is given in the thesis of W. R. Bishop which was kindly made available to the authors by Dr. Bradley T. Scheer (Department of Biology, University of Oregon, U.S.A.), and from which we quote nearly verbatim.

The animals are anesthetized by placing them in a jar containing a cotton swab with ether. Direct contact of the skin with the swab should be avoided. Care must be taken not to over-etherize the frogs which may result in anesthesia deaths. A better choice of applying anesthesia is to place the frogs in a 1 : 3000 solution of Tricaine–Sandoz (MS-222). (Bové, 1962).

When the frogs are sufficiently anesthetized, they are secured on a retaining board. Tongue and lower jaw are retracted and held in this position by a hemostat or by application of a suture fixed by straight pin to the board. The upper jaw must also be well fixed, by pushing a T pin through the end of the snout into the board. A medial-longitudinal incision is made through the mucous membrane lining the roof of the mouth. After application of two mosquito clamps to the lateral edges of the cut membranes, the parasphenoid bone is exposed. The base of the bone is freed from muscle and connective tissue using great care not to disturb the internal carotid plexus areas. With an electric hand-drill and a medium size bit, a hole is drilled through the bone to the capsule directly over the adenohypophysis. The point of penetration is exactly at the site of the junction of the posterior parasphenoid base and its anterior extension, at a position medial to, and at right angles from, the carotid plexus areas. The capsule itself is not penetrated by the drill but is opened with a sharp pointed scalpel. The hypophysis appears, then, as a pink-colored organ. A micropipette fitted with a rubber aspirator bulb is used to remove the adeno-hypophysis by suction, leaving the neurohypophysis intact and thus avoiding fatal hemorrhage. Occasional bleeding of the mucous membrane can be stopped by application of Gelfoam coagulant gauze. The hole in the bone is packed with surgical bone wax. This is followed by suturing the membrane flaps loosely together to allow for swelling and drainage. The animals are then rinsed with cold tap water, placed for a short period in a recovery tank and then in the regular frog container. Oral infections may be circumvented by keeping the water level in the container low.

EXPERIMENTS

1. ELECTRICAL ENERGY OUTPUT BY FROG SKIN (FRANCIS, 1933)

Objectives

A potential of 50 to 100 mV may be measured across frog skin with Ringer's solution on both sides of the skin. The epidermis is negative relative to the dermis. This experiment is designed to answer the following questions: what currents can be drawn from the shunted skin? What is the output of electrical energy?

Method of Investigation

A simple double chamber (glass or plastic) is constructed. It consists of two cylindrical cups with flat rims at the openings. Approximate dimensions are as follows: Length, 50 mm; i.d., 15 mm; membrane area, 1·8 cm². Midway in each hemichamber openings (10 mm i.d.) are made. These allow insertion of two short funnels with stem dimensions of 8 mm o.d. and 10 mm length. This part is filled with Ringer-agar. The funnel reservoir is filled with saturated KCl. End plates, tie rods, bolts and nuts are used to hold the "cell" together after placing a freshly prepared piece of abdominal skin between the cups. The cell is filled with salt solution containing per liter: 6·50 g NaCl; 0·15 g KCl; 0·2 g CaCl$_2$; 0·16 g NaHCO$_3$; 0·5 g glucose. The solution is oxygenated and adjusted to pH 7·5. Calomel cells are connected via KCl-agar bridges to a micro-ammeter and current readings are taken over a period of several hours. At the beginning and the end of the experiment, and several times during the experiment, the connection between the ammeter and one of the calomel cells is opened and the resistance of the total system is measured with a general laboratory ohm-meter. From the data, average values for current (I) and total resistance (R) are calculated.

Results and Comments

Francis (1933), who was the first to "short-circuit" the skin by a low resistance shunt, measured an average current output of 25 μA over a period of 12 h. Had the external resistance (chiefly bridges and solution) been closer to zero, the current would have been larger. Francis reported a total resistance of 1500 Ω. The skin probably contributed $1000/1 \cdot 8 = 560\ \Omega$ to the total (see Table III). Hence, approximately $\frac{2}{3}$ of the total resistance must have resided in the external circuit. Total output of electrical energy per second (w) may be calculated as: $E \times I$ (see pages 51 and 52). Alternatively, one may apply Ohm's law ($E = IR$) and calculate w $= I^2R$. Inserting average results obtained from the experiment, the calculation gives the following value: $(25 \times 10^{-6})^2 \times 1500 = 0 \cdot 94 \times 10^{-6}$ w, or 0·94 μw. This is equivalent to $0 \cdot 94 \times 10^{-6} \times 0 \cdot 239 \times 60 = 13 \cdot 5 \times 10^{-6}$ cal/min, or 13·5 microcal/min (see page 56). Referred to 1 cm^2 of skin, the values are $0 \cdot 94/1 \cdot 8 = 0 \cdot 52\ \mu$w/cm^2, or 7·5 microcal/(min $\times$ cm^2).

The study may be extended by obtaining the weight of skin involved in the electrical measurements. From metabolic data on wet frog skin which are available in the literature, the electrical energy output may then be compared with the total oxidative energy consumption. An average value for O_2 consumption of frog skin is 5 μl $\times$ min^{-1} $\times$ g^{-1} (wet). The area/weight ratio for skin (*R. pipiens*) is of the order of 45 cm^2/g. This ratio is probably higher for skin of *R. temporaria* (the European frog species) since the skin is thinner. Francis calculated that the electrical energy production is not better than 10% of the total energy consumption. The reason is that the measured current in the external circuit is probably only a fraction of the current which flows through the EMF source of the skin, because of internal shunts.

Although the energy output by frog skin is only of the order of 0·5 to 1·0 μw/cm^2, Karger (1967; 1968) has accomplished the task of setting a microwatt motor into motion by energy derived from isolated frog skin. Maximal useful energy production is obtained when the external resistance is equal to the membrane resistance.

2. THE EFFECT OF KCN ON CURRENT OUTPUT BY FROG SKIN (LUND, 1947)

Objective

It is known that the electrical potential across frog skin in Ringer's solution is observed only in "living" skin. Maintenance of cellular metabolism is a prerequisite for maintenance of the skin potential (Huf, 1935a; 1955; Huf

E

et al., 1957). This experiment is designed to answer the question: How does KCN poisoning affect the current that can be drawn from the skin by shunting it?

Method of Investigation

Two double glass chambers are constructed, as shown in Fig. 5. It is noteworthy that large lead amalgam electrodes (see page 73) are placed at the end of the cups. This is done to minimize the electrical resistance in the external circuit. The inside diameter of the chambers is approximately 28 mm.

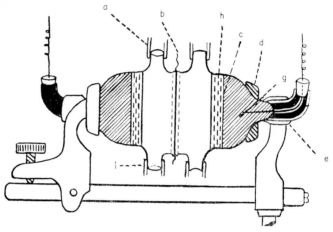

FIG. 5. Double glass chamber with frog skin (b) for measuring short circuit current. The skin is held between cloth nets (shown by dotted lines) which were fastened over the rims of the cups with rubber bands. Other components are as follows: (h) is a layer of 7% agar in physiological (0·65%) saline; (c) is a thin layer of lead chloride; (g) indicates the amalgam layer. Solution flows into the half cells through the bottom openings (i), and out of the cells at the top (a) Rubber washers (d) are placed between the half cells and the clamps. (From Fig. 1, E. J. Lund. *In* "Bioelectric Fields and Growth". The University of Texas Press, Austin, U.S.A., 1947, p. 255.)

This makes it possible to use a relatively large skin area ($\simeq 6\cdot2$ cm, $R \simeq 160\ \Omega$). The fluid volume in each half-cell is about 10 ml, which means that the depth of the free fluid compartment is 1·6 cm and the total depth of each chamber is approximately 3 cm. Such a double chamber, filled with Ringer's solution, has a resistance of 60–70 Ω. When not in use the "cell" is kept filled with Ringer's solution and shorted. Each half-chamber has an inlet (*i*) and an outlet (*a*) tube through which Ringer's solution (at constant temperature, if desired) flows at a rate of 4 ml/min. This serves two purposes. It insures against toxic effects on the skin from the electrode and it permits intermittent application of KCN to the skin. For this experiment Ringer's solution of the composition given above (Experiment No. 1) is used. A portion of the Ringer's solution contains KCN (MW $= 65 \cdot 1$). $65 \cdot 1$ mg KCN are dissolved in 1 liter of Ringer's solution, after which the pH must be adjusted to $7 \cdot 5$. Two symmetrical halves of belly skin from the same frog are mounted and, after filling the chambers, current is drawn from the skins by shunting the cells with a micro-ammeter of low resistance (Lund used $4 \cdot 5 \ \Omega$).

Results and Comments

A typical result is shown in Fig. 6. The current output was reversibly decreased by application of cyanide poison. The current produced by the control skin ($\simeq 35 \ \mu A$) was used to calculate the coulomb efficiency defined by Lund as follows:

$$\% \text{ Coulomb efficiency} = \frac{100 \times \text{total coulombs generated by skin}}{\text{coulomb equivalents of total oxygen consumed}}$$

This term was formulated by the author to state his postulate that electrical energy production is directly coupled with electron transfer to oxygen. Upon reduction, 8 g of O_2 ($= 22 \cdot 4 \times \frac{1}{4} = 5 \cdot 6$ l) take up 96 500 coulombs. The coulomb equivalent of the total amount of oxygen consumed by the skin ($6 \cdot 2 \ cm^2$) during the 5 h period (the average current flow was 35 μA) was calculated as follows:

$$\frac{96\ 500 \times 0 \cdot 0058 \times 6 \cdot 2 \times 5}{5600} = 3 \cdot 1 \text{ coulomb equivalent } O_2$$

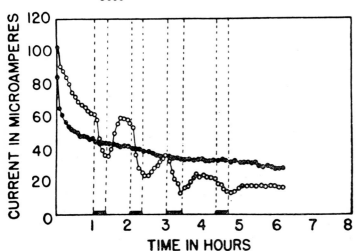

FIG. 6. Effect of KCN on current output by frog skin. The results of two individual experiments are shown: ●———● control experiment, ○———○ KCN experiment. At intervals 0·001M KCN in saline solution flowed through both half cells. The periods of application of KCN is indicated by the shaded portions of the base line. (From Fig. 4, E. J. Lund. *In* "Bioelectric Fields and Growth". The University of Texas Press, Austin, U.S.A., 1947, p. 267.)

Lund's figure for O_2 consumption of $0.0058 \, ml \times cm^{-2} \times h^{-1}$ was used. The total coulombs drawn from the skin was $35 \times 10^{-6} \, (A) \times 5 \times 3600 \, (sec) = 0.63$ coulombs. This gives a % coulomb efficiency of $0.63/3.1 = 20.4\%$. In other experiments Lund (1947) obtained coulomb efficiencies close to 100% which he used to support the theory that the EMF generation is linked to terminal electron transfer in the oxidative reaction chain. Cyanide is known to inhibit the oxidative reaction by blocking cytochrome oxidase. However, calculations of efficiencies must be viewed with criticism, since they are based on measurements of current flow in the external circuit. The amount of current which flows in the skin membrane and through the EMF source where conversion of chemical into electrical energy occurs is unknown. Calculation of this current depends on knowledge of shunts within the skin.

3. ELECTRICAL ENERGY OUTPUT OF THE DOG STOMACH (REHM, 1943, 1944)

Objectives

A variable potential difference exists across the wall of the resting dog stomach. The mucosa is negative relative to the serosa. Values close to 100 mV have been reported. This experiment is designed to answer the following questions: What currents can be drawn from the shunted stomach? What is the output of electrical energy? Does depolarization occur upon withdrawal of the current?

Method of Investigation

This experiment requires some experience in anesthetizing and operating upon warm blooded animals. Pernoston (a barbiturate, 60 to 80 mg/kg, s.c.) is recommended for anesthesia. An abdominal incision is made and, after ligation of the esophagus and pylorus, an incision is made in the ventral wall of the stomach. Warm saline is used to wash out the stomach. Two zinc-saturated zinc acetate agar (2%) electrodes, with an outer layer of Ringer-agar (see page 73), are placed in opposition to each other across the stomach so that the Ringer-agar surfaces touch to the mucosa and serosa firmly but without excessive pressure. The electrodes (11 to 12 cm^2), which are constructed in the form of circular cups, and the protruding wires attached to the zinc plate are connected to the external circuitry for electrical shunting of the wall of the stomach. The cups are filled with saturated $Zn(Ac)_2$ agar (2%) around the zinc plate. An outer layer of mammalian Ringer-agar (2%) is then applied to prevent $Zn(Ac)_2$ from coming in contact with the stomach. The electrode wires are connected to a variable resistance. The voltage drop across the chosen resistance may then be measured with a high impedance voltmeter. The current which flows through the system, including the portion of the wall of the stomach between the electrodes, is calculated from $I = V/r$. The chosen resistance is r, and V is the voltage drop across r. If r is expressed in ohms and V in mV, I is the current in mA. During the experiment care must be taken to keep the animal and stomach warm and deep anesthesia should be avoided. When fairly stable PD levels are observed, the dependence of PD on varying external resistance (a few ohms to several hundred ohms) is systematically studied. The electrodes prepared as described above have a resistance of 10 to 20 Ω. The Ringer's solution needed in this experiment should be "mammalian Ringer". One liter of solution contains the following salts: 9·00 g NaCl; 0·42 g KCl; 0·24 g $CaCl_2$; 0·2 g $NaHCO_3$.

Results and Comments

A typical result obtained by Rehm (1943) is shown in Fig. 7. The left half of this illustration gives a plot of total external resistance in ohms (electrode resistance + variable resistance from the resistance box) versus flow of

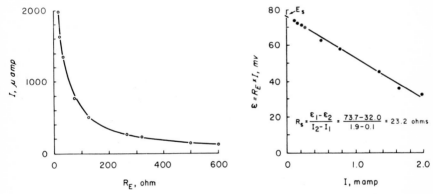

FIG. 7. Left side: dependence of flow of current (I), across the dog's stomach on resistance in the external circuit (R_E). Right side: Plot of $\epsilon = R_E \times I$ versus I. The straight line shown represents the equation $R_E I = E_s - R_s I$, in which E_s and R_s are the electromotive force of the stomach and its resistance, respectively. (From Fig. 1A, B, W. S. Rehm, *Am. J. Physiol.*, **139**, 1–8, 1943; redrawn.)

current in μA. The resulting graph shows the characteristics of a rectangular hyperbola, which one should obtain if Ohm's law applies. Since the total resistance (R_T) is the sum of the resistance of the wall of the stomach (R_S) and the external resistance (R_E), application of Ohm's law gives

$$I(R_S + R_E) = E_S \qquad (31)$$

or

$$R_E I = E_S - R_S I \qquad (32)$$

E_S is the EMF source within the stomach (mucosa), that gives rise to I. Both R_E and I are known from the experiment. When $R_E I$ was plotted against I, the graph shown in the right hand part of Fig. 7 was obtained which is the linear relationship predicted by equation (32). This implies that E_S remained constant. In other words, no depolarization of E_S occurred during flow of currents up to 2 mA. This graph demonstrates that Ohm's law holds for the wall of the dog's stomach under the conditions of this experiment. Furthermore, extrapolation of the straight line to intersect with the ordinate ($I = 0$) yields a value for $E_S = 76$ mV. Here, as in experiment No. 1, the true EMF within the mucosa of the stomach depends on the unknown internal shunts. However, it is likely that the EMF $> E_S$. From the slope of the lines, such as shown in Fig. 7, R_S was calculated as indicated. In this experiment R_S is 23·2 Ω. Multiplication of these values by the stomach area (11·6 cm^2) gives the specific membrane resistance: $23 \cdot 2 \times 11 \cdot 6 = 269\ \Omega \times$ cm^2 (see Table III). The electrical energy output of the stomach can be calculated from the experiment plotted in the left half of Fig. 7. The lowest total resistance was 16·5 (15·5 Ω, electrodes $+$ 1 Ω, box). Thus, the stomach was almost completely short-circuited and produced nearly maximal current in the external circuit of 2mA. Since depolarization of the EMF source did not occur, electrical energy output per sec may be calculated as follows: $w = E_S \times I = 0 \cdot 076 \times 0 \cdot 002 = 152 \times 10^{-6}$ w, or 152 μw. Referred to 1 cm^2 of stomach surface: $w = 152/11 \cdot 6 = 13 \cdot 1\ \mu$w/cm^2. Frog skin (Experiment No. 1) showed an electrical energy output of 0·52 μw/cm^2, i.e., about 1/25 that of dog stomach. However, dog stomach as compared to frog skin has a considerably greater O_2 consumption. Frog skin consumes O_2 at an approximate rate of $0 \cdot 05\ \mu l \times$ min$^{-1} \times$ cm^{-2} (wet). Rehm (1943) quotes a Q_{O_2} value of $4\ \mu l \times$ min$^{-1} \times$ g^{-1} (wet) for dog stomach. The area/weight ratio in the case of stomach is approximately 3 cm^2/g. It is about 45 cm^2/g for frog skin. Hence the Q_{O_2} for dog stomach can be given as close to $1 \cdot 33\ \mu l \times$ min$^{-1} \times$ cm^{-2}, which is about 1/25 of the Q_{O_2} value for frog skin. Thus, the efficiency of conversion of the total energy consumed into electrical energy in the dog's stomach is not greater than in the frog skin (see Experiment 1). Rehm (1943) calculated an efficiency of about 4%. He pointed out that this must be considered as an approximate, minimal figure because it is not known how much current flows via shunts within the mucosa of the stomach.

4. EFFECTS OF ELECTRIC CURRENT ON GASTRIC SECRETION AND POTENTIAL (REHM, 1945)

Objectives

In Experiment No. 3, it was pointed out that a potential difference exists across the "resting" dog's stomach. The mucosa is negative relative to the serosa. It is also known that the mucosa is the site of formation and secretion of HCl. This experiment is designed to answer the following two questions: How is the rate of HCl secretion affected by an applied electric current? Is there a correlation between rate of HCl secretion and potential difference across the wall of the stomach?

Method of Investigation

The procedures for the anesthetizing and operation are the same as described in Experiment No. 3. The dogs are fasted for 24 to 30 h before use. A double lucite chamber is constructed as shown in Fig. 8. In this illustration, the mucosa is oriented to the left and the serosa to the right. The opening of

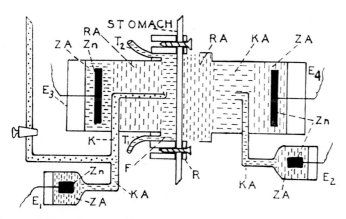

Fig. 8. Schematic drawing of a sagittal section of the apparatus with dog stomach in place. R refers to a lucite ring. This ring has an oblique cut in it so that the blood vessels (not shown) supplying the portion of the stomach in the chambers will not be occluded. RA refers to Ringer agar (or saline agar), KA to saturated KCl agar, ZA to saturated zinc acetate agar; K to saturated KCl solution; F to the fluid in the chamber. Electrodes E_1 and E_2 are connected to a potentiometer for measurement of the potential difference across the stomach. Electrodes E_3 and E_4 are used for sending current through the stomach. (From Fig. 1, W. S. Rehm, *Am. J. Physiol.*, **144**, 115–125, 1945.)

the tube (~ 0.5 mm i.d.) filled with saturated KCl solution establishes electrical connection between electrode E_1 and the saline solution in the chamber (F). The chamber F holds approximately 20 ml of fluid and the mucosal surface area is approximately 20 cm². The electrode on the serosal side makes contact with the tissue by the protruding Ringer-agar portion of the electrode. Its area is somewhat less than that of the mucosal surface electrode. This is to prevent pressure occlusion of blood vessels supplying the section of the stomach under investigation. The lucite ring (R), by which the wall of the stomach is held against the chamber F, is provided with an oblique cut to accommodate the blood vessels supplying the portion of the stomach in the chamber. Ten to twelve screws are used to fasten the ring to the chamber. The chamber is filled and flushed through the tubes T_1 and T_2. Currents of the order of a few $\mu A/cm^2$ are sent through the wall of the stomach via the electrodes E_3 and E_4, which are part of an external circuit. It consists of storage battery, variable resistance, milliammeter and a switch. Non polarizable $Zn/Zn(Ac)_2$ electrodes (E_1 and E_2) are connected to a high impedance millivolt meter for PD measurements when the external current is not passed through the chamber. After mounting the stomach, 0·9% NaCl solution (39°C) is flushed through the chamber to wash the mucosa. The chamber remains filled with the saline solution for 10 min. The contents are then drained and the chamber is rinsed out with fresh 0·9% NaCl solution to give a total collected volume of 100 ml. The pH of this sample is measured and the produced HCl is then titrated with 0·01N NaOH and phenolphtalein as indicator. Depending on secretory rate, NaOH solutions of lower or higher strength are used. A blank titration is also carried out on the saline solution. Furthermore, titrations are performed on mixtures of saline and HCl solutions which match the pH of the experimental sample. A series of such mixtures are prepared by pipetting accurately measured volumes of 0·159N HCl into 100 ml volumetric flasks and filling up to the mark with 0·9% saline. The purpose of titrating these pH matched HCl–NaCl mixtures is to prove that HCl, and not buffer acid, is secreted by the stomach. It is

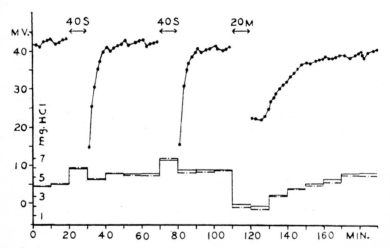

FIG. 9. Effect of applied electric current on potential and secretory rate of dog stomach. Solid dots represent potential in millivolts. Dash-dot lines represent milligrams of HCl secreted per ten minutes, as calculated from pH data; continuous lines represent milligrams of HCl as calculated from titration data. 40 S represents a 10-min period during which 40 mA were sent from serosa to mucosa. 20 M represents a 10-min period during which 20 mA were sent from mucosa to serosa. (From Fig. 2, W. S. Rehm, *Am. J. Physiol.*, **144**, 115–125, 1945.)

found that the titration results are the same for a given experimental sample and a pH matched HCl–NaCl mixture. Therefore, no appreciable amounts of buffer acid can be present in the sample collected from the stomach. The titration data are expressed in terms of mg HCl/100 ml. 10 ml 0·01N NaOH are equivalent to 3·65 mg of HCl.

Results and Comments

Data of a typical experiment are shown in Fig. 9. At zero time, a PD of 43 mV was measured across the wall of the stomach, mucosa negative relative to the serosa. The stomach secreted HCl at the rate of 4 mg/10 min. As the illustration shows, a current of 40 μA was then sent through the chamber and the wall of the stomach in the direction serosa $\rightarrow$ mucosa. PD measurements were discontinued during the period of current flow. The rate of the HCl secretion rose to 6 mg/10 min. Upon interruption of current flow, the PD across the stomach wall was low, but rapidly rose to its original level. Other observations are clearly described in Fig. 9. This experiment demonstrates that current flow in the direction serosa $\rightarrow$ mucosa increase HCl secretion. Current flow in the direction mucosa $\rightarrow$ serosa decreases HCl secretion. Regardless of the direction of flow of current through the wall of the stomach, the PD measured within seconds after breaking the current was always below the resting value. The portion of the graph to the right clearly shows a correlation between rate of HCl secretion and stomach potential. As the PD increases, so does rate of HCl secretion.

5. EQUIVALENCE OF SHORT-CIRCUIT CURRENT AND NET Na⁺ FLUX IN ISOLATED FROG SKIN (USSING AND ZERAHN, 1951)

Objectives

In 1936 the concept of "active transport" was introduced (Huf, 1936a). This was based on the observation that transport of salt and small amounts of water ("Reid's experiment") occurred from the outside to the inside of isolated frog skin bathed on both sides with identical Ringer's solution (Huf, 1935a, b; 1936b, c, d). It occurred also against a concentration gradient and against a small filtration pressure. Transport could be blocked by enzyme inhibitors and stimulated by nutrients, such as lactate. On the basis of these facts the term "active transport" was coined and described as "membrane activity seen in living and surviving membranes which force certain molecules across membranes in the absence of a diffusion gradient as well as against an existing partial pressure for particular molecule species at the two sides of the membrane" (Huf, 1936). For a more thorough discussion of definitions of active transport, see Rosenberg (1954), Patlak (1956), Scheer (1958), and Bresler (1967). In the earlier work referred to above the significance of the electrical factor in transport was neglected. The present experiment deals with two questions pertaining to the electrical factor. Does this "active salt transport" in frog skin also occur in the absence of the electrical gradient across the skin? Which ion is acted upon, Na$^+$ or Cl$^-$ ion, or both?

Method of Investigation

The plan of study is to completely short-circuit the skin and measure rates of Na$^+$ influx and Na$^+$ outflux with tracer quantities of isotopes. If Na$^+$ is the ion which is acted upon by a transport mechanism, the calculated net Na$^+$ flux (influx minus outflux) must be identical with the Na$^+$ equivalent of the measured short-circuit current (CFE, see page 52). This important experiment was first carried out by Ussing and Zerahn (1951). It is one of the land marks of the extensive field of research in "active transport" of ions. A Lucite double chamber is constructed in the fashion similar to the one designed by Rehm (1945, Fig. 8). Non-polarizable electrodes (calomel, or silver chloride) and bridges are used for measuring the skin potential and to annul it by

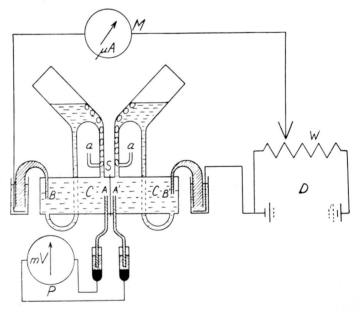

Fig. 10. Diagram of apparatus used for determining short-circuit current and Na$^+$ flux with the following components: (C) halves of a double chamber; each side contains 40 ml of Ringer's solution; (S) frog skin with epidermis to the left side; (a) inlets for air; (A) and (A′) Ringer-agar bridges, which connect outside and inside solutions, respectively, with calomel electrodes; (B) and (B′) Ringer-agar bridges used for application of outside EMF; (D) battery (+ pole at the right side end); (W) variable resistance; (M) microammeter; (P) millivolt meter. (From Fig. 1, H. H. Ussing and K. Zerahn, *Acta physiol. scand.*, **23**, 110–127, 1951.)

sending a current through the skin in the appropriate direction. In Fig. 10 the epidermis (which is negative relative to the dermis or corium) is to the left. The left hand current electrode is connected with the positive pole of the external battery and the right hand current electrode to the negative pole. By varying the resistance in the circuit the PD across the skin is annulled, i.e. the skin is short-circuited. It is important to emphasize that the potential electrodes must be brought as close as possible to the skin surfaces (see page 67). The double chamber is filled with frog Ringer's solution (see Experiment No. 1). The air lift system attached to each side of the chamber is a useful device for oxygenation and mixing. If the solutions are well oxygenated prior to use, this system is not necessary. Frog skin has a low metabolism and O_2 consumption of the skin diminishes significantly only at very low O_2 tensions (Huf, 1938). The solutions can be mixed by externally driven magnetic stirrers. During the first hour, unstable currents are often observed. When the short-circuit current has stabilized Na^{24} or Na^{22} is added to the solution on one side (0·02 to 0·03 $\mu c/ml$) and flux measurements are begun. At hourly intervals, 1 ml fluid samples are taken from the opposite side for counting of radioactivity. Throughout the period of study slight adjustments must be made in the external resistance to keep the skin completely short-circuited. A few minutes after the addition of Na^{24}, which allows for adequate mixing, a 1 ml fluid sample is taken from the same "hot" side. This sample is diluted $100\times$ and is used as Na^{24} standard. It may be counted simultaneously with the hourly experimental samples obtained from the "cold" side of the skin. In this manner no calculations for decay of Na^{24} need to be carried out. This is explained on page 57. When mixing time has elapsed, a fluid sample is also taken from the "cold" compartment. During the mixing period a small amount of Na^{24} has already entered this compartment. The respective count rate value is used as a "blank" value which is applied to all the following sample data. Use of Na^{22} instead of Na^{24} simplifies the counting procedure because of the relatively long half life of Na^{22} (2·6 year). Hence, a count rate measurement on the diluted "hot" sample, taken at any time during or after the experiment, suffices for all flux calculations.

Results and Comments

The experiment on equivalence of net sodium flux and short-circuit current has been repeated many times since it was first described by Ussing and Zerahn (1951) and their important results have been frequently confirmed. It seems fitting, therefore, to give as an illustration the original protocol published by these authors (Table V). The data presented are for Na^{24} influx, on which measurements were made over a period of 5 h. At hourly intervals, 1 ml samples were taken from the "inside" compartment for counting of activity. The PD of the skin at the beginning and the end of the experiment was 49 and 74 mV, respectively. The short-circuit current fell during the experimental time from 360 to 225 μA (6·6 cm² of skin of *Rana temporaria*). Sodium influx per hour and cm² of skin, $\overrightarrow{J}$, is calculated as follows (see page 57):

$$\overrightarrow{J} = \frac{\text{Total increase in activity of inside solution/(h} \times \text{cm}^2)}{\text{Activity of 1 ml outside solution/}(\mu\text{Eq Na}^+ \text{ per ml})}$$

Applied to the first hour data (Table V):

$$\overrightarrow{J} = \frac{1064/(1 \times 6\cdot6)}{100 \times 100/115} = 1\cdot85 \ \mu\text{Eq} \times \text{h}^{-1} \times \text{cm}^{-2}$$

The simultaneously measured short-circuit current, converted into its Na$^+$ flux equivalance (see page 52), is 1·80 μEq $\times$ h^{-1} $\times$ cm^{-2}. To compare CFE to net Na flux, a flux experiment must be carried out in which Na$^+$

TABLE V

Comparison of short-circuit current equivalent (CFE; page 52) and Na²⁴ influx in isolated frog skin (Rana temporaria) *exposed to Ringer's solution on both sides.* [Na⁺] = 115 mM. *Skin area 6·6 cm². (Data of Ussing and Zerahn, 1951)*

1	2	3	4	5	6	7
	Volume inside solution		Na²⁴ activity of inside solution compared to activity of 100 × diluted Na influx			
Time		CFE	outside solution (= 100% activity)			$\overrightarrow{J}$
		μEqNa⁺ × cm⁻²	per ml	increase/ml	total increase	μEqNa⁺ × cm⁻²
h	ml	× h⁻¹	%	%	%	× h⁻¹
0	40		2·2			
1	39	1·80	29·5	27·3	1064	1·85
2	38	1·68	57·3	27·8	1057	1·85
3	37	–*	70·9	13·6	504	0·88
4	36	–*	80·8	9·9	356	0·62
5	35	1·28	102·0	21·0	735	1·28

* Outside EMF source disconnected.

outflux $(\overleftarrow{J})$ is measured by the method identical to the influx experiment described, except that Na²⁴ (or Na²²) is added to the solution at the inside of the skin. In general, one finds that $\overleftarrow{J}$ is only a few per cent of $\overrightarrow{J}$. From a number of experiments and statistical treatment of the results, it has been firmly established that net Na$^+$ flux $(\overrightarrow{J} - \overleftarrow{J})$ and short-circuit current equivalence

(CFE) are identical. It should be stressed that this applies for the stated conditions of the experiments. Under other conditions this statement must be proven. This important experiment gives answers to the two questions raised above. First, it shows that net ion transport continues in the absence of a PD gradient across the skin. Secondly, it indicates that Na^+, and not Cl^- is acted

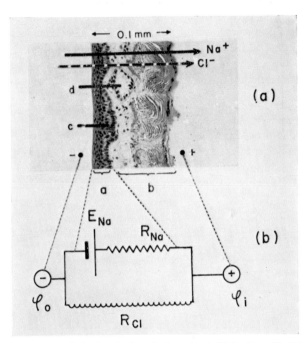

FIG. 11. Ussing and Zerahn's electrical equivalent circuit (b) for frog skin (a) with Ringer's solution on both sides with the following components: (E_{Na}) EMF of the "sodium pump", (R_{Na}) resistance for Na^+ movement in the active transport path; (R_{Cl}) resistance for Cl^- movement in the shunt pathway; (φ_o) and (φ_i), the electrical potentials of the "outside" and the "inside" Ringer's solution. a = epithelium, b = corium, c = stratum germinativum, d = mucous gland. (From Fig. 1, A. D. Campbell, W. D. Seward, T. E. Gilmer, Jr. and E. G. Huf, *Protoplasma*, **54**, 163–172, 1961.)

upon in the skin, for the total electrical current is carried by Na^+. No net movement of Cl^- occurs. In other words, with Ringer's solution on both sides of the short-circuited skin there is no "metabolic" force acting on the chloride ions. Electroneutrality in the two fluid compartments is maintained by the following electrode reactions: at the cathode (inside compartment) $Hg_2Cl_2 + 2e \rightarrow 2Hg + 2Cl^-$; at the anode (outside compartment), $2Hg - 2e + 2Cl^- \rightarrow Hg_2Cl_2$ (see page 71). On the basis of these results and other considerations, Ussing and Zerahn (1951) have proposed the "electrical equivalent circuit" for frog skin shown in Fig. 11b.

6. SHORT-CIRCUIT CURRENT MEASUREMENT IN THE SKIN OF LIVE FROGS
(WATLINGTON *ET AL.* 1964 ; CAMPBELL *ET AL.* 1961)

Objectives

The method of short-circuiting isolated frog skin introduced by Ussing and Zerahn (1951) can easily be adapted for investigation of the skin of live frogs. An *in vivo* method permits studies on mechanisms regulating ion transport of the skin in a setting approaching normal physiological conditions, especially in regard to humoral factors and innervation. This experiment is designed to demonstrate the effect of intraveneous injection of hypertonic mannitol solution on short-circuit current and PD in an *in vivo* skin preparation.

Method of Investigation

Agar Plugs. The procedure used employs principles applied by Rehm (1944 ; 1945) in studies on the dog stomach (see Experiments No. 3 and 4). Inside and outside of the skin are connected to the external electrical circuit via Ringer-agar plugs shown in Fig. 12. Details are given in the legend of this figure. Three

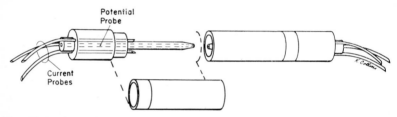

FIG. 12. Design of Lucite holders for "agar plugs": overall length = 50 mm; o.d. = 13 mm; i.d. = 10 mm; cross sectional area = 0·754 cm²; volume = 2 ml. (From Fig. 1, C. O. Watlington, A. D. Campbell and E. G. Huf, *J. cell comp. Physiol.*, **64**, 389–408, 1964.)

pieces of polyethylene tubing (12–15 cm long, 1 mm i.d.) are tightly fitted into one end of the plug, as shown in the illustration. Plugs and tubing are filled with 3 % agar Ringer's solution in such a way that a mound of agar protrudes from the free end after hardening. It is important to avoid trapped air-bubbles in the tubing. These tubings serve as electrical leads for sending the current through the skin. The center portion of the plug, between the three pieces of tubing, is also filled with 3 % Ringer-agar. This "probe" makes close contact with the skin for PD measurements. A simple salt solution (referred to here as Ringer's solution) can be used. It contains per liter of solution: 6·5 g NaCl, and 0·25 g KCl. Adjustment to an approximate pH value of 7·5 must be made on warm Ringer-agar before it has hardened. In practice, it is best to prepare a batch of Ringer-agar, cut it into blocks of suitable size, and store them in plastic bags in a cold room. This can also be done with a supply of filled plugs with their tubings attached. Preparation of Ringer-agar and melting of stored blocks of Ringer-agar must always be done slowly and at moderate temperature in a covered beaker to prevent evaporation.

Preparation of the Animal. Frogs are anesthetized with urethane, 3 mg/g body wt., injected into the dorsal lymph sac. Full anesthesia is seen after about 20 min and will last for several hours. Occasionally, additional small amounts of urethane must be administered. After a midline incision through the abdominal skin has been made, a No. 27 hypodermic needle which is attached to polyethylene tubing is inserted and tied into the abdominal vein. The frog is then placed with its back on a wet paper towel pad and the skin is lifted and supported as shown in Fig. 13. Undue tension of the skin must be avoided. Two plugs are then prepared by cutting away the mound of agar from the surface. After wetting the surfaces with Ringer's solution, two plugs are

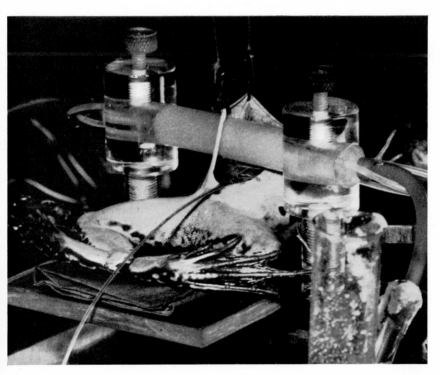

FIG. 13. Overall view of the experimental technique used for short-circuiting skin of live frogs, showing: anesthetized frog with cannula in the abdominal vein; agar plugs on either side of the skin of the abdominal wall; electrical leads connecting the plugs and the calomel half cells. The insertion of the cannula is made with the help of a micromanipulator and binocular optics. (From Fig. 2, C. O. Watlington, A. D. Campbell and E. G. Huf, *J. cell. comp. Physiol.*, **64**, 389–408, 1964.)

placed in opposition to each other with the skin flap between them. Some support for the plugs must be provided. It is best to construct a stage that permits one plug to be kept in a fixed position, and the other attached to a worm-gear drive. In this manner excessive pressure on the skin can easily be prevented when contact between skin and plugs is established.

Electrical Connections. Two pairs of calomel half-cells are positioned in close proximity to the ends of the plugs. One pair is used as current electrodes; they are connected through the three Ringer-agar filled, thin plastic tubings

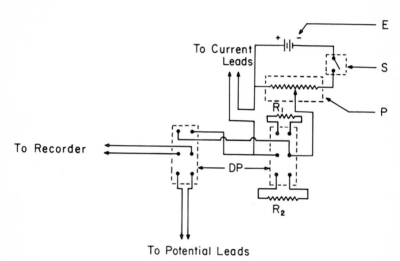

To Potential Leads

Fig. 14. Electric circuit diagram of a "switchbox", constructed from commercially available components, for measuring short-circuit current and "open" (spontaneous) membrane potential alternately. The use of this device is fully explained in the text. E C membrane potential alternately. The use of this device is fully explained in the text. E = external battery, 10 V or higher depending on total resistance in the system.

emerging from the plug. A second isoelectric pair of calomel electrodes is used for PD measurement. The connection is made through a piece of soft rubber tubing. One side is slipped over the emerging center portion of the plug (Fig. 12). The other end is dipped into the KCl solution of the calomel cell (Fig. 4). The tubing is then filled with KCl solution by aspiration from the KCl reservoir of the calomel cell. A hypodermic syringe and needle is used for this. The site of puncture of the rubber tubing is sealed with vaseline. It is quite important to check for continuity of electrical connection throughout the system, using an ohm meter (multimeter). It may be necessary to replace a defective plug by a fresh plug. The resistance in the current and PD circuit is of the order of 25 000 Ω, and 50 000 Ω, respectively.

Short-circuiting. This is accomplished by the method of Ussing and Zerahn

(1951). A simple "switch box" containing all the necessary electrical components may be built and manually operated for recording of the current and the open circuit, or "spontaneous" skin PD. A circuit diagram for such a simple device is given in Fig. 14. It requires more electronic skill to build a unit which automatically maintains zero potential across the skin and automatically interrupts current flow for short intervals for recording of "open circuit" skin PD. The essential circuit diagram of a unit which is used in the laboratory of the authors is shown in Fig. 15. A servo-balancing mechanism automatically and continuously maintains the potential difference across the membrane at zero (or at some pre-set fixed value) by regulating the voltage applied across the chamber. Similar automatic devices for short-circuiting experiments have been described by Mullins (1958) and by Menninger *et al.* (1960).

If the simple "switch box" circuitry shown in Fig. 14 is used, the operative steps are as follows. The potential and current leads are attached to the electrodes for measuring skin potential and short-circuit current, respectively, in such a way that their polarities are opposed. In the case of frog skin in Ringer solution the positive potential lead connects to the outside potential electrode. With switch S still open the skin potential is then determined by throwing the double-pole switch (DP) on the left so that the recorder is across the potential leads, i.e., downward referring to Fig. 14. A convenient recorder to use is a strip-chart null-balancing potentiometer with a 100 mV range, full scale. This recorder has effectively an infinite input resistance at the null-balance point and consequently does not draw current from the skin when it is balanced. To short-circuit the skin, switch S is closed with the recorder still across the potential leads. The potentiometer (P) is then adjusted so that the recorded potential is zero. At this point the skin is short-circuited. This operation can be done with the right-handed double-pole switch (DP) either across the 100 Ω resistor, (R_1), or across the 1000 Ω resistor, (R_2), depending on which one gives the best utilization of the recorder scale. After the skin is shorted, the left-handed double-pole switch is thrown upwards (referring to Fig. 14) to connect the recorder across the current leads. The potential thus recorded gives a determination of the short-circuit current from the relation

$$I_{sc} \, (\mu A) = \frac{1000 \times \text{millivolts recorded}}{\text{resistor value in ohms } (R_1 \text{ or } R_2)}$$

Care must be taken to short-circuit the skin and determine I_{sc} with the right-hand DP switch across the same resistor, R_1 or R_2. It is also important to check the zero setting of the recorder at the start of the experiment.

The steps described above must be repeated, in the sequence mentioned, more often at the beginning of the experiment than later since during the first 30 to 60 min the electrical characteristics of the membrane often show significant changes. Open skin PD's are measured by setting the right-hand DP switch in the middle position.

F

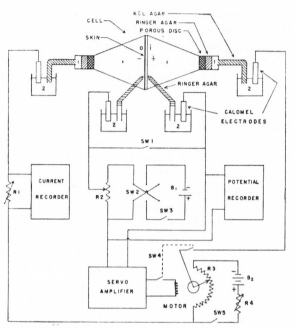

Fig. 15. Electric circuit diagram of an automatic short-circuiting device. If the membrane potential is different from that desired, a signal appears at the input of the servo amplifier causing it to activate the motor driving the potentiometer (R_3). The motor will drive in such a direction that the voltage applied to the chamber by means of this potentiometer is adjusted to reduce the input signal to zero. The current associated with this condition is measured by the voltage drop across the precision potentiometer (R_1) and is recorded. A voltage other than zero can be maintained across the skin with the circuit containing battery (B_1), switches (SW_2) and (SW_3) and the potential divider (R_2). With switch (SW_1) closed, this bias is applied to the potential recorder and thus can be set at the desired value. Current and potential recorders are strip-chart recorders (e.g. Varian G-10). A cycling switch (SW_4) opens and closes at regular intervals (e.g. every 3 or 10 min), thereby providing for alternate recording of the open circuit membrane potential and the short-circuit current. If SW_4 is kept in the open or in the closed position (by cutting off the cycling motor at the appropriate time) membrane potential or short-circuit current, respectively, are recorded continuously. The servo amplifier, motor, and potentiometer (R_3) are those contained in a Varian G-10 recorder. Alterations must be made to the circuit so that an external rather than an internal null is required for balance. The input has a high impedance in order not to draw excessive current from the skin. To reduce the amplitude of the oscillations the gear ratio between the motor and the potentiometer must be reduced by a factor of 40.

With the above arrangement, tests show that the apparatus responds to changes in skin potential greater than 0·25 mV and that the potential measurements are accurate to within 2 mV for the open circuit condition. When short-circuited, the potential is uniform within 1 mV over the surface of the skin. This was established through potential measurements between one of the fixed skin potential probes and an auxillary, movable Ringer-agar probe which was introduced through the filling opening of the half cell of the corresponding side. B_1, 1·3 V; B_2, 15 V; R_1, 100 Ω; R_2, 1 kΩ; R_3, 5 kΩ; R_4, 100 kΩ. Solutions used are Ringer's (1) and saturated KCl (2). (From Fig. 2, A. D. Campbell, W. S. Seward, J. E. Gilner, Jr. and E. G. Huf, *Protoplasma*, **54**, 163–172, 1961.)

Results and Comments

Figure 16 shows a record in which a rather stable current and PD occurred for 2 h. At regular intervals, the current was interrupted and a spot record of skin PD was obtained for 30 sec. At the end of the 2 h period, hypertonic mannitol was injected intravenously. A major decrease in current and a small decrease in PD resulted. This may be, in part, a direct osmotic effect on the

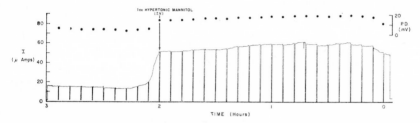

FIG. 16. Tracing of a record of short-circuit current ($I = I_{sc}$) and open skin PD in a live, anesthetized frog using a pair of agar plugs. Effect of i.v. injection of 1150 milliosmolar Ringer-mannitol solution on current and PD (From Fig. 7, C. O. Watlington, A. D. Campbell and E. G. Huf, *J. cell. comp. Physiol.*, **64**, 389–408, 1964.)

skin or a physiological response of the osmotic stimulus applied to the frog. The mechanism has not yet been studied. For other observations made with the *in vivo* method see Watlington *et al.* (1964) and Watlington (1968a). If one of the Ringer-agar plugs is made radioactive, e.g., contains Na^{22}, fluxes and current may be obtained simultaneously, as in isolated skin. The latter is a "closed system" and the *in vivo* preparation is an "open system" from the view point of flux of isotope material. Therefore, the evaluation of the *in vivo* flux data is considerably more complicated than evaluation of *in vitro* results. (Watlington *et al.* 1964).

7. EFFECT OF JANUS GREEN ON SHORT-CIRCUIT CURRENT IN ISOLATED FROG SKIN
(EUBANK *ET AL.* 1962)

Objectives

It is well known that optimal active Na^+ transport in frog skin is dependent on oxygen supply. In terms of cellular metabolism, it seems that Na^+ transport is in some way linked to intracellular oxidative-reductive reactions. In normal cellular metabolism there exists a steady state flow of nutients and oxygen. This maintains steady state equilibrium for several redox systems represented by the products of intermediary metabolism and their respective enzyme systems. The redox properties of such systems are commonly expressed by their E_o' value. This is the potential between a n-H_2 electrode and a blank Pt-electrode in a solution (under N_2) of a specified pH (usually 7) containing equimolar amounts of the oxidized and the reduced form of a redox substance. In taking these measurements, the two electrode systems are connected by a salt bridge. Arbitrarily the n-H_2 electrode is said to have zero potential. However, in practice the calomel cell is frequently used as a reference electrode. It is 0·245 V more positive than the n-H_2 electrode (see page 71). Therefore, one must add +0·245 V to a measured redox potential (with appropriate sign) to obtain the redox potential of a system under some arbitrary experimental conditions, for which the designation E_h is used. For example, the E_0' value for the lactate–pyruvate system (in the presence of DPN) is given as +0·18 V. Janus green is a redox dye whose E_0' value is −0·256 V. This dye (and others) may be used to "poise" the intracellular redox state. This is analogous to the effect of certain chemicals which "buffer" the acid-base state of cellular fluid. The following experiment is designed to answer the question: What are the effects of Janus green and Janus red on short-circuit current and potential in isolated frog skin?

Method of Investigation

The Double Chamber. It is constructed according to the ideas of Ussing and Zerahn (1951). A convenient material is Lucite which is ideal for machining work. A chamber system (or "cell") that has been useful in the laboratory of the authors for many years is shown in Fig. 17. Specifications with regard to size are given in the legend. The solutions are mixed by externally driven magnetic stirrers. This particular model is provided with a water jacket. Water of constant temperature is pumped through the jacket if rigid temperature control is desired.

Electrical Connections. The two "potential probes" are filled with 3 % Ringer-agar solution. After positioning them as close as possible to the surface of the skin (abdominal skin = 7·9 cm²), the free ends are connected to a pair of well matched calomel half cells (Fig. 4) via a piece of soft rubber tubing. The tubing is filled with saturated KCl from the calomel cell reservoir by aspiration with a hypodermic syringe. Vaseline applied to the point of penetration of the needle will seal off the site of puncture. Connections to the current electrodes are made in the following way: Ringer-agar is poured on to the porous disk shown in Fig. 17. After hardening, saturated KCl-agar is poured on top of the Ringer-agar. The rest of the space is filled with saturated KCl solution. A rubber stopper provided with a glass T-tube closes this area. Connection between the lower end of this tube and a calomel cell is made by a piece of rubber tubing. A short piece of rubber tubing, with screw clamp, is fitted to the upper end of the T-tube. Connection between chamber and calomel cell is established by aspiration of KCl solution. One must guard against air bubbles anywhere in the system. Continuity of circuits is evaluated with an ohm meter (multimeter). The resistance between the cells in the potential circuit is of the order of 10 000 Ω. Across the current circuit the resistance is also approximately 10 000 Ω.

Pt-electrodes for E_h *Measurement.* Two small, flamed bright Pt-wire coils are inserted through the filling openings of the chamber, and the respective calomel-half cell is used as a reference electrode. The E_h measurements at both

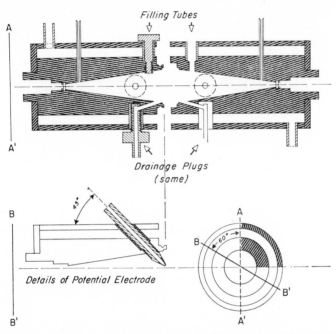

FIG. 17. Structural details of a cell used for study of isolated frog skin. The illustration includes the following: longitudinal cross section of the transport cell (dotted line indicates position of skin); details of a potential probe (longitudinal cross section in plate B–B'); and transverse cross section at A–A'. This illustration shows that a water jacket has been added to the skin chambers by enclosing the latter in large Lucite cylinders with endplates. However, it is recommended that the cell with its jacket be machined from one block of Lucite since this assures no electrical leaks. (From Fig. 4, A. D. Campbell, N. S. Seward, J. E. Gilmer, Jr. and E. G. Huf, *Protoplasma*, **54**, 163–172, 1961.)

sides of the chamber are completed within 2 min, during which time the measurements of the short-circuit current is interrupted.

Solutions. Ringer's solution is prepared by dissolving the following salts in 1 liter of distilled water: 6·5 g NaCl; 0·75 g KCl; 0·17 g NaHCO₃. The solution is adjusted to pH 7, after brief oxygenation. It contains approximately 2×10^{-4}M oxygen. Janus green ($C_{30}H_{31}N_6Cl$; MW = 511) in its oxidized form is commercially available. When 0·64 g are dissolved in 100 ml Ringer's solution one obtains a dye concentration of $12·5 \times 10^{-3}$M. Two ml of this solution are delivered to the bottom part of the chamber, allowing 2 ml of the 25 ml of Ringer's solution already in the chamber to overflow. Thus one obtains a final dye concentration of 1×10^{-3}M. More diluted dye solutions (1×10^{-4}M; 1×10^{-5}M) are prepared by appropriate dilutions of the above stock solution. The reduced form of Janus green (Janus red) is obtained by catalytic reduction of Janus green. This is done by bubbling H_2 gas through the dye solution (contained in a Erlenmeyer flask with side arm) in the presence of a small amount of commercially available Pt-asbestos as catalyst. If the gas inlet tube ends in a sintered glass plate. The solution containing Janus red can easily be separated from the asbestos by admitting H_2 gas through the side arm and pushing the reduced dye solution into an upper

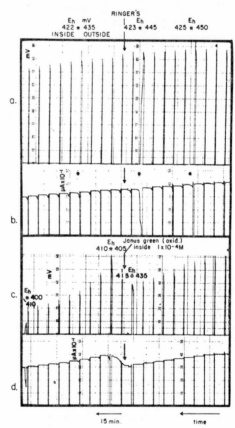

FIG. 18. Recordings of spontaneous skin potentials [a and c, inside (+), outside (−)] and short-circuit currents (b and d) in one control study (a and b) and one study with Janus green (c and d). Asterisks indicate the time when E_h measurements were made. The records should be read from right to left. (From Fig. 1, L. L. Eubank, E. G. Huf, A. D. Campbell and B. B. Taylor, *J. cell. comp. Physiol.*, **59**, 129–144, 1962.)

reservoir where it is kept under H_2 atmosphere. It is to be expected that re-oxidation of Janus red will occur when it is added to the oxygen containing Ringer solution in the chamber. The result will show, however, that autoxidation is a slow reaction.

Results and Comments

Figures 18 and 19 show that addition of Janus green or Janus red to the outside solution brought about an increase in short-circuit current. The effect on skin PD was, on the average, insignificant. The dye was also effective when added to the inside solution but the changes were less pronounced. The E_h

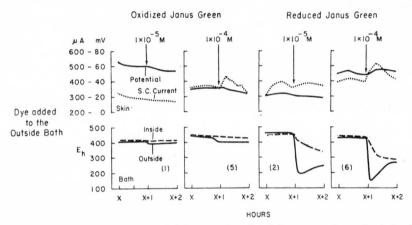

FIG. 19. Effects of Janus green and Janus red (reduced Janus green) on short-circuit current and spontaneous skin potential (average results). Number of experiments is given in parenthesis. On the abscissa, × indicates a time of approximately one hour after the mounting of the skin in the transport chamber. (From Fig. 5, L. L. Eubank, E. G. Huf, A. D. Campbell and B. B. Taylor, *J. cell. comp. Physiol.*, **59**, 129–144, 1962.)

measurements on Ringer's solution in the chamber suggest that slow autoxidation of the reduced dye occurred. Although the E_o' for Janus green is −0·256 V it was not expected that the E_h for Ringer's solution would reach decidedly negative values since Ringer's solution contained oxygen which was needed for the skin to carry on its active Na^+ transport function. It is not known why application of the dye increased the short-circuit current (and probably active Na^+ transport). It has been speculated that the reducing dye interacts with the flavoprotein system in the epithelial cells and shifts the intracellular E_h, which is probably slightly negative, in such a manner as to lead to increase in active Na^+ transport. Mention should also be made of the fact that redox substances with strong "oxidizing" properties (high $+ E_o'$ values) depress the short-circuit current and Na^+ transport, as does application of O_2 at several atmospheres of pressure (Eubank *et al.*, 1962).

8. EFFECT OF AMINOPHYLLINE ON SHORT-CIRCUIT CURRENT AND TOTAL CONDUCTANCE IN FROG SKIN (LINDERHOLM, 1952)

Objectives

The main aims in this study are to simultaneously measure short-circuit current and electrical conductance of frog skin in Ringer's solution, and to investigate the effects of aminophylline on current output and electrical conductance. Aminophylline is a drug which is known to affect biochemical and physiological processes. It mimics the effects of many hormones, e.g., antidiuretic hormone, epinephrine, ACTH.

Method of Investigation

Skin Chamber. The skin chamber designed by Linderholm has several special features, including electrodes for conductance measurements, which make it a very versatile tool for investigations of electrical properties of membranes. The chamber (Fig. 20) consists of two cylindrical Lucite half cells, with a fine-meshed plastic sieve on one side. Inlet (bottom) and outlet (top) tubes are provided for perfusion of Ringer's solution. Two pairs of platinized

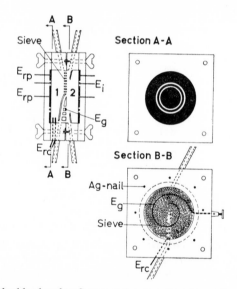

Fig. 20. Perspex double chamber for mounting frog skin. Frontal and two sagital cross sections (A–A and B–B) of chamber give details of construction showing the following: Sieve; inlet and outlet fluid jets; (E_{rp}) platinized Pt-electrodes for DC-resistance measurements on skin; (Eg) platinized Pt wire (0·2 mm) electrode on the skin side of the sieve, used as a recording electrode in the resistance bridge; (E_i) platinized annular Pt electrode for application of short-circuit current. Internal and external diameter 14·5 and 15·5 mm, respectively; (E_{rc}) platinized Pt-electrodes in chamber half No. 1 for measuring the conductance of the salt solution. Skin potentials are measured as shown in Figs 21 and 22. From Fig. 2, H. Linderholm, *Acta physiol. scand.*, **27**, Suppl. 97, 1–144, 1952.)

Pt-electrodes are shown. One pair (E_i) serves for the application of the short-circuit current, the other pair (E_{rp}) is used for conductance measurements on skins. The inner diameter of the cell is 3 cm, corresponding to a skin area of 7·1 cm². The depth of each half cell is 8 mm. Therefore, each half cell has a volume of 5·7 ml. Eight metal (Ag) nails fit into holes around the periphery of the right side cell, fix the skin membrane and keep the two half cells in position. Two cross sections of the chamber at the levels A and B are also shown in Fig. 20.

Electrical Circuits. Figure 21 gives a view of the electrical circuits applied to the skin chamber with its left (1) and right (2) halves. The three circuits shown are the skin potential circuit with the KCl-agar leads, the short-circuiting circuit with the E_i electrodes and the circuit for measurements of skin conductance with the electrodes E_{rp}.

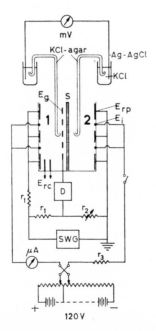

FIG. 21. Circuit of the bridge for measurements of the DC resistance of frog skin in the apparatus shown in Fig. 20. The arrangement for measurement of the electrical potential across the skin and the potential-controlling circuit are also shown. Additional components shown are as follows: (SWG) low-frequency square wave generator; Resistor, $r_1 = 100$ kΩ, $r_2 =$ variable precision decade resistance, $r_3 = 200$ kΩ, which is in series with the variable EMF and the μA-meter in the potential controlling circuit; (D) the detector, i.e., a DC amplifier and a cathode-ray oscilloscope; (S) the frog skin. The circuit shows the three electrode system (*cf.* text). When measuring the conductance of the solution in 1, the E_{rc} electrodes are connected to a similar bridge connected with a 1000 cyc/sec sine wave generator. (From Fig. 3, H. Linderholm, *Acta physiol. scand.*, **27**, Suppl. 97, 1–144, 1952.)

The Skin Potential Circuit. The electrodes are a considerable distance away from the skin. This is different from the Ussing's design of the short-circuiting cell (see Experiment No. 5). Since the outlet tubes for fluid circulation at the top of the chamber are very close (within 2 mm) to the surfaces of the skin membrane, the PD across the skin is accurately measured. Linderholm found that the PD drop across the bathing solution is very small and may be neglected. (See also the discussion on pages 61–68.)

The Short-circuiting Circuit. This needs no further explanation since it is very similar to the circuit already discussed in the instructions given for Experiments No. 5 and 6. The short-circuiting current is sent through the skin via ring-shaped platinized Pt-electrodes (E_i) which are separated by a 1mm gap from the conductance electrodes (E_{rp}).

The Conductance Measuring Circuit. The electrodes used to measure skin conductances are platinized electrodes, E_{rp} (at the ends of the chambers) and E_g (a wire electrode placed on the sieve). Conductance (or resistance) measurements are made between E_g and the E_{rp} electrodes in the right half of the chamber. Such measurements are carried out with and without skin, and the conductance of the skin is obtained from the difference between the results. Solution and skin between E_g and E_{rp} represent one of the four arms of a typical bridge circuit which is widely used in conductance measurements. The bridge itself contains a cathode-ray oscilloscope as detector (D) with its X and Y plates. The X plates are connected to the sine wave output of the generator (SWG). As long as the bridge is unbalanced, a standing Lissajou figure is seen on the screen of the oscilloscope. Upon balancing, this figure will closely approach a straight line. Linderholm describes in his 1952 paper how he employed a laboratory built amplifier in conjunction with a cathode-ray tube that was available at that time. This system can now be easily replaced by one of the modern cathode-ray oscilloscopes which has all the essential features needed for use of the oscilloscope as detector in the bridge system described. One such instrument is the Tektronix Oscilloscope, series 530, 540 or 550 with type 1A7A or G differential input. Another type is series 560 with type 2A61 or 2A63 differential input. Balancing is accomplished by adjusting the variable precision decade resistor r_2 (with trimming condensor in parallel) until the PD across the bridge has attained its established zero value. Thus, the unknown resistance (or conductance) is directly obtained from readings on r_2. When this method is applied to the chamber with and without the skin, the resistance (or conductance) of the skin is obtained from the difference between two readings. A generator is used which produces square waves of a frequency of 1000 cyc/sec and a synchronous low frequency pulse, 2 to 3 cyc/sec. The current density should not exceed $\pm 20 \mu A/cm^2$ since at higher densities the skin no longer reacts like a linear resistor. Linderholm recommends current densities of approximately 3 μA/cm^2. Square wave currents are pulsed across the E_{rp} electrodes such that a PD drop across the skin of no more than 10 mV results. Conductance measurements can be made on "open" as well as on short-circuited skins. This is made possible because of inclusion of the 200 kΩ resistance (r_3) in the potential controlling circuit. Whereas this is irrelevant for the measurement of I_{sc}, it assures that the total SWG pulse passes through the conducting measuring circuit. Good shielding is essential and the use of a Faraday cage is recommended.

Preparation of Platinized Pt-electrodes. The E_i and E_{rp} electrodes are platinized platinum electrodes. However, E_i is not a reversible electrode. It corresponds to the carbon electrode recommended earlier (page 73) for application of the short-circuit current. Linderholm has considered the possible effects on the skin of Cl$_2$ set free at the anodic E_i, but showed that only minute amounts of Cl$_2$ are liberated which does not seem to influence skin functions. Platinization, i.e. covering thoroughly cleaned Pt-metal evenly with a very fine, velvet like deposit of platinum black is done electrolytically. (See page 74.)

The Fluid Circulating System. This is shown in Fig. 22. The "air lift principle" suggested by Ussing (see Fig. 10) is used to circulate Ringer's solution in the

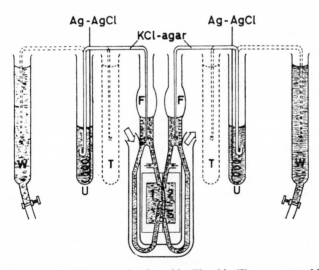

FIG. 22. Apparatus used for mounting frog skin. The skin (S) was mounted between two Perspex half cells, 1 and 2. Gas, usually air, entered at the small arrows → and circulated the fluid in the two compartments. The big arrows ⇒ indicate constant temperature water which passed through a rubber tube surrounding the narrow tubes for the fluid circulating in the two compartments of the cell. The electrode and KCl bridge arrangement for potential measurements is also shown. The electrodes for resistance measurements are shown in Figs 20 and 21. For further details see text. (From Fig. 1, H. Linderholm, *Acta physiol. scand.*, **27**, Suppl. 97, 1–144.)

upward direction through each half chamber. For temperature control, the outside fluid circulating tube, which is an extension of the funnel portion (F), is surrounded by a wide rubber tube through which water of constant temperature is circulated. The funnel and its legs are made of glass. This figure also shows the positioning of the KCl-agar bridges during and after the experiment. When not in use, the fine tips of the bridges are immersed into the test tubes, T, which contain saturated KCl solution. Before use, the bridges are thoroughly washed in distilled water kept in the tubes, W.

Ringer's Solution. Two stock solutions (A and B) are prepared. Solution A: dissolve in 1 liter distilled water: $6 \cdot 5$ g NaCl: $0 \cdot 27$ g KCl; $0 \cdot 21$ g $CaCl_2$. Solution B: dissolve in 1 liter distilled water: $12 \cdot 7$ g Na_2HPO_4; $1 \cdot 26$ g NaH_2PO_4. Working Ringer's solution is prepared by mixing 9 parts of A and 1 part of B. The pH is adjusted to $7 \cdot 4$.

Aminophylline. This is a molecular compound containing the active ingredient theophylline and ethylenediamine, which renders theophylline readily water soluble. For the experiment, 40 to 45 mg of aminophylline are dissolved in 1 ml of Ringer's solution and, at the appropriate time, $0 \cdot 1$ ml of this solution is added to the fluid in the funnel F (Fig. 22) containing the Ringer's solution which circulates at the inside of the skin.

Results and Comments

In this study emphasis was placed on measurement of short-circuit current and skin conductance. Figure 23 shows a typical result obtained on belly skin of *Rana temporaria*. After a control period of about 90 min, when stable current (I) and conductance (G) readings were obtained, aminophylline was added to the "inside" Ringer's solution to yield a concentration of 52 mg/100 ml. As can be seen, G sharply increased but the drug had little effect on I. An increase in G, which is the total ionic conductance of skin, is interpreted as increase in permeability for electrolytes.

When the bidirectional fluxes of Cl^- and Na^+ were also measured simultaneously with I (I_{sc}) and G, it was possible to obtain partial conductance values for Cl^- and Na^+ and the "active Na^+ transport potential". To obtain this additional information, Cl^{36} and Na^{24} were admitted into the funnel F, containing circulating Ringer's solution (Fig. 22). Samples were then removed at intervals for activity measurements. For details, see the publication of Linderholm (1952). Figure 23 gives results of such an extended experiment. Aminophylline increased the influx of chloride (ϕ_I^{Cl}) and of Na^+ (ϕ_{al}^{Na}). From the ion flux data, the partial conductances were calculated. Chloride conductance (G^{Cl}) is shown in Fig. 23 by the cross hatched area; sodium conductance (G_a^{Na}), referring to the actively transported ion, is shown by the dotted area. It can be seen that the sum of the partial conductances was nearly identical with the electrically measured total conductance, in the absence as well as in the presence of aminophylline. Aminophylline seemed to have no effect on the active Na^+ transport potential (Ψ_a^{Na}).

This study on the effects of aminophylline on the electrical and ion transport properties of frog skin is only one example of a great number of investigations

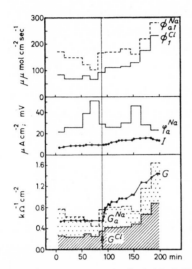

FIG. 23. Effect of aminophylline on a short-circuited skin in Ringer's solution. The drug was added to the inside solution as indicated by the arrow to give a concentration of 52 mg/100 ml. Results on Na^+ and Cl^- fluxes, measured inward through the skin are shown in the top part of the illustration. The following notations are used: (Φ_{a1}^{Na}) flux of actively transported Na^+, measured by a method "1"; (Φ_1^{Cl}) flux of passively moving Cl^-; (ψ_a^{Na}) active sodium transport potential; (I) short-circuit current; (G) total electrical conductance (G_a^{Na}) and (G^{Cl}) conductances for actively transported Na^+, and passively moving Cl^-, respectively. (From figure in, H. Linderholm. *Acta physiol. scand.* 27, Suppl. 97, 1–144, 1952.)

on the effects of metabolic inhibitors and drugs on membraneous biological tissues. The results of studies of this type have been summarized by Huf (1955), Ussing (1960).

When measurements of Na^+ fluxes across the skin are included in a study of the electrical properties of frog skin, some interesting calculations on the energetics of frog skin may be made, as has been pointed out by Linderholm (1952). One also needs data on O_2 consumption and the respiratory quotient (RQ). There are several standard methods available to obtain metabolic data on skin, but the description of these methods is beyond the scope of this article. A summary of calculations on the energetics of frog skin, untreated and treated with aminophylline follows. (See also Experiment No. 1.)

Energetics of frog skin before aminophylline
(Control Period, Fig. 23)

1. O_2 consumption: $4.8\ \mu l \times cm^{-2} \times h^{-1}$, or

$$1.33 \times 10^{-3}\ \mu l \times cm^{-2} \times sec^{-1}.$$

2. RQ: 0.85.

3. Caloric equivalent of O_2: $4.8\ cal/ml\ O_2$.

4. Energy from oxidative process:

$$1.33 \times 4.8 \times 10^{-6}\ \ 6.4\ \mu cal \times cm^{-2} \times sec^{-1}.$$
$$= 6.4 \times 4.184 = 26.8\ \mu w/cm^2.$$

5. Short-circuit current (I_{sc}): $10\ \mu A \times cm^{-2} = 10\ \mu coulomb/(sec \times cm^2)$.

6. Active Na^+ transport potential (Ψ_a^{Na}): 35 mV.

7. Na^+ conductance (G_a^{Na}): $0.40\ k\Omega^{-1} \times cm^{-2}$.

8. Electrical energy output:

$\Psi_a^{Na} \times I_{sc} = 35 \times 10^{-3} \times 10 \times 10^{-6} = 0.35\ \mu w/cm^2$.

or: $I_{sc}^2/G_a^{Na} = (10 \times 10^{-6})^2/(0.40 \times 10^{-3}) = 0.25\ \mu w/cm^2$.

9. Average electrical energy output: $0.30\ \mu w/cm^2$ ($0.52\ w/cm^2$ was found in Experiment No. 1).

10. Minimal overall efficiency, calculated from (4) and (9):

$$0.30 \times 100/26.8 = 1.1\%.$$

11. Minimal Coulomb efficiency, calculated as explained in Experiment No. 2, $(1\ ml\ O_2 = 17.3\ coulomb)$ and the data given in (1) and (5)

$$\% \text{ Coulomb efficiency} = \frac{100 \times 10 \times 10^{-6}}{17.3 \times 1.33 \times 10^{-6}} = 43\%$$

Energetics of frog skin after aminophylline
(Data from Fig. 23)

O_2 consumption: $7.7\ \mu l \times cm^{-2} \times h^{-1} = 2.14 \times 10^{-3}\ \mu l \times cm^{-2} \times sec^{-1}$.
Energy from oxidative process, calculated as above: $43\ \mu w/cm^2$.
Short-circuit current $(I_{sc}$ avg): $12\ \mu A \times cm^{-2} = 12\ \mu coulomb/(sec \times cm^2)$.
Active Na^+ transport potential $(\Psi_a^{Na}$ avg.): 32 mV.
Na^+ conductance $(G_a^{Na}$, avg.): $0.50\ k\Omega^{-1} \times cm^{-2}$.
Electrical energy output, calculated as above, and averaged: $0.34\ \mu w/cm^2$.
Minimal overall efficiency: $0.34 \times 100/43 = 0.8\%$.
Minimal Coulomb efficiency:

$$\% \text{ Coulomb efficiency} = \frac{100 \times 12 \times 10^{-6}}{17.3 \times 2.14 \times 10^{-6}} = 32\%$$

Thus it appears as if aminophylline decreases both the overall and the Coulomb efficiency, while it increases electrolyte permeability of the skin. It must be emphasized again, that the calculation of efficiencies are subject to revisions, depending on knowledge on current flows within the skin membrane which is presently not available.

9. OHM'S LAW IN SKIN OF NORMAL AND HYPOPHYSECTOMIZED FROGS (MYERS *ET AL.* 1961)

Objectives

On page 62 an equation has been derived (equation 18) which predicts a linear relationship between the flow of a current (I_B) and the voltage drop across a membrane producing within its boundaries an EMF of the voltage E'_a (Fig. 3; equation 17). A membrane which behaves in this manner is said to obey Ohm's law. The questions to which the following experiment is directed are: (1) To what extent does isolated frog skin obey Ohm's law?, (2) How does isolated skin of hypophysectomized frogs compare with skin of normal frogs in this regard?

Method of Investigation

Apparatus. This experiment may be carried out with the type of skin chamber described in Experiments No. 5, 7, or 8. The electrical circuit diagrams shown in Fig. 10 demonstrate that the variable resistance in the skin potential controlling circuit allows the experimenter to vary the current flow across the skin over wide ranges. In other words it is possible to short-circuit the skin, or to hypo-, or hyperpolarize it. By measuring the current flowing in the external circuit (I_B) and the voltage drop at two points close to the skin, in accordance with Fig. 10, the degree to which the skin follows Ohm's law can be ascertained. The experiment to be conducted is designed and carried out in a manner quite similar to Experiments No. 5, 7, and 8.

Salt Solutions. Dissolve in 1 liter distilled water 2·9 g NaCl; 0·37 g KCl; 0·25 g NaHCO₃. This gives a solution of 50mM NaCl, which is approximately half isotonic compared to ordinary frog Ringer's solution. Unpublished work by Dr. Flemming (Department of Biology, University of Oregon, U.S.A.), suggests that more stable skin potentials and currents are obtained with a 50mM NaCl solution.

Adenohypophysectomy. This requires some skill. It is performed on large frogs by the oral route as described on page 79. The success of the operation can be evaluated since removal of the gland leads to roughening and darkening of the skin. Completeness of the operation is confirmed by autopsy. Control animals are frogs that have undergone the same operative procedures without removal of the gland (sham operation). Frogs which seem to be adenohypophysectomized may be used within one week, and for 2 to 3 weeks after operation.

Results and Comments

A set of current-voltage readings was obtained by varying the resistance in the skin potential controlling circuit. When the data were plotted in the manner shown in Fig. 24, straight line relationships were obtained over the range indicated, both for normal skin and for skin of adenohypophysectomized frogs of the species *Rana pipiens*. To observe this result the required successive measurements were made within about 30 min. These experiments

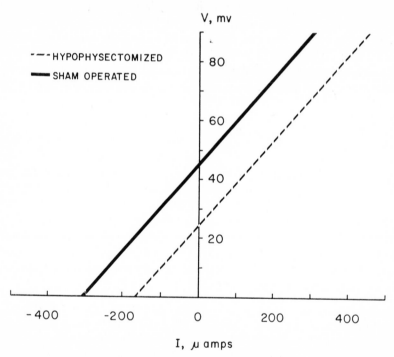

FIG. 24. Voltage-current relation in isolated frog skin of sham operated and adenohypophysectomized frogs. The fact that the corium side is positive relative to the epidermis is designated $+ V$. The equations for $V-I$ functions are as follows: $V = IR_T + E_a'$ (compare with equation (18) in the text, where the symbol I_B is used instead of I). R_T is the total skin resistance and E_a is the partially shunted active Na^+ transport potential; $E_a' = E_aR_S/(R_a+R_S)$ (see equation (17)). For $V = 0$, short circuit currents of $-308 \mu A$ and $-168 \mu A$ can be read from the graph for skins of sham operated and hypophysectomized frogs, respectively. (From Fig. 1, R. M. Myers, W. R. Bishop and B. T. Scheer, *Am. J. Physiol.*, **200**, 444–450, 1961; Redrawn.)

show that skins of normal (sham operated) and adenohypophysectomized frogs obey (within limits investigated) Ohm's law; in other words, the skins reacted like a simple conductor for which the equation (18) holds

$$V = I_B R_T + E'_a$$

In Fig. 24 the symbol I is used instead of I_B. $R_T = R_R + R_M$, i.e., the sum of the resistance of the Ringer solution between the potential probes at the two sides of the skin, and the skin membrane resistance. Since R_R is small relative to R_M one has $V \cong I_B R_M + E'_a$. If V is made zero, I_B becomes the short-circuit current I_{sc}. $I_{sc} = E'_a/R_M = E_a/R_a$ (See equation 19). From the points of intersection with the abscissa one can directly read the $-I_{sc}$ values for control skin and skin of operated frogs. The values are 308 μA, and 168 μA, respectively, for the total skin area. The reason for the lower short-circuit current in skins of adenohypophysectomized frogs is not evident from this type of experiment. Myers et al. (1961) have shown that Na$^+$ outflux is increased, with no change in Na$^+$ influx. Thus net flux of Na$^+$ (influx–outflux), and the short-circuit current is decreased. The decrease persists for 2 to 3 weeks following operation. I_{sc} carries the minus sign to express the fact that the short-circuit current flows across the skin from the negative epithelial side to the positive corium side. Figure 24 also shows that the resting potential i.e., the PD across the skins when the external flow of current is zero, is higher in control skins than in skins of adenohypophysectomized frogs. The values are $E'_a = E_a R_s/(R_a + R_s) = 45.5$ mV and 24·4 mV, respectively (equation 17). Finally, by applying Ohm's law one can calculate skin resistance for the two conditions (equation 28). One obtains $R_M = 148$ Ω for the control skin and $R_M = 145$ Ω for the skin of adenohypophysectomized frogs. Daily injections, for 7 days, of adenohypophysectomized frogs with 1 or 2 IU of ACTH or 10 μg of aldosterone accelerated return of skin function to control values.

10. VALIDITY OF OHM'S LAW IN RAT INTESTINE (ASANO, 1964)

Objective

It is often important to know whether Ohm's law is obeyed in studies on the electrical properties of biological membranes. The preceding experiment has shown that Ohm's law holds for isolated frog skin. The present experiment deals with the following question: To what extent does the intestinal wall of the rat obey Ohm's law?

Method of Investigation

Design of Apparatus and General Procedures. For the measurements of flow of current and electrical potentials across the wall of the gut, the same apparatus and procedure is used as was mentioned in the preceding text describing the experiment on frog skin. When working with frog skin, the experimenter can easily obtain 5 to 7 cm² of skin. When rat gut is used there may not be much more than 1 cm² of gut area available. Hence, a double chamber must be constructed of appropriate size to accommodate rat gut. The double chamber used by Asano (1964) provided for a free surface area of 1·06 cm² of gut. Five ml of salt solution are placed on each side of the tissue. Provisions must be made to conduct the experiment at 37°C. A simple way of doing this, is to enclose the chamber in a box with temperature-controlled air. When both sides of the gut are in contact with salt solution, it is found that the mucosa is negatively charged relative to the serosa.

Salt Solution

This is prepared by dissolving in 1 liter of distilled water: 7·3 g NaCl; 0·37 g KCl; 0·84 g $NaHCO_3$; 0·155 g $CaCl_2$; 0·144 g NaH_2PO_4; 2 g glucose. This solution is then saturated with a commercially available gas mixture of 5% CO_2 and 95% O_2. After the pH of the solution is adjusted to about 7·0, the solution is brought to 37°C before it is introduced into the chamber. A fine stream of the gas mixture is bubbled through the Ringer's solution in the chamber after the gut as been mounted.

Preparation of the Gut. Rats, weighing 100–250 g, are lightly anesthetized with ether, and an abdominal incision is made. From the middle section of the small intestine a 3 to 4 cm piece is separated from the rest of the gut, leaving the mesentery intact to ensure some blood supply to the isolated piece. The lumen of the short piece of gut is rinsed with warm, oxygenated Ringer's solution. This is followed by a longitudinal cut close to the mesentery. Thus, a sheet about 3 to 4 cm long and 1 to 1·5 cm wide is obtained which is then cut from its mesenteric attachment and mounted between the two halves of the chamber. Slight stretch may be applied. Mounting should be done quickly and oxygenated, warm Ringer's solution should be applied as soon as possible. The experiment may be conducted in such a manner that the open circuit PD across the intestinal wall is recorded for most of the time and at 5 min intervals currents of varying strength are sent for 30 to 40 sec through the chamber. Thus, in 30 to 40 min several current voltage readings can be obtained. To allow for early transient changes in the functions of the preparation it is recommended to obtain the data about one-half hour after completion of the mounting of the gut.

Results and Comments

A typical result is shown in Fig. 25. The plot of current (I_B) versus PD is similar to that for frog skin (Fig. 24). The "spontaneous" PD across the gut (condition of no flow of external current) was rather low, a few millivolts.

Figure 25 clearly indicates that Ohm's law holds over the range studied and one can apply again equation (18):

$$V = I_B R_T + E'_a$$

A value for R_T can be obtained from two correlated V and I_B readings.

$$R_T = (R_R + R_M) = \frac{V_1 - V_2}{I_{B_1} - I_{B_2}}$$

This is the slope of the current voltage relationship plotted in Fig. 25. One finds

$$R_T = (R_R + R_M) = \frac{7 \times 10^{-3}}{133 \times 10^{-6}} = 52.7 \ \Omega$$

for an area of 1·06 cm², or $52.7 \times 1.06 = 56 \ \Omega \times$ cm². From separate conductance measurements on the Ringer's solution used, T. Asano (personal communication) found $R_R = 11 \ \Omega \times$ cm², hence the resistance of the wall

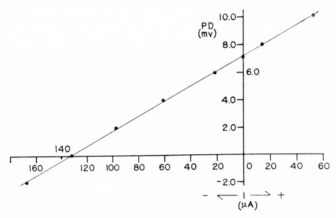

FIG. 25. Voltage–current relation across intestinal wall of the rat. The fact that the serosa is positive relative to the mucosa is designated by the V. The equation for the V–I function is: $V = IR_T + E_a$. Compare results with those shown in Fig. 24. For $V = 0$ a short-circuit current of $-133 \ \mu$A can be read from the graph. (From Fig. 2A, T. Asano, *Am. J. Physiol.*, **207**, 415–422, 1964.)

of the gut itself (R_M) is 45 $\Omega \times$ cm². Figure 26 shows transients, and eventual stabilization of several electrical properties of rat gut intestine investigated as described above. In the experiment shown in Fig. 26, I_{sc} per 1·06 cm² was calculated by applying equation (22). In this particular case I'_{sc} was 132 μA (14 min value). Hence, $I_{sc} = 132 \times 56/(56 - 11) = 164 \ \mu$A. This experiment was extended to include a study of the effects of various metabolic inhibitors. Results on the influence of Na-azide, phlorizin, and 2,4-dinitrophenol, added to the mucosal side, are shown in Fig. 27. The inhibitors were directly added to the Ringer's solution in the chamber. (Na-azide, MW = 65·0; phlorizin, MW = 472·4; 2·4 dinitrophenol, MW = 184·1.)

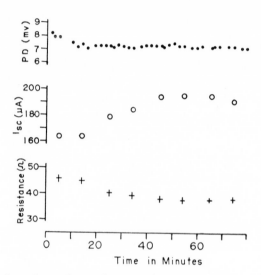

FIG. 26. Time dependence of potential (PD), short-circuit current (I_{sc}), and calculated resistance (Ω) of rat intestine with Ringer's solution on both sides of the wall. (From Fig. 2B, T. Asano, *Am. J. Physiol.*, **207**, 415–422, 1964.)

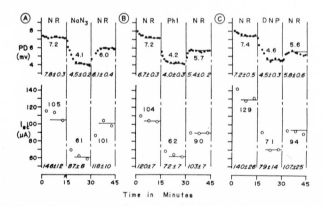

FIG. 27. Effects of metabolic inhibitors on PD and short-circuit current (I_{sc}) of rat intestine. NR indicates application of the normal Ringer's solution and NaN₃, Phl, and DNP indicate application of 1 mM sodium azide, 0·1 mM phlorizin, and 0·1 mM 2,4-dinitrophenol. Ordinate indicates PD in mV and I_{sc} in μA. Abscissa indicates time in minutes. Values of PD and I_{sc} representative for each period are shown, and the means and SE of results of five similar experiments are shown in italics. (From Fig. 3, T. Asano, *Am. J. Physiol.*, **207**, 415–422, 1964.)

11. EFFECT OF METHYL-GLUCOSE ON SHORT-CIRCUIT CURRENT IN RABBIT ILEUM
(SCHULTZ AND ZALUSKY, 1964b)

Objectives

It is known that the intestine is capable of active Na^+ and active sugar transport. Active Na^+ transport is measurable as a short-circuit current in a typical double chamber set-up as described in Experiments 5 through 10. Active sugar transport itself is not expected to produce an electrical current because the sugar molecule does not carry an electrical charge. For studies on active sugar transport 3–0 methylglucose is preferred to glucose, because the methylglucose is not metabolized. This experiment is designed to answer the question: Can methylglucose change the short-circuit current through interference with the active Na^+ transporting mechanism?

Method of Investigation

A Double Chamber. One like that described in the text of preceding experiments is used to accommodate a piece of rabbit ileum of a surface area of 1 to 1·5 cm². The double chamber is equipped with a gas-lift system (see Experiments No. 5 and 8). A gas mixture of 95% O_2 and 5% CO_2 is used. The volume of each chamber is 1 ml and the funnel part of the gas-lift system is designed to easily hold 9 ml of Ringer's solution. All equipment needed is identical with that needed for the previously described experiments.

Ringer's Solution. This is prepared containing in 1 liter distilled water: 8 g NaCl; 0·37 g KCl; 0·27 g $CaCl_2$; 0·21 g $MgCl_2$; 0·156 g Na_2HPO_4; 0·027 g KH_2PO_4; 0·21 g $NaHCO_3$. The pH is adjusted to 7·2. The solution is heated to 38·5°C, which is also the temperature at which the experiment is conducted.

Preparation of the Ileum. White rabbits, weighing approximately 2·5 to 5 kg, are anesthetized by intravenous administration of nembutal (20 mg/kg). After complete anesthesia the abdomen is opened and as quickly as possible the terminal 5 to 8 cm of ileum is excised. The ileum is that segment of gut which lies between the ileocecal junction and (proximally) a characteristic patch of lymphoid tissue. The excised piece is opened under warm Ringer's solution by making a cut along the mesenterium. After all intestinal contents are washed away from the mucosa, the sheet of gut is mounted and excess tissue is cut away. All these procedures can be done in about 4 min. Nine ml of Ringer's solution are placed on each side of the gut.

Results and Comments

Figure 28 shows the result of a typical experiment. A PD of approximately 5 mV was observed. The serosa is positive with respect to the mucosa. The short-circuit was of the order of 80 μA. After a very brief transient period, a stable short-circuit current was seen. At the time indicated, 1 ml of Ringer's solution containing 19·4 mg of 3–0 methylglucose (MW = 194·2) was added to both fluid compartments. A prompt rise in short-circuit current was seen. This effect was obtained only when the sugar was added to the mucosal solution. No similar effect was seen when the sugar was added to the serosal side of the gut. Approximately 15 min later, 1 ml of Ringer's solution was added to the serosal side, and 1 ml of Ringer's solution containing 2·6 mg of phlorizin (MW = 472·4) was pipetted into the mucosal fluid compartment.

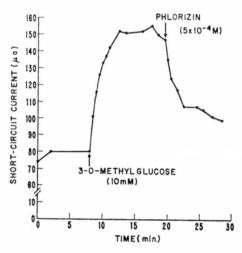

FIG. 28. The time course of the increase in the I_{sc} of rabbit ileum following the addition of 3–0 methylglucose to a sugar-free perfusion medium. The effect of phlorizin (5 × 10⁻⁴M). added to the mucosal solution alone, is also shown. (From Fig. 2, S. G. Schultz and R, Zalusky, *J. gen. Physiol.*, 47, 1043–1059, 1964.)

This resulted in a sharp reduction in short-circuit current. Further experimental studies showed that the effect of the sugar was attributable to its stimulatory action on active Na⁺ transport which occurs in the direction from mucosa to serosa. Since methyl-glucose is not metabolized by the gut it is clear that the increase in short-circuit current is not the result of a "nutrient" effect. Furthermore, the increase in short-circuit current seen upon addition of methyl-glucose to the mucosal side was dependent on presence of Na⁺ ions. Phlorizin depressed an elevated short-circuit current (rate of Na⁺ transport) because it inhibits active sugar transport. A hypothetical model of the Na-sugar interaction in the rabbit ileum is presented in the paper of Schultz and Zalusky (1964b).

12. EFFECT OF CURRENT FLOW ACROSS FROG SKIN ON UPTAKE OF K^+ FROM THE
CORIUM SIDE (CURRAN AND CEREIJIDO, 1965)

Objectives

It has been known for some time (Huf and Wills, 1951 ; Ussing, 1960) that inward active Na^+ transport across isolated frog skin is greatly diminished in the absence of K^+ ion from the bathing salt solutions. Small amounts (a few mM) must be present at the corium side of the skin to assure optimal active Na^+ transport. This has lead Huf, and Ussing to suggest a Na^+–K^+ coupled Na^+ pump. The Na^+ transport model proposed by Huf *et al.* (1957) and Winn *et al.* (1966) assumes that only a fraction of the cell K^+ (the "pump potassium") takes part in this ion exchange reaction at an "inner border" of the skin, and that this K^+ does not itself cross this border but cycles near the inner aspect of this border. The implication is that the Na^+ pump is electrogenic. According to this view the larger fraction of the cell K^+ ("bulk potassium") is not linked to the active Na^+ transport mechanism, but is maintained inside the cell by a separate metabolic pathway ("maintenance electolyte metabolism"). Koefoed-Johnson and Ussing (1958) have suggested a Na^+ transport model which does not explicitly assume compartmentalization of cellular K^+, all of which may be involved in an electroneutral Na^+–K^+ exchange reaction. In their view, K^+ does cross the "inner border" in exchange for Na^+. The present experiment is designed to answer the question: What is the rate of K^+ exchange between skin and the inside bathing solution in the short-circuited, the hyperpolarized, and the hypopolarized isolated frog skin during active transport?

Method of Investigation

Apparatus. A schematic diagram of the apparatus is shown in Fig. 29. The belly skin of *Rana pipiens* is tied (corium outward) into a groove on a cylindrical Lucite cylinder, 1·6 cm² i.d. This gives an effective skin area of 8 cm². The edges of the skin are painted with collodion in acetone which, when dry, provides for a leakproof seal. Four ml of salt solution are placed within the cylinder which is immersed in 30 ml of identical salt solution in the beaker. Agar bridges connected to calomel half cells are positioned as shown in Fig. 29. The short-circuit current is applied via Ag/AgCl electrodes which are insulated, except for the loop portions. The electrical circuitry and equipment needed for measuring and controlling PD and current flow is the same as used in Experiments No. 5, 6, and 7.

Salt Solutions. Dissolve in 1 liter of distilled water: 6·7 g NaCl; 0·25 g $KHCO_3$; 0·11 g $CaCl_2$.

Count Rate Measurements. K^{42} count rate measurements are done on skin and the salt solution in the beaker.

Measurements on the Skin. Before K^{42}Cl is added to the solution in the beaker, the skin is equilibrated for at least 30 min in "cold", non-radioactive solution. The cylinder with skin is then transferred into another beaker containing 30 ml salt solution to which 15 μc K^{42} have been added. Exactly 1 min later the cylinder is removed. The skin is rinsed for 6 sec in a large

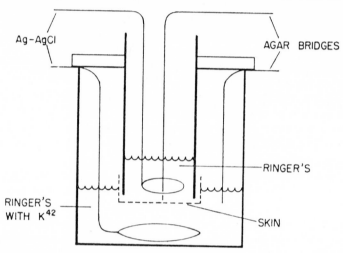

Fig. 29. Schematic diagram of apparatus for measuring K$^+$ uptake by isolated frog skin. The inside of the skin is in contact with the stirred solution in the beaker. The agar bridges are connected to calomel half cells for measurement of PD. Current is passed through the skin from an external source via the Ag–AgCl electrodes. (From Fig. 1, P. F. Curran and M. Cereijido, *J. gen. Physiol.*, **48**, 1011–1033, 1965.)

volume of "cold" salt solution and carefully blotted. The holder is then placed in a scintillation well counter in such a fashion that its position is reproducible in subsequent count rate measurements. Preservation of the same geometry in counting is crucial for obtaining meaningful results. The skin is counted for a period of 1 min and is then placed again for 1 min into the K^{42} salt solution. This procedure is continued for 10 min, or (increasing the intervals of removal) for 2 to 3 h. If the length of the experiment is limited to a 10 to 15 min period, no corrections need to be made for physical decay of K^{42}. The half life of K^{42} is 12·4 h, hence the activity of a 15 min sample is only 0·5% less than the activity of the sample at zero time. Corrections for decay must be applied if experiments are conducted which last for several hours. The calculations involved are explained on page 56. In long lasting experiments a second correction on the K^{42} count rates on skin should be applied, because during the course of the experiment a small amount of K^{42} has passed across the skin into the 4 ml of salt solution in the cylinder, bathing the epidermal side of the skin. The method used to obtain (under identical geometric counting conditions) a correction value is the same as the method applied to the "hot" salt solution in the beaker, which will now be described.

Measurements on Solutions. At the end of the experiment, i.e., after the activity of the skin has been counted for the last time, the skin is removed from the cylinder and a cellophane membrane is tied onto the cylinder. One ml of salt solution is pipetted into the cylinder and the cylinder is again positioned in the scintillation counter as in previous measurements. As an example, one may find a count rate for the bathing solution of 23 800 CPM. Since the salt solution contains 2·5 μEq K$^+$/ml, its specific K^{42} activity (s) is 23 800/2·5 = 9·520 CPM/μEq. (See page 57.)

Results and Comments

Kinetics of K$^+$ Uptake. Results of a typical experiment are shown in Fig. 30. K^{42} activity of the skin (CPM) on the ordinate is plotted versus time (min) on the abscissa. The data fitted the equation shown in Fig. 30. P_s is the activity of the skin at the time t, $P_{s\infty}$ is the final (steady state) activity of the skin, i.e., the CPM after elapse of a long ($t = \infty$) period of time. The rate constant λ is characteristic for K$^+$ uptake by skin. It will be seen that for $t = \infty$, $P_s = P_{s\infty}$. In this particular case, $P_{s\infty} = 68\ 500$ CPM. It is noteworthy that when the

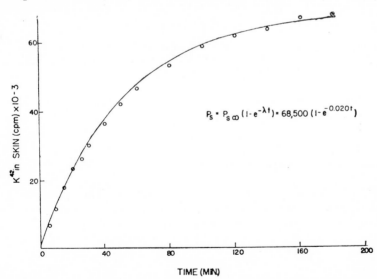

$$P_s = P_{s\infty}(1-e^{-\lambda t}) = 68{,}500\,(1-e^{-0.020t})$$

TIME (MIN)

FIG. 30. Uptake of K^{42} by frog skin with Ringer's solution on both sides of the skin. K^{42} was added to the corium side of the skin. The uptake curve is determined by the equation given. (From Fig. 2, P. F. Curran and M. Cereijido, *J. gen. Physiol.*, **48**, 1011–1033, 1965.)

total skin K^+ was estimated by flame-photometry, a value of 7·55 μEq was found by Curran and Cereijido (1965). Therefore, the specific activity of K^{42} in skin is 68 500/7·55 = 9073 CPM/μEq. Since the specific activity of K^{42} in the salt solution is 9520 CPM$^4\mu$Eq it was concluded that 96 % of the skin K^+ was in isotope equilibrium with the bath.

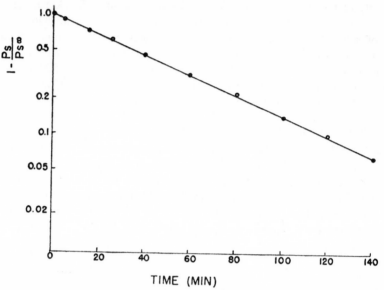

TIME (MIN)

Fig. 31. Plot of log $(1 - P_s/P_{s\infty})$ as a function of time, with $P_{s\infty}$ taken as 68 500 CPM. The line has been drawn by eye and has a slope of -0.02 min^{-1}. (From Fig. 2, P. F. Curran and M. Cereijido, *J. gen. Physiol.*, **48**, 1011–1033, 1965.)

To obtain a value for the rate constant (λ) the logarithmic form of the rearranged equation (36) was plotted, remembering that $\ln x = 2.3 \log x$:

$$P_s = P_{s\infty}(1 - e^{-\lambda t}) \tag{36}$$

or

$$2.3 \log (1 - P_s/P_{s\infty}) = -\lambda t \tag{37}$$

in which λ is the slope of line given by equation 37. This plot is shown in Fig. 31. Corresponding values read from this plot were inserted and the rate constant obtained. (Defares and Sneddon, 1961).

$$\lambda = \frac{2.3 (\log 1.0 - \log 0.1)}{0 - 120} = -0.019 \text{ min}^{-1}$$

Rate of K^+ Influx in the Short-circuited Skin. As was pointed out on page 57, the rate of flux of an ion, using the isotope method, is calculated by dividing the total increment in count rate per minute in a compartment by the specific activity of the ion species in question in the source compartment, i.e., $J = J^*/s$. When this is applied to the uptake of K^+ by the skin from its corium side one calculates for the average rate of K^+ influx (J_i^K):

$$J_i^K = \frac{60 \times J_i^*(1 + L)}{A \cdot s}$$

The factor 60 expresses the results in terms of hours. J_i^* is the total increase in activity/min, A is the skin area in cm^2, and s is the specific K^+ activity of the salt solution. The dimensionless correction factor (L) takes into account that K^+, which enters the cells of the epidermis from the corium side of the skin, encounters a diffusion delay in the region of the corium. Curran and Cereijido (1965) gave an average value of $L = 0.38$, but it varied with experimental conditions. For details, the original literature must be consulted.

Taking as an example the 120 min result on K^+ uptake shown in Fig. 30 one finds:

$$J_i^K = \frac{60 \times 62\,700\,(1 + 0.38)}{8 \times 9520 \times 120} = 0.57\ \mu EqK^+ \times cm^{-2} \times h^{-1}$$

Influence of Hyper- and Hypopolarization on K^+ Uptake. The results presented above are those obtained on short-circuited, i.e., on skins with zero (or near zero) PD across its total structure. When a current is sent across the skin in the direction epithelium → corium, hypopolarization of the skin occurs. Short-circuiting the skin is a special case of this situation. Hyperpolarization of the skin results if a current is sent in the direction corium → epithelium. The terms hypo- and hyperpolarization are used here with reference to frog skin bathed on both sides with Ringer's solution. In this case the epithelium is electrically negative relative to the corium. When K^+ influx experiments, as described above, were carried out under these altered conditions of skin polarizations, results such as shown in Table VI were obtained. It can be seen

TABLE VI

Effect of potential difference on K^+ influx. Samples of experiments on paired skins. Data of Curran and Cereijido (1965)

	Control	Experiment
	Shorted	Shorted
PD across skin, mV	0	0
K^+ influx, $\mu Eq \times h^{-1} \times cm^{-2}$	1·07	1·05
	Shorted	Hyperpolarized
PD across skin, mV	0	+200
K^+ influx, $\mu Eq \times h^{-1} \times cm^{-2}$	1·53	1·50
	Shorted	Hypopolarized
PD across skin, mV	0	−200
K^+ influx, $\mu Eq \times h^{-1} \times cm^{-2}$	1·03	1·20

that relatively large changes in skin potential had little or no effect on K^+ influx from the corium side of the skin. This is in support of the Ussing's concept of an electroneutral one for one Na^+–K^+ exchange pump. An extension of experiments of the kind described here, applying enzyme inhibitors and varying the Na^+ concentration at the epidermal side of the skin, led Curran and Cereijido (1965) to conclude that significant coupling between K^+ uptake from the inside solution and net active Na^+ transport across the skin does not exist. At best there is an exchange of one K^+ ion for every six Na^+ ions. This is in agreement with the transport model suggested by Huf *et al.* (1957). The role that K^+ ions play in active Na^+ transport is still an unsolved problem and an unequivocal interpretation of the results obtained is not yet possible.

13. EFFECT OF EPINEPHRINE ON SHORT-CIRCUIT CURRENT IN ISOLATED FROG SKIN AND TOAD BLADDER (LEAF *ET AL.* 1958)

Objectives

The isolated urinary bladder of the toad is a thin membrane consisting of a single layer of mucosal cells supported on a thin layer of connective tissue. The serosa is electrically positive relative to the mucosa with Ringer's solutions on both sides of the bladder. Active Na^+ occurs in the direction mucosa → serosa, and equivalence of Na^+ flux and short-circuit current exists. This is similar to what has been found in isolated frog skin. In both tissues, antidiuretic hormone stimulates active Na^+ transport and short-circuit current. Frog skin, as compared to toad bladder, has a much more complex histological structure. Large mucous glands, located in the dermis of the skin, are not found in toad bladder. Application of epinephrine to frog skin significantly increases the short-circuit current and it has been established that this is in part related to active Cl^- transport in the direction corium → epidermis. The suggestion has been made that epinephrine stimulates the mucous glands. Since toad bladder is devoid of mucous glands, the question is raised: Does epinephrine have an effect on the short-circuit current in toad bladder? The present experiment is designed to answer this question by comparing the effect of this hormone on bladder and skin.

Method of Investigation

Apparatus. After pithing the animals (*Bufo marinus*; *Bufo bufo*), one half-bladder is removed, rinsed in Ringer's solution and then mounted between two halves of a Lucite chamber identical in construction to any of those used in previously described experiments (No. 5 ; 7 ; 8). A second Lucite double chamber is used for mounting a piece of belly skin of *Rana pipiens*. The data shown below were obtained with a membrane surface area of 3.14 cm^2. Each chamber contained 10 ml of aerated Ringer's solution. Short-circuit current measurements are made as described earlier (Experiments No. 5; 6; 7; 8).

Salt solution. Dissolve in 1 liter of distilled water: 6·7 g NaCl; 0·14 g KCl; 0·2 g $NaHCO_3$; 0·10 g $CaCl_2$. Aerate solution.

Results and comments

Results of typical experiments are shown in Fig. 32. Short-circuit current/cm² of membrane area is plotted on the ordinate versus time in minutes on the abscissa. About 45 min from the start of the experiment 50 μg of

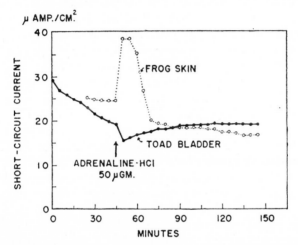

FIG. 32. Effect of adrenaline on short-circuit current in frog skin and toad bladder. The short-circuit current in the isolated frog skin is stimulated by adrenaline. No stimulatory effect of adrenaline was observed in toad bladder. (From Fig. 5, A. Leaf, J. Anderson and L. B. Page, *J. gen. Physiol.*, **41**, 657–668, 1958.)

epinephrine-HCl, dissolved in a small volume of saline (0·2 ml) was added to the solutions on both sides of the tissue membranes. A sharp, transient rise in short-circuit current was observed in the frog skin but not in the toad bladder. This supports the notion that the increase in current is the result of the action of epinephrine on the mucous gland of the skin. For a more thorough study on the effect of adrenergic drugs on isolated frog skin see Watlington (1967; 1968b). In the experiment described it is important to prepare the epinephrine-HCl solution fresh, just prior to its use since epinephrine is rapidly oxidized by room air. Further studies of this kind showed that the epinephrine effect on skin can be elicited by adding the hormone to the corium side of the skin only. Correlated experiments in which intact frogs are injected subcutaneously with 50 to 500 μg of epinephrine demonstrated profuse production of mucous covering the animals body surface. This is independent proof of the action of epinephrine on the mucous glands (Friedman *et al.*, 1967; Campbell *et al.*, 1967).

14. EFFECT OF AMPHOTERICIN B ON SHORT-CIRCUIT CURRENT AND WATER FLOW ACROSS ISOLATED TOAD BLADDER (LICHENSTEIN AND LEAF, 1965)

Objectives

Vasopressin stimulates both active Na^+ transport and bulk flow of water across isolated frog skin and toad bladder. For reasons stated in the paper referred to above, the concept has emerged that vasopressin may have a dual site of action on the mucosal barrier of the bladder epithelium. This has been visualized by assuming that the mucosal barrier consists of a double series barrier, an outer dense and an inner porous barrier. Vasopressin stimulates active Na^+ transport by increasing the permeability of the dense layer for Na^+ diffusion and thus, more Na^+ is made available to the "pump site" which is assumed to be located at the serosal barrier of the epidermis. By increasing the effective pore size of the porous layer, vasopressin leads to an increase in bulk (net) flow of water in the direction of an osmotic gradient. The assumption is also made that the dense layer is highly permeable for water. Suggestive evidence for this hypothesis of a dual site of action by vasopressin on Na^+ transport and water flow is provided by the experiment described below. An attempt is made to separate the Na^+ permeability effect from the effect on bulk water movement by employing amphotericin B, a polyene antibiotic. This substance is known to react with lipids (sterols) in cell membranes of microbiological systems and thereby increases membrane permeability. The present experiment is designed to answer the question: What is the effect of amphotericin B on the short-circuit current and bulk flow of water across isolated toad bladder?

Method of Investigation

Apparatus. Simultaneous measurements of both short-circuit current and net water flow are carried out with the apparatus shown in Fig. 33. The bladder (serosa on left side) is held firmly in place by nylon meshes covering the openings of the two halves of the Lucite chamber. The inside diameter of the chamber is of the order of 3 cm and other dimensions are in proportion to this. The left half of the chamber is provided with an air inlet tube through which air is continuously bubbled. This serves to aerate and mix the salt solution in this chamber. The right side chamber is a closed system, except for the small opening on the right side to which a calibrated pipette is attached. The connection is made with a rubber stopper. The 1 ml pipette is of the common laboratory type, graduated in 0·01 ml divisions. The upright, funnel shaped filling tube is provided with a glass stop-cock which is kept closed during the experiment. E is a draining tube with stop-cock, and D is a steel ball, rotated by an external magnet, thus mixing the salt solution in this compartment. The right side chamber is filled by syringe through E. One must be careful not to trap air bubbles in the region where the measuring capillary is connected to the

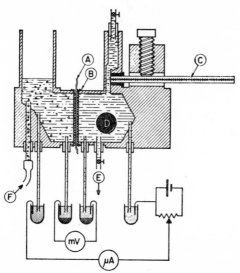

Fig. 33. Chamber used to measure short-circuit current and net water movement simultaneously. The components are designated as follows: (A) the toad bladder held firmly in place between the two halves of the Lucite chamber, each of which is covered by a nylon mesh support (B); (C) a calibrated pipette to measure net movement of water; (D) a steel ball in the chamber, which is acted upon by an external rotating magnet (not shown in the diagram) to stir the solution in the closed half chamber; (E) the outlet for the mucosal bathing medium; (F) a rubber tubing to an air outlet, which aerates and stirs the serosal bathing medium. The electrical short-circuit diagram is also illustrated. Bladder area is 7·07 cm². (From Fig. 1, N. S. Lichtenstein and A. Leaf, *J. clin. Invest.*, **44**, 1328–1342, 1965.)

chamber. Potential probes, positioned close to the surfaces of the bladder membrane, and short-circuiting electrodes (using calomel half cells) are also indicated in Fig. 33. For details on these points, see Experiments No. 5; 6; 7; 8. The serosa is electrically positive relative to the mucosa. Hence, the negative pole of the external battery is connected to the left chamber, the positive pole to the right chamber.

Salt Solution. Dissolve in 1 liter distilled water: 6·7 g NaCl; 0·26 g KCl; 0·24 g NaHCO₃; 0·10 g CaCl₂. Adjust the pH to 7·8.

Results and Comments

When the left side chamber is filled with the salt solution as described above (220 mosmols/kg water), and the right side chamber with 5 times diluted salt solutions, an osmotic gradient across the bladder membrane is established and water moves in the direction from mucosa → serosa. The rate of net water movement is read at the measuring capillary. Simultaneously the bladder is kept short-circuited and the short-circuit current is read or recorded. Results of a typical experiment are shown in Fig. 34. Approximately 45 min from the start of the experiment 12 μg/ml of water soluble amphotericin B (E. R. Squibb and Sons, New Brunswick, N.J.) were added via the cock at the top of

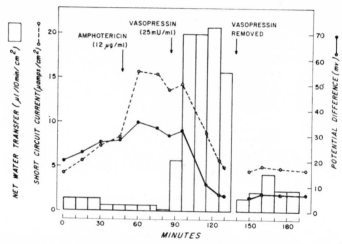

Fig. 34. Effects of amphotericin B and vasopressin on short-circuit current, potential difference, and net water movement across the toad bladder. Addition of amphotericin B to the mucosal medium produced a large increase in short-circuit current without affecting net movement of water. Subsequent addition of vasopressin failed to augment the short-circuit current, but produced its usual large effect on transport of water. When vasopressin was removed, the net transport of water was reduced. In this experiment sodium Ringer's solution was used as the serosal bathing medium and sodium Ringer's solution (diluted 1 : 5) as the mucosal bathing medium. (From Fig. 3, N. S. Lichtenstein and A. Leaf, *J. clin. Invest.*, **44**, 1328–1342, 1965.)

the funnel portion of the right side chamber and bulk flow of water and short-circuit current were again recorded. A prompt increase in current, but not of water flow occurred. Bladder PD also rose slightly. As indicated in Fig. 34, sometime later, 25 mU/ml vasopressin (Parke, Davis and Co., Detroit, Michigan) were added to the serosal solution. This greatly increased water flow, but short-circuit current gradually decreased. The effect of vasopressin was reversible and at the end of the experiment all measured parameters had similar values as measured at the start of the experiment.

In summary, amphotericin B, similar to vasopressin, increased the short-circuit current but only vasopressin and not amphotericin B increased the rate of bulk water flow. This is suggestive evidence that the effect of vasopressin on ion flux, which gives rise to the short-circuit current, is on a membrane structure separate from the structure in which vasopressin decreases resistance to osmotic water flow. The observations are in agreement with the concept of a double series barrier of the mucosal membrane.

Large ion gradients existed for several ions present in the salt solutions (predominantly Na^+ and Cl^-) and amphotericin B could have either stimulated active Na^+ transport in the direction mucosa $\rightarrow$ serosa, or increased the permeability for Cl^- in the direction serosa $\rightarrow$ mucosa, or both. Other data presented by Lichtenstein and Leaf (1965) indicate that amphotericin B can stimulate active Na^+ transport. Therefore, it was suggested that the antibiotic acted by increasing the permeability of "the dense barrier" for Na^+. Thus, greater amounts of Na^+ reached the unsaturated pump site near the serosa for active transport across the serosal barrier. It should be noted increased Na^+ transport was associated with considerable increase in O_2 consumption. Also, amphotericin B had no detectable effects on Na^+ transport (short-circuit current) or water flow when added to the serosal side of the bladder. The stimulatory effect of this antibiotic on short-circuit current was dose dependent, $2 \mu g/ml$ produced only a small effect, and $13 \mu g/ml$ produced near maximal change. Mendoza et al., (1967) have re-examined the effect of amphotericin B on toad bladder. Their results were not in agreement with the assumption of a single site of action of the antibiotic.

15. EFFECT OF ALDOSTERONE ON SHORT-CIRCUIT CURRENT IN ISOLATED TOAD BLADDER (SHARP AND LEAF, 1964)

Objectives

The existence of an active Na^+ transporting mechanism in epithelial membranes such as frog skin or toad bladder has stimulated biologists to study the effect of certain hormones known to regulate salt and water metabolism in the whole animal on the transport mechanism. The present experiment is designed to answer the question: What is the effect of d-aldosterone on the short-circuit current (active Na^+ transport) in isolated toad bladder?

Method of Investigation

Apparatus. Examination of the effect of aldosterone on toad bladder by using one half bladder for control, the other half bladder for the hormone experiment have been described in the literature. However, the variability of Na^+ transport in paired half-bladders often makes it difficult to draw unequivocal conclusions. An apparatus, therefore, was constructed which permits the comparison of one half of a half bladder with the other half of the same half bladder. A schematic illustration of such an apparatus is shown in Fig. 35.

G

Two double Lucite chambers of the type introduced by Ussing and Zerahn (see Experiment No. 5), holding 10 to 15 ml of fluid on each side, are placed side by side in such a way that two quarter bladders, A_1 and A_2, form a pair. Each quarter bladder divides the chamber into left side and right side fluid

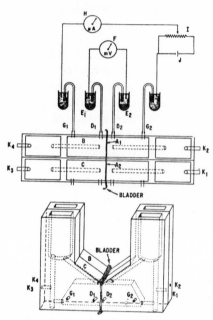

Fig. 35. Double chamber apparatus used to demonstrate stimulation of sodium transport by d-aldosterone. The upper figure is a horizontal section through the chamber as viewed from above. The bladder membrane is shown mounted as quarter bladders (A_1 and A_2) in the two parts (B and C) of the double chamber. Sodium Ringer's solution, bathing the two opposite surfaces of the bladders, is mixed and oxygenated by an air-bubble lift entering at K_1, K_2, K_3 and K_4. Potassium chloride–agar bridges (D_1 and D_2) connect the mucosal and serosal bathing media with calomel electrodes (E_1 and E_2) and the potentiometer (F). Two more bridges (G_1 and G_2) connect the media in the chambers with the external circuit made up of a microammeter (H), voltage divider (I) and power supply (J). The potential difference across the membrane may be reduced to zero by the applied EMF of the external circuit and the current recorded. Only one of the two identical circuits is shown, that connected to chamber B. In the lower figure the double chamber is shown in side view exposing the fluid compartments, air inlet and bridge leads of chamber C. (From Fig. 1 G. W. G. Sharp and A. Leaf, *Nature, Lond.*, **202**, 1185–1188, 1964.)

compartments. Salt solutions are admitted from the top, and some fluid is kept at all times in the funnel shaped reservoirs shown in Fig. 35. The main flux chambers are connected to the reservoirs via conduits drilled into the Lucite blocks. During the experiments, air is admitted through the openings K_1, K_2, K_3 and K_4. Thus, an "air lift fluid circulation system" is in operation to circulate the salt solutions through the flux chambers. The openings D_1, D_2, and G_1, G_2 establish, via KCl agar bridges, electrical connections to two pairs of calomel half cells for monitoring bladder PD and short-circuit current, respectively. This is done in the same manner as described earlier (see Experiments No. 5; 6; 7; 8).

Salt Solution. Dissolve in 1 liter distilled water: 6·7 g NaCl; 0·26 g KCl; 0·24 g NaHCO$_3$; 0·10 g CaCl$_2$.

Conditioning of the Toads. The toads are kept for at least 1 day (or preferably for several days) in 0·6% NaCl solution to reduce the endogenous production of aldosterone and other mineralocorticoids. The animals are placed in a plastic bucket containing one to two inches of the salt solution. The buckets are covered with a lid with adequate ventilation. It is important to keep the animals undisturbed. Their removal and pithing must be done rapidly so as to avoid endogenous aldosterone secretion at the time when their bladders are removed.

Results and Comments

A close parallelism was observed in the current output of two quarter bladders kept short-circuited for four hours, even when the current varied during this period of time. Thus, one can confidently ascribe deviations from parallelism in the time course of current output in a test experiment to the

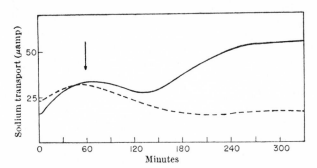

FIG. 36. Effect of *d*-aldosterone. 3·6 × 10^{-9}M on sodium transport in toad bladder. (From Fig. 3, G. W. G. Sharp and A. Leaf, *Nature, Lond.*, **202**, 1185–1188, 1964.)

action of aldosterone on the bladder. A typical result is shown in Fig. 36. One hour from the start of the experiment, *d*-aldosterone dissolved in a small volume (10 λ/ml salt solution) of methyl alcohol, was added to the serosal compartment of one of the double chambers. Alcohol without the hormone was added into the corresponding compartment of the control chamber. The final hormone concentration was 3·6 × 10^{-9}M. The molecular weight of aldosterone ($C_{21}H_{28}O_5 \cdot H_2O$) is 378·5 g. Therefore, one has to prepare a stock solution of 0·130 mg aldosterone/liter; it is more practical to dissolve 6·49 mg of aldosterone in 5 ml of methyl alcohol and make a two step dilution with alcohol, 1 : 100 each, to obtain the final stock solution. Ten λ added to 1 ml of salt solution gives the desired effective concentration of 3·6 × 10⁻⁹M. (See pages 76 and 77.)

The delay in onset of response of the treated bladder section, seen in Fig. 36, is typical for the effect of aldosterone on this tissue. These studies were extended in several directions. The site of action was evaluated. Sharp and Leaf's experiments suggest that aldosterone acts on the mucosal, rather than on the serosal bladder surface. These authors concluded that aldosterone increases the permeability of a mucosal border to Na⁺. Other studies established the minimal and optimal dose of aldosterone affecting short-circuit current. According to Sharp and Leaf the values are 3·3 × 10⁻¹⁰M, and 1 × 10⁻⁷M, respectively. With the method described the effects of other steroids and of steroid antagonists were investigated.

16. SHORT-CIRCUIT CURRENT AND Na²⁴ EFFLUX IN TOAD BLADDER (FRAZIER AND HAMMER, 1963)

Objectives

Toad bladder as compared to other membraneous tissues consists essentially of a single layer of epithelial cells. With identical salt solutions at the mucosal and serosal side, a short-circuit current can be drawn from this tissue which results from active Na⁺ transport in the direction mucosa → serosa. It would seem that the relatively simple histological structure of toad bladder makes it an ideal tissue for studies which aim at the better understanding of the mechanism of active Na⁺ transport. For instance, transmucosal Na⁺ transport may involve only two distinct steps : (1) diffusion of Na⁺ into the epithelial cell across the cell membrane oriented toward the mucosa ("mucosal barrier"). (2) Active transport of Na⁺ out of the epithelial cell across the cell membrane oriented towards the serosa ("serosa barrier"). The present experiment is designed to answer the following two questions : (1) What effect on short-circuit current has replacement of Na⁺ by choline ion at the mucosal side? (2) Is the rate of Na²⁴ efflux from preloaded bladders affected by the ion replacement?

Method of Investigation

The Double Chamber. To obtain answers to both questions simultaneously, Frazier and Hammer (1963) designed and constructed the chamber shown in Fig. 37. Dimensions of the chamber which accommodate one half of a toad bladder are given in the legend. The tissue is clamped between the two halves of the chamber as shown in the cross section illustration. Fluid is admitted into the chamber halves at the top, and fluid leaves the chamber at the bottom via stainless steel tubes. Except for the Na^{24} preloading phase (see below), flow of salt solution during the experiment is continuous and is kept at equal rates (4 to 6 ml/min) at the mucosal and serosal side of the bladder. The supply solutions are kept in 250 ml reservoirs. The outflowing solutions are collected

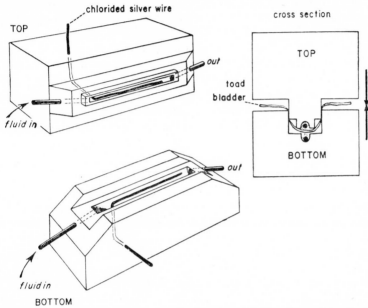

Fig. 37. Chamber used to measure Na^{24} efflux from bladder. It consists of a trough, 0·2 cm wide and 2·5 cm long, cut into a Lucite block. The total volume is 0·10 ml. Inlet and outlet tubes are stainless steel. The chloridized silver wire in the long axis of each chamber half is connected to an external battery and variable resistor to short-circuit the bladder. The transbladder PD is monitored from the reservoirs serving the two inlet tubes. The entire apparatus is electrostatically shielded. (From Fig. 1, H. S. Frazier and E. I. Hammer, *Am. J. Physiol.*, **205**, 718–722, 1963.)

in fractions for activity measurements. Information on measurements of the transbladder potential and short-circuit current is given in the legend. The measurements are carried out in exactly the same manner as discussed in previous experiments (No. 5; 6; 7; 8).

Ringer's Solution. This experiment requires two kinds of Ringer's solution. (1) Na^+ Ringer's: dissolve in 1 liter of distilled water, 6·5 g NaCl; 0·26 g KCl; 0·20 g $NaHCO_3$; 0·10 g $CaCl_2$. Adjust the pH to 7·5. (2) Choline Ringer's: composition as given above, except that 6·5 g of NaCl are replaced by 15·5 g choline chloride. A trace of Na^+ (0·5 mEq/liter) may be detectable in this solution.

Na²⁴ Preloading of Bladder. The small size of the Na⁺ tissue pool and its rapid turnover make it necessary to employ high specific activity of Na²⁴ (CPM Na²⁴/mEqNa²³) for labeling the bladder tissue. Na⁺ Ringer's solution with a specific activity of 20–60 mc/mEq is required. This is simply prepared by adding the appropriate amount of Na²⁴ (as obtained from the manufacturer) to Na⁺ Ringer's solution. Care must be taken to adjust the pH to 7·5 which is the pH at which the efflux experiment is conducted. Loading of the bladder is carried out from the mucosal side. Since it is likely that only small volumes of the "hot" Ringer's solution will be at hand, a small reservoir containing the radioactive solutions is connected to the mucosal chamber, and the fluid is recirculated for 10 to 15 min by means of an air bubble lift (see Fig. 10). During the loading period, "cold" Ringer's solution is passed through the serosal chamber in the manner mentioned above. At the end of the loading period, "cold" Ringer's solution is admitted to the mucosal chamber at the rate of 4–6 ml/min, while the flow of inactive Ringer's solution through the serosal chamber is continued as during the loading period. The effluent from both chambers is discarded for about 7 to 10 min. Thereafter, separate 2 min samples of the effluent from the two chambers are collected. The experiment is continued for 20 to 30 min. About midway during the experiment the flow of Na⁺ Ringer's through the mucosal chamber is discontinued and choline Ringer's solution passed through the mucosal compartment. Upon completion of the experiment, the collected samples are brought to equal volume with distilled water, if needed, and the Na²⁴ activity is determined with a suitable γ-counting system. Appropriate corrections for decay of Na²⁴ are applied as explained on pages 56 and 57.

Results and Comments

A typical result is shown in Fig. 38. In this experiment, thirteen 2 min effluent collections were obtained. The collections were started after a preceding wash-out period of 7 min. Short-circuit current measurements were taken at brief intervals throughout the half hour experiment. It can be seen from Fig. 38 that replacement of Na⁺ by choline⁺ on the mucosal side promptly lead to a reduction of the short-circuit current. Later, when choline⁺ was replaced by Na⁺ the current reappeared close to its original value. This suggests that the mucosa did not suffer damage during the exposure to choline. The upper portion of Fig. 38 demonstrates that the reduction of the short-circuit current to near zero values during the choline phase of the experiment was not associated with an alteration of the rates of Na²⁴ efflux from the bladder across the mucosal and serosal surface into the adjacent fluid compartment. This portion of Fig. 38 shows a semilog plot of count rate of the 2 min efflux samples (CPM/2 min) versus time in minutes. Na²⁴ efflux via the serosal surface was 4 to 5 times the value for Na²⁴ efflux via the mucosal surface.

Although the plot does not express a linear relationship between log efflux and time, both serosal and mucosal efflux ran a parallel course. If one makes the assumption that the log efflux-time relationships are in fact linear, one can write two efflux equations as follows:

$$\ln a_s^t = \ln a_m^7 - \lambda_s t \qquad \text{(serosal efflux)} \qquad (38)$$

and

$$\ln a_m^t = \ln a_m^7 - \lambda_m t \qquad \text{(mucosal efflux)} \qquad (39)$$

In these equations natural logarithms are used, whereas the semilog plot shown in the upper portion of Fig. 38 is based on Briggs' logarithms. This is

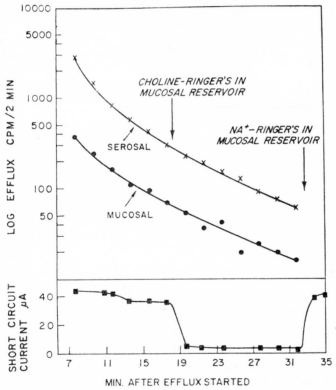

FIG. 38. Effect of altering the sodium concentration in the mucosal medium on rate of loss of Na[24] across the mucosal and serosal surfaces of the toad bladder. Initially, both mucosal and serosal media were ordinary Ringer's solution. At the time indicated by the first arrow, the mucosal medium was changed to a sodium-free choline Ringer's solution. At the second arrow, the mucosal solution was changed to the original Ringer's solution. The log of the activity in 2 min fluid samples (CPM/2 min) on the ordinate is plotted against time in minutes. The plot of short-circuit current in the lower part of the figure is a measure of the active transport of sodium across the bladder. (From Fig. 3, H. S. Frazier and E. I. Hammer, *Am. J. Physiol.*, **205**, 718–722, 1963.)

done because a linear plot, such as shown in Fig. 38 suggests that the physical law underlying the efflux of Na^{24} is represented by the well known decay equation of the general form $Y_t = Y_o e^{-\lambda t}$. When written in its logarithmic form, this expression contains natural logarithms and calculations for the rate constant λ must take this into account. In equations (38) and (39), a_s^t and a_m^t are used to express CPM/2 min sample for serosal and mucosal efflux, respectively. Similarly, a_s^7 and a_m^7 are the activity values for the first samples collected between the 7th and 9th min, and t is the time in minutes.

From the data shown in Fig. 38 (assuming a linear relationship) one can calculate values for λ as follows:

$$\lambda_s = \frac{2 \cdot 3 \, (\log a_s^7 - \log a_s^{31})}{7 - 31} = \frac{2 \cdot 3 \, (\log 2000 - \log 60)}{-24} = -0 \cdot 146 \text{ min}^{-1}$$

$$\lambda_m = \frac{2 \cdot 3 \, (\log_m^7 - \log_m^{31})}{7 - 31} = \frac{2 \cdot 3 \, (\log 400 - \log 12)}{-24} = -0 \cdot 146 \text{ min}^{-1}$$

Furthermore, a "half time value" for the efflux process $(a_s^{th}; a_m^{th})$ can be calculated, inserting in equations (38) and (39) the values of $a_s^{th} = 1/2 \, a_s^7$ and $a_m^{th} = 1/2 \, a_m^7$. Since the rate constants for serosal and mucosal efflux are the same, the "half time values" must also be the same. One finds:

$$t_h = \frac{\ln a^7 / a^{th}}{\lambda} = \frac{\ln 2}{\lambda} = \frac{0 \cdot 693}{0 \cdot 146} = 4 \cdot 8 \text{ min}$$

The fact that the half time for serosal and mucosal efflux samples are the same suggests that both serosal and mucosal efflux of Na^{24} came from a common pool and both fluxes obey first order kinetics. This, however, is only valid for a linear log efflux–time relationship.

17. EFFECTS OF OUABAIN ON SHORT-CIRCUIT CURRENT AND SODIUM TRANSPORT IN ISOLATED TOAD BLADDER (HERRERA, 1966)

Objectives

The relatively simple histological structure of toad bladder suggested to Herrera (1966) the application of a "three compartment model" for kinetic analysis of sodium transport, published earlier by Curran *et al.* (1963). The model assumes that Na^+ enters passively from the mucosal fluid compartment (1), moves across the mucosal cell membrane barrier into the cell compartment (2), and is actively transported across the serosal cell membrane into the serosal fluid compartment (3). The simple case of having identical salt solutions in compartments (1) and (3) is considered, and the following questions are asked: (1) What are the rate coefficients for unidirectional movement of Na^+ across the membrane barriers in the short-circuited bladder? (2) What is the size of the intracellular Na^+ pool? (3) What is the net rate of Na^+ transport across the bladder? (4) How and by what mechanism does ouabain affect active Na^+ transport?

Method of Investigation

In this experiment, in which Na^{22} is placed on the mucosal side of the bladder, several parameters are simultaneously measured, as follows: (1) the time course of accumulation of Na^{22} at the serosal side (CPM/min) before steady state is reached. (2) The steady state rate of accumulation of total Na^{22} at the serosal side (CPM/min). (3) The total amount of Na^{22} (CPM) involved in transport found in the bladder tissue under steady state conditions. (4) The total amount of Na^{22} (CPM) in the mucosal fluid compartment. (5) S, the total amount of non-radioactive Na^+ in the mucosal compartment. (6) The short-circuit current (SCC), and, by calculation, the CFE ($1 \mu A = 3.73 \times 10^{-2} \mu Eq$ ions $\times h^{-1}$; see page 52).

The Principles Applied in Measuring the Short-circuit Current. These are identical with those discussed earlier (Experiments No. 5; 7; 8). However, in the present experiment an apparatus is needed which allows for rapid and frequent replacement of the total solution at the serosal side of the bladder in order to obtain answers to questions (1) and (2) stated above. Such an apparatus is described in the following.

Rapid Sampling of Serosal Solution. Figure 39 shows a cylindrical double chamber with one half of the urinary bladder of *Bufo marinus* clamped between the two sections of the chamber. A nylon net, held taut in place by a rubber band, serves as support for the thin bladder membrane. The mucosal chamber contains 2·5 ml fluid. The volume of the serosal chamber is 1·2 ml. Exposed bladder area is 3·14 cm². Calomel half cells are used for monitoring bladder potentials. The short-circuit current is applied via Ag/AgCl electrodes. The serosal electrode is placed inside at the back of the chamber in the form of a chloridized Ag-spiral (dotted line). A Ringer agar bridge connects the left hand side AgCl electrode to the fluid chamber while the AgCl spiral in the right side chamber is connected by wire to the external circuit. The serosal chamber is connected to a fluid circulating system consisting of a reservoir (flask, containing 250 to 500 ml of aerated Ringer's solution), a miniature centrifugal pump, connecting tubing, double valve and a 5 ml syringe attachment, as shown in Fig. 39. During the equilibration period, following mounting of the bladder, the efflow tube of the serosal chamber is connected by a piece of tubing to the return tube of the reservoir. At the end of the equilibration period ($\frac{1}{2}$ to 1 h) a collecting tube, capacity about 10 ml, is attached to the efflow tube. This is for collection of a flush sample. Other samples are collected in separate collecting tubes. During the experiment when samples are taken for flux calculations the pump is shut off. To flush the serosal chamber, 5 ml of Ringer's solution are aspirated from the reservoir, and 4 to 5 portions of the fluid are used to flush the chamber. This can be accomplished in about 1 sec. Upon refilling the chamber with fresh saline solution at the end of the flush, a new flux period commences. With some

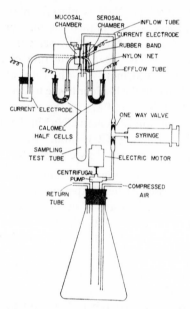

FIG. 39. Diagram of the apparatus employed in the flux build-up experiments. During the equilibration period a polyethylene tube was connected between the efflow tube of the serosal chamber and the return tube of the reservoir flask. Just before adding Na[22] to the mucosal bathing solution the motor-driven centrifugal pump was shut off and the return tube from the serosal chamber to the reservoir removed. (From Fig. 1, F. C. Herrera, *Am. J. Physiol.*, **210**, 980–986, 1966.)

care, all Na[22] containing fluid samples will be of approximately the same volume, and they can be conveniently counted for activity in a scintillation well spectrometer.

Two apparatus as shown in Fig. 39 are used simultaneously, each holding one half bladder from the same toad. One bladder serves as control, the other for the experiment with ouabain.

Amount of Na[22] in the Bladder Tissue. When all samples for flux calculations have been taken, the exposed tissue is removed, blotted on Whatman No. 1 filter paper, weighed, dried (24 h at 80°C) and re-weighed on tared metal foil. The bladders are then counted for Na[22] activity in a scintillation spectrometer.

Ringer's   Solution.   Dissolve   1   liter   distilled   water: 6·7 g NaCl;
0·17 g NaHCO₃; 0·15 g KCl; 0·06 g CaCl₂. Adjust pH to 8·3.

Results and Comments

Effect of Ouabain on Short-circuit Current. Figure 40 shows the time course of
the short-circuit current flowing across the 3·14 cm² bladder membrane. At
the time indicated, 18·2 mg ouabain (MW = 729) was added to the serosal

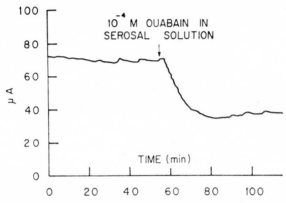

FIG. 40. Effect of serosal addition of ouabain on net sodium transport across the bladder
measured by the short-circuit current. (From Fig. 2, F. C. Herrera, *Am. J. Physiol.*, **210**,
980–986, 1966.)

fluid (250 ml). It can be seen that this reduced the short-circuit current to
approximately half its original value in about 20 min. If no other information
is desired, a simple double chamber such as shown in Fig. 10 may be used for
the experiment.

Effect of Ouabain on Rate Coefficients for Na⁺ Movements and Na⁺ Fluxes.
(Figure 41.) Bladder halves were mounted as described above. Ouabain,
18·2 mg, was added to the 250 ml serosal reservoir. When the short-circuit
current had stabilized (after approximately 20 to 30 min) 20 μc of Na²² were
added (through the admission opening shown in the upper left corner of
Fig. 39) to the mucosal fluid compartment. Immediately after addition of
Na²², 14 to 16 flush-out samples were taken from the serosal side at 30 sec
intervals, followed by 6 samples at 5 min intervals. As has been pointed out
above, the circulating pump was shut off during the sampling period of the
experiment. The samples taken at short intervals gave information on the rate
of Na⁺ transport before steady state was reached. The later samples gave the
rate of steady state flow of Na⁺. Throughout the experiment, the bladder
remained short-circuited. At the end of the flux studies, lasting for approximately 40 min, the Na²² activity of the samples was measured. Results of a

typical experiment are shown in Fig. 41. Time in minutes is plotted on the abscissa. On the ordinate is plotted the log of the following value: one minus the ratio of non-steady state rate/steady state rate of appearance of Na^{22} in

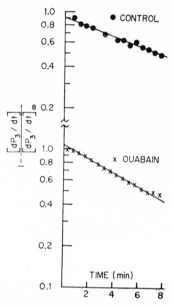

FIG. 41. Plots of log $[1 - (dP_3/dt)/(dP_3/dt)_\infty]$ as a function of time, for control and ouabain-treated bladder halves. The straight lines have been fitted by inspection. The slope of the lines gives values for $-(k_{21} + k_{23})/2.3$. See equation (40) and examples of calculations in the text. (From Fig. 3, F. C. Herrera, *Am. J. Physiol.*, **210**, 980–986, 1966.)

the serosal compartment (total CPM/min). To further analyse the results and give answers to the questions raised above the following expressions and equations, relating to the experimental data must be understood.

dP_3/dt = time course of appearance of the total amount of Na^{22} in the serosal compartment (CPM/min) before steady state has been reached.

$(dP_3/dt)_\infty$ = the steady state rate of appearance of the total amount of Na^{22} in the serosal compartment (CPM/min).

P_1 = total amount of Na^{22} in the mucosal compartment (CPM).

$P_{2\infty}$ = total amount of Na^{22} (CPM) in the exposed bladder area of 3.14 cm^2 ($\cong 10$ mg dry weight). It is assumed that practically all Na^{22} is present in the transporting cells. For justification see Herrera (1966). The ∞ sign used in this and previous definition refers to the end point of the experiment, when flux has become practically constant.

$S_1 =$ total amount of non-radioactive Na^+ in the mucosal compartment (μEq).

$S_2 =$ total amount of non-radioactive Na^+ in the transporting compartment (μEq).

$SCC =$ the short-circuit current (μA). From this the short-circuit current equivalent (CFE) is calculated. $1\ \mu A = 3.73 \times 10^{-2}\ \mu Eq/h$. It is known, and further evidence is presented below, that under the conditions of the experiment $CFE = J_n$, the net Na^+ flux across the bladder.

Calculations of rate coefficients for Na^+ movement and Na^+ fluxes are based on the theory (not presented here) of Curran et al. (1963), applied to the bladder model shown in the inset in Fig. 43. If back flux of Na^{22} from the serosal fluid into the bladder is neglected and several other assumptions are made which are stated in the theory, the following equations apply:

$$\ln\left[1 - (dP_3/dt)/(dP_3/dt)_\infty\right] = -(k_{21} + k_{23})\,t \tag{40}$$

$$k_{23} = \left(\frac{dP_3}{dt}\right)_\infty \bigg/ P_{2\infty} \tag{41}$$

$$k_{21} = \lambda - k_{23}; \qquad (\lambda = k_{21} + k_{23}) \tag{42}$$

$$k_{12} = P_{2\infty}(k_{21} + k_{23})/P_1 \tag{43}$$

$$S_2 = (k_{12}S_1 - J_n)/k_{21} \tag{44}$$

$(k_{21} + k_{23})$ will be recognized as the slope factor, λ, of equation (40). A numerical value can be obtained from the plot shown in Fig. 41 in which Briggs' logarithms and not natural logarithms, are employed ($\ln a = 2.3 \log a$). From a graphic extension of the regression lines shown in Fig. 41 (with time expressed in hours) it can be shown that in the control experiment

$$\lambda = (k_{21} + k_{23}) = 2.3\,\frac{\log 0.9 - \log 0.3}{(0-14)/60} = -\frac{2.3 \log 3}{0.234} = -4.7 \times h^{-1}$$

and the ouabain experiment

$$\lambda = (k_{21} + k_{23}) = 2.3\,\frac{\log 1.0 - \log 0.3}{(0.63 - 11.28)/60} = -\frac{2.3 \log 3.33}{0.178} = -6.8 \times h^{-1}$$

Once $(k_{21} + k_{23})$ is known, k_{23} and k_{12} can also be calculated from equations (41), (42), and (43), using the experimental data on $(dP_3/dt)_\infty$, $P_{2\infty}$, and P_1. The value of S_1 is known from the volume of the mucosal compartment ($V_m = 2.5$ ml) and the Na^+ concentration of Ringer's solution ($[Na^+]_m = 117\ \mu$Eq/ml). $S_1 = V_m \cdot [Na^+]_m$. From the CFE, J_n is calculated. Finally, S_2 can be calculated from equation (44). Since S_1 and S_2 are known, the fluxes for Na^+ across the cell barriers can be calculated from the relationships

$$J_{12} = k_{12}S_1 \tag{45}$$

$$J_{21} = k_{21}S_2 \tag{46}$$

$$J_{23} = k_{23}S_2 \tag{47}$$

The following tabulation of measured and calculated quantities illustrates typical results obtained on one pair of toad bladders (Table VII).

On the basis of numerous experiments and statistical treatment of the data, it was concluded that ouabain significantly lowers k_{23} and J_{23}. These parameters are most likely associated with the active Na^+ transport step, presumably located near the serosal side of the transporting epithelial cell. This explains why short-circuit current was also decreased. In ouabain treated

TABLE VII

Protocol of data on Na^+ flux in isolated toad bladder. Ouabain (1 × 10⁻⁴M) *was applied to the serosal side. Data of Herrera (1966)**

	Control bladder	Ouabain bladder
1. $[Na^+]_m$, μEq	117	117
2. V_1, ml	2·50	2·50
3. $S_1 = V_1 [Na^+]_m$, μEq†	292	292
4. Effective bladder area, cm²	3·14	3·14
5. Dry weight of tissue, mg/3·14 cm²	10·3	10·0
6. $SCC\ddagger$, μA/3·14 cm²	59·0	15·8
7. SCC,‡ μA/cm²	18·8	5·03
8. $J_n = CFE\S$, μEq/cm² × h	0·700	0·188
9. J_n, μEq/100 mg dry wt × h	21·3	5·90
10. $\lambda = (k_{21} + k_{23})$, h⁻¹	6·90	5·80
11. k_{12} × 10² (equation 43), h⁻¹	1·30	1·10
12. k_{21} (equation 42), h⁻¹	3·00	4·10
13. k_{23} (equation 41), h⁻¹	3·90	1·70
14. S_2 (equation 44), μEq/cm²	0·170	0·205
15. S_2, μEq/100 mg dry wt	5·20	6·45
16. J_{12} (equation 45) μEq/cm² × h	1·21	1·02
17. J_{12} μEq/100 mg dry wt × h	36·8	32·1
18. J_{21} (equation 46), μEq/cm² × h	0·51	0·84
19. J_{21}, μEq/100 mg dry wt × h	15·4	26·3
20. J_{23}, (equation 47), μEq/cm² × h	0·67	0·35
21. J_{23}, μEq/100 mg dry wt × h	20·4	11·0

* The figures presented are those of example No. 3 in Herrera's Tables I and II.
† $[Na^+]$ at the mucosal side of the bladder.
‡ SCC = short circuit current.
§ CFE = current flux equivalent. 1 μA = 3·73 × 10⁻² μEq/h.

bladders, k_{21} and J_{21} (efflux from the epithelial cells into the mucosal compartment) are significantly higher than the corresponding values found in control bladders. However, ouabain had no effect on k_{12} and J_{12}, and on S_2, the Na^+ pool in the bladder. The data presented in the protocol (and others found in the paper of Herrera) also show that J_{23} (obtained from flux measurement) approached J_n (net Na^+ flux as obtained from short-circuit measurement). When allowance was made for back flux (serosal fluid → bladder) it was found that $J_n = (J_{23} - J_{32})$, i.e., the total current was accounted for by movement of Na^+ ions. Furthermore, on a statistical basis Herrera's data also demonstrated that $(J_{12} - J_{21}) = (J_{23} - J_{32})$ as expected for a system in steady state. This was true for control and ouabain bladders.

18. EFFECTS OF INSULIN ON SHORT-CIRCUIT CURRENT AND SODIUM TRANSPORT IN ISOLATED TOAD BLADDER (HERRERA, 1965)

Objectives

The flow of short-circuit current and ions across tissue membranes can be altered by many chemical factors, including enzyme poisons and hormones. This experiment is concerned with the effects of insulin on toad bladder and is designed to give answers to the following questions: (1) What is the effect of insulin on the short-circuit current? (2) What are the rate coefficients for unidirectional movement of Na^+ across the membrane barriers? (3) What is the size of the intracellular Na^+ pool? (4) What is the net rate of Na^+ transport across the bladder? (5) By what mechanism does insulin affect active Na^+ transport?

Method of Investigation

If one is only interested in studying the effects of insulin on short-circuit current, a relatively simple double chamber with the proper attachments for PD and short-circuit current measurements can be used. A suitable chamber size for both mucosal and serosal compartment is 10 ml. For rate measurements of Na^+ movement across membrane barriers in the bladder tissue, the apparatus shown in Fig. 39 may be employed. Its design and mode of operation is described under Experiment 17. This text should also be consulted for estimation of Na^{22} in the bladder at the end of the experiment.

Ringer's Solution. The formula for preparing the solution is given under Experiment 17.

Insulin Stock Solution. 18·6 mg of crystalline pork insulin (MW = 5734) are dissolved in 1 ml of NaCl solution (0·67 gm/100 ml). For complete solution of the hormone the pH is adjusted to 3·0 with HCl. A NaCl solution (pH 3·0) without insulin must also be prepared. This is used in control experiments to assure that the effects seen with insulin are referable to the hormone, and not to the acid solution. Eight μl of the insulin stock solution (or acid vehicle) are added per ml of fluid in the chamber (i.e., 20 μl/2·5 ml; 80 μl/10 ml; 2 ml/250 ml (volume of the reservoir, Fig. 39).

Results and Comments

Effect of Insulin on Short-circuit Current. A typical result which shows the effect of insulin (final concentration 2·6 × 10^{-5}M) on short-circuit current is seen in Fig. 42. Two chambers were set up simultaneously. In one case (upper graph) the insulin was added first to the serosal solution and later to the

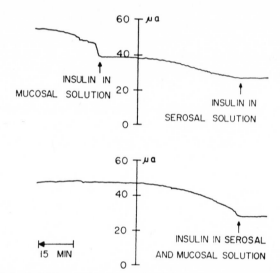

FIG. 42. Effect of addition of insulin on short-circuit current in toad bladder. Records must be read from right to left. Upper record shows effect of insulin on short-circuit current when it is added to serosal bathing solution and later to mucosal bathing solution. Lower record shows effect of insulin added simultaneously to both sides. (From Fig. 2, F. C. Herrera, *Am. J. Physiol.*, **209**, 819–824, 1965.)

mucosal solution. In the second case (lower graph) insulin was added at the same time to both serosal and mucosal solution. Serosal addition of insulin (upper graph) increased the short-circuit current from 28 to 38 μA/3·14 cm^2 (3·14 cm^2 was the effective bladder area). The later addition of insulin to the mucosal side resulted in a further increase of the short-circuit current from 38 to 54 μA/3·14 cm^2. The total increase in current was 26 μA/3·14 cm^2. Simultaneous addition of insulin to serosal and mucosal fluid raised the short-circuit current by 19 μA, from 29 to 48 μA/3·14 cm^2. When several experiments of this kind were carried out and the data treated statistically it was found that the sum of the partial increments was not different from the mean effect obtained when insulin was added to both sides simultaneously. Furthermore, from separate studies comparing the effects of acidic insulin solution and of acidic solvent alone it was established that the effects seen in Fig. 42 were the results of insulin administration. An increase in short-circuit current from 29 to 48 μA/3·14 cm^2 is equivalent to an increase in net Na$^+$ transport from 29 $\times$ 3·73 $\times$ 10^{-2} = 1·08, to 48 $\times$ 3·73 $\times$ 10^{-2} = 1·79 μEq/h per 3·14 cm^2 of bladder membrane.

Effect of Insulin on Rate Coefficients for Na$^+$ Movement and Na$^+$ Fluxes. To obtain data on rate coefficients, two bladder chambers were used, one serving as control and the other to investigate the effect of insulin. Both bladders were studied under short-circuiting conditions. When the current had become reasonably constant, insulin was added to the mucosal (or mucosal and serosal) fluid. These experiments and the analysis of the results is in every respect identical with the studies on the effects of ouabain on toad bladder (Experiment 17). Figure 43 gives the result of a typical control and an insulin experiment in which insulin was added to the mucosal fluid. Time in minutes is

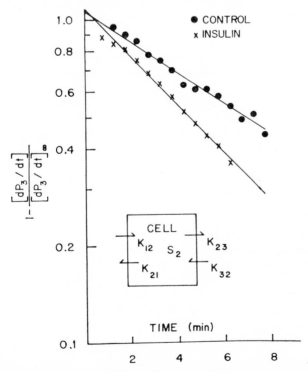

FIG. 43. Plots of log $[1 - (dP_3/dt)/(dP_3/dt)\infty]$ as a function of time for control and insulin-treated bladder halves. The straight lines have been fitted by inspection. The slopes of the lines give values for $-(k_{21} + k_{23})/2·3$. See equation (40) and examples of calculations in the text. (From Fig. 1, F. C. Herrera, *Am. J. Physiol.*, **209**, 819–824, 1965.)

plotted on the abscissa. On the ordinate is plotted the log of the following value: one minus the ratio of non-steady rate/steady state rate of appearance of Na^{22} in the serosal fluid (total CPM/min). From an extension of the regression lines shown in Fig. 43 one can calculate the following values for $(k_{21} + k_{23})$:

Control experiment:

$$(k_{21} + k_{23}) = 2 \cdot 3 \frac{\log 1 \cdot 0 - \log 0 \cdot 3}{(0 \cdot 56 - 11 \cdot 65)/60} = -\frac{2 \cdot 3 \log 3 \cdot 33}{0 \cdot 185} = -6 \cdot 5 \times h^{-1}$$

Insulin experiment:

$$(k_{21} + k_{23}) = 2 \cdot 3 \frac{\log 1 \cdot 0 - \log 0 \cdot 3}{(0 \cdot 56 - 7 \cdot 60)/60} = -\frac{2 \cdot 3 \log 3 \cdot 33}{0 \cdot 117} = -10 \cdot 3 \times h^{-1}$$

A protocol of another experiment in which insulin was added to both sides of the bladder is presented in Table VIII. Calculations of results are explained on pages 140–142. From a number of similar experiments and statistical analy-

TABLE VIII

Protocol of data on Na^+ flux in isolated toad bladder. Insulin $(2 \cdot 6 \times 10^{-5}M)$ was applied to both mucosal and serosal side. Data of Herrera (1965)*

	Control bladder	Insulin bladder
1. $[Na^+]_m$, μEq	117·00	117·00
2. V_1, ml	2·50	2·50
3. $S_1 = V_1 [Na]_m^+$, μEq	292·50	292·50
4. Effective bladder area, cm^2	3·14	3·14
5. $\lambda = (k_{21} + k_{23})$, h^{-1}	10·70	14·70
6. $k_{12} \times 10^2$ (equation 43), h^{-1}	4·10	3·70
7. k_{21} (equation 42), h^{-1}	8·10	9·70
8. k_{23} (equation 41), h^{-1}	2·60	5·00
9. S_2 (equation 44), μEq/3·14 cm^2	1·10	0·72
10. J_{12} (equation 45), μEq/3·14 cm$^2 \times$ h	1·20	1·08
11. J_{21} (equation 46), μEq/3·14 cm$^2 \times$ h	8·90	7·00
12. J_{23} (equation 47), μEq/3·14 cm$^2 \times$ h	2·86	3·60

* The figures presented are those of example No. 6 in Herrera's Table III.

sis of the results it was shown that the only significant difference between insulin treated and control bladders was the higher value of k_{23}, and hence of J_{23}. This suggests that insulin stimulated the active Na^+ transport mechanism, a result opposite to the one obtained when ouabain was applied. (Experiment No. 17.) Herrera (1965) also showed that the increase in J_{23} resulting from insulin treatment of bladders was matched by a nearly equivalent increase in short-circuit current. The stimulatory effect of insulin occurred in the absence of glucose in the bathing media.

19. SHORT-CIRCUIT CURRENT IN ISOLATED TURTLE BLADDER DURING ANEROBIOSIS (KLAHR AND BRICKER, 1964)

Objectives

By definition "active transport" is a process occurring in living cells and tissues which maintain the transport function by supplying metabolic energy to a mechanism whose mode of operation is not known. This holds true for all metabolizing, membraneous animal tissues, including bladder of the turtle (*Pseudemys scripta elegans*). In this tissue, as in frog skin or toad bladder, active Na^+ transport can be observed in the direction from mucosa to serosa. With Ringer's solution on both sides of isolated bladder tissue it is found that the serosa is electrically positive relative to the mucosa, and a short-circuit current can be drawn from this tissue as long as its metabolism is sustained. The following experiment is designed to answer the question: Is it possible to draw a short-circuit current under the conditions of anaerobiosis?

Method of Investigation

Double Chamber. To measure the PD across the bladder and short-circuit current that may be drawn from this tissue, a double chamber with appropriate attachment is used which is in every respect the same as the chambers described in earlier experiments (No. 5 and 7). Within limits the dimensions of the chambers are not critical. The data presented below were obtained with hemi-chamber volumes of 20 ml, and a bladder area of 7 cm². Oxygen is continuously bubbled through the fluid in the chambers in studies designed to investigate the function of the bladder under aerobic conditions. Anaerobic conditions are attained by bubbling 100% N_2 from a tank through the chamber fluids.

Ringer's Solution. Dissolve in 1 liter of distilled water: 6·7 g NaCl; 0·18 g KCl; 0·16 g $CaCl_2$; 0·19 g $MgCl_2$; 0·29 g Na_2HPO_4; 3·8 g glucose; adjust pH to 7·4.

Results and Comments

Results of a representative experiment are shown in Fig. 44. An aerobic period of 30 min was followed by a 50 min period of anaerobiosis. Data are given of short-circuit current (*SCC*, in $\mu A/7$ cm²), "open" bladder PD (measured intermittently, mV) and bladder resistance in ohms, referable to 7 cm² of bladder surface. The resistance values were calculated by applying Ohm's law, $R = E/I$ in which E is the PD of the "open" bladder, and I is the concurrent short-circuit current (see page 68). To obtain the specific membrane resistance in units of $\Omega \times cm^2$ (see page 51), the R values must be multiplied by $A = 7$ cm^2.

Although occasionally no changes in SCC, PD and R were seen upon removal of O_2 from the solution bathing the bladder, more often a decrease in both SCC and PD and an increase in R (Fig. 44) were observed. However,

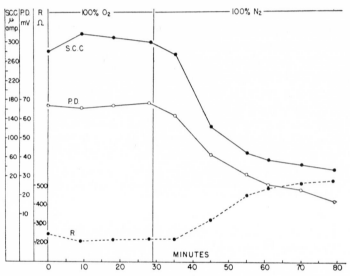

FIG. 44. Bioelectric properties of the isolated turtle bladder studied under anerobic conditions. Initial values depicted in the graphs (in O_2) were obtained after SCC (I_{sc}) and PD had recovered from the initial drop. (From Fig. 3, S. Klahr and N. S. Bricker, *Am. J. Physiol.*, **206**, 1333–1339, 1964.)

the important fact remains that in the absence of analytically detectable amounts of O_2, a considerable PD across the bladder persisted, and for periods exceeding 3 h of anaerobiosis a short-circuit current could be drawn from several bladders. It would appear, therefore, that glycolysis plays a major role in the energy supply to support active ion transport in turtle bladder.

More insight in the ion transport function of this tissue was obtained from several extensions of the experiment described. This included simultaneous Na^{22} and Na^{24} influx and outflux measurements; application of 1×10^{-3}M KCN; studies on bladders of turtles after a prolonged period of diving. Results related to these conditions are found in the paper of Klahr and Bricker (1964). One of their notable observations was that under conditions of anaerobiosis, net Na$^+$ flux considerably exceeded the short-circuit current flux equivalent (CFE, see page 52). This suggests active anion transport in this tissue. The following experiment (No. 20) will give proof that turtle bladder is able to actively transport Cl^- ions from the mucosal to the serosal side. Active transport of HCO_3^- ions also occurs in this tissue in the direction mucosa → serosa (Gonzales *et al.*, 1967).

20. SHORT-CIRCUIT CURRENT AND CHLORIDE FLUX IN ISOLATED TURTLE BLADDER (GONZALES *ET AL.* 1967)

Objectives

It is known that when isolated turtle bladder is bathed on both sides with sodium free choline Ringer's solution, which contains as anions both Cl^- and HCO_3^-, the mucosal side is electrically positive relative to the serosa, i.e., $(\Psi m - \Psi s) > 0$. The symbols Ψm and Ψs designate the potentials of the mucosal and serosal fluid, respectively. If Na^+ is present in the solution (see Experiment 19) it is found that $(\Psi m - \Psi s) < 0$. From short-circuit current and Cl^- flux measurements on bladders in sodium free choline Ringer's, results such as the following may be obtained: $\Psi m - \Psi s = 39\cdot8$ mV; rate of Cl^- flux in the direction mucosa → serosa, $J_{ms} = 1\cdot06$ μEq $\times$ h^{-1}; rate of Cl^- flux in the direction serosa → mucosa $J_{ms} = 0\cdot38$ μEq $\times$ h^{-1}; hence, net Cl^- flux $= (J_{ms} - J_{sm}) = 0\cdot68$ μEq $\times$ h^{-1}; short-circuit current, $SCC = 35\cdot6$ μA, and current flux equivalent, CFE $= 35\cdot6 \times 3\cdot73 \times 10^{-2} = 1\cdot33$ μEq $\times$ h^{-1}. Thus, the net Cl^- flux accounts for only 51 % of the short-circuit current. The remaining electrical current (49 %) is the result of active HCO_3^- transport. The present experiment is designed to answer the following question: What is the quantitative relationship between short-circuit current and Cl^- flux in bladders suspended in media free of HCO_3^- and free of Na^+?

Method of Investigation

Flux Chambers. The double Lucite flux chamber needed for simultaneous measurements on paired halves of a given urinary bladder of *Pseudomys scripta* is shown in Fig. 45. As can be seen from Fig. 45C, the two bladder halves are side by side in the double chamber, each consisting of a left side and right side compartment. The exposed areas of bladder tissue between compartments are $1\cdot2$ cm². Gonzales *et al.* (1967) have described the mounting of the bladders as follows: after removal of the bladder from the turtle, the tissue is placed in Na^+ free choline Ringer solution. The edge of the bladder is grasped with 10 small clips (minigators) to which pieces of threads are attached. The bladder is then moved into a cork ring, 14 cm in diameter and the tissue is held in place by securing the threads to 10 thumb tacks arranged in a circle on the cork ring. This is done with as little stretch as possible. After the bladder has been kept for $\frac{1}{2}$ h in the salt solution the tissue is mounted into the flux chamber.

Ten fine stainless steel needles, arranged in a circle, are embedded into the Lucite block constituting one half chamber. The matching Lucite block of the opposite side is provided with appropriate holes to accommodate the pins which hold the bladder membrane. The serosal surface of the bladder rests on a fine-mesh tantalum screen. Leakage is prevented by placing rubber O-rings on both sides of the membrane before positioning the two half cells. The half cells are forced against each other by some appropriate clamping device.

Air Lift System. This device (Fig. 45A) holds approximately 10 ml of salt solution (see also Figs 10 and 22). The mucosal fluid is gassed with 100% O_2, the serosal fluid with 99% + 1% CO_2. The tip of the air inlet tube (not shown in

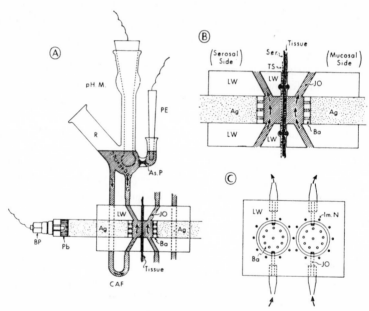

FIG. 45. Schema of bladder interposed between two circulating fluids, showing component parts of Lucite chamber and the mode of mounting of tissue. *Inset A*: (pH.M) glass electrode for pH determinations; (PE) probe electrode (calomel) for measurement of transbladder PD; (As.P) asbestos plug; (R) reservoir for circulating fluid; (G) position of emission of gas mixture through a finebore polyethylene tube, not shown, in which white dots denote gas bubbling upward, and dark arrows denote direction of flow of fluid; (BP) banana plug for current sending electrode consisting of metallic lead (Pb) plus agar layers (Ag) of saturated Pb acetate, KCl, and choline sulfate (stippled); (Ba) baffle with agar filled holes; (CAF) circulating ambient fluids (diagonal lines); (JO) jet orifice. *Inset B*: enlarged view of tissue mounting site showing O-rings (solid dots) which seal tissue and tantalum screen (TS) against which serosal surface of tissue rests. *Inset C*: end view of chamber with tissue removed showing (Im.N) impaling needles; concentric circles which enclose groove into which O-rings are placed. (LW) Lucite wall. (From Fig. 1, C. F. Gonzales, Y. E. Shamoo and W. A. Brodsky, *Am. J. Physiol.*, **212**, 641–650, 1967.)

Fig. 45) is placed 8 cm below the fluid level in the system. A fluid movement of 30 ml/min, passing at high velocity over the membrane surface, is obtained by providing 1·5 mm wide jet openings in the top and the bottom of each chamber. The centers of these openings should be 1 mm away from the surfaces of the bladder. The gas-lift reservoirs are equipped with pH glass electrodes and calomel half cells as shown in Fig. 45. The calomel cells serve to measure and monitor the bladder potential. Since the bladder tissue has a high electrical resistance, relative to the resistance of the fluid layers between the jet openings and the surfaces of the bladder, the PD between the electrodes is very nearly the bladder membrane PD (see pages 61–68).

Current Sending Electrodes. Details of construction of these reversible lead/lead acetate electrodes are shown in Fig. 45. The dimensions of the Lucite cylinder are : $2\frac{7}{8}$ in. in length ; $\frac{5}{8}$ in. o.d., and $\frac{1}{2}$ in. i.d. The left hand side of the illustration shows the metallic lead disk which is penetrated by a banana plug. On the right hand side, a Lucite baffle plate is depicted with 10 holes, each 1 mm in diameter. The cylinders are filled with 3% agar layers of : saturated $PbAc_2$ ($\frac{1}{3}$), saturated KCl ($\frac{1}{3}$), choline Cl^- ($\frac{1}{3}$, mucosal side), or choline Ringer's ($\frac{1}{3}$, serosal side). The agar mixture penetrates the holes in the baffle plate. PD measurements and short-circuiting the bladder are accomplished with equipment described already earlier (Experiments No. 5; 6; 7).

Salt Solutions. The mucosal side of the bladder is bathed with "choline chloride", the serosal side with "choline Ringer's solution". Preparation of choline chloride solution : dissolve in 1 liter of distilled water : 12·57 g choline chloride ; 13·7 g sucrose (to raise the total osmolarity to $\cong$ 220 mosmoles) Preparation of choline Ringer's : dissolve in 1 liter of distilled water : 11·6 g choline chloride ; 2·8 g choline bicarbonate ; 0·30 g KCl ; 0·11 g KH_2PO_4 ; 0·096 g $Mg\,SO_4$; 0·22 g $CaCl_2$. Choline bicarbonate is sold by some supply houses in form of a 40 to 50% solution from which the needed solution is prepared. It should be noted that both types of salt solutions have the same chloride concentration. The total osmolarity of this solution is $\cong$ 220 mosmoles. To match both types of salt solutions exactly, osmometric measurements must be carried out, and final adjustments are made with sucrose. When the solutions are in contact with the bladder and are gassed as mentioned above, pH values of 7·5 to 7·6 can be maintained throughout the experiment.

Chloride Fluxes. Bidirectional fluxes (J_{ms} and J_{sm}) are measured separately on two bladder halves using the Cl^{36} isotope in the form of choline Cl^{36}. This is prepared by titrating choline bicarbonate with HCl^{36} (which is commercially available) to reach an endpoint of pH 3·0 after boiling the mixture. Shortly before adding the acid Cl^{36} solution to the appropriate chambers, the pH of the salt solutions is raised to 7·6 with diluted KOH. For measurements of chloride flux in the direction mucosa→serosa (J_{ms}), 10 μC of Cl^{36} in 0·05 ml fluid are added to the mucosal compartment. For flux measurements in the opposite direction (J_{sm}) 20 to 30 μc Cl^{36} in 0·1 ml fluid are added to the serosal compartment. For count rate measurements (at least 10 000 counts per period) a Packard Tri-Carb liquid scintillation spectrometer (or a similar type of equipment) may be employed. Under the conditions of the experiments as illustrated below, the total radioactivity in the fluid into which the isotope moves will never exceed 1% of the total radioactivity. Hence, backflux of isotope may be neglected.

Experiment. Paired halves of a turtle bladder are mounted simultaneously in the double chamber. Only bladders without visible evidence of surface damage should be used. Furthermore, best results are obtained by selecting a "well-matched" pair, i.e. a pair in which the half-bladders differ by less than 10% in their spontaneous bladder PD. When the PD has become reasonably stabilized, flux experiments are started. At about 10 min periods the short-circuit current is interrupted for about 1 sec for "open-bladder" PD measurements. Chloride isotope is added to the appropriate compartment for flux measurements. At half hour intervals fluid samples are taken from the "cold" side for count rate measurements. A yield of 10 000 counts per sample assures sufficient counting accuracy. The original activity of the "hot" solution is obtained by taking a sample from the "hot" compartment soon after Cl^{36} addition, allowing sufficient time for mixing. The result may be checked by taking an additional sample at the end of the 4 to 5 h experiment. Chloride fluxes are calculated by dividing the total increment of count rate in the compartment into which Cl^{36} has moved by the specific activity of chloride in the compartment to which Cl^{36} was added (see page 57). Net flux, J_n, is calculated as ($J_{ms} - J_{sm}$). The net Cl^- flux thus obtained for a given period of time and the given bladder area (1·2 cm²) may then be expressed as flow of current by using the relationship: $1 \mu A = 6·22 \times 10^{-4} \mu Eq \times min^{-1}$ (see page 53).

Results and Comments

Results of a typical experiment are shown in Fig. 46. It can be seen from the PD record that the data apply to a well matched pair of bladders. Over a period of 4·5 h PD, short-circuit current (I_{sc}) and Cl^- flux gradually decreased. Near equivalence between the measured I_{sc}, and the I_{sc} calculated from chloride fluxes existed. In this experiment six flux periods were chosen. When a number of similar experiments were conducted and the results were analysed statistically, full equivalence of flux and current was found. This suggests that turtle bladder actively transports Cl⁻ in the direction from mucosa → serosa. If HCO_3^- is also present in the salt solution at the mucosal side, it can be shown that the bladder actively transports HCO_3^- ions, in addition to Cl⁻ ions, as has been mentioned under "Objectives" of this experiment.

In the middle section of Fig. 46, flux ratio are given for the five flux periods studied. For instance, in period I the flux ratio $J_{ms}/J_{sm} = 23{\cdot}6/10{\cdot}4 = 2{\cdot}27$.

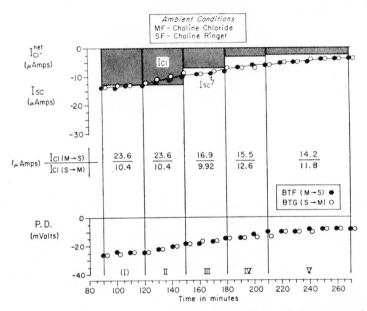

FIG. 46. Chloride fluxes (I_{Cl}), short-circuiting current (I_{sc}), and PD versus time in absence of mucosal bicarbonate. Values for flux ratios are given in the middle section of the illustration. (From Fig. 4, C. F. Gonzales, Y. E. Shamoo and W. A. Brodsky, *Am. J. Physiol.*, **212**, 641–650, 1967.)

One may now apply the Ussing–Teorell independence equation as follows:

$$\frac{J_{ms}}{J_{sm}} = \frac{[Cl^-]_m}{[Cl^-]_s} \cdot e^{(zF/RT)\,(\Psi_m-\Psi_s)} \tag{48}$$

As has been mentioned under "salt solution", $[Cl^-]_m = [Cl^-]_s$. $z = -1$; $F/RT = 38{\cdot}9 \times V^{-1}$ (see page 56). $\Psi_m - \Psi_s = 0$ (under short-circuit conditions). Inserting these values in equation (48) one calculates for

$$\frac{J_{ms}}{J_{sm}} = e^0 = 1{\cdot}00$$

The fact that the calculated flux ratio is far less than the experimentally found flux ratio (2·27) suggests that active chloride transport occurs in turtle bladder.

One may also apply an extended form of the independence equation (Ussing and Zerahn, 1951) and calculate a minimal value for the active transport potential, E_{Cl}, of the active hypothetical "chloride pump" by solving equation (48) for E_{Cl}:

$$2\cdot27 = e^{(zF/RT)\,[(\Psi\ -\Psi_s)+E_{Cl}]}$$

The result is:

$$E_{Cl} = -\frac{2\cdot3 \log 2\cdot27}{38\cdot9} = -0\cdot021\ V$$

In other words, to explain the flux results the data suggest the operation of an active chloride pump which generates a pump potential of at least -21 mV during period I (Fig. 46) of the flux measurement.

CONCLUDING REMARKS

This article was written to stimulate interest among younger biologists, who have an appreciation for the principles of physical chemistry applied to biology and who desire to do research on some properties of biological membranes on which so many conditions for life depend. It is hoped that those who perform similar experiments share in the satisfaction that comes with the conduction of experiments which aim at the establishment of quantitative relationships between a number of measurable variables. This presentation placed emphasis on:

(1) Summarizing several important physical and chemical principles related to the overall objective.

(2) Description of construction and mode of operation of several pieces of general laboratory equipment.

(3) Design of special equipment needed to do research work on a variety of biological tissues which present themselves in the form of "membranes", although of highly complex histological structure.

In dealing with a particular experiment, as many details as were available or could be obtained through correspondence with authors of papers were searched for and are presented here. All this has been done with judgment based on the practical experience of the authors of this article.

It is clear that this article is primarily written for the non-expert in the field often broadly referred to as Membrane Transport. In selecting the experiments described in this text, the authors were guided by methodological viewpoints, leaving it to the future to decide on the outcome of controversial conclusions drawn from their results. These experiments are presented to illustrate the kind of observations which can be made with the various methods of study. Experiments introducing some new feature in design of equipment were given particular attention, and in some respects were applied to the historical development of the area of investigation of tissue membranes. Once the novice has acquired some skill in the handling of equipment and understands the reasons why it has been designed as proposed, he may then be better prepared to apply modifications which may be necessary to solve a new problem of his own choosing.

Experts in the field of membrane transport will readily recognize that a considerable number of important contributions are not mentioned in this article. The aims mentioned above explain these omissions. The diligent student will soon discover that the list of reference will guide him well along the ramified pathways to the work of most investigations in the field of Membrane Transport.

ACKNOWLEDGEMENTS

The authors gratefully acknowledge the assistance received from several scientists by giving additional information on technical aspects of their work, not found in their publications. All authors, as well as the editors of Journals, have kindly given us permission for reproduction of numerous illustrations shown in this article. For this, too, we are very grateful. Acknowledgment of permission for reproduction of illustrations is expressed by full quotation of the source from which the material was taken. The writing of this article was supported by several Grants:

Special Fellowship, 5F3AM–18664 (C. O. Watlington)
NSF Fellowship (T. C. Smith)
Career Award KO6 GM 16 687 (E. G. Huf)
NIH Research Grant AM–06481 (C. O. Watlington) and GM–03545 (E. G. Huf)

LIST OF SYMBOLS

(Symbols not listed here are explained in the text).

EMF (E)	electromotive force, mV.
PD (ΔV; V)	potential difference, mV.
ψ_o; ψ_i	potentials of the solutions at the "outside" and the "inside", respectively, of a membrane, mV.
$I(i)$	electrical current, mA, or μA.
I_{sc}	true short-circuit current, μA.
I'_{sc}	apparent short-circuit current μA.
$R(r)$	resistance, ohm. (R is also used for the gas constant.)

R_R, R_M resistance of Ringer's solution, and membrane resistance, ohm. Specific resistances are given as ohm $\times$ cm^2.

G conductance ($1/G$), ohm^{-1} (mho); or mho/cm^2 to express specific conductance.

Λ equivalence conductance, ohm^{-1} $\times$ cm^2/Eq.

(ϕ)   flux, μEq $\times$ cm^{-2} $\times$ h^{-1}, or μEq $\times$ cm^{-2} $\times$ sec^{-1}.

CFE   current flux equivalent, as defined on page 52.

MW   molecular weight, g.

REFERENCES

Asano, T. (1964). Metabolic disturbances and short-circuit current across intestinal wall of rat. *Am. J. Physiol.*, **207**, 415–422.

Bové, F. J. (1962). MS-222 Sandoz—The anesthetic of choice for fish and other cold-blooded organisms. *Sandoz News*, No. 3, 1–8.

Bresler, E. H. (1967). On criteria for active transport. *J. theoret. Biol.*, **16**, 135–146.

Brown, A. C. and Kastella, K. G. (1965). The AC impedance of frog skin and its relation to active transport. *Biophys. J.*, **5**, 591–606.

Campbell, A. D., Seward, W. D., Gilmer, T. E., Jr. and Huf, E. G. (1961). Automatic recording of electric potential and ion transport in frog skin. *Protoplasma*, **54**, 164–172.

Campbell, J. P., Aiyawar, R. M., Berry, E. R. and Huf, E. G. (1967). Electrolytes in frog skin secretions, *Comp. Biochem. Physiol.*, **23**, 213–223.

Chase, G. D., and Rabinowitz, J. L. (1965). *In* "Principles of Radioisotope Methodology". Burgess Publishing Company. Minneapolis, Minnesota, U.S.A.

Clark, W. M. (1952). *In* "Topics in Physical Chemistry". The Williams and Wilkins Company, Baltimore, Maryland, U.S.A.

Cooperstein, I. L. and Hogben, C. A. M. (1959). Ionic transfer across the isolated frog large intestine. *J. gen. Physiol.*, **42**, 461–473.

Curran, P. F. and Cereijido, M. (1965). K. Fluxes in frog skin. *J. gen. Physiol.*, **48**, 1011–1033.

Curran, P. F., Herrera, F. C. and Flanigan, W. J. (1963). The effect of Ca and anti-diuretic hormone on Na transport across frog skin. *J. gen. Physiol.*, **46**, 1011–1027.

Curran, P. F., Taylor, A. E. and Solomon, A. K. (1967). Tracer diffusion and uni-directional fluxes. *Biophys. J.*, **7**, 879–901.

Defares, J. G. and Sneddon, I. N. (1961). *In* "The Mathematics of Medicine and Biology". Year Book Medical Publishers, Inc., Chicago, U.S.A.

Dobson, J.G., Jr. and Kidder, G. W., III (1968). Edge damage effect in *in vitro* frog skin preparations. *Am. J. Physiol.*, **214**, 719–724.

Durbin, R. P. and Heinz, E. (1958). Electromotive chloride transport and gastric acid secretion in the frog. *J. gen. Physiol.*, **41**, 1035–1047.

Eubank, L. L., Huf, E. G., Campbell, A. D. and Taylor, B. B. (1962). Effects of redox systems on active ion transport in frog skin. *J. cell. comp. Physiol.*, **59**, 129–144.

Francis, W. L. (1933). Output of electrical energy by frog skin. *Nature, Lond.*, **131**, 805.

Frazier, H. S. and Hammer, E. I. (1963). Efflux of sodium from isolated toad bladder, *Am. J. Physiol.*, **205**, 718–722.

Friedman, R. T., LaPrade, N. S., Aiyawar, R. M. and Huf, E. G. (1967). Chemical basis for the [H$^+$] gradient across frog skin. *Am. J. Physiol.*, **212**, 962–972.

Fukuda, T. R. (1944). Über die Froschhautimpedanz im niedrigen Frequenzbereich. *Jap. J. med. Sci Trans. Abstr.* (Part III, Biophys.), X, 63–76.

Gerstner, H. (1939a). Polarisierbarkeit and Permeabilität der Froschhaut. *Pflügers Arch. ges Physiol.*, 113–125.

Gerstner, H. (1939b). Blind-und Wirkwiderstand der Froschhaut in Tonfrequenzbereich und ihre Beziehungen zur Permeabilität. *Pflügers Arch. ges. Physiol.*, **242**, 587–616.

Glasstone, S. (1946). *In* "Textbook of Physical Chemistry". D. Van Nostrand Company, Inc., Princeton, N.Y., U.S.A.

Gonzales, E. F., Shamoo, Y. E. and Brodsky, W. A. (1967). Electrical nature of active chloride transport across short-circuited turtle bladders. *Am. J. Physiol.*, **212**, 641–650.

Heinz, E. and Durbin, R. P. (1957). Studies on the chloride transport in the gastric mucosa of the frog. *J. gen. Physiol.*, **41**, 101–117.

Henderson, P. (1907). Zur Thermodynamik der Flüssigkeitsketten. *Z. phys. Chem.*, **59**, 118–127.

Henderson, P. (1908). Zur Thermodynamik der Flüssigkeitsketten. *Z. phys. Chem.*, 325–345.

Herrera, F. C. (1965). Effect of insulin on short-circuit current and sodium transport across toad urinary bladder. *Am. J. Physiol.*, **209**, 819–824.

Herrera, F. C. (1966). Action of ouabain on sodium transport in the toad urinary bladder. *Am. J. Physiol.*, **210**, 980–986.

Hills, G. J. and Ives, D. J. (1961). The calomel electrode and other mercury-mercurous salt electrodes. *In* "Reference Electrodes, Theory and Practice". D. G. Ives and G. J. Janz, ed.). Chapter 3, p. 127. Academic Press, New York and London.

Hogben, C. A. M. (1955). Active transport of chloride by isolated frog gastric epithelium. Origin of the gastric mucosal potential. *Am. J. Physiol.*, **180**, 641–649.

Huf, E. G. (1935a). Versuche über den Zusammenhang zwischen Stoffwechsel, Potentialbildung und Funktion der Froschhaut. *Pflügers Arch. ges. Physiol.*, **235**, 655–673.

Huf, E. G. (1935b). Über den Anteil vitaler Kräfte bei der Resorption von Flüssigkeit durch die Froschhaut. *Pflügers Arch. ges. Physiol.*, **236**, 1–19.

Huf, E. G. (1936a). Über aktiven Wasser-und Salztransport durch die Froschhaut. *Pflügers Arch. ges. Physiol.*, **237**, 143–166.

Huf, E. G. (1936b). Die Reproduzierbarkeit des Reid'schen Versuchs. *Pflügers Arch. ges. Physiol.*, **238**, 97–102.

Huf, E. G. (1936c). Die Bedeutung der Atmungsvorgäuge für die Resorptions-leistung and Potentialbildung bei der Froschhaut. *Biochem. Z.*, **288**, 116–122.

Huf, E. G. (1936d). Über irreziproke (gerichtete) Osmosis durch die Froschhaut. *Protoplasma*, **26**, 614–619.

Huf, E. G. (1938). Der Sauerstoffverbrauch der isolierten Froschhaut und der Einfluss von Cyanid. *Pflügers Arch. ges. Physiol.*, **240**, 573–577.

Huf, E. G. (1955). Ion transport and ion exchange in frog skin. *In* "Electrolytes in Biological Systems" (A. M. Shanes, ed.). American Physiological Society, Washington, D.C., p. 215.

Huf, E. G. and Wills, J. (1951). Influence of some inorganic cations on active salt and water uptake by isolated frog skin. *Am. J. Physiol.*, **167**, 255–260.

Huf, E. G., Doss, N. S. and Wills, J. P. (1957). Effects of metabolic inhibitors and drugs on ion transport and oxygen consumption in isolated frog skin. *J. gen. Physiol.*, **41**, 297–417.

Ives, D. J. and Janz, G. J. (1961). *In* "Reference Electrodes, Theory and Practice". (D. J. Ives and G. J. Janz, eds). Academic Press, New York and London.

Janz, G. J. (1961). Silver-silver halide electrodes. *In* "Reference Electrodes, Theory and Practice". D. G. Ives and G. J. Janz, eds.). Chapter 4, p. 179. Academic Press, New York and London.

Karger, W. (1959). Über eine Variation der Kurzschlussmethodik von H. H. Ussing zum aktiven Ionentransport. *Z. Naturf.*, **14B**, 118–124.

Karger, W. (1967). Aktiver Natriumtransport an der isolierten Froschhaut als Antrieb für einen Mikrowattmessmotor. *Ber. der Bunsenges.*, **71**, 887–890.

Karger, W. (1968). Abgabe elektrischer Energie aus einer Froschhaut. *Naturwissenchaften*, **55**, 109–112.

Kedem, O. and Essig, A. (1965). Isotope flows and flux ratios in biological membranes. *J. gen. Physiol.*, **48**, 1047–1070.

Klahr, S. and Bricker, N. S. (1964). Na transport by isolated turtle bladder during anaerobiosis and exposure to KCN. *Am. J. Physiol.*, **206**, 1333–1339.

Koefoed-Johnson, V., Ussing, H. H. and Zerahn, K. (1952). The origin of the short-circuit current in the adrenaline stimulated frog skin. *Acta physiol. scand.*, **27**, 38–48.

Koefoed-Johnson, V. and Ussing, H. H. (1958). The nature of the frog skin potential. *Acta physiol. scand.*, **42**, 298–308.

Leaf, A., Anderson, J. and Page, L. B. (1958). Active sodium transport by the isolated toad bladder. *J. gen. Physiol.*, **41**, 657–668.

Lichtenstein, N. S. and Leaf, A. (1965). Effect of amphotericin B on the permeability of the toad bladder. *J. clin. Invest.*, **44**, 1328–1342.

Linderholm, H. (1950). Ion Permeability and electrical conductivity of isolated frog skin. *Acta physiol scand.*, **20**, 185–202.

Linderholm, H. (1952). Active transport of ions through frog skin with special reference to the action of certain diuretics. *Acta physiol. scand.*, **27**, Suppl. 97, 1-144.

Lund, E. J. (1947). *In* "Bioelectric Fields and Growth". The University of Texas Press, Austin, U.S.A.

Mendoza, S. A., Handler, J. S. and Orloff, J. (1967). Effect of amphotericin B on permeability and short-circuit current in toad bladder. *Am. J. Physiol.*, **213**, 1263–1268.

Menninger, J. R., Snell, F. M. and Spangler, R. A. (1960). Voltage clamp for biological investigation. *Rev. Scient. Instrum.*, **31**, 519–521.

Mullins, L. J. (1958). Penetration of anions through frog skin. *Am. J. Physiol.*, **194**, 369–372.

Myers, R. M., Bishop, W. R. and Scheer, B. T. (1961). Anterior pituitary control of active sodium transport across frog skin. *Am. J. Physiol.*, **200**, 444–450.

Netter, H. (1959). *In* "Theoretische Biochemie". Springer Verlag, Berlin Göttingen, Heidelberg.

Patlak, C. S. (1956). Contributions to the theory of active transport. *Bull. math. Biophys.*, **18**, 271–315.

Rehm, W. S. (1943). Electrical energy output of the resting stomach as determined by shunting its potential. *Am. J. Physiol.*, **139**, 1–8.

Rehm, W. S. (1944). The effect of histamine and HCl on gastric secretion and potential. *Am. J. Physiol.*, **141**, 537–548.

Rehm, W. S. (1945). The effect of electric current on gastric secretion and potential. *Am. J. Physiol.*, **144**, 115–125.

Rehm, W. S. (1953). Electrical resistance of resting and secreting stomach. *Am. J. Physiol.*, **172**, 689–699.

Rosenberg, T. (1954). The concept of definition of active transport. *Symp. Soc. exp. Biol.*, **8**, 25–41.

Scheer, B. T. (1958). Active Transport: Definitions and criteria. *Bull. math. Biophys.*, **20**, 231–244.

Schultz, S. G. and Zalusky, R. (1964a). Ion transport in isolated rabbit ileum. I. Short circuit current and Na fluxes. *J. gen. Physiol.*, **47**, 567–584.

Schultz, S. G. and Zalusky, R. (1964b). Ion transport in isolated rabbit ileum. II. The interaction between active sodium and active sugar transport. *J. gen. Physiol.*, **47**, 1043–1059.

Sharp, G. W. G. and Leaf, A. (1964). Biological action of aldosterone *in vitro*. *Nature, Lond.*, **202**, 1185–1188.

Ussing, H. H. (1960). The alkali metal ions in isolated systems and tissues. *In* "The Alkali Metal Ions in Biology". (O. Eichler and A. Farah, eds) Handbuch der Experimentellen Pharmakologie.

Ussing, H. H. and Zerahn, K. (1951). Active transport of sodium as the source of electric current in the short-circuited isolated frog skin. *Acta physiol. scand.*, **23**, 110–127.

Watlington, C. O. (1967). Adrenergic stimulation and sodium transport. *Med. Coll. Virginia Quart.*, **3**, 157–162.

Watlington, C. O. (1968a). Effect of adrenergic stimulation on ion transport across skin of living frogs. *Comp. Biochem. Physiol.*, **24**, 965–974.

Watlington, C. O. (1968b). Effect of catecholamines and adrenergic blockade on sodium transport of isolated frog skin. *Am. J. Physiol.*, **214**, 1001–1007.

Watlington, C. O., Campbell, A. D. and Huf, E. G. (1964). Ion transport in skin of live frogs. *J. cell. comp. Physiol.*, **64**, 389–408.

Watlington, C. O., Burke, P. K., Campbell, A. D. and Huf, E. G. (1965). Systemic effects of epinephrine in the frog. *J. cell. comp. Physiol.*, **65**, 337–354.

Winn, P. M., LaPrade, N. S., Tolbert, W. R. and Huf, E. G. (1966). On the nature of the resting frog skin potential. *Med. Coll. Virginia Quart.*, **2**, 116–126.

Exp. in Physiol. and Biochem. (1970). 3, 161–180.

5 | Experiments on the Transmembrane Potential of Chromatophores

ALAN R. FREEMAN

Department of Physiology, Rutgers Medical School,
New Brunswick, New Jersey, U.S.A.

and

MILTON FINGERMAN

Department of Biology, Tulane University, New Orleans,
Louisiana, U.S.A.

GENERAL PRINCIPLES

The object of this experiment is to apply electrophysiological methods of investigation in characterizing the cell boundary of a specific chromatophore. It is anticipated that the information so gained will be useful towards a better understanding of the physiology of chromatophore responses in general.

The erythrophores of Crustacea are chosen here as the experimental object for a number of reasons. Technologically, the dissection procedure is relatively simple and the cells will tolerate microelectrode impalement with minimal damage. Physiologically, pigment migration in these chromatophores is controlled entirely by blood-borne substances, the cells being free of innervation (Fingerman, 1965). In addition, the sources of both pigment-dispersing and pigment-concentrating substances have been localized, i.e., in the prawn *Palaemonetes vulgaris* (Fingerman, 1965).

Experimental methodology and data interpretation are discussed in as much detail as is consistent with a reasonable space consumption presupposing that the reader is familiar with the fundamental concepts of electricity and electrochemistry. When specific sources for items of equipment such as amplifiers, oscilloscope, etc., are given these should be regarded as only a single suggestion of many available which would serve equally well. The techniques described are independent of unique features of any individual piece of apparatus.

H

APPARATUS

Dissecting microscope
Microdissection instruments
Micromanipulator and
  microelectrode holder
Oscilloscope
High impedance amplifier
Calibration unit
Petri dish
Histological staining jar

Microcapillary puller
0·8 mm (o.d.) pyrex capillary tubing
Ordinary laboratory glassware
No. 20 gauge fine silver wire (about
  1 meter in length)
1·5 V battery
10 megohm resistor
1000 Ω resistor
31 gauge hypodermic needle and
  5 ml syringe

CHEMICALS

Sodium chloride
Potassium chloride
1/10N HCl

Microelectrodes

Since no unique requirements are imposed by the chromatophores under investigation, a wide variety of methods for microelectrode fabrication may be employed.

The following method is suggested because of its ability to produce suitable electrodes simply and in a relatively short period of time.

Prepare about 15 lengths of 0·8 mm pyrex capillary tubing measuring roughly 10 cm each. Starting with arbitrary heat settings on the micro-electrode puller (such as that of Industrial Science Associates, Ridgewood, N.Y., U.S.A.) begin pulling capillaries until the product appears to have approximately a 4 mm shoulder-to-tip taper and possesses a smooth contour when viewed under the low power light microscope. Because the final tip of an acceptable electrode is not visible under high power, it is generally regarded that the tip aperture is less than 0·5 μ in diameter. Fix 10 or so of the pulled capillaries, now about 5 cm long, to a microscope slide being careful to recess the fragile tips so as to prevent mechanical damage. A snugly fitting elastic band may be used to secure the microelectrodes which should be oriented with the tips facing downward. Introduce distilled water using a long 31 gauge hypodermic needle which has been inserted as far down into the electrode tip as possible. Place the slides supporting the water-filled capillaries into a histological staining jar which is about $\frac{1}{3}$ filled with filtered 3M KCl. The jar is then covered and allowed to remain under the heat of a 60 W lamp at a distance of 3 cm or so for 12 to 24 h. (Time varies according to electrode geometry.) During this time the combined forces of capillarity and differential vapor pressure, augmented by the added heat gradient usually cause the KCl to rise sufficiently high in the tip so that either a small air gap or no gap at all exists between the KCl and the distilled water. The 31 gauge needle, this time filled with filtered 3M KCl, is once again introduced and the capillary completely rinsed. A fine wire, such as the cleaning wire provided with the 31 gauge needle, may sometimes be necessary to dislodge a stubborn air bubble which might remain in the microelectrode tip.

After manufacture those electrodes are selected for use whose electrical resistance measures between 10 and 20 megohms. A method for determining the electrode resistance is presented later in this article.

An extensive treatment of the subject of microelectrodes may be found in the article by Frank and Becker (1964).

TROUBLESHOOTING MICROELECTRODES

Although occasionally problems associated with the use of microelectrodes may appear mystical in nature, certain difficulties are more likely to occur than others. From time to time a completed electrode may have excessively high resistance and/or a relatively high potential appearing across its tip ("tip potential"). If this problem is encountered frequently it may be necessary to boil the KCl before filtering in order to suppress microorganism growth. In addition, thorough acid cleaning of the capillary tubing might be advisable. Sometimes high resistance is seen in individual electrodes of a particular batch and not in others. In this case wide variations in geometry may be looked for and the possibility always exists that a very fine air gap exists so far into the tip as to go unnoticed by the naked eye. Inspection of microelectrodes in the light microscope is recommended as a standard procedure before their experimental application.

METAL ELECTRODES

Silver-silver chloride half cells are suggested for both the reference electrode and also the lead from the KCl-filled microelectrodes. The often used "salt bridge" is not essential here due to the fact that the chloride ion activity of the bathing medium is maintained constant throughout the experiment and more importantly all potentials are measured in the steady state and are always referred to the zero point by withdrawal from the cell.

Two arbitrary lengths of No. 20 gauge fine silver wire are coiled at one end and connected jointly at the opposite end to the positive pole (anode) of a 1·5 V battery. Coil lengths might be 1–2 cm with the diameter sufficiently designed so as to fit the particular microelectrode holder employed. It should be remembered that a continuous column of fluid forms the junction between the micropipette and metal wire.

The negative pole of the battery (cathode) is connected to a 1000 Ω resistor which is in turn joined to a third coiled silver wire. The three coils are then immersed in a beaker containing 0·1N HCl as shown in Fig. 1. This

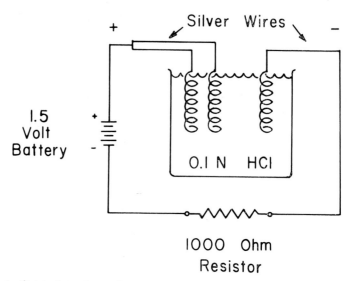

FIG. 1. Metal electrode coating arrangement. Current of about $1·5 \times 10^{-3}$ amperes $(I = E/R)$ is passed for several hours creating an Ag–AgCl electrode system at the anode ($+$).

electrolytic arrangement causes AgCl to form on the two coils connected to the battery anode. The electric current may be allowed to flow for several hours after which time the coated Ag-AgCl half cells should have taken on an even grayish appearance and are ready for use.

TROUBLESHOOTING METAL ELECTRODES

While it is not essential that metal electrodes be perfectly matched due to the fact that asymmetry potentials are balanced out electrically in our experiments, poorly coated electrodes may give rise to unstable readings. If this problem occurs, a number of aspects of the coating process might be inspected.

Silver wire should be of the "fine silver" quality not the "sterling" variety which contains considerable copper contamination. The wire should be thoroughly cleaned with organic solvents after the coils have been prepared and the coil ends should not be touched at any time after this point.

During the electrolysis, bubbles of hydrogen may collect on the cathode as this electrode polarizes. These bubbles should be removed by lightly tapping the beaker. If the problem persists, increase the value of the series resistor to about 2000 Ω and increase the length of time to 12 h for completion. It is advisable that the cathode coil be as large as possible in order to offer sufficient surface area to minimize polarization.

Lastly, be sure that all soldered connections are clean and insulated because drops of saline coming into contact with a silver-copper union may cause formation of an unstable junction potential.

ELECTRONIC ARRANGEMENT

The scheme of electronic components is diagrammed in Fig. 2. Though it is assumed that the experimenter is somewhat familiar with the use of the oscilloscope and the general concepts of amplifier function, brief clarification on certain aspects of the arrangement should be mentioned here. The high

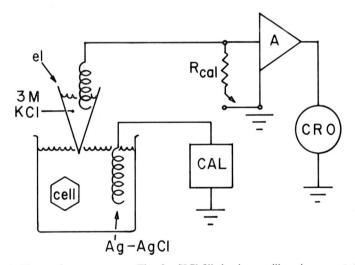

FIG. 2. Electronic arrangement. The 3M KCl-filled microcapillary is connected via an Ag–AgCl metal electrode to the high impedance amplifier (A) and cathode ray oscilloscope (CRO). The calibrator (CAL) inserts a known reference voltage (V_{cal}, Fig. 3) between bath and ground. Resistor (R_{cal}) is used for purposes of microelectrode resistance check.

impedance amplifier (A) serves as an intermediate between the recording microelectrode and the cathode ray oscilloscope (CRO). This amplifier is employed in order to properly match the high electrical resistance (10–20 megohms) of the potential measuring micropipette to the relatively low input resistance (perhaps 1 megohm) of the oscilloscope. Thus, this amplifier serves specifically as an impedance matching element and need not necessarily have higher than unity gain. The importance of the foregoing point will be made clearer later in this section. One such unit is the NF-1 wide band electrometer (Bioelectric Instruments Inc., Hastings-on-Hudson, New York, U.S.A.) which also incorporates a convenient in-built circuit for measuring microelectrode resistances. Alternative methods for this determination will be given later in this section. A relatively inexpensive oscilloscope suitable for use in these experiments is the model 503 supplied by Tektronix Inc., Beaverton, Oregon, U.S.A.

An accurate calibrated voltage standard may be obtained with the use of a calibration unit such as the CA5 calibrator (Bioelectric Instruments) designated (CAL) in Fig. 2.

As seen in the figure the AgCl wire leading from the bath is returned to ground through this calibrator thus serving to present a known voltage to the microelectrode and amplifier system.

The 10 megohm resistor (R_{cal}) when switched in the circuit as shown, provides a method for the determination of electrode resistance where the appropriate hardware is not built into the particular amplifier used by the investigator.

The equivalent circuit representing the situation with R_{cal} in the circuit is shown in Fig. 3. With the known voltage of the calibrator (V_{cal}), Kirchhoff's laws may be applied in deriving a simple formula for calculating the electrode resistance (R_{el}). Since the amplifier is now measuring the fraction of the total

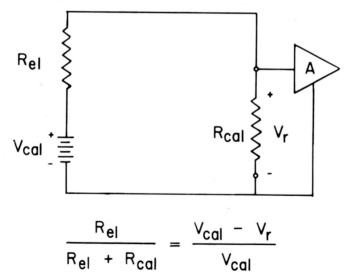

$$\frac{R_{el}}{R_{el} + R_{cal}} = \frac{V_{cal} - V_r}{V_{cal}}$$

FIG. 3. Equivalent circuit for microelectrode resistance measurement. R_{el} represents the electrical resistance of the microelectrode; R_{cal}, the 10 megohm calibration resistor; V_r, the voltage recorded across R_{cal}; V_{cal}, the reference voltage of the calibrator. (CAL, Fig. 2.)

voltage (V_{cal}) which appears across the calibration resistor (V_r) it follows that R_{el} is given by the following proportion and R_{el} is easily computed.

$$\frac{R_{el}}{R_{el} + R_{cal}} = \frac{V_{cal} - V_r}{V_{cal}}$$

Obviously, R_{cal} is present here only for the purpose of the electrode resistance determination and must be switched out of the circuit when normal experimental potential measurements are made.

The importance of the high impedance amplifier mentioned earlier, should now become clear. For example, considering a given high quality electrometer or field effect transistor amplifier, the input resistance is so high as to be considered infinity for purposes of demonstration.

Equivalently, this implies that R_{cal} in the equation rises to infinity. Clearly then the fraction of voltage which falls across the "source resistance" (in this case the membrane resistance, solution resistances, and microelectrode resistance) falls to zero and all the potential appears across the input of the amplifier thereby faithfully reproducing the desired signal.

The distortion which would arise if the low resistance oscilloscope were directly connected to the microelectrode should now be clear and the importance of impedance matching obvious.

TROUBLESHOOTING THE ELECTRONIC ARRANGEMENT

With the assumption that the calibration unit, high impedance amplifier and oscilloscope are in good working order, certain problems unique to the particular component arrangement might be encountered. Erratic readings might occur due to poorly coated metal electrodes or unprotected or poorly joined soldered connections. Remedies in this case have been discussed earlier.

Possibly more often associated with microelectrode measurements is AC interference as characterized by a high sine wave component on the oscilloscope face. Often improper grounding is the source of such difficulty. Be sure that all metal components on the work table are connected to a common ground point on the oscilloscope by individual wires leading to each item. This includes the dissecting microscope manipulator, lamps, etc. Also be sure the investigator is grounded to the same point. If high level AC is still recorded after the grounding procedure, shielding from electromagnetic radiation may be necessary.

Simply shortening the wire lead to the microelectrode or shielding this lead by the use of a coaxial cable rather than hook-up wire may solve the problem. (Implying that the Ag-AgCl electrode be kept very short and a protected soldered joint be made to a shielded cable leading to the amplifier.)

Lastly, a screened cage might be resorted to as discussed by Wolbarsht (1964). It should be pointed out that the investigator need not strive for complete elimination of AC interference since first, this is not practicable and secondly the steady-state nature of the measurements on chromatophore potentials allows that they be recorded in the presence of low-level sine wave interference (less than one millivolt).

Mechanical Components

A device which combines freedom of motion with sufficient mass to damp vibrations must be employed for positioning microelectrodes. The mechanical system must also allow for the liquid coupling between the 3M KCl within the micropipette and the Ag-AgCl lead. For these purposes we have employed the PBL-2 manipulator with the HP-2 microdrive and microelectrode holder; Fig. 4 (Beryllium Manufacturing Corp. Valley Stream, Long Island, New York, U.S.A.).

The microdrive is particularly important in performing the described chromatophore potential measurements due to the fact that extremely delicate technique must be exercised by the experimenter. For this reason the microdrive must combine stability with very fine control over forward motion.

Animal Preparation

Specimens of *Palaemonetes* should be placed in black containers for a period of at least one hour before an experiment is begun. This procedure induces maximal dispersion of the red pigment, Fig. 5, staged according to the system of Hogben and Slome (1931). Stage 5 represents maximal pigment dispersion; stage 1, maximal concentration; stages 2, 3 and 4 intermediate conditions. Cut with small scissors a 3 mm square portion and carefully free the carapace dorsal to the heart, Figs 6, 7, 8. The chromatophore-containing epidermis should remain adhering to this piece of exoskeleton. For this reason molting animals should be avoided. The preparation may then be transferred to a flat-bottom glass or lucite chamber containing physiological saline. A small Petri dish would serve well in this capacity. Dabs of vaseline applied to the perimeter of the carapace permit convenient anchoring and allow for minor adjustments in position. With the epidermis facing upward the preparation is ready for microelectrode impalement.

The physiological saline employed in the described experiments is detailed in the following table.

	Molarity	gm/liter
NaCl	0·325	19·0
KCl	0·01	0·745

KCl stock solution for use in later experiments.

	Molarity	gm/liter
KCl	0·325	24·2

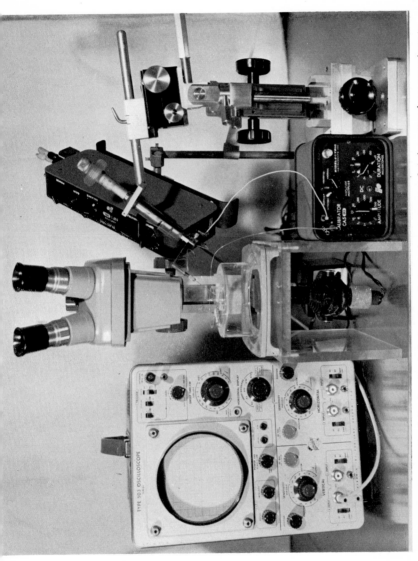

FIG. 4. Photograph of the described electronic and physical arrangement for chromatophore experiments. Section of chromatophore-containing carapace is placed epidermis upward in the Petri dish and positioned to receive the voltage-recording micropipette shown.

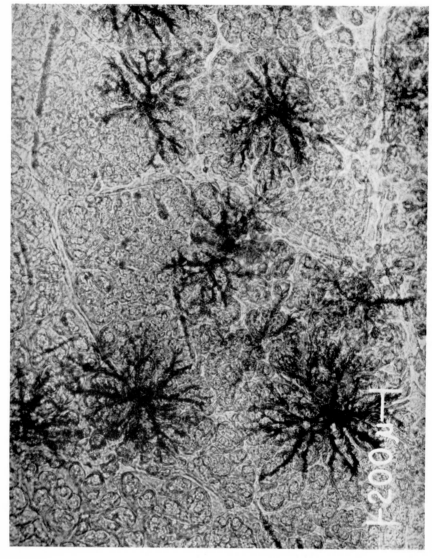

FIG. 5. Low power light micrograph showing a representative group of prawn erythrophores. As shown

THE TRANSMEMBRANE POTENTIAL OF THE PRAWN CHROMATOPHORE

In order to measure transmembrane potentials in the described normal saline a recording microelectrode should be advanced at an angle of about 30° toward the central region of a chromatophore, Fig. 9. This angle was found optimal by us in producing minimal cell damage. Using substage illumination the path of the advancing electrode is visible in the dissecting microscope and the particular position of entry into the chromatophore may be observed. Upon reaching close proximity to, but before piercing the central area of the cell, a number of sharp 10–30 mV negative potential jumps will be encountered. These voltages are often unstable and usually dissipate within several minutes. When the micropipette is introduced into the chromatophore center, as visualized in the dissecting microscope, a sudden large inside-negative voltage drop will be recorded. This potential might range between 40 and 80 mV depending on the cell and should be stable for long periods of time. Further advancement of the electrode should result in a sharp loss in the negative potential back to the zero line. This would be expected if the electrode tip were emerging from the opposite side of the cell. The same

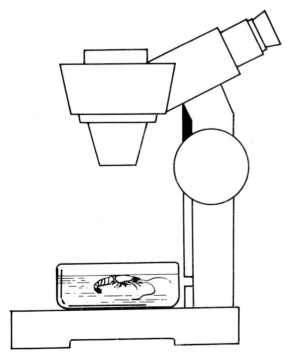

FIG. 6. Dissection arrangement showing chamber containing an animal viewed under the stereomicroscope. Prawn may be secured with pins to a wax layer on the floor of the dish.

FIG. 7. Photograph of the prawn *Palaemonetes* taken as viewed through the dissecting microscope. Carapace just dorsal to the visibly beating heart of the animal is removed and set up for experiments as described in the text and figures.

potential should be recoverable by carefully retracting the electrode through the same path thereby showing that the membrane had not been seriously damaged during the back and forth procedure. This maneuver should be repeatable successfully several times without significant diminution in the negative potential.

Since the red chromatophores of *Palaemonetes* are highly branched, the small unstable potentials recorded initially might be interpreted as representing the resting potentials of fine branches. As used here the term "resting potential" designates a time-invariant steady state voltage and does not imply an absence of participation by cell metabolism in the maintenance of such a steady state. Due to the instability encountered one might conclude that damage phenomena preclude the accurate measurement of potentials in these cell processes. However, reliable, stable resting potentials can be routinely secured in the central region of the chromatophore. The average resting potential and standard deviation for 24 individual cells from 12 separate animals was calculated by Freeman *et al.* (1968) to be: 55 mV $\pm$ 15 mV inside negative. The standard deviation of 15 mV indicated a rather high degree of variability among individual chromatophores. At least a portion of this variability might arise from differences in intracellular potassium activity as will be discussed in the next section.

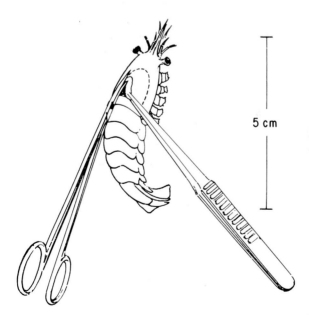

5 cm

FIG. 8. View of the dissection procedure showing region of carapace employed in the described experiments. Chromatophore-containing epidermis remains adhering to this portion of the transparent exoskeleton.

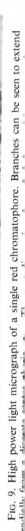

FIG. 9. High power light micrograph of a single red chromatophore. Branches can be seen to extend
radially from a discrete center where the

THE RELATIONSHIP OF THE IONIC ENVIRONMENT TO THE PRAWN CHROMATOPHORE RESTING POTENTIAL

It is well established that the transmembrane potential of a variety of cells is related to certain ionic concentration gradients (Grundfest, 1964; Hodgkin, 1951).

Thus, our next experimental task might appropriately be to examine the effect of changing the external potassium level on the already observed chromatophore resting potentials.

A general protocol for this purpose might be as follows.

A given cell is impaled and the resting potential recorded. The potassium concentration of the bathing medium is then raised in systematic, isosmotic increments and any corresponding alterations in the potential recorded, the electrode remaining within the cell during the entire experiment. After all desired additions have been made the electrode is withdrawn and the voltage change recorded. The total of all the K-induced potential changes plus that seen on removal of the micropipette should summate to the original resting potential with an error of less than 3 mV. If a greater discrepancy occurs the experiment must be discarded and amplifiers checked for excessive drift.

Since the recording microelectrode is to remain inserted intracellularly while the external saline is being altered, the experiment must be designed so as to minimize mechanical agitation. For this reason it is recommended that amounts of the KCl stock solution, previously described, be carefully added to the bathing medium which has had an equal volume of fluid previously removed, thereby maintaining the total volume constant and causing minimal disturbance to the preparation.

The desired isosmotic increments might be achieved by a protocol such as the following. (An arbitrary volume of 20 ml has been selected for demonstration purposes.)

A—the existing bathing medium before addition of the next volume of KCl stock solution

B—KCl stock solution

A ml present in the bath	B ml added to the bath	Total external potassium concentration mEq/litre
20	0	10 (normal saline)
19	1	26
18	2	56
16	4	110
10	10	217
0*	20	325

* This requires that the solution be totally removed and replaced with B. Special caution to prevent agitation should be exercised.

The results are plotted in a semilogarithmic relationship as shown in the sample experiment portrayed in Fig. 10. Membrane potentials appear arithmetically on the ordinate while the abscissa presents a logarithmic display of the external potassium-concentration ($[K_{out}]$). Above 20–30 mEq/l the resting potential decreased linearly with the logarithm of the external potassium level. This finding prompts one to test the applicability of the familiar Nernst equation. Since the Nernst relationship for a single ion species represents an equilibrium condition, application of this equation presupposes a unique membrane selectively toward this ion with the exclusion of other cations in the system. This assumption is only a first approximation as will be discussed later. The transmembrane or equilibrium potential E_m is related to the internal and the external potassium concentrations in the following manner.

$$E_m = \frac{RT}{F} \ln \frac{[K^+]_{out}}{[K^+]_{in}}$$

where R = the gas constant

T = the absolute temperature

F = the Faraday

$[K^+]$ = potassium concentration in milliequivalents per liter

E_m = the potassium equilibrium potential

Assuming $[K^+]_{in}$ to be constant we find the relationship between the resting potential and changes in $[K^+]_{out}$ by differentiating:

$$dE_m = \frac{RT}{F} d \ln [K^+]_{out}$$

rearranging and converting to the base 10 yields:

$$\frac{\Delta E_m}{\Delta \log_{10} [K^+]_{out}} = 58$$

That is, a membrane in which potassium is distributed in electrochemical equilibrium, would respond with a 58 mV alteration in the potential per tenfold change in the external concentration of this ion.

Inspection of the equation reveals that when $[K^+]_{in} = [K^+]_{out}$, E_m becomes zero. In other words, the external potassium level at which the measured membrane potential is zero theoretically equals the intra-cellular potassium concentration. (It is assumed that ion activities are the same on both sides of the membrane.) The zero-potential point in the curve shown in Fig. 4

occurs at 450 mEq/l. The Nernst equation would therefore predict that 450 mEq/l of potassium is contained within the chromatophore. The accuracy of this figure must be seriously challenged, however, as evidenced by the fact that the slope of the $E_m/\log_{10}$ [K^+]$_{out}$ line does not equal 58 but rather 45. Among other possibilities the discrepancy between the theoretical and actual slope could arise due to the assumption of a constant internal potassium concentration. For example, if changes in cell geometry were to take place during the measurement such as assumption would be invalid.

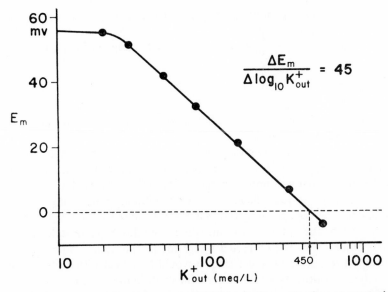

FIG. 10. Ordinate: transmembrane potential (E_m); abscissa: potassium concentration in the bathing medium. Potassium was substituted isosmotically for sodium. (After Freeman *et al.*, 1968.)

The addition of KCl is known to cause pigment concentration in fish melanophores (Kinosita, 1953). We have also observed this phenomenon in the prawn erythrophore. It is conceivable that the pigment-filled compartment in which the recording electrode is lodged could undergo a loss in volume upon the addition of KCl resulting in an increase in [K^+]$_{in}$. As seen in the Nernst equation an increase in [K^+]$_{in}$ would tend to oppose the effect of an elevation in [K^+]$_{out}$, yielding the slope of less than 58 mV per decade change. Therefore the possibility exists that compartmental volume change occurring persuant to the elevation in external potassium level could account for the lack of agreement between the actual and theoretical data.

Considering then, that cell shrinkage does indeed take place during KCl

I

addition, it should be possible to predict the magnitude of such a change by a rearrangement of the Nernst equation:

$$d \ln [K^+]_{in} = -\frac{dE}{\dfrac{RT}{F}} + d \ln [K^+]_{out}$$

since $$[K^+]_{in} = \frac{K^+}{V}$$

where V = cell volume and

K$^+$ = absolute quantity in milliequivalents

$$\log_{10} \frac{V_1}{V_2} = -\frac{45}{58} + 1 \text{ (for a ten-fold change in } [K^+]_{out})$$

$$\therefore \quad \frac{V_2}{V_1} = 0.60 \quad \text{and} \quad V_1 - V_2 = 40\%$$

In other language, the equation predicts a 40% loss in cell volume per ten-fold increase in external potassium concentration.

Applying similar reasoning the new calculated value for internal potassium becomes approximately 200 mEq/l rather than the previously discussed figure of 450 mEq/l which was not corrected for volume changes. The uncorrected value represents at least 900 milliosmolar without considering other cell components thereby yielding the cell interior unreasonably hyperosmotic with respect to the bathing medium which contains 650 mosmoles per liter. On the other hand, the corrected figure for $[K^+]_{in}$ seems more reasonable with respect to osmotic balance since it would be expected that other osmotically active constituents would be contained within the cell and could account for 250 mosmoles per liter. An examination of the internal ion profiles of other cells will show that this could easily be the case (Brinley, 1965).

It should be re-emphasized here that the foregoing treatment implies a condition of electrochemical equilibrium for the potassium ion in the linear portion of the E_m versus $\log_{10} [K^+]_{out}$ plot. As previously pointed out, the initial portion of the curve shown in Fig. 2 (up to 20 or 30 millimolar external potassium) does not obey this relation.

Thus, it appears possible that within certain limits, the membrane potential of the prawn red chromatophore is predominantly a function of the trans-membrane potassium gradient.

However, since the relationship between the resting potential and the log of $[K^+]_{out}$ deviates markedly from linearity at potassium concentrations below 30 mEq/l, other ions could make significant contributions to this potential in the prescribed region and appeared similar to the situation arising in other tissues (Grundfest, 1961; Hodgkin, 1951).

The predominance of sodium in the medium makes this ion a logical candidate. This situation would then be somewhat analogous to that seen in the squid giant axon where the mixed contribution of potassium and sodium to membrane resting potentials has been treated in detail (Hodgkin and Katz, 1949). According to this idea the concentration gradient for sodium ion (high extracellular and low intracellular) would contribute a depolarizing influence to the resting potential, the magnitude of which would be a function of the relative permeabilities of the two ion species. This point is clearly seen by inspection of the equation derived by Hodgkin and Katz (1949) utilizing the constant field theory of Goldman (1943).

$$E_m = \frac{RT}{F} \ln \left[\frac{P_k[K^+]_{out} + P_{Na}[Na^+]_{out} + P_{Cl}[Cl^-]_{in}}{P_k[K^+]_{in} + P_{Na}[Na^+]_{in} + P_{Cl}[Cl^-]_{out}} \right]$$

where RT/F is a constant and P represents the membrane permeability coefficient for the particular ion.

Though no specific evidence regarding the contribution of other ions to the prawn transmembrane potential has been obtained in these experiments this equation is presented as a possible suggestion for future investigations.

Indeed, data (Freeman and Fingerman, 1968) obtained by using the drug tetrodotoxin, known to block sodium pathways in certain membranes, are consistent with this idea.

BIBLIOGRAPHY

Brinley, F. J. (1965). Sodium, potassium, and chloride concentrations and fluxes in the isolated giant axon of *Homarus*. *J. Neurophysiol.*, **28**, 742–772.

Fingerman, M. (1965). Chromatophores. *Physiol. Rev.*, **45**, 296–339.

Frank, K. and Becker, M. C. (1964) Microelectrodes for recording and stimulation. *In* "Physical Techniques in Biological Research", Vol. 5 (W. L. Nastuk, ed.), pp. 22–87. Academic Press, New York and London.

Freeman, A. R., Connell, P. M. and Fingerman, M. (1968). An electrophysiological study of the red chromatophore of the prawn *Palaemonetes*: Observations on the action of red pigment-concentrating hormone. *Compl Biochem. Physiol.*, **26**, 1015–1030.

Freeman, A. R. and Fingerman, M. (1968). Action of tetrodotoxin and observations on the characteristics of the chromatophore membrane of the prawn, *Palaemonetes*. *Comp. Biochem. Physiol.* (In Press.)

Goldman, D. E. (1943). Potential, impedance and rectification in membranes. *J. gen. Physiol.*, **27**, 37–60.

Grundfest, H. (1961). Ionic mechanisms in electrogenesis. *Ann. NY. Acad. Sci.*, **94**, 405–457.

Grundfest, H. (1964). General introduction to membrane physiology. *In* "Electrophysiology of the Heart". (Proceedings of the Milan meeting), pp. 25–51. Pergamon Press, New York.

Hodgkin, A. L. and Katz, B. (1949). Effect of sodium ions on the electrical activity of the giant axon of the squid. *J. Physiol., Lond.*, **108**, 37–77.

Hodgkin, A. L. (1951). The ionic basis of electrical activity in nerve and muscle. *Biol. Rev.*, **26**, 339–409.

Hogben, L. and Slome D. (1931). The pigmentary effector system. VI. The dual character of endocrine co-ordination in amphibian colour change. *Proc. R. Soc.*, Series B, **108**, 10–53.

Kinosita, H. (1953). Studies on the mechanism of pigment migration within fish melanophores with special reference to their electric potentials. *Annotne zool. jap.*, **26**, 115–129.

Wolbarsht, M. L. (1964). Interference and its elimination. *In* "Physical Techniques in Biological Research", Vol. 5. (W. L. Nastuk, ed.), pp. 353–372. Academic Press, New York and London.

xp. in Physiol. and Biochem. (1970). 3, 181–210.

6 | Electrical Measurements on Insect Cuticle and Integument

PAUL O. SCHEIE

Department of Biophysics, The Pennsylvania State University,
University Park, Pennsylvania, U.S.A.

INTRODUCTION

Electrical measurements on insect cuticle and integument consist of apply-ng well-established physical techniques to a remarkable and vital organ of he insect. The cuticle forms the outer, hard, thick membrane often perforated by pore canals and dermal gland ducts. It provides protection, structural strength and the route for most material and information exchanged by an nsect with its environment. Beneath the cuticle and attached to it lies a single layer of epidermal cells whose versatility and diverse functions bestow upon it a commanding role in the life of an insect. During the molt cycle these cells lay down new cuticle while digesting and reabsorbing the old and these processes are performed in synchrony over the whole surface. At the same time, these cells reportedly are capable of differentiating into any of several kinds of specialized cells including bristle-forming cells, socket-forming cells, sensory neurons, and neurolemma cells. The combination of cuticle plus epidermal layer comprises the integument, a complex membrane and an intriguing system for experimental study.

Certain electrical measurements can provide information concerning the passage of ions in solution across such membranes and will detect any mechanism acting as an ion pump or ion separator. However, electrical studies on either cuticle or integument have been few. Jahn (1936) and Cole and Jahn (1937) made electrical measurements on grasshopper egg membranes. They were able to detect large changes in electrical resistance and capacitance at the time of diapause, and they attributed the changes to the formation of thin, highly impermeable membrane. Richards (1957) and Schmitt (1955), using more sophisticated instrumentation showed complex responses by blow fly and cockroach cuticles to alternating current (AC), indicating asymmetric permeabilities. In addition, they found higher electrical resistance (lower permeabilities to ions) through cuticle than through intact integument, and they concluded that the main barrier to ions in the cuticle of blow fly larvae was associated with the outermost surface layers. Beament (1961) reported finding significant potential differences across excised cockroach cuticle indicating the presence of an ion pump, and he suggested that the external mobile grease behaves as an electret. Scheie and Smyth (1967, 1968) and Scheie (1969) unable to repeat Beament's measurements, went on to make other electrical measurements on both excised cockroach cuticle and intact cockroach integument. They reported lower ion permeabilities through intact integument than through excised cuticles, and did not find a major ion barrier near the outer surface. They preferred to interpret their result in terms of ion passage through large channels such as the dermal gland duct instead of holding to the more conventional view that permeation occurs by diffusion across a laminated chitin-protein complex. More significant perhaps, for future studies were their experiments on groups of live animals in which the same animals were used for a series of measurements over extended periods of time. These provided a monitor for changes in the integument of individual insects. Large increases in electrical resistance were found across the integument of nymphs several days prior to a molt, during the first day following a molt, and in adult integument after several weeks of isolation from others of the species.

The following experiments illustrate the techniques for obtaining electrical parameters under several conditions, first for excised cuticle and then for intact integument. Emphasis is on the methods, although suggestions for interpretations are included. Similar techniques could be extended to other conditions, to other species of cockroaches and to other insects.

Specimen Preparation and Basic Equipment

Most of the electrical measurements dealt with in these experiments depend on determining the potential difference between 2 contacts, one on each side of the cuticle. Figure 1 illustrates a simple arrangement for accomplishing this. The various components are:

The excised cuticle.

The electrolyte comprising the conducting bridge between cuticle and electrodes.

The electrodes which connect the electrolyte with conventional metal hook-up wires.

The instrument that measures potential difference, the voltmeter.

The Excised Cuticle

Size is an important factor in the selection of an insect for initial measurements; larger animals can provide larger pieces of cuticle that are easier to work with. The cockroach, *Periplaneta americana*, is convenient in having a broad, generally flat, and relatively hairless surface on the pronotum which is a favorable object for study.

The animal can be anesthetized by cooling, with CO_2, or the excision can be performed without anesthesia. It is important, however, to avoid touching the surface of the section to be excised or to cause abrasion to it from other sources. Electrical and histological studies indicate that most abrasions received by *P. americana* during normal contact within a colony can be healed by keeping the insect away from such contact for at least 6 h.

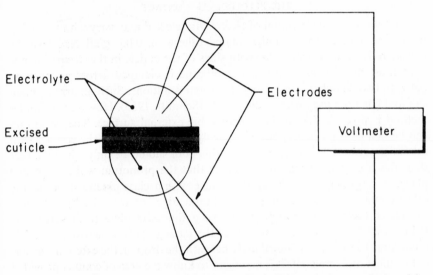

FIG. 1. Basic diagram for measuring the potential difference across excised cuticle.

The pronotum is removed and freed from most of the adhering tissue with a pair of scissors. If the posterior edge is then clasped with forceps and the anterior edge braced against a table top, another pair of forceps can be used to gently scrape off most of the remaining tissue—without bringing the outer surface into contact with the table or bending the cuticle. Excess grease on the outer surface plus loose debris on the inner surface can be removed by playing a small stream of distilled water over these surfaces for a few seconds. The cuticle is ready for measurements at this point, or it can be stored by floating it, outer side up, on the surface of a suitable aqueous solution. The exact solution used for this has not been found to be critical. Distilled water is satisfactory, although there are two points that should be kept in mind: (1) pH and ionic strength of the solution are likely to affect the hydration of the endocuticle which involves approximately the inner one-half of the total thickness, and (2) floating cuticles on the solution which will be in contact with the inner surface during measurements helps ensure that contact is not modified by an unstirred layer of another solution.

Meaningful data require measurements on several specimens so that it is advisable to prepare at least 8–10 pronotums. In addition, there are some changes that occur in the cuticle during the first few hours after excision and unless these changes are being studied, it is well to prepare cuticles 4–8 h before making measurements.

THE ELECTROLYTE CONTACT

The type and concentration of electrolyte selected may vary with the information sought. However, unless stated otherwise, 0·058 g/ml NaCl will be considered as the electrolyte for both sides of the cuticle in these experiments.

In most membrane studies the membrane is clamped across an opening between two chambers containing electrolyte solutions. Such an arrangement can and has been used with insect cuticle (Schmitt, 1955). However, a simpler method is possible due to the hydrophobic external surface. The pronotum can be floated on a small pool of electrolyte which provides the contact with the inner surface. The surface area of this pool should be only slightly larger than the size of the pronotum in order that the pronotum will stay in one place. A drop placed on the upper surface with a glass pipette serves as the other contact. Surface tension of the liquid together with the hydrophobic surface of the pronotum combine to keep this electrolyte from spreading. It has been found safe to assume that the passage of ions across the cuticle is confined to the region immediately beneath the drop on the external surface.

For most measurements it is necessary to know the area of contact provided by the drop on the outer surface. It is possible, with a little practice, to produce a reasonably consistent drop size on the cuticle with the aid of a dissecting microscope. A contact diameter of 3 mm is a convenient size on *P. americana*. This drop size obviously is a possible source of considerable error, random as well as systematic. Checks on the errors involved can be obtained by making several measurements on the same sample using drops of different sizes. Other factors, however, such as variations between animals have permitted use of this technique with no more than ordinary caution. For those who still might worry, the situation can be improved by punching out discs of filter paper, wetting them with electrolyte, and placing these on the outer surface in lieu of the drop.

ELECTRODES

Silver wire 2–5 cm long and about 0·05 cm in diameter provides suitable electrodes for use with chloride electrolytes. One end can be soldered to a convenient hook-up wire; the other end must be coated with silver chloride.

An electrolytic chloriding arrangement is shown in Fig. 2. The electrode is made positive in a solution of concentrated NaCl where another silver wire is maintained negative. The resulting electric current causes silver chloride to be deposited on the positive wire which is indicated by a change in color of the wire. Care must be taken to avoid letting the solder or the hook-up wire contact the electrolyte during this process. Electrodes for precise work require care in the chloriding process; however, for the purpose of the experiments dealt with here it is adequate to use a current that causes slight bubbling for

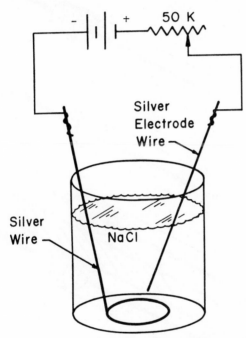

FIG. 2. Schematic for chloriding silver wire.

10–15 sec. Under these conditions the electrode surface will turn reddish-brown. Another method, slower but less trouble, consists of keeping the cleaned silver immersed in a chloride solution for a day or two. In this case the color change probably will not be noticed. In either case, the electrical characteristics are the important factors.

One should prevent the chlorided electrodes from drying out. A simple scheme to accomplish this is to insert the electrode into a glass tube filled with an NaCl solution, one end of which has been drawn out and a short piece of cotton string inserted as a wick (see Fig. 3). The other end is sealed with paraffin to hold the electrolyte in the tube. This arrangement will be referred to as a pipette electrode. One useful modification of this includes filling the drawn out section with a melted 2% agar solution which when cool forms a porous plug. This makes the seal at the other end less critical for preventing the tube from leaking. Another modification consists of fastening two of these electrodes together with their wicks joined (Fig. 3c). One such double electrode plus two of the single varieties are sufficient for any of the

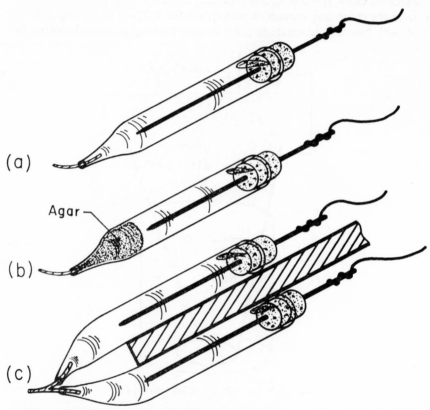

(a)

Agar

(b)

(c)

Fig. 3. Diagram of pipette electrodes. (a) Single pipette electrode; (b) single pipette electrode with agar-filled tip; (c) double pipette electrode.

experiments mentioned here. They can be stored for some time if they are well sealed and the tips kept immersed in NaCl solutions between experiments.

A word about the electrode size may be helpful. There are three considerations to be weighed. (1) Ease in manipulation decreases when the electrodes get too large. Glass tubing 10 cm long and 1 cm in diameter is at the upper limit for convenience. (2) Low electrode resistance is achieved by having a large contact area between the silver wire and the electrolyte. A single, straight wire lends itself to cleaning more readily, although greater contact area may be achieved by coiling a longer piece of silver wire. (3) A large volume of electrolyte in the electrode reduces the effect on its concentration produced by molecules diffusing in or out through the tip along a concentration gradient during a measurement.

Various devices can be used for mounting these electrodes. Some models of micromanipulators are excellent. It is desirable to have good control over the positioning of the electrodes since adhesion between the wicks and the drop on the cuticle surface permits the electrode to be used in adjusting the amount of contact the drop has with the surface. Raising the electrode will pull the drop up also and thereby reduce the contact with the cuticle.

THE VOLTMETER

A voltmeter is used to measure the potential difference between the silver wires. To do this the potential difference must be used to drive a small amount of current through the meter to energize it. Unfortunately, this current can change both the characteristics of the electrodes and the specimen being studied. Thus, it is necessary to minimize this current. Another way of saying this is that a high input resistance voltmeter is required. Acceptable values are in excess of 10^9 Ω, and most ordinary voltmeters do not meet this requirement. A workable system consists of placing a high input resistance amplifier between the electrodes and the voltmeter. Any good physiological DC amplifier should serve for this purpose (for example, a Grass P-6 with cathode follower probe or a Bioelectric NF1). An oscilloscope functioning as a voltmeter is more versatile and preferable to a simple voltmeter. Warm-up time of $\frac{1}{2}$ h should be allowed for electronic components containing vacuum tubes.

POTENTIAL DIFFERENCE ACROSS EXCISED CUTICLE

The most straightforward electrical measurement on an excised cuticle is that of the potential difference between inside and outside. This can be accomplished by coupling appropriate electrodes to each side with electrolyte and measuring on a voltmeter the potential difference between the electrodes. With the same electrolyte on each side and with electrodes which are matched so as not to introduce an appreciable potential difference by themselves the value measured can be assumed to be a property of the cuticle. If the same electrolyte is used on both sides, and also if the voltmeter has a very high electrical resistance, the current through the cuticle can be assumed negligible and a reading of potential difference becomes a good approximation for the electromotive force (EMF) of the system. The presence of such an

EMF would indicate that the cuticle behaves as a battery and is capable of separating electric charges.

When the contact electrolytes are of different concentrations a measurable potential difference is expected. Its value depends on the electrodes used, but in general will consist of both concentration potentials and diffusion potentials. Interpretation of this value provides a measure of the ratio of mobilities of the ions in the solutions used.

EXPERIMENT 1—A CHECK ON THE EQUIPMENT

Purpose: to establish the characteristics of the electrodes and the voltmeter.

1. Electrical set-up: the schematic is shown in Fig. 4. The cuticle is not needed, but a separate source of potential difference is necessary. A $1\frac{1}{2}$ V battery will suffice.

Electrolytes: 0·058 g/ml NaCl

Electrodes: 2 single pipette electrodes filled with 0·058 g/ml NaCl.

2. The amplifier-oscilloscope system for measuring potential difference must be calibrated. This is done under the assumption that the oscilloscope

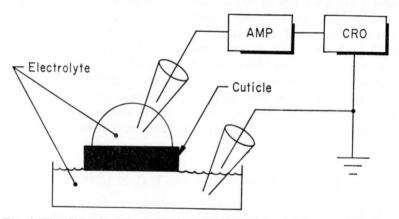

FIG. 4. Electrical set-up for making potential difference measurements including an amplifier to provide a high input resistance, and an oscilloscope on which to display the results.

itself is calibrated (the instruction manual for the instrument should tell how to do this). Disconnect the electrodes and connect a small battery across the input to the oscilloscope. Record the potential difference as the product of the vertical deflection of the trace and the vertical sensitivity. Then connect the battery to the input of the amplifier and note the new potential difference indicated on the oscilloscope. Obtain the amplification factor by dividing this second measurement by the first. Subsequent references to potential differ-ence will refer to values to which this factor has been applied. $V = $ (ampli-fication factor) $\times$ (vertical sensitivity) $\times$ (vertical deflection).

3. Connect the electrodes, lower them into a pool of NaCl solution and note the potential difference. It should be within $\pm$ 0·2 mV of zero if the electrodes have been properly prepared.

Notes:

(a) The most convenient amplification factor is 1·0. This can be arranged by means of the continuous amplification control on either the amplifier or oscilloscope when such controls are available. The Grass P-6 amplifier does not provide continuous control over amplification, and the setting for an amplification of 1 cannot be assumed to provide an amplification of 1·0.

(b) Frequent checks on the electrode balance are advisable. Some amplifiers provide a means for electronically canceling variations in electrodes. For some measurements this may be satisfactory; however, if it involves passing current between the electrodes and thereby through the specimen, the specimen may be altered by such current.

EXPERIMENT 2—POTENTIAL DIFFERENCE ACROSS CUTICLE WITH THE
SAME ELECTROLYTE ON BOTH SIDES

Purpose: to detect sources of EMF within the cuticle.

1. Electrical set-up: the schematic is shown in Fig. 4.

Electrolyte: 0·058 g/ml NaCl

Electrodes: 2 single pipette electrodes filled with 0·058 g/ml NaCl.

2. Place the excised cuticle, outside surface up, on a pool of NaCl solution. Place a drop of the same solution on the outer surface, and lower one electrode to contact it. Place the other electrode in contact with the pool, and record the potential difference.

3. Raise the upper electrode and blot the drop away. Another drop can then be placed on a different area of the same cuticle, or another cuticle can be sampled.

Notes:

(a) The size of the external drop is not critical in this experiment and need not be measured. It may be preferable to keep it small enough to permit sampling several areas on the same cuticle.

(b) It is recommended that the midline of the pronotum be avoided for these and the following measurements except as an extension to them. The cuticle is structurally different in this region.

(c) Some controversy exists as to whether there will be a measurable potential difference under these conditions. Beament (1961) has reported one exists while Scheie and Smyth (1967) found none.

EXPERIMENT 3—POTENTIAL DIFFERENCES ACROSS CUTICLE WITH
DIFFERENT CONCENTRATIONS OF THE SAME ELECTROLYTE ON EACH SIDE

Purpose: to find the mobility ratios of ions as they pass through the cuticle.
1. Electrical set-up: the schematic is shown in Fig. 4.
Electrolytes: 0·058 g/ml and 0·58 g/ml NaCl
Electrodes: two single pipette electrodes filled with 0·58 g/ml NaCl.
2. Allow the cuticles to float several minutes on a large volume (250 ml) of
0·58 g/ml solution.
3. Dip the two electrodes in a pool of 0·58 g/ml NaCl to check on electrode
balance. The potential difference should read within ± 0·2 mV of zero.
4. Fill two 100 ml beakers with the NaCl solutions, one with the concentration of 0·058 g/ml and the other with 0·58 g/ml. Connect these beakers with an
agar bridge (see notes). Introduce an electrode into each solution and note
the potential difference. The value at 20°C should be near 11 mV, the electrode
in the more dilute side negative (assuming that the ion mobilities in the agar
are equal to those in water). When the electrodes are reversed the potential
difference should have the same magnitude.
5. Float a cuticle on a pool of 0·58 g/ml NaCl and add an external drop of
0·058 g/ml NaCl. Place the grounded electrode in contact with the pool while
the other contacts the drop. Record the potential difference and sample
another portion of the cuticle in the same manner. Blot off the external drops
and return the cuticle to the surface of 250 ml 0·058 g/ml NaCl.
6. When all cuticles have been measured in this manner they are ready to be
measured with the concentrations reversed.
7. Compute the mobility ratios for the chloride and sodium ions with the aid
of the equation

$$\frac{v'}{u'} = \frac{750 - 11\cdot3\ V}{495 + 11\cdot3\ V}$$

where V is the measured potential difference, v' is the anion (chloride)
mobility, and u' is the cation (sodium) mobility.
8. A reasonable potential difference should be in the range of 5–20 mV,
measured with 0·58 g/ml solution against the inside surface. For a measured
value of 13 mV one obtains a ratio of 0·95. A ratio close to 1·0 suggests that
the cuticle does not select either ion for easier passage. Therefore, the channels
must be very wide or the walls uncharged to account for a measured potential
difference near 13 mV.
Notes:
(a) Derivation of the equation used to determine mobility ratios can be
found in Scheie and Smyth (1967).
(b) Agar bridges are constructed as follows: heat a 2% agar solution made

up in 0·058 g/ml NaCl until the agar melts. Before this solution gels pour it into a section of glass tubing bent in the form of a U and large enough to bridge two beakers adjacent to each other. Care should be taken to fill the tube completely to avoid any air bubbles either in the middle or at the ends.

(c) Other combinations of NaCl concentrations can be used. The corresponding values for mobility ratios will vary slightly with time after excision, temperature, position of the external drop and pretreatment of the cuticle (such as abrasion or a chloroform rinse). There will be considerable variation among cuticles and it will take measurements on 10–20 in order to obtain an acceptable distribution curve and mean value. Repeated measurements on the same cuticle will demonstrate whether or not the source of variation is in the measuring technique.

(d) Other electrolytes can be used. The working equation will differ slightly for other uni-univalent combinations, but for more complex electrolytes the problems are more involved and a treatise on electro-chemistry should be consulted.

(e) Both pipette electrodes were filled with the same electrolyte in order to eliminate concentration potentials. When not in use they should be kept in contact with a reservoir of 0·58 g/ml NaCl.

(f) It is assumed that during the time of making a measurement while one electrode is in contact with the 0·058 g/ml drop there is no significant change in the concentration of the drop. Agar-filled electrode tips will help keep this assumption valid. Any change in concentration can be monitored, of course, by looking for a change in potential as a function of the time the electrode is in contact with the drop.

DC RESISTANCE

When there is no source of EMF within the cuticle it is necessary to obtain current from an external source in order to make any non-zero electrical measurements. Such can be obtained using different concentrations of electrolyte on either side or by using an external power supply such as a battery. In either case, however, it becomes important to know the response of the cuticle to direction and magnitude of current. For a simple, well-behaved system one might expect the potential difference across the cuticle to vary directly as the current through it and to be symmetrical to the direction of current. When such is the case, the ratio of potential difference to current is the transverse direct current (DC) resistance of the cuticle and the cuticle can be described as obeying Ohm's law.

The schematic for making these experiments with an external current supply is shown in Fig. 5. It consists of the same potential measuring circuit as before with two added arrangements. One provides for using the oscilloscope to measure simultaneously both the potential difference and the current through the cuticle. The other addition provides an external source of current. This particular design permits continuous variation of the current via the 50 K potentiometer between limits determined by the battery size, while the use of the oscilloscope as both voltmeter and ammeter means that as the current is varied the spot on the oscilloscope will trace out a potential versus current (*V* versus *I*) curve. The current is measured by determining

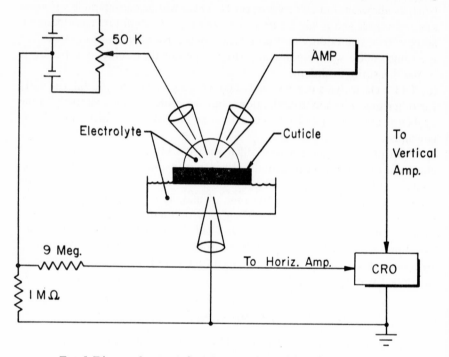

FIG. 5. Diagram for measuring current–voltage chracteristics of cuticle.

the potential difference it produces across the 1 megohm resistor. (This is then applied to the horizontal deflection plates while the potential difference across the cuticle still controls the vertical deflection.) The 9 megohm resistor is used to ensure that most of the current passes through the 1 megohm resistor and not through the oscilloscope circuit. Its use in series with an oscilloscope input resistance of 1 megohm also results in the oscilloscope deflection being attenuated by a factor of 10. This must be taken into account when computing the current passing through the cuticle.

Readings can be taken visually from the oscilloscope screen or the trace can be photographed for a permanent record of the entire *V* versus *I* relation.

EXPERIMENT 4—ELECTRODE RESISTANCE

Purpose: to measure the DC resistance of a pipette electrode and to note polarization effects.

1. Electrical set-up: the schematic is shown in Fig. 5.

Electrolytes: 0·058 g/ml NaCl

Electrodes: 1 single and 1 double pipette electrode filled with 0·058 g/ml NaCl. Connect the single electrode to ground.

2. Place the double electrode in the pool of 0·058 g/ml NaCl containing the grounded electrode.

3. Rotate the 50 K potentiometer back and forth through its maximum excursion as evenly as possible at about 1 cyc per 5 sec. The trace on the oscilloscope should look similar to the drawing in Fig. 6b if the electrodes were initially balanced. The slope of the almost horizontal lines indicates the DC resistance of the grounded electrode. This electrode is the only one through which the current is passing *and* across which the potential difference is being measured. Calculate the resistance using the equation $R = V/I$ at a representative point on the trace. V (in volts) is given by the product of amplification factor, vertical scope sensitivity and vertical deflection, while the current I (in amps) is given by $10 \times$ horizontal sensitivity $\times$ horizontal deflection $\times 10^{-6}$.

4. Subsequent measurements of cuticle resistance will have to be corrected by the amount of this electrode resistance.

Notes:

(a) The curvature in the lines of V versus I, particularly at maximum I (Fig. 6b), indicates an increase in electrode resistance due to polarization. The effect is undesirable; however, if small, it is not of great importance when measuring resistance of cuticles.

(b) Electrode resistances should be as small as possible with acceptable values under 1000 Ω per electrode.

EXPERIMENT 5—CURRENT-VOLTAGE CHARACTERISTICS OF CUTICLE: LINEARITY AND RECTIFICATION

Purpose: to investigate variations in cuticle resistance as current intensity and direction are altered.

1. Electrical set-up: the schematic is shown in Fig. 5.

Electrolyte: 0·058 g/ml NaCl

Electrodes: 1 single and 1 double pipette electrode, each filled with 0·058 g/ml NaCl.

2. Place a water-washed, excised cuticle on a pool of 0·058 g/ml NaCl, and place a drop of the same electrolyte on the outer surface of the cuticle. Lower the double electrode to contact the drop, and adjust the drop size—either

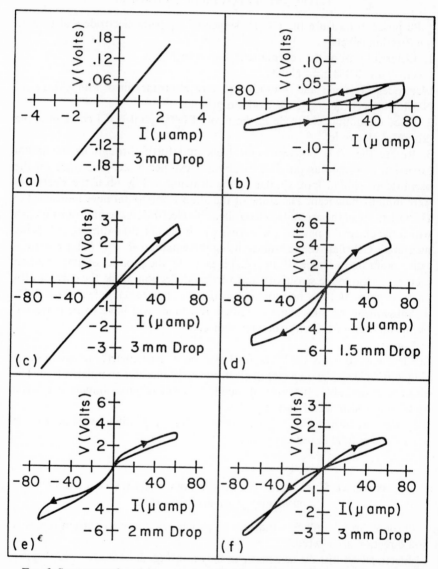

FIG. 6. Some examples of V versus I curves traced from oscillograms. (a) Low current density; (b) cuticle shorted, demonstrating electrode polarization; (c) representative pattern at current densities up to $30\,\mu A/cm^2$; (d) pattern for highest current density attempted, $4 \times 10^3\,\mu A/cm^2$; (e) and (f) variations found in the patterns (from *Comp. Biochem. Physiol.* **21**, 547–571, 1967.)

by changing volume of the drop or by varying the height of the double electrode—until the area of contact with the cuticle approximates a 3 mm diameter circle.

3. Vary the current on both sides of zero to maximum values of $\pm$ 2–3 μA. The trace should indicate a reasonably straight line passing through the origin (Fig. 6a). This signifies that the cuticle is obeying Ohm's law and that there is no rectification; hence, the resistance does not depend on the magnitude or direction of the current. For the circuit in Fig. 5 positive current represents positive charges flowing from outside to inside through the cuticle.

Notes:

(a) At higher currents (e.g., 60 μA) through the same size drop the shape of the V versus I curve will likely change to a complex form which is neither linear nor symmetrical (Fig. 6c–f). There may also be a difference between the first trace and subsequent ones and it has been found convenient to cycle the current several times to eliminate this effect before a reading is taken. Of course, there is additional information in these complex curves but it is more difficult to interpret and will not be considered here.

(b) It would be advisable to adjust the circuit in order that the maximum variation of the potentiometer results in a current which stays within the range of linear response. This can be accomplished either by changing the size of the batteries or by adding equal resistors to each end of the potentiometer. A combination of a 45 V battery and 120 K Ω resistors so placed has been found workable.

(c) It is a good idea to adjust the sensitivities of the oscilloscope amplifiers so as to utilize as large a portion of the oscilloscope screen as is convenient.

EXPERIMENT 6—RESISTANCE OF EXCISED CUTICLE USING AN EXTERNAL
SOURCE OF CURRENT

Purpose: to obtain the specific DC resistance of excised cuticle using an external battery as the source of current.

1. Electrical set-up: the schematic is shown in Fig. 5.

Electrolytes: 0·058 g/ml NaCl

Electrodes: 1 single and 1 double pipette electrode, each filled with 0·058 g/ml NaCl.

2. Excise 5–10 pronotum cuticles, wash them with water, and float them, outside surface up, on 200 ml of 0·058 g/ml NaCl.

3. If Experiment 5 has shown cuticle to be well behaved (electrically) it is possible to choose a value of current, note the corresponding potential difference as the current is brought to that value, and calculate the resistance from

$R = V/I$. Example: in Fig. 6a at a current of $+ 2$ μA the potential difference is 0·13 V from which the resistance is calculated to be

$$R = \frac{V}{I} = \frac{0·13 \text{ V}}{2·0 \times 10^{-6} \text{ A}} = 6·5 \times 10^4 \ \Omega$$

4. This value of R must be corrected for electrode resistance by subtracting a value obtained as demonstrated in Experiment 4.

5. Four determinations of resistance using 3 mm drops in each of the four quadrants of 5–10 pronotums should provide an idea of the variations among different cuticles and among different areas on any given cuticle.

6. It is convenient and customary to convert such resistance values into specific resistances which are independent of the size drop used, and instead reflect a property only of the cuticle. This is accomplished by multiplying the resistance by the size of the contact area of the drop (0·071 cm² for a 3 mm drop) with the tacit assumption that the drop defines the region through which all the current passes transversely across the cuticle. The value obtained is the specific areal resistance, and has units of ohm-cm². If $R = 6·5 \times 10^4 \ \Omega$ for a 3 mm drop as in the example above, and if the total electrode resistance is $0·2 \times 10^4 \ \Omega$, areal resistance, $R_s = 6·3 \times 10^4 \ \Omega \times 0·071$ cm² = 4·5 $\times 10^3$ ohm-cm².

Notes:

(a) It will be realized that the measured drop size is a possible source of appreciable error. Larger drops decrease the relative error in their measurement, but the larger areas covered also blur variations which may be present over the surface. Three mm diameter drops seem a reasonable compromise for the *P. americana* pronotum. It is a good idea to try drops of other sizes and to compare the values of specific areal resistance which should be independent of drop size for homogeneous material.

(b) An alternative to using drops of electrolyte consists of punching out solid circles from filter paper, wetting them in electrolyte, and laying them on the cuticle surface.

(c) An important extension of these measurements is the determination of the DC specific areal resistance as a function of electrolyte concentration. A dependence of specific resistance on this concentration would imply electrolytic conduction through the cuticle whereas lack of such a dependence would suggest electronic conduction.

(d) There has been some confusion over units of specific resistance in biological literature and an attempt at clarification can be found in Scheie (1967).

(e) A 10 cm length of 1 mm diameter glass tubing filled with electrolyte can be trimmed so that it provides an ohmic resistance close to that of the cuticle, and it can be substituted for the cuticle in order to establish the behavior of the equipment. This is especially useful when the apparent cuticle response is not linear and one needs to determine whether it is indeed a characteristic of the cuticle or of the instrument.

EXPERIMENT 7—RESISTANCE OF EXCISED CUTICLE USING CONCENTRATION POTENTIALS AS A SOURCE OF CURRENT

Purpose: to obtain specific DC resistance of excised cuticle using concentration potentials to provide the current.

1. Electrical set-up: the schematic is shown in Fig. 7.

Electrolytes: 0·058 g/ml and 0·58 g/ml NaCl

Electrodes: 1 single pipette electrode filled with 0·58 g/ml NaCl; 1 single pipette electrode filled with 0·058 g/ml NaCl.

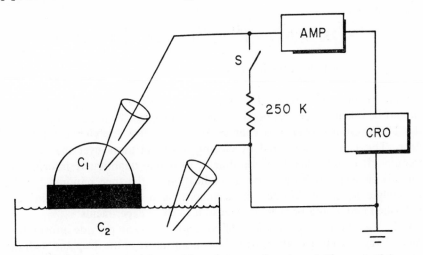

FIG. 7. Diagram for obtaining cuticle resistance using concentration potentials as a source of current.

2. Float a cuticle on 0·058 g/ml NaCl and place a 3 mm diameter drop of 0·58 g/ml NaCl on the outer surface. Place electrodes having similar concentrations of electrolyte in contact with these electrolytes.

3. Record the potential difference, with switch S open (V) and again with it closed (V').

4. Determine the resistance from $R = R_0 \dfrac{(V - V')}{V'}$ where $R_0 = 250$ K Ω.

Cuticle resistance, R_c, is this value minus the electrode resistance which must be measured as in Experiment 4 (see also note d). Hence, $R_c = R - R_e$ and the specific areal resistance, R_s, is found by using $R_s = R_c A$, where $A = 0·071$ cm^2 for 3 mm drops.

Combining these in one equation gives

$$R_s = \left(R_0 \frac{V - V'}{V'} - R_e \right) A$$

or

$$R_s = \left(250 \times 10^3 \, \Omega \times \frac{V - V'}{V'} - R_e \right) \times 0{\cdot}071 \text{ cm}^2$$

5. Sample results are

$V = 41$ mV

$V' = 37$ mV

$R_e = 2000 \, \Omega$ (see note d)

from which

$$R_s = \left[250 \times 10^3 \, \Omega \times \left(\frac{41 - 37}{37} \right) - 2000 \, \Omega \right] \times 0{\cdot}071 \text{ cm}^2$$

$$= 1700 \text{ ohm-cm}^2.$$

Notes:

(a) The potential difference, V', may change while S is closed. The reading should be taken as soon as possible and S should not be left closed.

(b) The resistance may also change with time after applying the external drop. This can be monitored by closing S several times over the first few minutes. It is only slightly more difficult to obtain quantitative information on this change which may give an indication of the time required for the electrolyte to fill the conduction channels. Such information remains unpublished and would be a good extension to these experiments.

(c) The use of other combinations of concentrations can provide information on how the resistance changes with the concentration of the drop and with the concentration of the pool. Previous data have shown this resistance to be more sensitive to the concentration of the external drop which has led to the suggestion that cuticles prepared in the manner prescribed give easier access to the conducting channels from the outer surface.

(d) The electrode resistance in this case can be obtained by connecting the two electrodes with a drop of 0·058 g/ml NaCl and proceeding either as prescribed in this experiment (with no cuticle) or as in Experiment 4. The assumption is made that the concentration changes in the electrodes are negligible during the course of this procedure. The resulting resistance will be the sum of the resistances of both of these electrodes since the current passes through both and the potential difference is measured across both.

(e) The equation $R = R_0 \dfrac{(V - V')}{V'}$ is obtained as follows:

The cuticle preparation with electrolyte is assumed to be a source of EMF (a battery) with internal resistance R. When S is open, $V =$ EMF since it is assumed that no current passes through the cuticle under these conditions. When S is closed conservation of energy requires charges to lose as much energy as they gain when moving around the closed loop containing R_0, the electrodes and the cuticle. This requirement can be expressed mathematically as EMF $= R_0 I + RI$ or $V = R_0 I + RI$ where I is the current present in this loop. The value V' obtained when S is closed is the potential difference across R_0 produced by the current I and is related to this current by $V' = IR_0$. Hence, $I = V'/R_0$ which, when substituted in $V = R_0 I + RI$, leaves $V = R_0 V'/R_0 + RV'/R_0$. Solving for R gives $R = R_0 \dfrac{(V - V')}{V'}$.

RESPONSE OF EXCISED CUTICLE TO ALTERNATING CURRENT

An advantage of using alternating, or pulsed current, over direct current lies in being able to detect transient responses to changes in applied current. Electrically, this means detecting capacitive or inductive elements in addition to pure resistances. In terms of insect cuticle, DC resistance gives information concerning paths of least resistance to ion movement, whereas determination of capacitance can provide information about the barriers to ion movement. Inductive components are assumed missing. A simple model for cockroach cuticle might have the layer of external grease comprising the major barrier to ions with occasional holes to allow ion movement across this barrier. Capacitance would then be indicative of the ratio of the dielectric constant of this grease layer and its thickness. At the same time, it must be pointed out that these measurements require more equipment, more time, and that the interpretation of the results is somewhat equivocal.

THE AC BRIDGE

The basic idea of the bridge technique is to approximate the cuticle behavior with electronic components, in this case a capacitance and resistance in parallel (see Fig. 8). The bridge is balanced when the detector reads zero potential difference between points 2 and 4. This will be true only when the potential drop from 1 to 2 equals that from 1 to 4, and when the potential drop from 2 to 3 equals that from 4 to 3. R and C are adjusted until this condition is achieved, at which point the cuticle could be replaced by such a combination without unbalancing the bridge. This balancing procedure must be repeated for several frequencies of applied current since most dielectrics have frequency dependent dielectric constants. In addition, analysis of data at several frequencies is necessary to determine the degree to which it is legitimate to use a simple combination of R and C as an electrical model for the cuticle.

The standard analysis proceeds by converting the parallel combination values of R and C obtained by balancing the bridge to a series combination having an equivalent impedance. This is most readily accomplished by introducing complex number notation. Thus, the impedance of the series combination is written as

$$Z_s = Xj' + R'$$

and that of the parallel combination as

$$Z = \frac{RX}{Rj + X}$$

where X is capacitive reactance,

$$X' = 1/(2\pi f C') = 1/\omega C',$$
$$X = 1/(2\pi f C) = 1/\omega C,$$

and $j = \sqrt{-1}.$

R and C are the experimentally determined values.

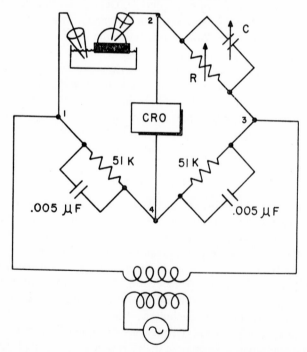

FIG. 8. AC bridge circuit. Variable components R and C consist of decade boxes. The oscilloscope (CRO) is operated in the mode which applies the difference in potential between the two inputs to the vertical deflection plates—without either of the inputs grounded.

By setting $Z_s = Z$, a series capacitance and resistance can be found by equating first the real and then the imaginary parts to give

$$R' = \frac{1/R}{(1/R)^2 + (\omega C)^2}, \quad C' = \frac{(1/R)^2 + \omega^2 C^2}{\omega^2 C}, \quad \text{and} \quad X' = \frac{\omega C}{(1/R)^2 + (\omega C)^2}.$$

These R's and X's are calculated from the experimental values of R and C and then the series reactance X' is plotted as a function of the series resistance R'. Capacitive reactance is usually considered to be negative; however, in this application it is customary to plot X' so that it appears along the positive y axis. The curve on such a plot gives the complex impedance loci. The two intercepts on the R axis define the zero frequency (DC) resistance and the infinite frequency resistance (the capacitance shorted). If the cuticle does behave as a frequency independent resistance and capacitance in parallel the curve will be a semicircle. If it is not a semicircle but the arc of a circle whose origin lies below the R' axis, the cuticle may be represented by any of the combinations shown in Fig. 9 where R_3 and C depend on frequency. In such a case it is misleading to speak of cuticle capacitance without specifying frequency. If, on the other hand, the points do not lie on an arc of a circle any firm association with a particular model is quite difficult.

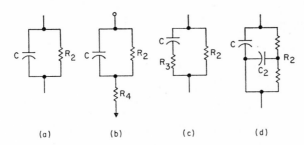

(a)   (b)   (c)   (d)

FIG. 9. Possible electrical models for cockroach cuticle.

EXPERIMENT 8—COMPLEX IMPEDANCE LOCI FOR EXCISED CUTICLE

Purpose: to determine the response of excised cuticle to alternating current using an AC bridge.

1. Electrical set-up: the schematic is shown in Fig. 8.
Equipment used for the first time in this series of experiments includes:
a signal generator, 100 cyc/sec to 20 000 cyc/sec
an isolation transformer
a decade resistance box (see note a)
a decade capacitance box (see note a)
Electrolyte: 0·058 g/ml NaCl
Electrodes: 2 single pipette electrodes filled with 0·058 g/ml NaCl.

2. The cuticle and electrodes in place, disconnect the lead to the CRO from point 4 in Fig. 8 and connect it through a 10 megohm resistor to point 1. Short the variable resistor R with a short length of hook-up wire. Set the signal generator at 20 000 cyc/sec and vary its intensity until the peak to peak potential difference across the cuticle is less than 20 mV. This procedure insures against having current values at which the current-voltage character-istics are non-linear in the cuticle. When this procedure has been carried out reconnect the components as shown in Fig. 8.

3. Adjust R and C until a minimum deflection is obtained on the oscilloscope when $f = 20\,000$ cyc/sec. Record these values of R, C, and f. Then reduce the frequency in convenient steps and repeat the balancing process. A reasonable lower limit is 100 cyc/sec.

4. For each frequency used calculate an R' and an X' from

$$R' = \frac{1/R}{(1/R)^2 + (\omega C)^2}$$

$$X' = \frac{\omega C}{(1/R)^2 + (\omega C)^2}$$

Example:

$f = 1000$ cyc/sec

$C = 0 \cdot 0007 \mu\text{F}\ (7 \times 10^{-10}\ \text{F})$

$R = 47\,000\ \Omega$

$$R' = \frac{\dfrac{1}{47\,000\ \Omega}}{\left(\dfrac{1}{47\,000\ \Omega}\right)^2 + (2\pi \times 1000\ \text{cyc/sec} \times 7 \times 10^{-10}\ \text{F})^2} = 45\,000\ \Omega$$

$$X' = \frac{2\pi \times 1000\ \text{cyc/sec} \times 7 \times 10^{-10}\ \text{F}}{\left(\dfrac{1}{47\,000\ \Omega}\right)^2 + (2\pi \times 1000\ \text{cyc/sec} \times 7 \times 10^{-10}\ \text{F})^2} = 9300\ \Omega$$

5. Plot the X's as functions of the R's, and draw the best circular arc through these points as in Fig. 10. This curve constitutes the complex impedance loci.

6. Determine the phase angle from the impedance loci as indicated in Fig. 10.

Notes:

(a) With single decade boxes for R and C in the bridge circuit it may not be possible to completely balance the bridge at all frequencies. The values that bring it closest to balance usually are adequate. More precise measurements can be obtained by inserting additional decade boxes so as to provide smaller steps in the variation of R and C.

(b) For those not acquainted with bridge techniques it may be helpful to begin by substituting a known resistance and capacitance for the cuticle in order to gain some familiarity with the apparatus and procedure.

(c) Stray capacitance can cause problems. It will depend somewhat on the orientation of the electrodes, and can be measured experimentally by removing the cuticle, connecting the electrodes, and proceeding to balance the bridge at various frequencies. A discussion of the effect of stray capacitance can be found in Eisenberg (1967). Electrode resistance has been assumed negligible in this experiment.

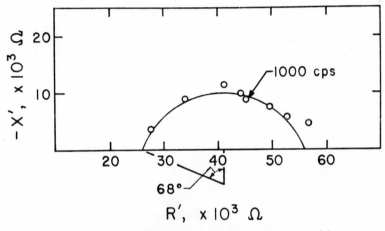

FIG. 10. Example of impedance loci for *P. americana* cuticle.

(d) Interesting variations in impedance loci can be obtained by using freshly molted animals or by treating excised cuticle with a lipid solvent such as chloroform.

(e) The intercept farthest out on the R' axis, which corresponds to zero frequency, indicates the DC resistance and should compare favorably with DC resistance determined as in Experiment 6.

RESPONSE OF EXCISED CUTICLE TO PULSED CURRENT

The response of cuticle to pulsed current provides information pertaining to the resistance and capacitance of the cuticle just as does an AC bridge. It even has been shown that values from either type of measurement can be transformed into those of the other (see Teorell, 1946). Pulsed current requires slightly more sophisticated equipment, but measurements are obtained faster and more easily than those using a bridge.

The procedure consists of applying a rectangular pulse of current across the cuticle and monitoring the resulting potential difference across the same area. The circuits employed are shown in Fig. 11a. The incident pulse and the expected response are shown in Fig. 11b. It is convenient to consider this response in terms of electrical models of the cuticle such as are shown in Fig. 9. The response is interpreted as follows. The potential difference immediately rises to a value depending on the effective resistance with C shorted. (For a circuit such as Fig. 9a the resistance would be zero and the potential difference would not make an initial jump.) It then rises exponentially as the

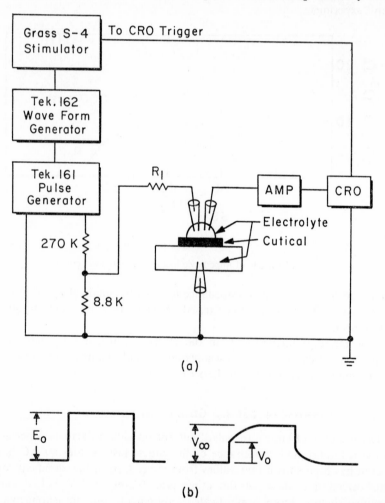

(a)

(b)

FIG. 11. (a) Diagram of the circuit used to impose a square wave on insect cuticle and measuring the time course of the resulting potential difference; (b) The expected response from a circuit such as shown in Fig. 9b or c.

capacitor is being charged to a final value determined by the total DC resistance when no current passes through the capacitor.

The DC resistance of the cuticle is found by using Ohm's law, dividing the potential difference across the cuticle by the current through it. When the potential difference is V_∞ and the current is the same as through R_1 which, by Ohm's law, is

$$\frac{E_0 - V_\infty}{R_1}.$$

Hence,

$$R_{DC} = \frac{V_\infty}{E_0/R_1 - V_\infty/R_1} = \frac{V_\infty R_1}{E_0 - V_\infty}.$$

The value of V_0 indicates the magnitude of an R_3 or an R_4. Assuming C to be effectively shorted during the transient portion of the voltage response to the pulse, one again can apply Ohm's law and write

$$R_3 = \frac{R_1 V_0}{E_0 - \left(\dfrac{R_2 + R_1}{R_2}\right) V_0}$$

or

$$R_4 = \frac{R_1 V_0}{E_0 - V_0}.$$

It is not possible to distinguish between an R_4 and an R_3 electrically.

Some indication of the capacitance can be obtained from the rise time of the exponential portion of the response curve (Fig. 11b). For a model such as shown in Fig. 9a where R_3 and R_4 are neglected, this term becomes relatively simple. The following equations mathematically describe the situation that is drawn in a more illustrative fashion in Fig. 12.

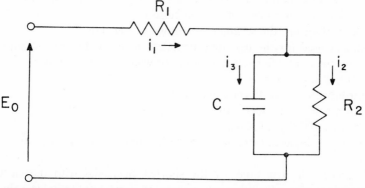

FIG. 12. The circuit used to obtain an expression of capacitance as a function of the rise time of the applied pulse.

$$E_0 - R_1 i_1 - R_2 i_2 = 0$$

$$Q/C = R_2 i_2 \qquad\qquad R_3 = R_4 = 0$$

$$i_1 = i_2 + i_3$$

$$i_3 = dQ/dt$$

These can be solved for Q/C which is the potential difference across the capacitor and the quantity subject to experimental measurement. The integrated solution is

$$Q/C = \frac{E_0}{1 + \dfrac{R_1}{R_2}}\left(1 - e^{-\frac{t}{c}\frac{R_1 + R_2}{R_1 R_2}}\right) \quad \text{or} \quad V = V_\infty\left(1 - e^{-\frac{t}{\tau}}\right)$$

from which the time constant, or rise time, τ, is given by

$$\tau = C\frac{R_1 R_2}{R_1 + R_2}.$$

Having just measured R_2 ($R_2 = R_{DC}$) it is possible to compute a C by first determining τ. τ can be measured directly for it is the time required for the potential difference to reach a value $V_\tau = (1 - 1/e)V_\infty$. V_τ can be computed when V_∞ is measured and the corresponding time can be read off the oscilloscope. Another means of determining τ also provides a check on the assumption that the cuticle can be approximated by this mathematical model: When $\ln(V_\infty - V)$ is plotted as a function of time, the curve should be a straight line with a slope $1/\tau$.

EXPERIMENT 9—CUTICLE CAPACITANCE

Purpose: to demonstrate the use of electrical transients and to obtain a measure of the capacitance of excised cuticle.

1. Electrical set-up: the schematic is shown in Fig. 11a.

Equipment used for the first time includes apparatus to provide adjustable pulses of potential difference. Examples of what can be used are:

a Grass S-4 Stimulator

a Tektronix 162 Wave Form Generator

a Tektronix 161 Pulse Generator

Electrolytes: 0·058 g/ml NaCl

Electrodes: 1 single and 1 double pipette electrode, each filled with 0·058 g/ml NaCl.

2. Determine the rise time for the shorted electrodes with the electrodes connected to each other through a drop of electrolyte. Suitable values are no larger than 5 μsec.

3. Insert the prepared cuticle into the circuit and apply electrodes as before. Adjust the pulse duration so that the pulses are long ($> \times 10$) compared to the rise time across the cuticle, and adjust the frequency to give intervals between pulses approximately equal to the pulse duration. With the CRO properly adjusted repetitive pulses will always appear at the same position on the screen so they may be measured or photographed.

4. Note the value for V_0 and V_∞ and determine the time constant from the trace on the oscilloscope screen. This will be the value of t when V is within $1/e$ of $(V_\infty - V_0)$ or when $V = 0.73 (V_\infty - V_0)$.

5. Plot a graph of $\ln (V_\infty - V)$ versus time. A straight line indicates any of the models in Fig. 9 may be valid. (However, a straight line is not likely.) A measurable value for V_0 would restrict the model to those of Figs 9b–d. (V_0 has been found negligible in most experiments with pronotum cuticle performed by the author.)

6. Now, compute C with the aid of the equation

$$\tau = C \frac{R_1 R_2}{R_1 + R_2} \quad \text{or} \quad C = \tau \frac{R_1 + R_2}{R_1 R_2}.$$

When τ is expressed in sec and the Rs are expressed in megohms C will be given in microfarads. Once again it is desirable to normalize this quantity to a piece of cuticle 1 cm^2 which in this instance ideally gives the specific areal capacitance. This is done by dividing the capacitance by the area of the contact on the outer surface. $C_s = C/A$. It must be emphasized that capacitance appeared to depend on frequency in Experiment 8; furthermore, the equation used in the above paragraph was derived from a model that is not necessarily correct. Thus, the value obtained here must be used with some caution. It should not be construed to imply a complete or accurate description of the capacitance unless the assumptions underlying its calculation can be verified. At the same time, it is reasonably safe to assume that long rise times are the result of large capacitive elements being present.

Notes:

(a) The applied pulse should have as fast a rise time as possible. The components shown in Fig. 11a for obtaining such a pulse are not unique, but represent a workable arrangement with equipment readily available.

(b) Undetectable values for V_0 also imply that electrode resistance is negligible.

(c) It is convenient to set V, with the cuticle shorted, at some value (i.e., 140 mV). This value serves then as E_0. Too large a value for E_0 would mean operating in a region where the current voltage characteristics of the cuticle are non-linear.

(d) The response to the trailing edge of the pulse should provide the same information as the response to the leading edge if assumptions as to the possible models are valid.

(e) The lack of clean, unequivocal results from these experiments points out that more research needs to be done in this area. Anyone performing these experiments should do so with eyes open for ways of improving the techniques and interpretations.

(f) This technique is more useful for comparisons either among cuticles or with information obtained on a given cuticle with the AC bridge than it is for determining any absolute values. Interesting comparisons can be found by looking at cuticle excised at various times after a molt or after treatment with chemicals, heat, or abrasives.

(g) Scheie and Smyth (1968) suggested an electrical model such as Fig. 9d to account for the cuticular responses they reported in 1967. Their paper can be consulted for the details of their argument.

MEASUREMENTS ON INTACT INTEGUMENT

From a physiological point of view an excised cuticle is a mutilated biological specimen, and a more satisfactory arrangement would require a study of intact integument. This is possible with slight modification of the techniques used with cuticles, although only DC resistance measurements have been reported to date for such systems.

EXPERIMENT 10—DC RESISTANCE OF INTACT INTEGUMENT

Purpose: to determine the DC specific resistance of intact integument by measuring the resistance between 2 electrolyte drops on the external surface.

1. Electrical set-up: the schematic is shown in Fig. 5.
Electrolytes: 0·058 g/ml NaCl
Electrodes: 1 single and 1 double pipette electrode, each filled with 0·058 g/ml NaCl.

2. Cut a soft plastic sponge to fit a small box with a removable cover. A box measuring 2 cm × 4 cm × 6 cm has been used successfully.

3. Capture a live adult *P. americana*, taking care not to touch or rub the upper surface of the pronotum. After rinsing the pronotum with water, place the animal upright on the sponge with its head against one end of the box and then place the cover such that the animal is pressed into the sponge leaving head and pronotum exposed. The head can be immobilized by sticking it to the end with a small piece of dental periphery wax.

4. Apply two 3 mm diameter drops of electrolyte to the surface of the pronotum taking care to avoid the midline; lower electrodes and determine the resistance between the two drops as was done with cuticle in Experiment 6.

5. Calculate specific areal resistance by using $\frac{1}{2}$ the measured resistance and multiplying it by the area of contact under one of the drops (0·071 cm²). This calculation assumes equal size drops and lack of current paths other than transverse to the plane of cuticle beneath the drops.

6. Release the insect and return it to the appropriate container. Careful handling causes little apparent injury and subsequent measurements can be made on the same specimen.

Notes:

(a) A check on the assumption that current direction is transverse to the plane of the integument can be made in two ways: (1) by using smaller drops and measuring resistance as a function of the separation of these drops. Increased resistance with increased separation would indicate the assumption is not valid and (2) by inserting the grounded electrode through the soft integument under the pronotum, measuring the resistance between each drop and the inside, and comparing the sum of these with the resistance between the two drops. Measurements with this electrode inserted into the animal also permit detection of any asymmetry with current direction. These same ideas also apply to excised cuticle.

(b) Interesting variations in the value of this resistance can be found, (1) by isolating animals from each other and making measurements every few days. The resistance should begin to rise after 40–60 days of isolation and is partially reversible when the animals are reunited; (2) by doing the same with isolated nymphs through several molt cycles. The resistance will rise quite high within 10 days before molt and drop quite low immediately following a molt; (3) by abrading the outer surface or rinsing it with a lipid solvent.

(c) As of this writing no one has published attempts at measuring the integument capacitance of live animals.

(d) Similar measurements can be made on the other portions of the integument or on other species.

REFERENCES

This is not intended to be an exhaustive bibliography. It does, however, include most of the published reports of electrical measurements on insect cuticle and integument. In addition, attention is directed to a few of the more general publications involving insect integument as well as to some useful articles on electrical measurements.

ELECTRICAL MEASUREMENTS ON INSECT CUTICLE AND INTEGUMENT

Beament, J. W. L. (1961). Electrical properties of oriented lipid on a biological membrane. *Nature Lond.*, **191**, 217–221.

Beament, J. W. L. (1964). The active transport and passive movement of water in insects. *Adv. insect Physiol.*, **2**, 67–130.

K

Beament, J. W. L. (1965). The active transport of water: Evidence, models, and mechanisms. *Symp. Soc. exp. Biol.*, **19**, 273–298.

Cole, K. S. and Jahn, T. L. (1937). The nature and permeability of grasshopper egg membranes. IV. The alternating current impedance over a wide frequency range. *J. cell. comp. Physiol.*, **10**, 265–275.

Jahn, T. L. (1936). Studies on the nature and permeability of grasshopper egg membranes. III. Changes in electrical properties of the membrane during development. *J. cell. comp. Physiol.*, **8**, 289–300.

Richards, A. G. (1957). Studies on arthropod cuticle. XIII. The penetration of dissolved oxygen and electrolytes in relation to the multiple barriers of the cuticle. *J. insect Physiol.*, **1**, 23–39.

Scheie, P. O. (1969). Electrical resistance of intact integument throughout the molt cycle of a cockroach. *Comp. Biochem. Physiol.*, **29**, 479–482.

Scheie, P. O. and Smyth, T., Jr. (1967). Electrical measurements on cuticles excised from adult male *Periplaneta americana* (L.). *Comp. Biochem. Physiol.*, **21**, 547–571.

Scheie, P. O. and Smyth, T., Jr. (1968). The electrical resistance of intact integument of *Periplaneta americana* (L). *Comp. Biochem. Physiol.*, **26**, 399–414.

Schmitt, O. H. (1955). Dynamic negative admittance components in statically stable membranes. *In* "Electrochemistry in Biology and Medicine". (Shedlovsky, T. ed.). 91–120, Wiley, New York, U.S.A.

GENERAL ASPECTS OF INSECT INTEGUMENT

Guthrie, D. M. and Tindall, A. R. (1968). The Biology of the Cockroach. Edward Arnold, Great Britain.

Richards, A. G. (1951). "The Integument of Arthropods". University of Minnesota Press, Minneapolis, U.S.A.

Richards, A. G. (1958). The Cuticle of Arthropods. *Ergebn. Biol.*, **20**, 1–26.

Rockstein, M. (ed.) (1964). "The Physiology of Insecta". Vol. III, Academic Press, New York and London.

Wigglesworth, V. B. (1967) "Insect Physiology". Wiley, New York, U.S.A.

OTHER USEFUL REFERENCES INVOLVING ELECTRICAL MEASUREMENTS ON MEMBRANES

Bureš, J., Petráň, M., and Zachar, J. (1962). "Electrophysiological Methods in Biological Research" Czech. Acad. of Sci., Prague.

Cole, K. S. (1932). Electric phase angle of cell membranes. *J. gen. Physiol.*, **15**, 641–649.

Cole, K. S. (1968) "Membranes, Ions and Impulses. U. of Calif. Press, Berkeley, U.S.A.

Eisenberg, R. S. (1967). The equivalent circuit of single crab muscle fibres as determined by impedance measurements with intracellular electrodes. *J. gen. Physiol.*, **50**, 1785–1806.

Ives, D. J. and Janz, G. J. (1961). "Reference Electrodes". Academic Press, New York and London.

Scheie, P. O. (1967). Ohms, mhos, farads, and membranes. *Bioscience*, **17**, 907–911.

Schwann, H. P. (1957). Electrical properties of tissue and cell suspensions. *In* "Advances in Biological and Medical Physics" (J. H. Lawrence and C. A. Tobias, eds) Vol. 5. Academic Press, New York and London. 147–209.

Teorell, T. (1946). Application of "square wave analysis" to bioelectric studies *Acta physiol. scand.*, **12**, 235–254.

Exp. in Physiol. and Biochem. (1970). 3, 211–232.

7 | Experiments on Synaptic Transmission using the Frog Sartorius Nerve-Muscle Preparation

BARBARA J. EXCELL

Department of Physiology, Queen Elizabeth College,
University of London, England

In vertebrate striated muscle the arrival of a nerve impulse at the motor nerve endings leads to the release of the transmitter acetylcholine. This diffuses across the synapse to fit into receptors in the post-synaptic membrane and produces an increase in the permeability of the membrane to sodium and potassium ions. The resultant depolarization is termed an end-plate potential and normally gives rise to a propagated action potential which passes down the muscle fibre and initiates contraction. The following experiments have been chosen to illustrate certain features of synaptic transmission, particularly in relation to transmitter release.

EXPERIMENT 1—TO RECORD THE END-PLATE POTENTIAL AND ILLUSTRATE SYNAPTIC FACILITATION AND DEPRESSION

By employing d-tubocurarine to partially block the acetylcholine receptors on the post-synaptic membrane, the time course of the e.p.p. may be followed without the complication of the action potential (Fatt and Katz, 1951).

If a second impulse arrives between 2 msec and 75–100 msec after the first impulse the size of the second e.p.p. increases markedly. This phenomenon is termed facilitation or potentiation. It is due to two processes (1) summation of the second e.p.p. with the residual e.p.p. from the previous stimulus and (2) increased output of transmitter as a result of the previous stimulation.

Repetitive stimulation leads to a depression of the e.p.p. in a curarized preparation (Wedenski inhibition) and is associated with a reduction in the amount of transmitter available for release.

MATERIALS

Apparatus

Micro-manipulator. For simple experiments the design is not critical, movements in the horizontal plane as given by a modified microscope stage being sufficient. Vertical movements should have fine and coarse adjustments similar to a standard microscope. Micrometer scales attached to the horizontal movements are useful to allow co-ordinates to be taken. Suitable commercial instruments include the relatively cheap Narishige MM3 and Prior micro-manipulators, as well as the Zeiss micro-manipulator. The holder for carrying the micro-electrode should have a metal tube allowing the greater part of the electrode to be shielded. The particular design is not important but depends partly on the method of connecting the micro-electrode to the cathode follower. If the refinement of measuring the tip potential of the micro-electrode is required, the micro-electrode must fit into a saline-agar holder containing the Ag/AgCl lead passing to the cathode follower. The agar holder is similar to the indifferent electrode and steady potentials from this part of the system can be balanced out before the attachment of the micro-electrode. In the simpler system the Ag/AgCl wire passes directly into the micro-electrode containing the 3M KCl.

Cathode Follower. The noise level must be less than 25 μV under short circuit and a cathode follower using a ME 1400 valve has been found satisfactory. To reduce interference to a minimum the cathode follower must be positioned close to the micro-electrode and the connecting silver wire kept as short as possible.

Cathode Ray Oscilloscope. A two-channel oscilloscope is required such that the resting potential may be monitored on one beam, the end-plate potential on the second beam (AC sensitivity up to 200 μV/cm). Recordings can be made by either camera or pen recorder though the latter is particularly suitable when the mean value of a large number of amplitudes is required. The Mingograf-34 pen recorder with frequency response of 700 cyc/sec gives good reproduction of the waveform.

Preparation Bath. This is made of clear perspex and has the following features: (Fig. 1).

1. A detachable curved perspex platform upon which the preparation is mounted. The curved portion is 13 mm wide by 50 mm long rising to a maximum height of 3 mm above the base plate.

   The surface of the platform is covered with thin polythene which is fixed in position with nylon screws at each end. This allows micropins to be used in setting up the muscle. Alternatively the polythene covering may be omitted, and the muscle attached by threads to stainless steel hooks inserted at the ends of the platform. The platform is firmly held in the base of the bath by a peg and hole fixture.

2. A side chamber containing stimulating electrodes placed approximately halfway along the length of the chamber. The nerve passes through a small slit (1 mm) into the chamber.

3. An inlet and outlet to allow perfusion. The volume of the bath should

be kept low (10 ml or less) to reduce the volume needed for perfusion replacement. The outlet is so arranged that the opening is in the horizontal plane and at such a height that the muscle is only covered by 2–3 mm fluid. Removal of perfusion fluid is assisted by gentle suction from a water pump. This facility is optional for Experiment 2 as fluid may be exchanged using a syringe and needle. However it is preferable, and for continuous recording as in Experiment 5, essential.

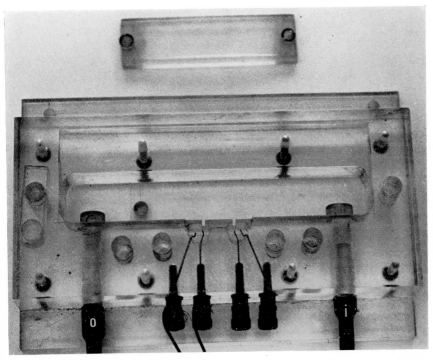

FIG. 1. The preparation bath. The platform on which the muscle is pinned is shown above the bath. i, inlet; o, outlet. (By courtesy of Professor B. Katz.)

Dissecting Microscope with Range × 10 *to* × 40. If available, × 80 is useful. A micrometer eyepiece is also helpful. The muscle is of the order of 30 mm long and end-plates may be found over approximately 10 mm of this length. The total field may be scanned by use of a microscope head mounted on a transverse rack and pinion, and in this case the bath is placed on a clear-based, rigid stand. However, if a fixed head microscope is used, the bath is mounted on a clear perspex plate attached to a microscope stage at the base of the stand.

Microscope Lamp with Adjustable Intensity. The lamp is placed at a distance and the light directed through the preparation by means of a concave microscope mirror below. Better illumination is obtained if the light passes through a ground glass plate. A water-filled perspex container in front of the lamp acts as a heat filter.

Stimulator with Variable Frequency Pulse. For Experiment 1 a double pulse with separation from 1 msec to 50–100 msec is required. The stimulus passes through a radio-frequency probe to allow isolation from earth.

Micro-electrodes filled with 3*M KCl.* To reduce interference the electrode resistance should be kept in the region of 5–25 MΩ. The electrodes are filled by gently boiling in filtered KCl, under reduced pressure. The pressure is released periodically. If difficulty is encountered with fine bubbles trapped in the shaft, cooling overnight in the refrigerator allows their reabsorption. The electrodes may be stored in the refrigerator for several days. Before use the electrode is rinsed in distilled water, dried, and a small amount of KCl removed from the stem and replaced by paraffin, to prevent surface crystallization.

The indifferent electrode contains 0·5% agar in Ringer solution with Ag/AgCl wire as a lead.

Pulse Generator. DC Pulses of 200 μV, 1, 5, 10 and 100 mV are required.

Screened Cage. The bath with its associated apparatus and the cathode follower should be set up on a heavy, rigid surface as free as possible from vibration, and enclosed in a wire-screen cage with hinged front. The remainder of the electrical apparatus is carried on a trolley or rack nearby.

Circuit. The micro-electrode is connected through the cathode follower to the active side of both channels 1 and 2 of the CRO. The indifferent electrode is connected to one side of the pulse generator, the other side passing to the earthed sides of the cathode follower and CRO.

Animals

Rana esculenta and *Rana temporaria* are preferable to other species as the preparation is relatively easily freed of connective tissue.

Chemical solutions

Ringer solution of normal ionic composition as given in Table I (A), d-tubocurarine Cl (Burroughs Wellcome) 200 μg/ml.

EXPERIMENTAL DETAILS

Dissection

The sartorius is a superficial muscle running slightly obliquely along the ventral surface of the thigh with attachments to the tibio-fibula and the pelvic bones (Fig. 2). Its motor nerve branches off from the dorsally situated sciatic nerve and a long length of nerve is obtained by dissecting the sciatic nerve from its origin in the sacral vertebra.

1. Pith and skin the frog. Place the preparation supine and cut across the vertebral column just below the forelimbs. Cut the muscle on either side of the lower backbone extending the cut onto the outer side of both ilia. Remove

TABLE I

Composition of Ringer solutions

| Compound | (A) Normal ionic concentrations | | | |
	Stock soln (g/100 ml)	Vol taken (ml)	Ion	Final concn (mM/1)
KCl	1·86	10	K^+	2·5
$CaCl_2.2H_2O$*	2·62	10	Ca^{++}	1·8
$NaH_2PO_4.2H_2O$	0·70	10	H_2PO_4'	0·45
Na_2HPO_4	1·81	20	HPO_4''	2·55
NaCl	13·0	50	Na^+	116·5
H_2O (dist)		to 1000 ml	Cl'	117·1
(B) High magnesium low calcium concentrations				
$CaCl_2.2H_2O$*	2·62	5	Ca^{++}	0·9
$MgSO_4.7H_2O$	24·65	6	Mg^{++}	6·0
NaCl	13·0	48	Na^+	112
Other compounds as in (A)				
(C) Varying calcium ion concentrations				
NaCl	13·0	5·2	Na^+	116
KCl	1·86	1·0	K^+	2·5
$CaCl_2.2H_2O$*	2·62	0·5	Ca^{++}	0·9
		1·0		1·8
		2·0		3·6
		4·0		7·2
H_2O (dist)		to 100 ml		

* To be added near final volume of Ringer to prevent precipitation of calcium phosphate.

the upper part of the body and viscera by holding the lower portion of the vertebral column so that the viscera fall away from it; cut the connecting tissue. The sacral outflow of nerves running on either side of the urostyle can now be seen. Place the preparation prone. Hold up the urostyle, and with the tips of the scissors pointing upwards, cut the muscle along either side of the urostyle; remove the urostyle at its base. Place the preparation supine. Cut across each ilium at the pelvic and vertebral ends and remove with attached muscle.

2. Pass a short ligature under the sacral nerve outflow and tie close to the vertebra; cut each nerve bundle above the ligature. Place the preparation prone and carefully free the sciatic nerve as it passes across the pelvis to enter the dorsal aspect of the hindlimb. Cut the large medial muscle of the hindlimb (mainly semimembranosus) close to its pelvic attachment and gently reflect (Fig. 3a). The branch containing the motor nerve to the sartorius can now be seen leaving the sciatic trunk medially. Cut the sciatic nerve beyond the bifurcation and carefully free. The point at which the sartorius

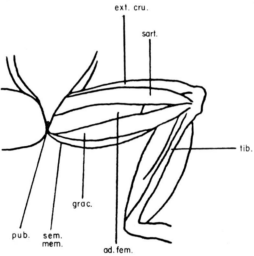

FIG. 2. The ventral view of the thigh muscles of the frog. Note the motor nerve passing over the adductor femoris to enter the sartorius muscle. ad. fem., adductor femoris; ext. cru., extensor cruris; grac., gracilis; pub., pubes; sart., sartorius; sem. mem., semimembranosus; tib., tibia–fibula.

nerve leaves this secondary trunk is best determined by dissecting backwards from the point of entry of the nerve into the sartorius muscle. A dissecting microscope of approximately × 10 is useful at this point.

3. Place the preparation supine. Dissect out the tibial tendon of the sartorius at the knee-joint and ligature firmly. Gently reflect the muscle and, using very fine scissors, cut the connective tissue on either side of the muscle leaving a small edge for pinning out the preparation. Carefully cut the connective tissue as close to the under (dorsal) surface as possible. This is important for subsequent trouble-free penetration of the end-plate region. Continue as far as the motor nerve entering onto the dorsal surface from the medial side approximately one third distance from the tibial end. The nerve can be seen passing a short distance over the adductor femoris then turning downwards into the fascia between the femoris and adjacent gracilis muscle.

Carefully cut the connective tissue *above* the nerve at this fascial junction and extend the cut to separate the gracilis and femoris muscles as far as the pelvis. Cut across the gracilis at its pelvic attachment and reflect.

4. Gently reflect the sartorius muscle about the line of nerve entry, (Fig. 3b), and by very gently pulling the underlying femoris muscle forward, the connective tissue holding the nerve at its point of entry can be cleared. Beyond this point the nerve is very firmly held to the femoris and it is inadvisable to clear it at this stage as the nerve is easily stretched and the nerve endings, particularly those lying superficially, are damaged. This is the most common

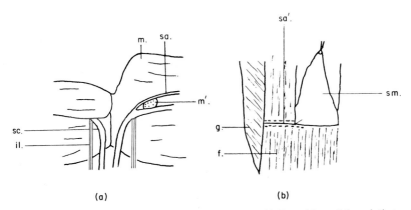

(a)   (b)

FIG. 3. Stages in the dissection of the sartorius nerve. (a) Branching of the sciatic trunk immediately it enters the dorsal surface of the hind-limb. (b) Freeing the sartorius nerve close to the point of entry into the muscle. f., femoris muscle with lines of cut – – –; g., gracilis muscle, reflected; il., stump of ilium; m., cut and reflected dorso-medial thigh muscle; m′, cut muscle; sa., branch containing the sartorius nerve; sa′., sartorius nerve; sc., sciatic trunk; sm., sartorius muscle partly reflected.

cause of the failure to find end-plates. Cut the superficial fibres of the femoris muscle on both sides of the nerve (Fig. 3b); the muscle fragments can be cleared at a later stage. The nerve lies in muscle fascia running downwards and medially on its way to joining the dorsally lying sciatic nerve. In order to expose the complete course of the nerve it is necessary to cut along the fascial line of two medial deep muscles as far as their pelvic attachment, cut across their tendons and reflect gently. Nerve branches are cut. The preparation will be slowly rotated from the ventral to the dorsal surface and is steadied by pinning the feet. In freeing the nerve from the sciatic bifurcation to the sartorius muscle no traction must be placed on the nerve. The nerve should be reflected and allowed to lie flat whilst the connective tissue is cleared from beneath its length. The freed portion can usually be gently pushed forward.

5. Reflect the sartorius muscle and drape the freed nerve along the under-surface so that it is held loosely by surface tension. Any spontaneous twitching denotes damage to the nerve. Continue to carefully free and clear the muscle up to its attachment to the upper part of the pubes. With a scalpel bisect the pubes commencing on the ventral surface near the ilial stump and following the pubic curvature. Reflect the muscle completely and separate the cartilaginous process with attached sartorius nerve-muscle preparation.

Setting up the Preparation

Place the muscle on the curved perspex platform such that the dorsal surface (underneath surface) is uppermost. Micropins are carefully inserted through the pelvic and tibial tendons and through the fine strip of connective tissue along each edge. The muscle should lie flat but slightly stretched to its *in vivo* length. The nerve is placed on the stimulating electrodes and the side chamber sealed off with a greased coverslip with vaseline in the slit. A small piece of moistened filter paper placed over the nerve at the point of exit prevents drying.

For the best visual contrast between the superficial nerve fibres and the underlying muscle fibres the concave mirror is angled to give oblique rays with the light falling parallel to the muscle fibres but transversely to the nerve fibres. It is important to determine the optimum angle and intensity of the light. Although the full pattern of branching indicated in Fig. 4a may not be visible in every muscle sufficient should be seen to act as landmarks.

Add d-tubocurarine Cl to give a final bath concentration of 3 μg/ml and test for complete block over 45–60 min. In some preparations it may be necessary to increase the final concentration to 4–5 μg/ml.

Whilst waiting for the block the micro-electrode should be tested. The

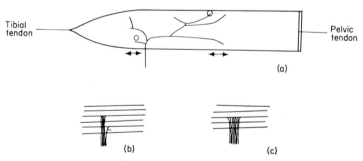

Fig. 4. Stages in locating likely sites of end-plates. (a) Motor innervation as seen on the dorsal surface of the sartorius muscle. The end-plate zones are indicated by arrows, and most easily detected sites ringed. (b) The appearance of a motor nerve as it branches close to an end-plate. (c) The appearance of a motor nerve as it dives below the surface muscle fibres.

resistance should be kept as low as possible although electrodes up to 25 MΩ are suitable. The majority of e.p.p.'s range from 1–5 mV and the amount of interference being picked up should be checked by turning up the AC beam sensitivity to 500 μV/cm. There should be no 50 cyc/sec hum with the screen down (see trouble-shooting), but if the irregular noise level is still high discard the electrode. As a final check determine the resting potential of any muscle fibre; the value should be of the order of 90 mV and no lower than 70 mV.

Set the time sweep of the CRO at 5 msec/cm and arrange that the sweep is triggered by the stimulus.

Locating the End-plate

Many of the muscle fibres have a double innervation and the majority of these end-plates are distributed into 2 zones as indicated in Fig. 4a. Using × 40 magnification, look for a site in these zones where the apparent ending of the nerve is very fine and likely to be dividing into single fibres passing to end-plates (Fig. 4b). These are more easily detected near the edges of the muscle. The electrode is inserted at this point and the presence of an e.p.p. determined by nerve stimulation. At many end-plates the fibres are not visible and the site is only found by trial and error. However once a site is found, end-plates are usually detected in the same position in several

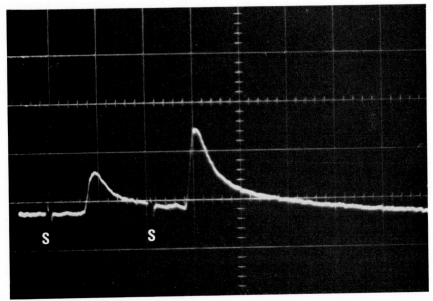

Fig. 5. End-plate potentials following a double stimulus (s). The two stimuli are separated by 11 msec. Vertical scale, 2 mV/cm; horizontal scale, 5 msec/cm.

of the nearby fibres. In the tibial zone the end-plates are restricted to a narrower band.

The position of the centre of the end-plate is determined from the shape of the e.p.p.; at this point the amplitude and rise and fall times are maximal, the time from onset to peak being just over 1 msec and the time from onset to half decline around 4 msec (Fig. 5). Although under the present conditions of blocking the e.p.p.'s are mainly between 1 and 5 mV, the variation between junctions may be more than 10-fold. The spatial decay is such that at 500 μ from the centre the amplitude has dropped by 50% and the respective times are 1·8 and 6·5 msec. At increasing distances the rise and fall times are slowed and at 2 mm the height is reduced to 20% of maximum. Steps of approximately 100 μ may be necessary for the final positioning of the electrode.

To Illustrate Facilitation and Depression

Apply double stimuli every 30 sec using pulse separations of 0, 5, 10, 20, 50 and 100 msec. Determine the total height of the second e.p.p. and express as % height of a single e.p.p.; plot the time course of facilitation. On the same graph show the proportion due to increased transmitter release by plotting the height of the second e.p.p. above its new baseline as % height of a single e.p.p.

Record several e.p.p.'s at a stimulus frequency no greater than 20/min and 20 or so e.p.p.'s during a tetanus of 40/sec. Determine the rate of recovery using single stimuli at intervals. Plot the height of successive e.p.p.'s as % control height.

RESULTS

The maximal degree of facilitation is obtained with double stimuli of 5 msec separation when the second e.p.p. rises to 200% or more of a single e.p.p. By 11 msec separation, facilitation is nearly completely due to increased transmitter release (Fig. 5).

At the start of tetanic stimulation facilitation is apparent, but a depression is gradually superimposed. At some end-plates the decline in height may show a sudden break indicative of conduction failure in a terminal nerve branch. This is usually intermittent (Fig. 6).

TROUBLE SHOOTING

Low Resting Potential

This may be due to either a broken electrode tip or the gradient at the tip being too sharp resulting in damage to the membrane. In the latter case an increase in the pulling heat may be required.

Absence of End-plates

Damage to the nerve endings by stretch applied during the dissection and setting up procedures is the most likely cause. Larger e.p.p.'s may be obtained by increasing the calcium concentration to 3·6 mM/l or by using a final concentration of 2 μg/ml d-tubocurarine. In both cases the time to block is considerably increased and with the lower concentration of curare a few fibres may fail to block. This movement may interfere with recording.

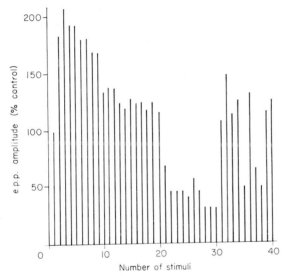

Fig. 6. The effect of a tetanus of 40/sec on the amplitude of the end-plate potentials. Recorded in the presence of d-tubocurarine.

Interference

1. AC of 50 cyc/sec from the mains. Each piece of equipment must be earthed, but at one point only to prevent interference arising from earth loops. Leads should be shielded but care taken that this does not provide a second earth leak. In practice the oscilloscope is connected to earth via the mains, and the cathode follower, stimulator and pen recorder earthed by their oscilloscope connections; the cage, micromanipulator etc. are earthed by connections to the cathode follower. The source of any troublesome AC is found by progressive exclusion of parts of the apparatus, leads etc.

2. Irregular noise. If the noise level of the micro-electrode is acceptable when it is in the fluid but increases markedly upon insertion into the fibre, connective tissue above this particular site is likely to be the cause. If the general noise level of the electrode has increased the tip is probably blocked with

protein and this should be reflected in an increased electrode resistance. The electrode resistance should be periodically checked, any change in either direction making the electrode suspect and to be discarded. Good dissection and good electrodes are the two essentials.

Stability

The resting potential and e.p.p. should be stable for 5–6 h. DC drift in the apparatus usually necessitates the removal of the electrode after an hour as a check on the resting potential, but the electrode can be re-inserted several times in the same spot or very close by. A marked variation in the size of e.p.p. indicates impairment of the nerve endings. In prolonged testing the stimuli should be no closer than 1/4 sec to prevent depression. The Ringer-curare solution should be replaced every 1–2 h to avoid changes in osmotic pressure due to evaporation.

EXPERIMENT 2—TO DETERMINE THE EFFECT OF CALCIUM ION CONCENTRATION ON THE SIZE OF THE END-PLATE POTENTIAL

The concentration of calcium ions in the external medium controls the amount of transmitter released from the nerve endings following the arrival of a nerve impulse. It has been suggested that, as a result of depolarization, calcium ions move inwards and activate a carrier molecule involved in the release of acetylcholine.

MATERIALS

The experimental requirements are similar to Experiment 1 with the addition of Ringer solutions of varying calcium concentration (Table IC). It is advisable to make up several hundred mls of the normal calcium solution (1·8 mm/1). The tonicity of the solutions range from 99–107% but this should not affect the recordings.

EXPERIMENTAL DETAILS

1. Locate an end-plate as described previously using the normal calcium solution containing 3 μg/ml d-tubocurarine. Record the resting potential and several e.p.p.'s at a stimulus frequency no greater than 20/min.
2. Add curare to the other calcium solutions to give an identical final concentration.
3. Exchange the bathing fluid in either of the following ways.
(a) Withdraw the electrode to just above the fibre but do not alter the position otherwise. Carefully remove the bathing fluid with syringe and needle and

replace with an equal volume of solution of calcium 0·9 mM/1. Allow the preparation to equilibrate for 10 min then replace with more of this solution. Re-insert the electrode and record both the resting potential and several e.p.p.'s. Repeat the procedure using calcium solutions of 3·6, 7·2 and finally 1·8 mM/l. The equilibration time is longer following a marked reduction in the calcium concentration and 20 min or more may be required.

(b) With the electrode *in situ* change the solution by gently flowing approximately 50 ml of the low calcium solution through the chamber over 2–3 min. Record the resting potential and several e.p.p.'s when the preparation has equilibrated and repeat for the calcium solutions of 3·6, 7·2 and 1·8 mM/l.

RESULTS

A plot of mean e.p.p. against log of the calcium concentration gives a straight line. The resting potential is virtually unchanged and the effect of calcium completely reversible.

TROUBLE SHOOTING

Fluid exchange

The efficiency of the clearance of the chamber by perfusion should previously be tested using a dye such as methylene blue. Dead spaces can often be eliminated by filling with paraffin wax,

EXPERIMENT 3—TO MEASURE THE FREQUENCY AND AMPLITUDE OF SPONTANEOUS MINIATURE END-PLATE POTENTIALS AND TO DETERMINE THE MEAN QUANTAL CONTENT OF AN END-PLATE POTENTIAL

At the unblocked neuro-muscular junction, small random depolarizations termed miniature end-plate potentials (m.e.p.p.'s) can be observed (Fatt and Katz, 1952). Their amplitude is depressed by curare and enhanced by anti-acetylcholinesterases (neostigmine) as with e.p.p.'s.

Magnesium ions compete with calcium ions for the release of acetylcholine following a nerve impulse and reduce the output of acetylcholine considerably. At high magnesium concentrations the sensitivity of the post-synaptic membrane to acetylcholine is depressed, but by lowering the calcium concentration and raising the magnesium concentration both e.p.p.'s and m.e.p.p.'s can be recorded at the same junction. Furthermore, in the frog, magnesium ions do not significantly affect the frequency of m.e.p.p.'s.

If a nerve stimulus is applied to a preparation highly blocked with magnesium, there may be failure of response or an e.p.p. recorded of the size of the mean m.e.p.p. or multiples of this size. It has been considered that m.e.p.p.'s are associated with the spontaneous release of single packets or quanta of acetylcholine and represent unit potential, whilst e.p.p.'s result from the synchronous release of a large number of these quanta following depolarization of the nerve terminal.

As the amplitudes of the e.p.p.'s fluctuate markedly in the presence of magnesium, it is necessary to estimate the average number of quanta released per stimulus. Assuming the quantal nature of the process, the mean quantum content (m) is obtained by dividing the mean e.p.p. by the mean m.e.p.p. If the variation in size of individual e.p.p.'s is due to the low probability of release of a quantum from a relatively large store of quanta in the nerve endings, the frequency of occurrence of amplitudes of varying quantal number should be given by the Poisson distribution from which the average occurrence (average quantal content) may be estimated. Close agreement of the calculations based on m.e.p.p. size and the Poisson distribution lends strong support to the concept of the quantal nature of transmission (del Castillo and Katz, 1954a). It has been estimated that at the frog neuro-muscular junction, on the average, 100 quanta (m) are released per stimulus, with an average probability (p) of release of 0·14, and thus the store (n) is of the order of 700 quanta (m = np).

MATERIALS

Apparatus and animals

As for Experiment 1.

Chemicals

Ringer of normal composition (Table IA), Ringer of high magnesium, low calcium concentrations (Table IB). Neostigmine methyl sulphate (Prostigmin, Roche) 100 μg/ml.

EXPERIMENTAL DETAILS

1. Neostigmine is used to increase the size of the m.e.p.p.'s but as the amplitudes will still only be of the order of 200–500 μV, the noise level must be kept as low as possible, i.e. around 100 μV with the micro-electrode in circuit. To achieve this, micro-electrodes of relatively low resistance (5–10 MΩ) are usually necessary and there must be stringent exclusion of AC by shielding and checking on earth connections.

2. Set up the frog sartorius nerve-muscle preparation as in Experiment 1 and block with the magnesium Ringer containing neostigmine 1 μg/ml. Locate an end-plate from the shape of the e.p.p.; neostigmine increases the

duration as well as the amplitude of the e.p.p. so that at the centre of the end-plate the time from onset to peak potential is nearly 2 msec and from onset to half decline about 8 msec. The amplitude will fluctuate markedly.

3. Check for the presence of m.e.p.p.'s by turning the gain to 500 μV/cm and letting the time base run freely at a slow sweep, e.g. 1 sec/cm (Fig. 7). Further identify the small potentials by increasing the sweep speed and note that the time course is similar to that of the e.p.p. (Fig. 8).

Accurate localization of the end-plate is necessary. If the amplitudes of

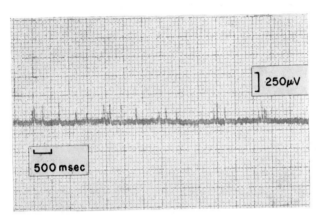

FIG. 7. Miniature end-plate potentials recorded at a slow sweep. Neostigmine was added to the bath to increase the amplitude. Vertical scale, 250 μV; horizontal scale, 500 msec.

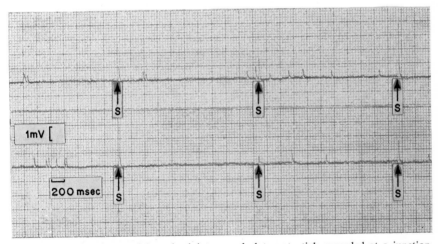

FIG. 8. End-plate potentials and miniature end-plate potentials recorded at a junction highly blocked with magnesium ions. Neostigmine was present. A stimulus was applied at S. Vertical scale, 1 mV; horizontal scale, 200 msec.

the m.e.p.p.'s are close to the noise level look for an end-plate in a narrow fibre in the vicinity. The mean size of a quantum is not thought to vary between end-plates, but the resulting response is directly related to the membrane resistance and thus inversely related to the fibre diameter.

4. Record m.e.p.p.'s for approximately 3 min (according to frequency) and measure the height of each potential taking the centre of the noise band as baseline. Determine the mean amplitude ($\bar{v}_1$) and plot the distribution of the amplitudes as a histogram (Fig. 9). Determine the frequency of firing.

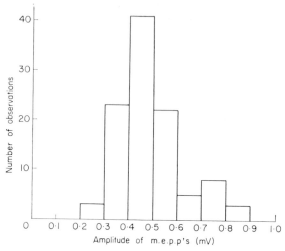

Fig. 9. The distribution of amplitudes of the spontaneous potentials recorded at the end-plate illustrated in Fig. 8.

5. Record 50–100 e.p.p.'s with an upper stimulus frequency of 30–60/min. Measure the height of each potential and determine the mean amplitude ($\bar{v}$). The position of the stimulus artefact allows the identification of a failure and also determines whether a small potential arose spontaneously or in response to nerve stimulation. This can be a problem in a highly blocked end-plate where there is also a high frequency of m.e.p.p.'s.

If there is an appreciable number of failures make a count of their number (n_0) as well as the total number of stimuli (N).

6. Time permitting, Experiment 4 may now be carried out.

RESULTS

The mean amplitudes of the m.e.p.p.'s in Figs 7 and 8 are 200 μV and 475 μV respectively, and Fig. 9 gives the distribution of m.e.p.p.'s at the latter end-plate. With a mean m.e.p.p. amplitude of 200 μV, there will be a loss of the smallest m.e.p.p.'s in the noise band due to the low signal to noise ratio. The normal distribution of amplitude is thought to reflect, at least partly, a small variation in the size of the individual quanta or a variation in the density of receptor molecules. The simultaneous but random release of several units occasionally occurs.

The frequency of firing is 158/min and 65/min respectively at the above two end-plates, even lower frequencies are common. In the course of the experiment the frequency may change, being relatively labile, but the mean amplitude remains constant provided the resting potential is stable.

In Fig. 8 the fluctuation in amplitude of the e.p.p.'s can be seen to include two values within the range of size of the m.e.p.p.'s.

The average number of quanta released per stimulus (m) is given by

$$m = \bar{v}/\bar{v}_1$$

where $\bar{v}$ is the mean size of the e.p.p.'s and $\bar{v}_1$ the mean size of m.e.p.p.'s. For the end-plate in Fig. 8

$$\bar{v} \text{ (mV)} = 2 \cdot 0, \bar{v}_1 \text{ (mV)} = 0 \cdot 475$$
$$m = 2 \cdot 0/0 \cdot 475$$
$$= 4 \cdot 2$$

The average quantal content of the e.p.p. may also be calculated from the proportion of failures; this corresponds to the first term in the Poisson distribution.

$$m = \ln (N/n_0)$$

where N is the total number of trials and n_0 the number of failures. At another end-plate, in 106 trials there were 30 failures.

$$m = \ln (106/30)$$
$$= 1 \cdot 3$$

If the mean e.p.p. is greater than 5% of the R.P. (m is greater than 10), there is non-linear summation of the individual units i.e. the amount of potential change contributed by each quantum will decrease as the number of quanta increase. For strict accuracy this should be taken into account when calculating m (Martin, 1955). The corrected estimate (m') is given by

$$m' = m (1 - \bar{v}/V_0)^{-1}$$
$$= m (V_0/V_0 - \bar{v})$$

where V_0 is the difference between the R.P. and the equilibrium potential for the neuromuscular junction. This latter value is 15 mV below zero and V_0 represents the driving force for the e.p.p. $(V_0 - \bar{v})$ gives the potential across the membrane at the height of the e.p.p. Thus at an end-plate with an R.P. of 84 mV, mean e.p.p. of 7·1 mV, and uncorrected average quantal content of 15·8,

$$V_0 = 84 - 15 = 69$$
$$V_0 - \bar{v} = 69 - 7\cdot1 = 61\cdot9$$
$$m' = 15\cdot8 \times 69/61\cdot9 = 17\cdot7$$

These methods of calculating m cannot be used if recording in the presence of curare. However, the Poisson distribution gives a relationship beween m and the coefficient of variation $(C.V.)$ of the amplitudes of the e.p.p.'s such that $m = 1/(C.V.)^2$

The main problem is achieving a satisfactory signal to noise ratio. Mean values of 260 μV and 620 μV have been obtained for m.e.p.p.'s in fibres of 140 μ and 76 μ respectively (Katz and Thesleff, 1957). Narrow fibres need more care in penetration and it is essential to carefully centre the electrode above the fibre just prior to penetration. If the electrode passes obliquely between fibres the noise level increases markedly. The end-plate region must also be clear of connective tissue.

Preparations may vary markedly in the amount of magnesium required to block all fibres. Above a magnesium concentration of 10 mM/1 the reduction in m.e.p.p. size becomes marked and in such cases a lower calcium concentration should be used, e.g. Ca 0·45 mM/1, magnesium 5 mM/1.

EXPERIMENT 4—TO DETERMINE THE EFFECT OF TETANUS ON END-PLATE POTENTIALS AND MINIATURE END-PLATE POTENTIALS IN THE PRESENCE OF MAGNESIUM

Repetitive stimulation markedly increases the frequency of m.e.p.p.'s though their amplitude remains unaffected. Due to the low quantal output per stimulus with magnesium blockade tetanus does not lead to depression but, on the contrary, facilitation is clearly seen.

Facilitation occurs even if a stimulus fails to release transmitter and is considered to involve an increase in the probability of release of a quantum (del Castillo and Katz, 1954b). According to one theory facilitation may be due to a residue of calcium ions attached to an active release site. The mechanism of increase of m.e.p.p. frequency is not clear but may have the same origin.

The experimental set-up is identical to Experiment 3.

1. Locate an end-plate using magnesium-neostigmine Ringer as described in Experiment 3.
2. Record 50–100 m.e.p.p.'s and e.p.p.'s using a stimulus frequency of 1/sec. This allows the estimation of the control m.e.p.p. frequency and amplitude, and the mean amplitude and quantal content of the e.p.p.
3. The time course of build-up of facilitation and its subsequent decay is determined by recording, at a fast speed, a tetanus of 20/sec for 5 sec then immediately testing at 1/sec for the following 90–120 sec. Usually both m.e.p.p.'s and e.p.p.'s can be recorded on the same sensitivity range for the control and post-tetanic periods. The fast recording speed should be continued for a short time into the post-tetanic period in order to follow the increase in m.e.p.p. frequency. Higher stimulating frequencies may be used but the total number of stimuli kept at 50–100 otherwise a depression of release will be seen after the decay of facilitation.
4. Calculate the mean e.p.p. for each successive 20 stimuli during tetanus and express as a ratio of the control mean value. In the post-tetanic period obtain the mean value following 10 stimuli for the first 30 sec, and then the mean of 20 consecutive responses for the remainder of the period. Express the values as a ratio of control and plot the time course of facilitation and its decay.

Determine the mean amplitude and frequency of m.e.p.p.'s following tetanus and compare with control values. Note that facilitation is due to an increase in the mean quantal release per stimulus.
5. Repeat the experiment if the m.e.p.p.'s cannot be recorded simultaneously with the e.p.p.'s.

RESULTS

Facilitation is cumulative and under the present conditions may increase by nearly 7-fold. The decay is initially very rapid but a residual facilitation is apparent for at least 60 sec (Fig. 10). In the same experiment the m.e.p.p. frequency increased by 6-fold immediately following tetanus, but had returned to normal after 30 sec. The increase in m.e.p.p. frequency following a tetanus is lessened by the presence of magnesium ions which appear to have a stabilizing effect on the pre-synaptic membrane.

EXPERIMENT 5—TO DETERMINE THE EFFECT OF POTASSIUM IONS AND HYPERTONICITY ON THE FREQUENCY OF MINIATURE END-PLATE POTENTIALS

According to the quantum hypothesis depolarization of the nerve terminals should result in an increase in m.e.p.p. frequency. This is seen when cathodal currents are applied to the nerve endings or more easily, by increasing the external concentration of potassium ions.

Hypertonicity increases the frequency of the m.e.p.p.'s, but the fact that it has no effect on the mean amplitude lends support to the concept of the quantal nature of m.e.p.p.'s. Magnesium ions markedly reduce the effect of potassium ions and hypertonicity presumably by stabilizing the pre-synaptic membrane.

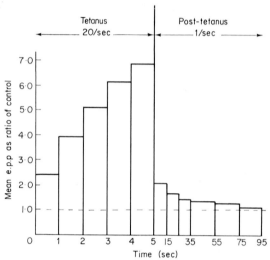

FIG. 10. The onset and decay of facilitation resulting from tetanic stimulation in the presence of magnesium ions. Neostigmine was present. Note the change in time scale.

MATERIALS

If the experimenter is familiar with the probable location of the end-plates, m.e.p.p.'s may be located without the use of stimulation. Otherwise the apparatus is as before for measuring m.e.p.p.'s with the inclusion of a facility for changing solutions by exchange perfusion.

Chemicals

Normal Ringer solution (Table IA). High magnesium, low calcium Ringer (Table IB) optional. High potassium Ringer solution (7·5 mM/l). Add 2 ml stock KCl to 98 ml normal Ringer solution. Neostigmine 100 μg/ml. 1·12 M sucrose solution (38·3 g %).

Hypertonic Ringer solution (125% tonicity). Add 5 ml 1·12 M sucrose to 95 ml normal Ringer solution.

EXPERIMENTAL DETAILS

1. Add neostigmine to normal, high magnesium, high potassium and hyper-tonic Ringer solutions to give a final concentration of 1 μg/ml.
2. Locate an end-plate by recording m.e.p.p.'s in the presence of normal

Ringer-neostigmine solution or by following the time course of the e.p.p. produced under magnesium blockade. Replace the latter solution with normal Ringer-neostigmine solution.

3. Note the R.P. and record the frequency of m.e.p.p.'s for several minutes over a period of 10 min.

4. Leaving the electrode *in situ*, change to the high potassium solution (see Experiment 2). Allow the preparation to equilibrate for 5 min, note the R.P. and record the m.e.p.p. frequency and amplitude for several minutes over 10–15 min.

5. Return to normal Ringer solution and record at intervals over 15 min. Note the R.P.

6. Change to the hypertonic Ringer. Take recordings after 5 min over a 10–15 min period.

7. Return to normal Ringer and record at intervals over 15 min. An increase of tonicity to 150% may be carried out. All these recordings can be made with the electrode continuously *in situ*.

RESULTS

The depolarization of the nerve endings induced by the high potassium concentration raises the m.e.p.p. frequency by more than 2-fold. The associated depolarization of the muscle membrane will cause the mean amplitude of the m.e.p.p.'s to fall but a correction may be made for this. The equilibrium potential of the post-synaptic membrane is 15 mV below zero so that for a normal R.P. of 90 mV the driving force is 90–15 or 75 mV. For a R.P. of V mV the driving force is $V-15$ and this effect may be allowed for by multiplying the mean m.e.p.p. by $75/(V-15)$. It is important that the m.e.p.p.'s are well above the noise level or the frequency change may be obscured by loss of units into the background.

Hypertonicity markedly increases the frequency of the m.e.p.p.'s, again by more than 2-fold, but has no effect on the mean amplitude.

FURTHER EXPERIMENTS

The basic techniques illustrated in the foregoing experiments can be used to elucidate the site of action of compounds affecting neuromuscular transmission. Examples of compounds acting at a pre-synaptic site are guanidine (Otsuka and Endo, 1960), hemicholinium (Elmqvist and Quastel, 1965) and sodium pump inhibitors (Birks and Cohen, 1968). Post-synaptic block is produced by such compounds as succinylcholine (Thesleff, 1955) and the neurotoxin of cobra venom (Chang and Lee, 1966).

232   B. J. EXCELL

With increasing familiarity with the preparation, a second micro-electrode can be placed in an extra-cellular position at the junction for the ionophoretic application of compounds (del Castillo and Katz, 1955).

Permeability changes at the end-plate may also be determined by recording the end-plate current when the membrane is clamped at a constant potential (Takeuchi and Takeuchi, 1959).

BIBLIOGRAPHY

Birks, R. I. and Cohen, M. W. (1968). The action of sodium pump inhibitors on neuro-muscular transmission. *Proc. R. Soc.*, B, **170**, 381–399.
Chang, C. C. and Lee, C. Y. (1966). Electrophysiological study of neuromuscular blocking action of cobra neurotoxin. *Br. J. Pharmac. Chemother.*, **28**, 172–181.
del Castillo, J. and Katz, B. (1954a). Quantal components of the end-plate potential. *J. Physiol. Lond.*, **124**, 560–573.
del Castillo, J. and Katz, B. (1954b). Statistical factors involved in neuromuscular facilitation and depression. *J. Physiol. Lond.*, **124**, 574–585.
del Castillo, J. and Katz, B. (1955). On the localization of acetylcholine receptors. *J. Physiol. Lond.*, **128**, 157–181.
Elmqvist, D. and Quastel, D. M. J. (1965). Presynaptic action of hemicholinium at the neuromuscular junction. *J. Physiol. Lond.*, **177**, 463–482.
Fatt, P. and Katz, B. (1951). An analysis of the end-plate potential recorded with an intra-cellular electrode. *J. Physiol. Lond.*, **115**, 320–370.
Fatt, P. and Katz, B. (1952). Spontaneous subthreshold activity at motor nerve endings. *J. Physiol. Lond.*, **117**, 109–128.
Katz, B. (1962). The Croonian lecture. The transmission of impulses from nerve to muscle, and the subcellular unit of synaptic action. *Proc. R. Soc.*, B, **155**, 455–477.
Katz, B. (1966). "Nerve, muscle and synapse". McGraw-Hill, New York, U.S.A.
Katz, B. and Thesleff, S. (1957). On the factors which determine the amplitude of the miniature end-plate potential. *J. Physiol. Lond.*, **137**, 267–278.
Martin, A. R. (1955). A further study of the statistical composition of the end-plate potential. *J. Physiol. Lond.*, **130**, 114–122.
Martin, A. R. and Veale, J. L. (1967). The nervous system at the cellular level. *A. Rev. Physiol.*, **29**, 401–426.
Otsuka, M. and Endo, M. (1960). The effect of guanidine on neuro-muscular transmission. *J. Pharmac. exp. Ther.*, **128**, 273–282.
Takeuchi, A. and Takeuchi, N. (1959). Active phase of frog's end-plate potential. *J. Neurophysiol.*, **22**, 395–411.
Thesleff, S. (1955). The mode of neuromuscular block caused by acetylcholine, nicotine, decamethonium and succinylcholine. *Acta physiol. scand.*, **34**, 218–231.

Exp. in Physiol. and Biochem. (1970). 3, 233–293.

8 | Experiments on Amphibian Respiratory and Circulatory Systems

DAVID R. JONES*

Department of Zoology, Bristol University, Bristol, England

INTRODUCTION

Studying the respiratory and circulatory systems of amphibians has been popular with experimentalists for over 100 years. The investigations of Krogh (1904) and Willem (1920) can be regarded as the corner-stones of much of the current work on amphibian respiratory systems. Precise studies on the circulatory system are somewhat more recent and much of the present day interest has been based on fields pioneered by Foxon in the late 1940s (see Foxon's review, 1955). Consequently it can be no surprise that many of the techniques still used are modified versions of methods which have been in the literature for many years. However, due to the recent advances in electronic instrumentation, older techniques may now be considerably improved and new ones incorporated into this field of study. The purpose of this chapter is to describe in detail selected experiments utilizing current techniques. In most cases the experiments are those with which I can claim some familiarity although, for the sake of completeness, outlines of other techniques which could be used are sometimes given. The title of this chapter should be qualified in that the experimental descriptions concern "whole animals" and not "isolated preparations". In most cases the experiments are only applicable to adult amphibians and some adjustment of measurements, injection volumes, etc., will have to be made if one is lucky enough to have animals of over 100 g body weight available. Since different types of equipment can often be made to do more or less the same job references to apparatus, when describing experiments, are in general rather than specific terms.

A recipe for amphibian Ringer's solution is given by Lockwood (1961). Several anaesthetics are suitable for use with amphibia. Deep anaesthesia may be induced by injecting paraldehyde (0·02 ml/10 g body weight) into the dorsal lymph sac or by immersion in aqueous solutions of Sandoz MS 222 (300 mg/l) or urethane (5 g/l). More recently I have been using barbiturates but suitable dose levels have yet to be ascertained. Light anaesthesia, which may be maintained for periods of over 24 h, is best achieved by continuous immersion in MS 222 (20–50 mg/l) or Urethane (50–80 mg/l).

* Present address: Department of Zoology, University of British Columbia, Vancouver, B.C., Canada.

In many experiments it is necessary to prevent excessive movements by the animals. Anurans and urodeles up to about 100 g can be restrained, on a cork board, by a series of pins around the limbs. The limbs are flexed and at each joint, one pin is placed inside the bend with two outside it so that the animal cannot then straighten the limb. Movement of upper joints of limbs is prevented by crossed pins. With urodeles one or two pins placed along the length of the body restrict lateral movement. For animals exceeding 100 g clamps are more suitable for holding the limbs. The faces of the clamps should be protected with sponge rubber in order to prevent occlusion of blood vessels.

EXPERIMENTS ON THE RESPIRATORY SYSTEM

RECORDING BREATHING MOVEMENTS

Air is moved in and out of the lungs of amphibians by movement of the floor of the buccal cavity which acts alternately as a force and suction pump. At least two types of movement of the buccal floor are made; one in which air is pumped, from outside, in and out of the buccal cavity and the other in which air is pumped into or sucked out of the lungs. At present there is no good agreement as to the precise relationship of these events. For studies of respiratory dynamics it is necessary to record the volumes of and pressures within the lungs and buccal cavity. The techniques used for this are applicable to a wide range of other experiments.

Pressure within the Buccal Cavity and Lungs

Cannulation of the Buccal Cavity. Various techniques of cannulation of the buccal cavity have been used, the principal ones being either to intubate a nostril or to exteriorize the cannula by piercing the tympanic membrane. The results shown in Fig. 1 were obtained using the latter approach.

1. One end of a short piece of polyethylene tube, 2–3 cm in length, $\frac{1}{2}$–1 mm bore, is held over a low flame until a flat disc (1–2 mm diameter) is formed, taking care to avoid constriction of the bore of the tube. The other end is cut to a pointed taper.

2. The buccal cavity of an anaesthetized animal is opened and a hypodermic needle, about half the diameter of the polyethylene tube, is pushed from the inside of the mouth through the tympanic membrane.

3. The needle is removed and the polyethylene tube is forced through the hole until the disc-shaped end abuts the inside of the tympanic membrane. By using a hypodermic needle smaller than the tube an air-tight seal is assured when the tube is in position.

4. A tight fitting collar of rubber or nylon is placed over the free end of the

cannula and advanced until it reaches the outside of the tympanic membrane. This serves to fix the cannula firmly in position.

Cannulation of the Lungs. The simplest and most permanent period of cannulation is to tie a tube into the lung itself. This is advantageous in that bleeding around the point of insertion of the cannula is prevented. It is much easier to cannulate the lungs if they are inflated but in anaesthetized animals

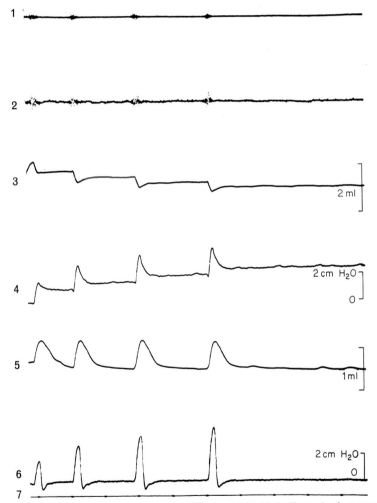

FIG. 1. Breathing movements of a frog (*Rana pipiens* 30 g). Trace 1, electromyogram. Activity in the muscle signals closure of the external nares. Trace 2, electromyogram from a muscle which, on contraction, opens the glottis. Trace 3, lung volume recorded using an R.C.A. mechano-electric transducer (down on trace = increase in volume). Trace 4, lung pressure. Trace 5, buccal cavity volume recorded photoelectrically (down on trace = increase in volume). Trace 6, buccal cavity pressure. Trace 7, time (sec).

the lungs usually collapse, so the first step of the procedure is to re-inflate the lungs.

1. Intubate the glottis and close the mouth, thereby holding the tube in position. Inflate the lungs by blowing gently down the tube. As the lungs expand their outline can be readily determined externally. Clamp the tubing with a pair of haemostats.

2. Make an incision, 0·5 cm long, in the body wall near the posterior border of the lung and exteriorise the tip of the lung. Ensure that there are no major blood vessels in the area of the proposed cannulation.

3. Place a cotton loop around and exposed lung. Holding the lung tip in forceps, tear a small hole and insert the cannula. Tie the cannula into the lung. Mucous inside the lung tends to occlude the hole when it is torn so that the lung usually remains inflated. The free end of the cannula should be blocked to prevent collapse of the lungs as it is inserted. Despite these precautions air may escape from the lungs during insertion and the lung wall may be damaged if the cannula is forced in under these circumstances. It is often useful to maintain a steady state of lung inflation, throughout the period of insertion, by blowing down the tube inserted in the glottis.

4. The cannula should be fairly large, 2 cm long and 1–2 mm i.d. for a 30 g animal, preferably soft walled and the end for insertion should be cut into a long blunt taper. Small perforations in the wall of the tubing opposite the taper will assist in maintaining the cannula patent should the lung wall collapse and occlude the taper during deflation.

5. Sew up the body wall, securing the cannula to the body wall at the same time. This tends to reduce traction on the wall of the lung if a long term implant is envisaged.

Connexion of lung and buccal cavity cannulae to pressure transducers permits the recording of pressures. Of course these cannulae can also be used for artificial ventilation or for gas sampling from the buccal cavity and lungs. When recording pressures one must ensure that the cannulae do not become occluded by mucous in the mouth or lung. Use of large bore cannulae is advantageous and connexion to the manometer should be made by means of a 3-way tap so that air can be forced through the cannula from the side arm to blow out obstructions which may occur during an experiment. A true pressure recording will not be obtained unless the dynamic characteristics of the pressure transducer are adequate. The dynamic response of the manometer, with its attached cannula, should be checked before the experiment (see Appendix).

Volume of the Buccal Cavity and Lungs

Changes in the volume of the buccal cavity during the breathing cycle are seldom measured. Photo-cells have been used to monitor form and rate of movement of the floor of the buccal cavity (Jones and Shelton, 1964; Jones, 1967). Photo-electric recording systems have the advantage of imposing no load on the system and can be used to record buccal cavity volume in small amphibians under 100 g body wt.

1. Position the animal's head between a light source, 6 or 12 V DC, preferably with some degree of focussing, and a photocell. If the animal is fixed to a board the floor of the buccal cavity must be held away from the board. Locating a small block of cork under the extreme anterior border of the head is a convenient way of doing this, but on many occasions the animal will lift its head clear of its own volition. Arrange the animal's head so that a shadow of the head is thrown onto the photocell.

2. Calibrate the system by injecting known volumes of air into the buccal cavity from a syringe. Air can be injected through the cannula used for pressure recording. Unfortunately calibration can only be performed on animals in which breathing movements are temporarily arrested. This can be done by deep anaestheia or more conveniently by passing a stream of $N_2 + 10\%$ CO_2 over the nostrils. After initial stimulation breathing movements slow and finally cease. Air is injected in 100 μl steps and the system is linear over the range of volumes which are recorded from the normal animal (Fig. 1 and Fig. 2a). Consequently the volume of the buccal cavity at any instant in time can be estimated.

Lung volume is difficult to measure satisfactorily. Although one could think of several very sophisticated devices for doing this, the simplest method of obtaining estimates of volume change is to use a mechano-electric transducer. A flexible arm attached to the transducer is placed in contact with the body wall and as the lungs are filled the displacement of the arm is monitored. By suitable arrangement of the length of the arm, and its position, a linear response may be obtained over the physiological range of volumes. For calibration air is injected through the lung cannula. Since the lungs are connected together an injection of 1 ml should be divided equally between both lungs. In the experiment shown in Fig. 1 the response of the transducer was originally nonlinear, but insertion of a piece of thin card (1 cm × 0·5 cm) under the end of the arm where it contacted the body wall made the response linear over the physiological range.

The chief purpose of recording lung and buccal cavity pressure and volume is to enable detailed studies on the mechanics of breathing to be made. The traces obtained represent rate of change of pressure and volume with time. Plotting pressure against volume for coincident points in time allows estimates to be made of the work done in breathing.

It is customary to measure the pressures in g cm^{-2} (i.e. cm of water) and the volumes in cm^3 so that the resulting values of external work done are in g cm. Plots can be done mechanically from the traces which are obtained during an experiment (Fig. 2b). Alternatively, if a dual beam oscilloscope with the facility for X-Y plotting is available, then estimates of work done can be obtained directly by switching one beam from the X to the Y axis. Leaving an illuminated graticule (i.e. 1 cm markings) over the oscilloscope face allows the scale to be assessed. Whichever way the plots are made measurement of the area enclosed by the loops gives the work done in a breathing cycle.

With small amphibians, particularly when recording pressures from the buccal cavity, care must be taken to keep the volume of the transducer and cannula as small as is compatible with an adequate dynamic response of the recording system. If the volume of the buccal cavity is doubled, by attachment of the transducer and cannula, then the movements of the buccal

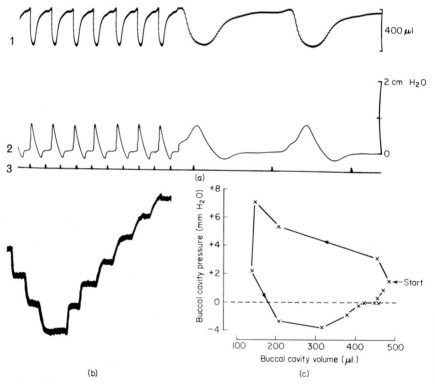

Fig. 2. Volume of and pressure within the buccal cavity of a frog (*R. temporaria* 20 g). (a) Trace 1, buccal cavity volume recorded photoelectrically (down on trace = decrease in volume). Trace 2, pressure within the buccal cavity. Trace 3, time (sec). (b) Calibration of the photoelectric recording system. The buccal cavity was inflated and deflated, in steps, by injection and removal of 0·1 ml of air. (c) Pressure and volume relationships in the buccal cavity during a single breathing cycle. The loop starts at the arrow and cycles in an anti-clockwise direction. The points are 0·1 sec apart.

floor will have to be twice as great to produce the same pressure change as before. Consequently the "attached" volume must be small compared to the volume of the buccal cavity, or else the recorded volume and pressure changes will be significantly greater or smaller, respectively, than in the normal animal. The important thing here may be not only the constant factor by which the records have to be corrected but also that a large "attached" volume may upset the animal and cause its muscles to behave abnormally. It is possible to record lung and buccal cavity pressure and buccal cavity volume in unrestrained animals by the methods already outlined.

X-ray Techniques

Movements of the hyoid bone and the opening and closing of the glottis etc. may be investigated by using X-ray techniques. The full potential of these techniques in the study of breathing movements of amphibians has yet to be realized, although G. E. H. Foxon (personal communication) has made some interesting films. With most X-ray apparatus which is routinely available adequate contrast is only obtained when using large animals (over 50 g body wt).

X-rays alone are usually not sufficient for a complete analysis; one may also need to record pressure and volume. This raises the complication of how to link pressure traces, recorded on an oscilloscope or pen writer, with the X-ray cine films so that the events can be related. With most X-ray apparatus the cine-camera is locked onto the image intensifier so that "split-frame" photography is not possible. Two met hods of tracelinking are described below.

1. As shown in Fig. 3, one or two frames per second were sacrificed in order to provide a linking pulse with pressure traces recorded from an oscilloscope. A small light bulb or neon, activated by a stimulator, was fixed into the camera hood. A neon is preferable to a light bulb since the latter often takes a relatively long time to light up and darken but, of course, this may be overcome by having a pre-heating circuit on the light bulb. The stimulator was also connected to one beam of a double beam oscilloscope, so that when the light flashed a pulse was also registered on the oscilloscope. The cine and oscilloscope cameras were set running and the stimulator was adjusted to give a long pulse ($\frac{1}{2}$ sec or so), followed by 1/20th sec pulses at intervals of 1 sec. The long pulse provides a marker and traces can be analysed from the first short pulse after this. Several breathing movements were filmed so that the blank frames of one cycle could be filled in from inspection of other similar cycles. A short length of lead (1 cm) was placed alongside the animal so that the scale of the prints from the cine films could be assessed. (Fig. 3).

2. A more convenient method is to place a lead tipped arm of a galvanometer (a pen recorder galvanometer is most satisfactory) alongside the animal being X-rayed. The galvanometer records the output of the pressure trans-

ducer. Two fixed markers can be placed behind the galvanometer arm in positions representing zero pressure and the calibration pressure. Consequently the pressure within the buccal cavity is recorded instantaneously on the ciné-film. The movement of the lead tip is obviously curvilinear, but if one regards a 2% error as acceptable then a curvilinear amplitude may be measured with a straight ruler providing the deviation, from the midline, does not exceed 0·35 cm × pen radius (in cm). The frequency response of the galvanometer should be checked after it has been loaded with the lead tip.

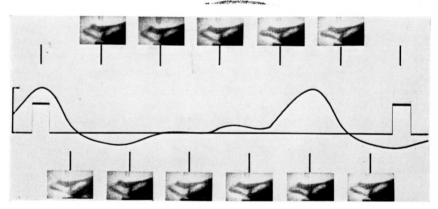

Fig. 3. X-ray ciné-photographs of the breathing movements of a frog (*R. esculenta* 40 g) linked to pressure changes in the buccal cavity, recorded at the same time. The linking pulse (0·05 sec duration at 1 sec intervals) shows on the pressure records as a deflection of one beam, marking zero pressure, of a dual beam oscilloscope and on the cine films as an overexposed frame (omitted). One ciné frame in two is shown. The size marker, a piece of lead wire 1 cm long, has been retouched on the first frame.

ACTIVITY OF MUSCLES DURING BREATHING

Action potentials can easily be detected in active muscles. Electro-myography is obviously important for investigations of the role of various muscles in the respiratory cycle, but this technique can also be used to monitor events which are difficult to record by other means. For instance, the opening of the glottis during the breathing cycle can be signalled by monitoring activity in the muscle responsible for this action. Surface electrodes are not suitable for small amphibians and the electrodes must usually be placed on or in the muscle itself.

Superficial Muscles

1. Prepare electrodes from 100–250 μ diameter varnished copper wire by stripping the varnish from one end, by abrasion with fine emery paper or melting with a hot soldering iron, to expose about 1 mm or less of bare wire.
2. Thread the wire through the eye of a fine sewing needle and sew it into

the muscle so that the exposed portion of copper wire is completely embedded in the muscle. Loop the free end of the wire through connective tissue or skin to hold the electrode firmly in position.

3. Sew another electrode alongside the first. Earth the skin of the animal and connect the copper wires to a pre-amplifier.

Deep Muscles

1. Thread one or two varnished copper wires through a hypodermic needle and bend them back over the taper. Cut the wires close to the taper leaving, at most, 1 mm free. Clean the varnish from these free ends. The ends of the electrodes are now hook-shaped.

2. Insert the tip of the hypodermic needle into the muscle and slowly withdraw the body of the needle, taking care not to snag and drag out the electrodes. Since the electrodes are hook-shaped at their ends they should be held quite firmly but they may be further secured by tying them to the skin or connective tissue with cotton.

3. If possible the position of the electrodes should be checked by post-mortem.

Electro-myograms may be displayed on an oscilloscope or pen recorder. In amphibia the discharge frequencies of muscle action potentials are in the range 0·5–500 cyc/sec so higher frequencies will be lost when using pen recorders. However, pen recorders are quite satisfactory if the electro-myogram is being monitored solely as an indication of a muscle's activity. Figure 1 shows electro-myograms from a muscle which, when active, closes the nostril (electrodes inserted by the first method above) and a muscle which, by its contraction, opens the glottis (electrodes inserted by second method). The only problem one meets using this technique is, if no activity is recorded from a muscle, to decide whether it is quiescent or the electrodes have short-circuited. With experience this is easily resolved since the noise level is much lower on short circuit.

Very few studies have been made on the activity of the respiratory muscles in amphibians and in this sense there is much to be done (but first see Shinkai and Narita, 1957; Oka 1957). Furthermore, by using integrated electro-myograms from all the respiratory muscles it may be possible to get estimates of the work done in breathing. Other problems spring to mind which may be resolved by electromyography. For example, controversy exists as to whether the flanks actively co-operate in expelling air from the lungs: this problem could be investigated by recording electro-myograms from the muscles of the flanks during cycles of lung ventilation.

GASEOUS EXCHANGE

Systems for measuring gas exchange can be divided into two types, closed and open. With both open and the more complex closed systems the gaseous

L

environment is rigidly controlled. In all types temperature must be kept constant, since not only does the animal's rate of gaseous exchange change with temperature but, with most systems, the output of recording devices will also change with temperature.

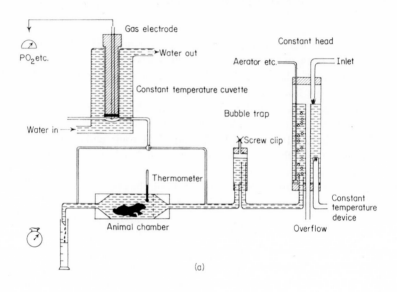

(a)

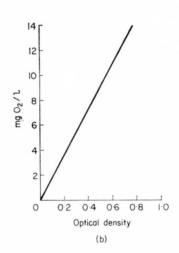

(b)

FIG. 4. (a) An open respirometer for measuring cutaneous gaseous exchange of amphibians. (b) Relationship between optical density of liberated iodine (Winkler's Method) and oxygen content of the water. The optical density of the iodine solution was measured on an EEL absorptiometer using an Ilford 601 filter (peak transmission at about 425 mμ).

Open Systems

With small amphibians these are only really satisfactory for recording gas exchange in water, since water at 20°C only contains some 6–7 ml O_2/l whereas air contains around 200 ml O_2/l. The major advantage of the open system is that environmental concentrations of oxygen and carbon dioxide presented to the animal can be rigidly controlled.

1. The apparatus required is shown in Fig. 4.

2. The water flow is adjusted so that there is an accurately measureable difference in oxygen content between the inflowing and outflowing water. The flow rate is measured either with an "in-circuit" flowmeter or by catching the effluent in a measuring cylinder.

3. Oxygen consumption can be assessed from measurements of the oxygen content of the inlet and outlet water, providing flowrate is known. The oxygen content can be obtained polarographically (which gives partial pressure of oxygen, which is related to content by physical constants) or by Winkler's titration. Jones and Shelton (1964), using the latter method, found it more convenient to measure the optical density of the liberated iodine rather than proceeding with the titration. A fixed quantity of reagent must be added to a fixed sample volume. A reagent blank is made up using deoxygenated water (boiled) and the sample and reagent blank are read against distilled water.

O.D. due to liberated iodine = O.D. sample − O.D. reagent blank. A typical curve is shown in Fig. 4b.

4. Carbon dioxide production can be assessed by measuring the CO_2 content or partial pressure of CO_2, with a CO_2 electrode, in the inlet and outlet water. If PCO_2 measurements are made below 7–8 mm Hg, since the sensitivity of carbon dioxide electrodes is not constant this part of the range must be carefully calibrated. Carbon dioxide content of water can be obtained by measuring the pH if alkalinity is known (Moore, 1939). Alternatively the following equation may be used:—

$$\text{ml } CO_2/l = \frac{22 \cdot 4}{K_1} \cdot [HCO'_3] \cdot [H^{\cdot}]$$

where K_1 = first dissociation constant for CO_2 at the experimental temperature.

the first dissociation is $H_2CO_3 \rightleftharpoons H^{\cdot} + HCO'_3$

and at equilibrium $K_1 = \dfrac{C_{H^{\cdot}} \times C_{HCO'_3}}{C_{H_2CO_3}}$

$K_1 = 2 \cdot 647 \times 10^{-7}$ (at 0°C);
$\quad = 3 \cdot 430 \times 10^{-7}$ (at 10°C);
$\quad = 4 \cdot 147 \times 10^{-7}$ (at 20°C);
$\quad = 4 \cdot 710 \times 10^{-7}$ (at 30°C).

HCO'_3 = alkalinity expressed as one equivalent part per million ml. Obtained by titrating 100 ml of water with $N/10$ HCl or H_2SO_4 to pH4 using a pH meter or methyl orange indicator. HCO'_3 = number of ml of $N/10$ acid required.

$H^{\cdot}$ = hydrogen ion concentration in equivalents/litre. If the pH of the water is measured then $H^{\cdot} = 10^{-pH}$.

Precautions.

1. Due to the high oxygen content of air, bubbles of air must not be allowed to accumulate in the respirometer.

2. The water in the respirometer should be completely exchanged in a time which is short compared to the period of recording. Obviously this is aided by keeping the respirometer small. Pockets of water which do not mix with the through-flowing water are undesirable and these can be eliminated by using a circular respirometer with conical ends and mesh screens near the inlet to promote turbulence and good mixing. Injection of dye solution (Evans blue) into the inlet water permits assessment of the turnover time and degree of mixing of water flowing through the respirometer.

Calculations.

1. Oxygen uptake

Temperature $= 20°C$ 1 litre of aerated water ($PO_2 = 150$ mm Hg) contains 6·57 ml of O_2 (from Winkler's titration)

Water flow $= 20$ ml/min $\therefore$ Solubility of O_2 in water $= 0·0000438$ ml/ml/mm Hg

PO_2 inlet water $= 150$ mm Hg
PO_2 outlet water $= 100$ mm Hg
PO_2 difference $= 50$ mm Hg (inlet and outlet water)

Oxygen uptake (ml/min) $= PO_2$ difference $\times$ solubility $=$ flow rate ml/mm
$$= 50 \times 0·0000438 \times 20$$
$$= 0·0438 \text{ ml/min} = 2·628 \text{ ml/h}$$

2. Carbon dioxide production

Temperature $= 20°C$ 1 litre of water with PCO_2 of 7·5 mm Hg contains 8·9 ml of CO_2.
Water flow $= 20$ ml/min $\therefore$ Solubility of CO_2 in water $= 0·001187$ ml/ml/mm Hg
PCO_2 inlet water $= 7·5$ mm Hg

PCO_2 inlet water $= 7·5$ mm Hg
PCO_2 outlet water $= 9·5$ mm Hg
PCO_2 difference $= 2·0$ mm Hg

CO_2 produced (ml/min) = PCO_2 difference $\times$ Solubility $\times$ flow rate ml/min

$$= 2 \cdot 0 \times 0 \cdot 001187 \times 20$$

$$= 0 \cdot 0475 \text{ ml/min} = 2 \cdot 85 \text{ ml/h}$$

$\therefore$ Respiratory quotient $= \dfrac{CO_2 \text{ produced}}{O_2 \text{ consumed}}$

$$= \frac{2 \cdot 85}{2 \cdot 628} = 1 \cdot 084$$

If oxygen or carbon dioxide electrodes are not available, oxygen uptake and carbon dioxide output may be measured directly using the Winkler method for oxygen and one of the two above methods for carbon dioxide. In the latter case samples are either taken directly into bottles, with the stopper ground to a rough point to prevent trapping air bubbles when sealing, or collected and stored under liquid paraffin (specific gravity 0·85).

A similar procedure can be used for air flow but, for the same flow rate of air as of water in the example, the PO_2 difference will be 1/25th of the above value. This difference cannot be measured with great accuracy and consequently the flow rate of air must be reduced.

Although systems such as these have been used extensively in studies of fish respiration they have not been applied to amphibia. There are many possibilities for this type of experiment. For instance if cutaneous gas exchange is studied at various water flow rates it may be possible to extrapolate the result to give gas exchange at zero flow, a parameter which is difficult to measure except in some closed systems which have a number of disadvantages. Furthermore cutaneous gas exchange can be studied at various environmental concentrations of CO_2 and O_2 since the tensions of CO_2 and O_2 in the inlet water can be varied at will.

Closed systems

Basically two types of closed respirometer have been used with amphibia. In simple systems no attempt is made to control the environmental gas concentrations presented to the animal whereas in more complicated set-ups the gaseous environment is usually controlled within very fine limits.

Simple Systems. A sealed box, containing the animal and some means of determining changes in oxygen or carbon dioxide in air or water is all that is required for these systems. As stated above the major disadvantage of these systems is that the gaseous environment presented to the animal is continually changing, although when the box is air-filled increases in environmental carbon dioxide concentration can be prevented by chemical absorption of carbon dioxide produced by the animal. If one decides to use these systems for determination of respiratory dependence curves there are a couple of points worth noting:

Air Filled Systems. If the carbon dioxide given out by the animal is absorbed (or R.Q. is less than one when it is not absorbed) as the animal consumes oxygen the pressure in the box falls below atmospheric. For example, vol. of box $= 100$ ml, animal consumes 10 ml $O_2/(CO_2$ absorbed). Pressure in box at start $= 760$ mm Hg.

After one hour:

$$\text{Pressure change in box} = \frac{\text{Pressure at start} \times \text{vol. change}}{\text{Vol. of the box}}$$

$$\text{P change} = \frac{760 \times -10}{100}$$

$$= -76 \text{ mm Hg}$$

If an oxygen electrode is sealed in the box, providing the sub-atmospheric pressure does not affect the output of the electrode, it will record a change in PO_2 of 76 mm Hg. However if a sample is now taken from the box and analysed at atmospheric pressure, PO_2 in the sample will be increased by a factor of $\frac{760}{684}$. Hence, to obtain the PO_2 in the box the measured PO_2 ($= x$ mm Hg) must be adjusted.

$$\therefore PO_2 \text{ in box} = x \cdot \frac{760 - x}{760} \cdot \text{mm Hg}$$

Water-filled Systems. The major complication here is sampling. In order to remove water from the respirometer an equivalent volume must be injected, or the volume of the container must be reduced. There are several methods of doing this but in all cases corrections have to be made to the results.

Complex Systems: Differential Respirometers. Many types of differential respirometer have been described for measuring gaseous exchange of amphibians. A differential respirometer consists of two closed boxes connected by a manometer. One chamber contains the animal (animal chamber) and the other only air and/or water (compensation chamber). If the CO_2 produced by the animal is absorbed then as the animal consumes oxygen the pressure in the animal chamber falls; this pressure change is shown by the manometer. Oxygen is then injected into the animal chamber to restore the pressure; the amount injected is measured and this represents the oxygen uptake of the animal in the period since the previous restoration. Pressure changes in the animal chamber are monitored with reference to the constant pressure in the other chamber (compensation chamber) so that changes in atmospheric pressure during the experiment do not affect the results. The respirometer is placed in a thermostatically controlled water bath and slight changes in temperature during the experiment are automatically compensated since these slight fluctuations in temperature will cause equal changes in pressure in both chambers of the respirometer. In this respect the blank chamber need not be the same size as the animal chamber but if they are of equal dimensions then temperature change will occur in both chambers at the same rate, which is obviously advantageous.

Construction of a Differential Respirometer. A differential respirometer, used by Jones (in preparation), is shown in Fig. 5. A rectangular perspex box, of 2–4 l capacity, and wall thickness 1 cm is divided by a central partition and sealed by a lid covering both chambers. Silicone grease or silicone rubber sealant may be used on this joint to obtain an air tight seal. The chambers are connected to a pressure measuring device, either a U-tube manometer containing an aqueous solution of Brodie's fluid or a differential pressure transducer, by taps A and B (Fig. 5). A small hole, later to be sealed with a rubber bung, is made in the lid over each chamber.

Gaseous Exchange in Air : Oxygen Consumption.

1. Place the respirometer in a water bath at the experimental temperature.
2. Put the animal into the animal chamber either free or attached to a cork board.
3. Place the carbon dioxide absorbent and a small beaker containing 5–10 ml amphibian Ringer's solution in each chamber. This ensures that an identical vapour pressure equilibrium is established in each chamber.
4. Screw the lid onto the animal chamber with the manometer taps open to the atmosphere.
5. Connect the tap to the manometer alone and test both chambers for leaks. Inject 10–20 ml of air, from a syringe, through the rubber bung in the lid over the chamber. The pressure change shown by the manometer will be maintained if the chamber is leak-proof.
6. Connect the chambers to the atmosphere to restore the pressure. Reconnect to the manometer and leave the respirometer for 30–60 min for temperature and vapour pressure equilibration. Values for oxygen uptake recorded during this period are unreliable.
7. After this period inject into the animal chamber enough oxygen to restore the manometer and then record the amount of oxygen required to equalize the pressure every ten minutes. Oxygen is injected, from a tuberculin syringe (100 div in 1 ml), by means of a hypodermic needle which pierces the rubber bung in the top of the animal chamber. Ideally the injected oxygen should be at the same temperature and pressure as the air in the animal chamber. The former is most easily achieved by working in a temperature controlled room at the same temperature as the water bath. To prevent heating the syringe, as it is handled, place a short piece of rubber tubing over the barrel and grip this. If the volume of air in the animal chamber is large compared

to the volume injected correction for changes in barometric pressure during the experiment are unnecessary.

Carbon Dioxide Production. Several methods are available for measuring carbon dioxide production. If KOH is used, as an absorbant for CO_2, total CO_2 production during the experiment can be obtained by titrating the KOH

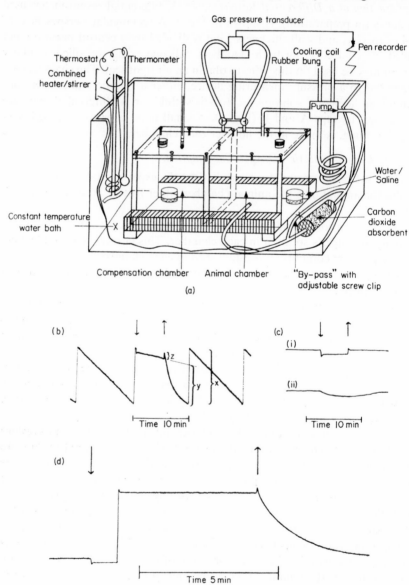

Gas pressure transducer

Thermostat   Thermometer

Combined heater/stirrer

Cooling coil   Pen recorder

Rubber bung

Pump

Water / Saline

Constant temperature water bath

Carbon dioxide absorbent

Compensation chamber   Animal chamber   "By-pass" with adjustable screw clip

(a)

(b)

Time 10 min

(c)

(i)

(ii)

Time 10 min

(d)

Time 5 min

with acid at the end of the experiment. However as oxygen uptake is measured perhaps every 10 min, it seems advantageous, particularly from the point of view of R.Q. determinations, to measure CO_2 production during this period of time. If the dead space of a long hypodermic needle and micrometer syringe is filled with mercury, and the needle is inserted through a rubber bung in the lid of the animal chamber into the KOH solution, accurately measured samples of KOH can be withdrawn for later analysis. Of course if 0·5 ml of KOH soln. is removed then 0·5 ml of air has to be injected to equalize the pressure. This procedure can be repeated every 10 min if desired. Several methods of analysis may be used. A convenient one is to mix the measured volume of KOH with strong acid (5 N H_2SO_4) in a Warburg manometer and to measure the volume of CO_2 evolved. A small quantity of glass wool in the manometer flask aids evolution of CO_2. After the determination check the pH in the flask, this should be less than pH4. All volumes of KOH, including that contained in the animal chamber at the start of the experiment, must be accurately measured since the volume of CO_2 in the sample must be multiplied by a factor (= total volume of KOH in animal chamber divided by sample volume) to obtain the output of the animal.

Since oxygen uptake is known the CO_2 production can be estimated by closing off the CO_2 absorber for a short time (5 min) and comparing the change in pressure during this period with the pressure change which occurs when CO_2 is absorbed (Fig. 5b). Elimination of the CO_2 absorbent from the animal chamber can be achieved by several means:

1. If the CO_2 absorbent is contained within the animal chamber itself a lid may be lowered over the container. Raising and lowering the lid can be done by a wire which passes through a mercury seal in the lid of the animal chamber. A hypodermic needle is passed through a rubber bung in the lid

---

FIG. 5. (Facing page) (a) A differential respirometer suitable for recording cutaneous and pulmonary gas exchange of amphibians. (b) Determination of R.Q. by comparing the pressure change occurring when the carbon dioxide absorbent is "out of circuit" with that occurring when carbon dioxide is absorbed.

Total oxygen consumption in 10 min	= x mm.
By extrapolation, CO_2 production in 10 min	= y mm.
Pressure change caused by switching off the air circulating pump	= z mm.

$$\therefore \text{R.Q.} = \frac{y + z}{x}$$

(c) Records from test runs. The animal chamber contains a volume of saline equal to the volume of the animal. (i) Pressure change caused by switching the air circulating pump off (downward pointing arrow) and on (upward pointing arrow). (ii) Pressure change caused by closing (downward arrow) and opening (upward arrow) the lid over a pot of KOH solution contained within the animal chamber. (d) Test run. Pressure change caused by injection of 1 ml of CO_2 into the animal chamber when the CO_2 absorbent is "out of circuit" (air circulating pump off) and rate of absorption of CO_2 after the pump is switched on (upward pointing arrow).

of the animal chamber and the wire is threaded through the needle. The hub of the needle, on the outside of the respirometer, is filled with mercury.

2. If an air circulating system is used, so that the CO_2 absorbent is outside the animal chamber, a by-pass can be used. If the CO_2 absorbent is completely closed off then the volumes of both circuits must be the same or else switching from one to the other will cause slight pressure changes. This problem is avoided if the tube, conducting air through the absorbent, is only closed off upstream. Furthermore the resistances of both limbs to air-flow must be the same. To equalize the resistances the diameter of the by-pass tubing is reduced, using a screw clip, until no detectable change is shown on the manometer when changing from one air pathway to the other. In theory this is the best system but in practice I have never found it easy to use or very satisfactory if high levels of accuracy are required.

3. A simpler method of achieving the above result is to switch off the air pump. This causes a small change in pressure in the animal chamber which must be taken into account in calculations of CO_2 production (Fig. 5c). A small "bleeder tube" can be connected across the absorbent chamber. This serves the purpose of (a) preventing large scale pressure changes in the animal chamber should the air-flow resistance of the absorber increase dramatically (i.e. tube block) and (b) the amount of air being pumped through the absorbent can be adjusted to give any desired rate of absorption of carbon dioxide.

A non-deliquescent solid CO_2 absorbent is preferable to say KOH solution due to the difference in vapour pressure between water/saline and KOH solution. Under normal circumstances a dynamic equilibrium between the vapour pressures of water/saline and KOH solution will be established. However, if the KOH solution is then taken "out of circuit" the vapour pressure will change to that of water/saline and then back to the dynamic equilibrium when KOH solution is brought back "in circuit". The pressure difference is slight but has a significant effect on R.Q.'s especially when oxygen uptake is low (i.e. during apnoea). Solid absorbents do not have this effect providing they are saturated with water vapour before the experiment. Floating the absorbent, spread evenly in a Petri dish, on a water surface in a closed container for 5–10 h is sufficient for saturation.

Accuracy. Using a fluid filled U-tube manometer 1 ml of air, injected into the animal chamber, can be removed with an accuracy of $\pm$ 20 μl by reading the manometer. Since the pressure changes are small, mercury is too heavy as a manometric fluid and aqueous solutions of Brodie's or Kreb's fluid are most suitable. The manometer must be cleaned regularly with chromic acid and the addition of one or two drops of wetting agent per litre of manometric fluid reduces unwanted surface tension effects in the manometer. Accuracies of the level of $\pm$ 5 μl may be achieved using a sensitive pressure transducer. If a pen writer is employed to record the pressure changes the pen deflection can be directly transposed to volume in an experiment without the necessity of measuring the volume of oxygen injected. Calibration is achieved by measuring the pen deflection caused by injection and removal of a fixed volume of air.

Test Runs. The response of the system to the various experimental procedures can be checked by test runs. The respirometer is set up, as in an experiment, but the animal is replaced by a suitable volume of water or Ringer's solution. The following can then be checked.

1. Stability—after equilibration the pressure should remain sensibly constant over periods similar to that at which the experiment will be conducted. Complete stability is rarely achieved and a drift rate of $\pm$ 1–2% of the animal's oxygen uptake/h, in terms of pressure changes, is acceptable in most applications.

2. Rate of absorption of CO_2—inject 1 ml of 100% CO_2 with the absorbent "out of circuit" and note rate of absorption/unit time. Ideally this should be zero over the period for which the absorbent will be "out of circuit" during an experiment (Fig. 5e). With the absorbent "in-circuit" note the time for 90% of the injected CO_2 to be absorbed. Absorption of CO_2 occurs exponentially (Fig. 5e) and 90% will have been absorbed after 2·303 time constants. If 90% of the injected CO_2 is absorbed after 3 min then the time constant (T) would be $\frac{3}{2 \cdot 3 0 3}$ or 1·30 min. The time constant is smaller if more surface area of the absorbent is exposed to the CO_2. The rate of absorption of CO_2 is proportional to the concentration, the factor being the reciprocal of the time constant, say $\dfrac{E}{T}$ where E is the environmental concentration and T the absorption time constant. If during an experiment the CO_2 concentration is kept constant by the frog's output (F) then

$$F = \frac{E}{T}$$

If $F = 0 \cdot 1$ ml/min and $T = 1 \cdot 30$ min

then $E = 0 \cdot 13$ ml in the volume of the box.

To increase the rate of absorption of CO_2 a lattice work of filter paper dipping into the KOH may be used. Alternatively, if a solid absorbent is used it can either be spread out more, or else the amount of air going through the by-pass can be reduced.

3. Pressure changes—caused by switching the pump on and off or by redirecting air flow etc. can be checked.

4. Accuracy of system—inject 1 ml of air and remove it by reading the manometer. The level of accuracy required will obviously affect the precautions,

such as test runs, taken. The ratio of test runs to experiments in my work is about 1:3.

Precautions.

1. After the respirometer is first closed values for oxygen uptake are unreliable for some 30–60 min. This raises the problem that when the pressures are equalized one may add too little or too much oxygen. This effect becomes really important if the volume of the animal chamber is small. Making conditions identical, apart from the animal, in both chambers of the respirometer tends to minimize the error. As an aid to precise restoration an oxygen electrode can be placed in the animal chamber and oxygen injected until it reads the same pO_2 as at the start of the experiment.

2. During the setting up procedure a gas leak between the animal and compensation chambers may not be immediately apparent since, although the pressure recorded by the manometer will fall, no air bubbles will be seen leaving the respirometer. With both chambers closed measure the pressure in one chamber with reference to the atmosphere. The pressure change caused by injection of air into the chamber will decline and stabilize when the pressure in both chambers is the same. However the stabilized pressure will be above atmospheric.

3. Condensation in the tubing of air circulation systems must be avoided. This is most easily achieved by having as much of the tubing as possible within the water bath and by maintaining room temperature at or slightly above the temperature of the water bath.

Determination of the Volume of the Respirometer. This may be done by filling the respirometer with water and measuring the volume of water required. When circulating systems are involved this is not practicable and volume is best determined by injecting a known volume of air and measuring the pressure change produced. Of course, this method assumes no elasticity in any of the components.

$$\text{Volume of respirometer} = \frac{\text{Atmospheric Pressure} \times \text{Injected Volume}}{\text{Pressure change}}$$

e.g. Injected volume $= 5$ ml

Pressure change $= 5{\cdot}0$ cm H_2O

Atmospheric Pressure $= 1030$ cm H_2O

$$\text{Volume of respirometer} = \frac{1030 \times 5}{5{\cdot}0} = 1030 \text{ ml}$$

Gaseous exchange in water. The animal chamber is $\frac{1}{2}$–$\frac{3}{4}$ filled with water which is agitated so that oxygen and carbon dioxide, in both the water and air-phase, are in equilibrium. Water may be agitated by a magnetic stirrer bar attached to one side of the animal chamber or by a paddle introduced through a mercury seal. With an animal in water in a respirometer Jones (1967) recorded a maximum difference of 2–4 mm Hg PO_2 between the oxygen tensions of the air and water at stirring rates of 200 + rev/min (using a 6 cm $\times$ 0·5 cm diameter magnetic stirrer bar). If an air circulating system is used the air may be bubbled continuously through the water.

Water agitation of this type may affect amphibians in two ways. First, physical disturbance might affect the animal's responses but this effect can be minimized by long periods of acclimation to the respirometer (5–20 h). Second, the flow of water probably facilitates cutaneous respiratory exchange and this should be borne in mind when basing conclusions on results obtained by this method (Jones, 1967).

Precautions and Test Runs. These are similar to those outlined above except (1) the efficiency of equilibration is tested by substituting an equal amount of deoxygenated water for water in the stabilized system and recording the time for re-equilibration; (2) to ensure even thermal equilibration the compensation chamber should also contain water which is stirred.

Recently Chase *et al.* (1968) have described an electrolytic respirometer which would seem preferable to the above type for long term recording although its range would have to be extended. Using respirometers many other parameters can be monitored along with oxygen uptake and CO_2 production. A cannula may be brought from an artery through a mercury seal in the lid of the box so that blood PO_2, PCO_2 and pH may be determined. Breathing frequency can be monitored by a light and photocell located outside the animal chamber. Heart rate and electromyograms can be recorded by copper wire electrodes brought out through the lid of the box. Respiratory dependence curves may be constructed by replacing the consumed oxygen with nitrogen and monitoring the PO_2 of the animal chamber. The effects of carbon monoxide on respiratory and circulatory metabolism may also be studied (Jones, in preparation). A double differential respirometer has been used by Whitford and Hutchison (1963) to monitor simultaneously cutaneous and pulmonary gas exchange in the spotted salamander.

ARTIFICIAL VENTILATION

Single cycles of inflation and deflation of the lungs or buccal cavity can be done by hand from a hypodermic syringe. If rhythmic ventilation is required some form of mechanical pump must be used. A respiratory pump, for use with small amphibians, is shown in Fig. 6b. Either 5 or 10 ml syringes can be used. The pump is driven from a variable speed motor, connected to a shaft on which a worm gear drives the pinion, A, which rotates the valve, B. Gear

ratios of the order of 40:1 to 80:1 are suitable. The valve (B) fits into a
barrel, D, which has a central valve port, a, to the syringe and three other
"in line" openings (b, c and d) at right angles to a. The latter are asymetrically
arranged, two to one side (b and c) and one to the other (d) of the central
valve port. The valve extends beyond the end of the barrel and the driving
arm, F, is fixed to the valve by an eccentric cam, E. The cam consists of a
lipped circular plate eccentrically attached to the valve. The driving arm

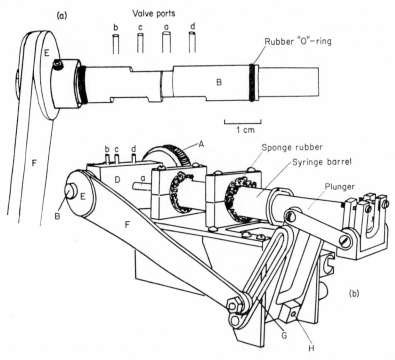

Fig. 6. (a) The rotating valve with its connexion to the driving arm. (b) Diagram of the
respiratory pump described in the text.

forms a running fit over the lip of the arm and a further plate is fixed outside
of this to hold it in position. Consequently the rotational movement of the
valve is translated into a reciprocating movement of the end of the driving
arm. The end of the driving arm is fixed to a slotted crank arm, G, which via
a series of linkages operates the piston of the pump. The position of the
driving arm on the slotted crank arm controls the stroke volume of the pump
and the dead space of the pump can be adjusted by altering the position of the
linkages relative to the slotted crank arm by means of the screw, H.

The valve (Fig. 6a) has a central annular groove (opposite port a) and flats, milled on a round shaft, as valve ports for b, c and d. On the back-stroke d is connected to the syringe and b and c are connected together. Fresh air is drawn into the syringe through d and air contained in the lungs escapes through b and c. On the instroke d and b are closed and the syringe is connected to c, air contained in the syringe is forced into the lungs through port c.

If artificial ventilation is being performed on an animal in a closed respiro-meter, large pressure changes will occur as the piston moves in and out. To prevent this another syringe must be arranged to pump into the animal chamber, in the opposite direction to the respiratory pump, so that the volume of the respirometer remains constant. Careful adjustment of the stroke of this syringe can reduce the pressure fluctuation until it is equivalent to 5% of the total pressure change recorded during a ten minute period.

EXPERIMENTS ON THE CIRCULATORY SYSTEM

RECORDING HEART RATE

The electrocardiogram (e.c.g.) can be recorded bipolarly or unipolarly. In the latter case the indifferent electrode is placed on the skin. Copper wire electrodes may be used and their preparation is the same as for recording electromyograms. The live electrode is sewn ventrally under the skin in the mid-line between the fore limbs. Sewing the wire back on itself through the skin and passing the free end through the loop so formed gives a knot, when the wire is pulled taught, and serves to fix the electrode in position. In anuran amphibians a second electrode, if required, is most conveniently sited under the skin of one of the hind legs. However, with urodeles positioning the second electrode dorsally, directly above the other electrode, has proved more satisfactory (Fig. 7a). For studies on unrestrained animals the wires can be twisted into wide springs which are held over the animals. The method proved satisfactory for studies on diving bradycadia of unrestrained frogs (Jones and Shelton, 1964) but during long term recordings—several days—the animals tend to become tangled in the wires which results in termination of the experiment (Jones, 1968). Other methods, for long term recording of heart rate, present as many difficulties. Small radio-transmitters can be used with larger amphibians. Figure 7b shows ventricular contractions, as recorded from the movement of the body wall, transmitted over a distance of 1–2 metres. A wide band transmission from a continuous wave oscillator, frequency modulated by movement of a ferrite bead in the oscillator coil, was received on a normal portable radio. The movements of the ferrite bead were caused by the slight movements of the body wall over the heart. The signal was demodulated by a simple pulse counting circuit and displayed on a pen recorder (Fig. 7b). Due to the low frequency of transmission it was only possible to receive over 5–10 cm if the animal was submerged. Furthermore the batteries ran down after 4–5 h which meant that this device was not suitable for prolonged recordings.

RECORDING BLOOD PRESSURE

Virtually all recordings of blood pressure are made using liquid filled electro-manometers. To record pressure oscillations faithfully the characteristics of the manometric system must be rigidly controlled. McDonald (1960) concludes that in order to record pressure pulses up to about 20 cyc/sec the

a)

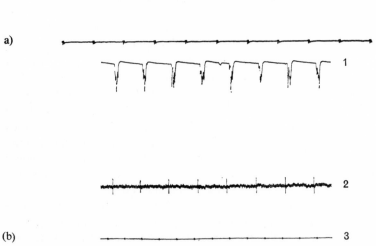

1

2

(b)

3

FIG. 7. Two methods of recording heart rate from unrestrained animals. (a) (Upper) Contractions of the ventricle recorded by a movement transducer strapped to the chest wall and transmitted over a distance of 1–2 m. Downward movement of the trace = ventricular contraction. Lower trace, time (sec). (b) (Lower) Trace 1, ventricular contractions of a submerged toad (*Bufo bufo* 25 g) recorded with an ultrasonic blood flow detector (Doptone, Smith & Kline Instruments Co.). Trace 2, unipolar recording of e.c.g. using a copper wire electrode. Trace 3, time (sec). The probe is positioned above the animal and detects the doppler shift caused by cardiac movements. The ultrasonic beam, at 5 MHz, was focused at 3 cm but it was possible to record ventricular contractions when the probe was at least 10 cm away from the animal. The tip of the probe was kept just under the water surface to avoid undue reflection at the air–water interface. Other probes can be focused at greater distances (20 cm) so the range over which recordings can be made should be considerably increased. This technique should be applicable to recording heart rate during prolonged submergence, e.g. during hibernation. (Record: Jones and Preece, in preparation.)

natural frequency of the manometer must be at least five times this frequency, with damping of not more than 0·1 of critical damping (See Appendix). The frequency response of a manometer depends on two factors, the stiffness of the membrane in the manometer and the bore and length of any attached cannulae. Highest frequencies are obtained with a very stiff membrane and short, wide catheters, although bore is more important than length in this respect. The total movement of liquid in modern electromanometers is very small and the presence of minute air bubbles greatly reduces the frequency response since air is some several million times more compressible than water. The viscous resistance of the liquid in the catheter causes damping and as with the frequency response, the bore of the catheter systems affects damping much more than the length. A narrow catheter will increase the damping.

General Principles of Pressure Measurement

The pressure recorded at any point in the circulation may not reflect the true driving force for flow. The "true" blood pressure, at any point, will be recorded only if the tip of the catheter is at right angles to the flowing blood and is in the same horizontal plane as the heart. The latter, hydrostatic factor, is taken care of when the zero level of the manometer is established (see later). Flowing blood possess kinetic energy and if the catheter faces the on coming blood stream, flow is prevented and kinetic energy transformed into pressure energy. Consequently the manometer records a pressure which is higher than the blood pressure by $\frac{1}{2}\rho v^2$ (where ρ = density of blood; v = velocity of the blood flow). If the catheter points downstream the pressure recorded is lower than the pressure in the fluid by some fraction of $\frac{1}{2}\rho v^2$. Only when the catheter is at right angles to the flowing blood is the pressure at that point accurately recorded. In small amphibians correction for the kinetic energy of the flowing blood can be ignored but in larger animals, particularly in regions of high blood velocity (arterial arches), correction may be necessary.

Zero level of the manometer is best established by connecting the manometer to a column of water whose meniscus is at the same level as the tip of the catheter in the blood vessel. If the animals are submerged then obviously zero level is the water surface of the tank. In this way errors due to differences in fluid level, not only within the circulation, but also between the membrane of the manometer and the recording site, are eliminated. Connecting the manometer to a reservoir of saline, h cm above the zero level, allows calibration of the manometer in terms of static pressure (Fig. 8).

When the manometers are filled with saline great care must be taken to ensure that no air bubbles remain in the manometer or attached catheters. Manometers are usually filled with de-aerated saline (boiled or vacuum rinsed). A few drops of wetting agent added to each litre of saline helps to

M

prevent bubble entrapment. If a reservoir system is used for flushing out the manometer before each experiment then air, which gradually enters the saline in the reservoir, may appear as bubbles if the working temperature of the apparatus increases. The surface of the saline, in the reservoir, may be covered with a layer of paraffin oil (sp. gr. 0·85) but this is rather messy and I have found it easier to change the saline every couple of days.

Blood clotting within the catheter reduces the frequency response and

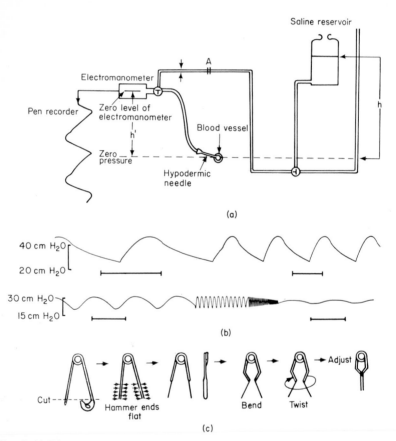

FIG. 8. (a) Diagrammatic experimental set up for recording blood pressure. h = calibration pressure (h cm saline) with respect to zero pressure (atmospheric). h′ = factor by which records must be corrected to obtain pressure values with respect to zero, if the zero level is not established. "A" shows position of haemostats, when flushing the catheter to clear blood clots. (b) Upper trace, pressure pulse recorded from the systemic arch. Lower trace, pressure pulse recorded from the systemic arch with a catheter partially occluded by a blood clot—the occlusion becomes progressively worse as the trace proceeds. Marker = time, 1 sec. (c) Manufacture of artery clamps, from brass safety pins, for closing blood vessels of small amphibians.

increases the damping of the manometer since the effective bore of the catheter is diminished. Coating catheters with silicone fluid and addition of 10–40 i.u. of Heparin to each ml of saline considerably reduces the risk of clotting. When clotting occurs it must be dealt with on the spot or else one's interpretation of pressure relationships may be based on erroneous results. Experience is the best guide to assessing whether the dynamic characteristics of the manometer have changed but in general the pressure traces become smoother as the high frequency components are lost and the pulse pressure tends to decrease (Fig. 8b). Blood clots can be cleared by flushing the catheter with fresh saline. This can be done passively by raising the level of the saline reservoir well in excess of the peak blood pressure and then connecting the reservoir to the catheter. If the clot resists this pressure a slug of saline must be forced through the catheter. Using a set-up similar to that shown in Fig. 8 the procedure is as follows:

1. The tubing at A is occluded with a pair of haemostats.
2. The stopcock of the manometer is turned to connect the catheter to the side arm. Care must be taken to ensure that the manometer is completely closed off or else it may be damaged.
3. The tubing between the stopcock and clamps at A is squeezed and saline forced out through the catheter.
4. While maintaining the pressure on the tubing connect the catheter to the manometer and remove the haemostats, then release the tubing. This last order of events is quite important for if the pressure on the side arm tubing is released when the catheter is still connected to the side arm, blood will be sucked back increasing the chances of further clotting. Even if the pressure is released after disconnection of the catheter, before removal of the haemostats, the elastic recoil of the tubing may be sufficient to cause bubble formation, either by drawing gases from solution or air in around joints in the tubing.

Most manometers have very low volume displacements and consequently the material of the catheters must be chosen with care. If the catheter material is very elastic it will show an appreciable change of volume in response to the applied pressure, reducing the frequency response of the manometer. For the highest natural frequencies rigid connexions of copper or lead tubing are required. For flexible connexions nylon is preferable to polythene, polypropylene, polyvinylchloride or rubber because, for a given wall thickness, it is less elastic. The rigidity of nylon tubing often presents problems, particularly if pressures are being monitored in unrestrained animals since it is prone to kinking and in the final analysis choice of catheter material is often a matter of compromise. Also, with unrestrained animals, there is the added hazard of large movement artefacts. Surges of pressure may be caused by suprisingly small movements. Movement artefact can be reduced by using as short a catheter as possible and arranging the apparatus so that as much of the flexible catheter as possible is at right angles to the direction of anticipated movements.

Blood Pressure in the Heart and Central Blood Vessels

The dissection of the heart and central blood vessels can be done quickly and simply if the animal is to be restrained in a fixed position.

1. Fix the animal to a board and cut through the skin in the mid-ventral line. The edges of the cut skin may be cauterized to prevent bleeding.
2. Raise the pectoral girdle holding it anteriorly with forceps. In anuran amphibia this is done by holding and raising the episternum.
3. With the front of the girdle raised carefully push a scalpel or the flats of a pair of scissors posteriorly so that the pericardium and muscles to the sides of it are freed from the girdle.
4. Cut through the girdle, either side of the mid-line, to the end of the pericardium.
5. To complete exposure of the arterial arches, jugular veins and posterior vena cava, muscle bands overlying this region may have to be removed. Cut through the muscles near their caudal insertions and turn them forwards. Cauterize or ligature the cut ends of the muscle.
6. Carefully remove, by tearing, the connective tissue which surrounds the major arteries.

The type of catheter being used determines the procedure for insertion into the blood vessel. If rigid connections of wide bore copper or lead tubing are made between the manometer and recording needle the technique is different from that for nylon and polythene catheters.

Rigid Connections. Adjust the needle tip until it lies over and parallel with the blood vessel. Pull the vessel back past the tip of the needle, holding onto connective tissue strands on either side of the blood vessel. Raise the vessel in line with the tip of the needle and pull the vessel forward onto the needle. Manipulate the needle into the same "lie" as the blood vessel. For piercing the chambers of the heart the pericardium is held and the needle advanced.

Flexible Connections. A tip of a hypodermic needle may be force-fitted into the end of the catheter, which is pushed through the wall of the blood vessel. Alternatively the vessel may be clamped either side of the projected recording site. A hole is made with a needle in the walls, between the clamps, and the catheter fed through it into the blood vessel. The catheter can be ligatured to connective tissue etc. Then the clamps are removed. Most commercially available haemostats damage amphibian blood vessels and clamps are best manufactured from 1–2 cm brass safety pins. Figure 8c illustrates manufacture of these clamps.

The advantage of flexible catheters is that the animal does not need to be restrained so firmly. Also it is much easier to record side rather than downstream pressures since the open end of the catheter may be closed and a hole bored in the side wall of the catheter using a hot needle.

In order to record pressure from unrestrained animals the dissection must be greatly reduced and pliable catheters must be used. Results obtained from free rather than restrained animals are less suspect on many counts and it is in this direction that many worthwhile investigations may be made.

Blood Pressure in Peripheral Blood Vessels

In some instances blood pressure, say in limb blood vessels, may be recorded using similar techniques as have been described for recording from central blood vessels. However if the vessel is small the catheter may reduce or even prevent blood flow. In these cases T-piece catheters must be used. The side arm is made of nylon and cross piece of polythene tubing. Polythene is preferred since it can be pulled, over a low flame, to give smaller diameter cross pieces than are available commercially.

Manufacture of Small T-pieces

1. The end of a length of nylon tube is held over a low flame until it flares and bends at right angles to the main body of the tube.
2. The cross bar of the "T" is made by threading a piece of copper or steel wire through the bore of a short length of polythene tube and burning a small hole, in the mid position, by touching the wall with a hot needle.
3. A needle, of the same diameter as the polythene tubing, is pushed into the bore of the flared end of the nylon tube and out through the wall at the right angled bend.
4. The polythene tube is threaded through the flared end of the nylon tube and out of the hole at the right angled bend, until the hole in its mid position is opposite the main lumen of the nylon tube.
5. The joints between the polythene and nylon tubing are sealed with molten nylon (melt nylon tube in a low flame) and coated with varnish.
6. The copper or steel wire is removed from the bore of the polythene crosspiece and each end of the cross-piece is cut to a short pointed taper.

Insertion of T-pieces into Blood Vessels. As the cross-piece can be made no shorter than about 1 cm length at least 1–2 cm of vessel must be exposed before attempting to insert the T-piece.

1. Place clamps at both ends of the exposed blood vessel and make a small incision in the vessel wall between the clamps. Ideally the vessel should not be completely bisected at this stage.
2. Push the tips of watchmakers forceps (closed), through the incision, into the vessel and allow them to open slightly so that the wall is stretched. Repeat

this procedure until the blood vessel wall, either side of the incision, has stretched enough to allow easy insertion of the cross-piece.

3. Having siliconed and filled the T-piece with heparinized saline, insert one arm of the cross-piece into the vessel, using a micromanipulator. Tie the vessel to the cross-piece with thin cotton.

4. Completely divide the blood vessel and holding the free end in forceps, pull it onto the other arm of the cross-piece. Tie it in position.

5. Ligature the T-piece to surrounding muscle, etc. and sew up the animal.

With practice it is possible to insert T-pieces into arteries of anuran amphibians weighing about 10 g. These T-pieces can also be used to take blood samples for analysis of blood gas tensions, etc.

Pressures in the Microcirculation.

Obviously for studies on the microcirculation catheters must be of very small diameter, which will adversely affect both the frequency response and damping of the manometer. Rappaport *et al* (1959), using a low-volume displacement pressure gauge and rigid connections to micropipettes of 75–20 μ diameter, successfully recorded pulsatile pressures in arteries and arterioles down to 30 μ in diameter. Wiederheilm *et al.* (1964) used micropressure transducers with tip diameters of 0·5–5 μ. In principle their device works to prevent entry of serum into the micropipette by means of a counter-pressure which is generated by a servo-system. The counter-pressure applied to the hydraulic system reflects the pressure in the blood vessel and is measured by a commercial pressure transducer.

CARDIAC OUTPUT

Apart from direct measurement of the amount of blood flowing from the ventricle all methods of assessing cardiac output are open to a number of objections. The choice, given here, is between measurements (i.e. ventricular length, area or circumference) which must be converted to volume changes by mathematical approximations or by direct measurement of volume change albeit applying some external load to the ventricle. Of course some other systems will suffer both of these disadvantages.

Ciné films of the heart have the advantage that no extra load is imposed on the heart and with suitable approximations, changes in volume of the cardiac chambers can be calculated (Shelton and Jones, 1965b). Reflection of highlights from the heart and surrounding regions can be avoided by running Ringer solution into the receptacle which holds the frog so that the heart is just submerged while the nostrils remain clear of the water surface. Volumes must be calculated from a single view of the heart. Shelton and Jones (1965b) regarded the truncus arteriosus and conus arteriosus as cylinders, the mean diameter and length being measured on prints of the ciné film (Fig. 9). The ventricle was assumed to be circular in cross-section and the volumes at the extremes of the range were calculated on this basis. This was a time consuming procedure and was simplified by converting these figures into a factor based on the area of the ventricular outline. Multiplication by this factor of the area of the ventricular outline, measured by a planimeter on the photographs, gave ventricular volumes between the extremes of the range.

Synchronization with simultaneously recorded blood pressures was achieved by including a rotating disk with two easily distinguishable sectors in the camera field (Fig. 9a). The disc rotated once every second and was connected to contacts which acted as a switch for a neon in the hood of the recording camera. This provided a time calibration and a means of synchronizing precisely the ciné and pressure films (Fig. 9a).

Cardiometers have been used to record cardiac output but the extra inertial and resistive load placed on the heart by these devices is undesirable particularly if a moment to moment analysis is required. The cardiometer used by Shelton and Jones (1965a) consisted of a small cylindrical perspex cup the end of which was covered by a rubber membrane, with a hole through which the ventricle was pushed. It is essential that a good "fit" is obtained and for this reason a fresh membrane was prepared for each experiment. The cup was directly connected, on one side, to a 1 ml syringe barrel containing a small free running metal plunger and on the other to a saline reservoir. In use the syringe was arranged horizontally. After introduction of the ventricle into the cardiometer, saline was run in from the reservoir, air being forced out through a small hole in the wall of the cardiometer opposite the saline inlet. When the cardiometer was completely full of saline the reservoir was closed off and the hole blocked with plasticine. Volume change in the saline filled system was recorded, from the movement of the piston, by a mechano-electric transducer. The whole moving assembly weighed 1·1 gm and moved through a distance of 8 mm (maximum). The volume of saline in the apparatus was about 1 ml. There seems little doubt that the absolute values for cardiac output were reduced by the external loading on the ventricle but qualitatively the results gave much new information (Fig. 9b).

BLOOD FLOW

Blood Flow through the Heart.

Much attention has been directed to a study of blood flow through the amphibian heart with particular reference to the problem of whether separation of oxygenated and de-oxygenated blood occurs in the undivided ventricle. The majority of techniques have concentrated on the injection of foreign substances into the circulation and monitoring their pathway through the heart. (Foxon, 1947; De Graaf 1957; Simons, 1959). At best it can only be said that the problem has been investigated under experimental conditions. More recently Johansen (1963) and G. Shelton (personal communication) have attacked this problem in animals under more normal conditions. Blood

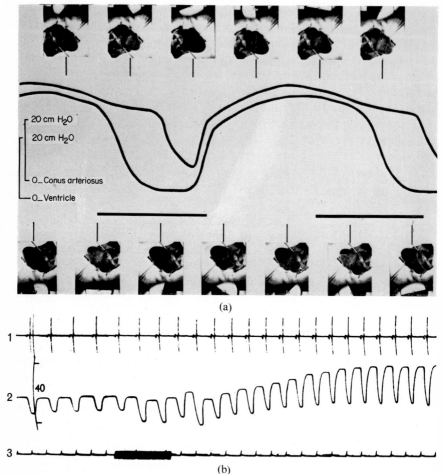

FIG. 9. (a) Prints from ciné films of the heart of a frog taken at the same time as blood pressures within the conus arteriosus and ventricle were recorded. A 1 cm diameter black and white disc, rotating once every second against a black and white background, was included in the camera field. At like on like the rotating disc operated a pair of contacts which acted as a switch for a neon located in the oscilloscope camera hood which gave the $\frac{1}{2}$ sec time marker under the pressure traces. One ciné frame in three is illustrated. Top pressure trace—conus arteriosus, bottom—ventricle (Shelton and Jones, 1965b). (b) Cardiometer recordings of total and stroke volume of the ventricle of *R. pipiens* (21 g). Trace 1, electrocardiogram; trace 2, stroke volume (μl), up on trace = decrease in volume; trace 3, time (sec). At the mark the animal was brought to the surface after a period of submergence in water. (Shelton and Jones, 1965a.)

gas tensions are measured in blood samples taken from the heart and arterial arches by exteriorized catheters. However, blood must be withdrawn from the circulation which may affect flow through the heart.

In the ideal system, flow through the heart should be investigated without the need for change in volume of the circulatory system. Furthermore, it should be applicable to the unrestrained animal. In a current series of experiments the blood in either auricle is heated about 1°C and the distribution of this warmed blood is monitored with small thermocouples located in the arterial arches. (Jones, in preparation).

Construction of Thermocouples and Heating Coils. Thermocouples are constructed from insulated, 100 μ diameter, copper and constantin wire. Two to three mm of the ends of the wires are bared, twisted together, soldered and lightly varnished. The thermocouple is connected to a DC amplifier with the constantin at earth. The response of the thermocouple is tested by subjecting it to a sudden temperature change. At present thermocouples are dropped into a beaker of water 1–2°C above or below ambient. Response times of the order of 0·01 to 0·1 sec are obtained if the varnish is not too thick (Fig. 10a). If faster response times are required unvarnished thermocouples can be used. The amplifiers should be adjusted so that output on the recorder from all thermocouples is identical. For stability another thermocouple must be used as a reference. Heating coils are wound from constantin or other suitable materials and varnished.

Experimental Procedure

1. Expose the heart and arterial arches of the animal leaving the pericardium intact.
2. Sew cotton loops into the pericardium, either side of the auricles, and push the heating coils through the wall of the pericardium to lie alongside the right and left auricles. Tie them in position with the cotton.
3. Clamp the truncus arteriosus of one side and one of the arterial arches downstream of this clamp. Pierce the wall of the arterial arch with a fine pin (sewing needles sharpened electrolytically are ideal) and push the thermocouple into the vessel. Hold it in position by means of a ligature to surrounding connective tissue. Repeat this procedure with the other arterial arches.
4. Place the reference thermocouple in the animal's anus or under the skin of the body wall.
5. Connect the heating coils to a 12 V battery through a tapping key and reversing switch. The tapping key may be wired to activate a marker connected to the recorder. Heat the left or right auricle and monitor the distribution of the warmed blood (Fig. 10b). Thermocouples located within the auricles allow a finer control of the heating system.

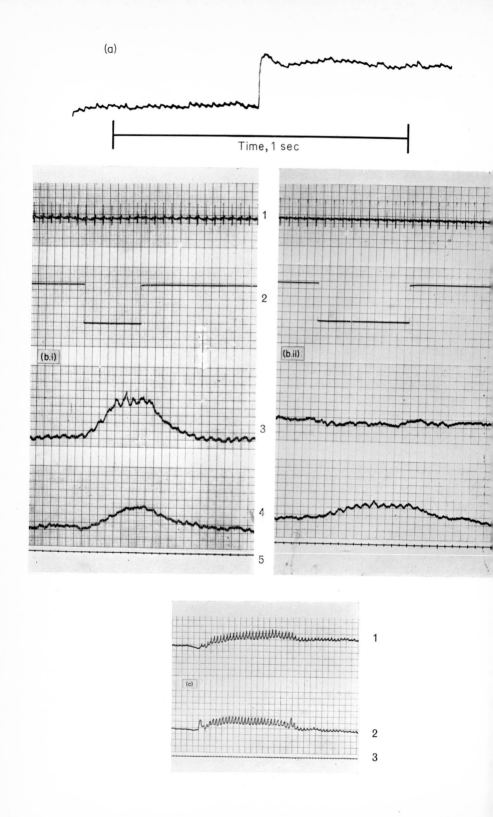

(a)

Time, 1 sec

6. Response of thermocouples can be tested *in situ* by placing a small piece of ice on the outside of the blood vessels over the thermocouples (Fig. 10c).

The pacemaker of the amphibian heart is sited in the sinus venosus and no changes in heart rate are caused by warming the blood in the auricles (Fig. 10b). Since the heating coils and thermocouples are small and can be fixed firmly in position it is hoped to extend this technique to unrestrained animals. Qualitatively this technique has a lot to offer but quantitatively has still to be proven. The major problem at the moment is that heating is applied unevenly and indiscriminately to the auricular blood. If one is able to calculate the amount of heat applied to the blood then, providing the specific heat of blood and the temperature increase are known, the volume of blood which is warmed may be estimated. To this end a new heating system is being designed which will be placed inside the auricle along with four or five thermocouples.

Direct Measurement of Blood Flow

For the microcirculation, flow can only be assessed by direct observation. Poczopco (1957, 1958, 1959) recorded changes in the number of open capillaries in the web of a frog under normal conditions and during periods of respiratory stress. These experiments have yielded valuable information on blood flow distribution under these conditions.

Flowmeter probes of suitable dimensions are now available for use on the major arteries of even small amphibians (Fig. 11). Unfortunately, there is no possibility of using these probes to record flow in unrestrained animals of less than 3–500 g wt. With small animals the probes must usually be held in clamps. Zero flow is obtained by occluding the vessel, downstream of the flow probe. Upstream occlusion is satisfactory in the case of the systemic arch but with the pulmocutaneous arch the vessel usually collapses when upstream occlusions are effected. Vessels may be occluded with forceps (with electro-magnetic flowmeters plastic or wooded forceps must be used) or various types of snare. G. Shelton (personal communication) has used a snare consisting of a length of cord with passes around the vessel and is then threaded through holes in a perspex rod. Pulling the cord constricts the vessel over the end of the rod. It is possible to use pneumatic constrictors

FIG. 10. (Facing page) Thermocouple technique for investigating blood distribution from the undivided ventricle of amphibians. (a) Response of a Copper/Constantin thermocouple to a sudden change in temperature of 1°C. (b) Distribution of warmed blood from the right (i) and left (ii) auricles. Trace 1, e.c.g.; trace 2, marker showing period for which the auricles were heated (down on trace = heating auricle); trace 3, response of a thermocouple in the systemic arch; trace 4, thermocouple in the pulmocutaneous arch; trace 5, time (sec). (c) Testing response of the thermocouples *in situ* by placing a block of ice on the arterial arches. Trace 1, systemic arch; trace 2, pulmocutaneous arch; trace 3, time (sec).

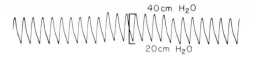

(a.i)

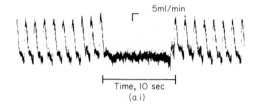

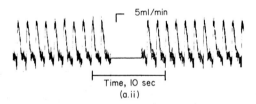

(a.ii)

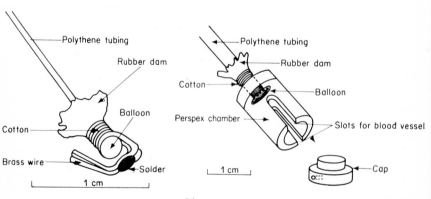

(b)

even with animals as small as 30 g wt (Fig. 11b). Two types of pneumatic constrictors which are simple and cheap to construct are shown in Fig. 11b. In principle the constrictor consists of a balloon enclosed with a rigid chamber through which the blood vessel runs. As the balloon is inflated the vessel is constricted against the wall of the chamber and occluded when pressure in the balloon exceeds that in the blood vessel. A brief outline of their construction is given below.

1. A piece of rubber dental dam is bound over a slightly flared end of a length of polythene tubing. This is force-fitted into the main body of the occlusion chamber.

2. The chamber may be a piece of brass wire shaped as shown in Fig. 11b or a short (0·5 cm) length of perspex tube with slots in the sides to accommodate the blood vessel.

3. In the case of the wire chamber the vessel is inserted through the gap between the free ends of the wire and the balloon. The chamber is then squeezed to close this gap and prevent the blood vessel falling out during an experiment. With the perspex chamber, the slots are placed over the vessel and a cap is force-fitted into the open end of the chamber. A hole may be bored through the cap so that it can be held in forceps.

4. Inflation is effected by a hypodermic syringe attached to the free end of the polythene tube.

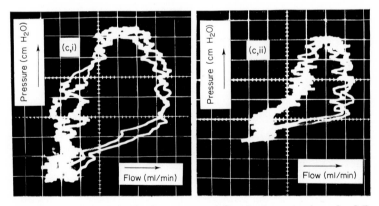

FIG. 11. (a) (Facing page) Blood pressure and flow in the systemic arch of *R. pipiens* (30 g). Flow was recorded with an electromagnetic blood flowmeter. (i) Vessel occluded downstream of the flow probe by inflation of a pneumatic occluder. Notice the slight "pounding" during the occlusion. (ii) "Electronic zero"—compare with occlusion zero. (b) (Facing page) Two types of pneumatic occluder which are suitable for use with small amphibians. (c) (Above) Pressure and flow relationships in the systemic arch of *Xenopus laevis* (40 g). Loops photographed from an oscilloscope with the facility for X–Y plotting. (i) Normal, (ii) after application of ACh to the venticle. Two complete cycles were filmed in each case. The loops cycle in an anti-clockwise direction.

BLOOD GAS TENSIONS AND GAS VOLUMES

Commercially available cuvettes, requiring only 30–100 μl of blood, allied to the appropriate electrodes makes determination of blood PO_2, PCO_2 and pH relatively simple. In most systems cuvettes can be filled by the blood pressure and after a reading has been obtained blood may be returned to the animal. Adequate details of calibration and operation are given by most manufacturers' manuals. A point here might be made about choice of material for catheters. If long catheters are to be used, in which the blood will remain for some time, the lower the permeability of the catheter wall to gases the better, particularly if large differences are expected between the gas tensions of blood and ambient air. For a given thickness the permeability of nylon to oxygen and carbon dioxide is some 50–70 times less than that of low density polyethylene.

Regarding determination of gas volumes the major problem with small amphibians is that only small quantities of blood can be taken for analysis. Tucker (1967) has described in detail a method utilizing an oxygen electrode for measuring oxygen content of 7 μl samples of blood. Using the Natleson microgasometer (Scientific Industries Inc., New York, U.S.A.) both oxygen and carbon dioxide content can be determined from 30 μl blood samples. Dissociation curves can be obtained using these methods. If large quantities of blood are available the simplest method for determining an oxygen dissociation curve is to equilibrate blood samples with a high (200 mm Hg) and a low PO_2 (10 mm Hg). The oxygen content of the blood is measured as accurately as possible at these two values. Mixing blood taken from each sample, in various proportions, allied to measurement of the PO_2 of the mixed blood allows construction of an oxygen dissociation curve in terms of vol. % versus partial pressure of oxygen.

In order to assess the importance of haemoglobin in oxygen transport and consequently aerobic metabolism, the haemoglobin can be poisoned with carbon monoxide. However, a reliable method for determining the % saturation of haemoglobin with carbon monoxide is required. Many of the techniques used in human physiology are not very satisfactory due to the large volume of blood that is required. If a spectrophotometer is available the following technique may be used for blood volumes of the order of 10–50 μl. The technique is based on the principle that at 509 mμ the optical densities of carboxy- and reduced haemoglobin are the same (isosbestic wavelength) whereas at 600 mμ they are very different. Two standards, of 100% carboxy-haemoglobin and completely reduced amphibian haemoglobin, must be prepared first.

1. Withdraw up to 50 μl of blood by cardiac puncture into a test tube.
2. Add distilled water until a good red colour is obtained (about 5 ml).

3. Shake the test tube for 1 min and then centrifuge at 3000 rev/min for 1–2 min.

4. Add 2 ml of supernatant to a 4 × 1 × 1 cm cuvette : R red.

5. Bubble 100% CO through the remaining solution in the test tube for 1 min. To prevent evaporation of the sample the carbon monoxide is first humidified by bubbling through distilled water.

6. Add 2 ml of the carboxy-haemoglobin sample to a 4 × 1 × 1 cm cuvette: R carb.

7. Add 1·5–2 ml of saturated dithionite solution ($Na_2S_2O_4$) to both cuvettes— mix thoroughly by inversion.

8. Read the optical density of the solutions at 509 and 600 mμ against distilled water.

$$\text{Standards : R carb} = \frac{\text{O.D. 600}}{\text{O.D. 509}} \simeq 0\cdot5$$

$$\text{R red} = \frac{\text{O.D. 600}}{\text{O.D. 509}} \simeq 1\cdot0$$

$$\% \text{ Hb CO} = 100\left(\frac{\text{R red} - \text{R test}}{\text{R red} - \text{R carb}}\right)$$

$$\text{where R test} = \frac{\text{O.D. 600}}{\text{O.D. 509}}$$

R test is obtained by following steps 1–4, 7 and 8 of the above procedure.

Precautions

1. On some occasions solutions tend to go cloudy after addition of dithionite solution. The use of freshly made up dithionite solution tends to prevent this.

2. This method appears to give results which are about 5% too low. As the blood is haemolysed and consequently the diffusion distance between the water and haemoglobin molecules is effectively zero some CO is probably released from combination with the haemoglobin to the water. This effect can be greatly reduced by using larger samples of blood or by diluting the blood with water of the same CO tension as that to which the animal was exposed.

BLOOD VOLUME

The proportion of red cells to plasma can be determined from the haematocrit. Consequently measurement of plasma or red cell volume alone can be used to assess total blood volume providing the haematocrit is known. Apart from Wilson *et al.* (1960) who labelled cells or plasma with radioisotopes, most other estimates of amphibian blood volume have been based on determination of plasma volume by use of the dye method. The blood volume is expressed in terms of % of the wet body weight. Chien and Gregersen (1962) have extensively reviewed this subject and for more precise details of techniques and precautions the reader is referred to their article.

Determination of Plasma Volume.

The two substances most commonly used to determine plasma volume are Evans blue dye (T-1824) and radioactive iodinated albumin (I^{131} — albumin).

Determination of Plasma Volume using Evans blue.

1. Make up a solution of Evans blue dye in heparinized saline (0·5 — 2mg/ml).
2. Prepare a standard curve of optical density against mg dye solution/ml.

Unless one is prepared to sacrifice a considerable number of amphibians to obtain a large volume of plasma, dilutions are best made with Ringer's solution. However in an experiment plasma taken from the animal, may have to be diluted 1 : 20 or so with Ringer's solution in order to give sufficient volume for spectrophotometric analysis. Consequently a like dilution of plasma in saline is required when constructing the standard curve. The reason for this is that the spectral absorption curve for Evans blue in Ringer's solution is changed considerably with the addition of even small quantities of plasma. For amphibian Ringer the peak absorption is between 610 and 615 mμ whereas with a 13 times dilution of amphibian plasma in Ringer the peak absorption is at 620–625 mμ. Evans blue in solutions of human plasma and amphibian plasma has more or less the same peak absorption (human 620 mμ, frog 622·5 mμ) and it is possible to substitute human for frog plasma in test runs without a noticeable loss of accuracy.

Inject a small drop of dye solution, from a syringe, into a tared volumetric flask. Reweigh the flask with the dye solution and determine the weight of the dye. Fill the volumetric flask to the calibration mark with a solution of 1:20 or whatever is appropriate, plasma in Ringer's solution. Determine the peak absorption of an aliquot of the dye solution, reading against clear plasma in Ringer's solution. Of course, readings can be made against distilled water in which case the optical densities of both the dye solution and clear Ringer-plasma solution must be determined at peak absorption. A standard solution contains x mg dye soln/ml and will have an optical density D_I. If the samples are read against distilled water then the optical density of the dye solution is the measured optical density, minus the optical density of the clear Ringer-plasma solution. A number of standard solutions are made and their optical densities are obtained and plotted on a graph of dye solution concentration against optical density (Fig. 12a). The standards should bracket the optical densities likely to be obtained experimentally (0·1–0·7).

3. Anaesthetize and weigh the animal.
4. Make a small incision in the animal's sternum and insert a nylon catheter,

tipped with the end of a hypodermic needle, into the ventricle. Tie the catheter in position with ligatures to the skin. The catheter is closed with a clip. Five to ten μl of Heparin may be injected at this stage.

5. Place the free end of the catheter into a calibrated glass tube, sealed at one end, remove the clip and withdraw about 150 μl of blood. Centrifuge (5000 rev/min for 5 min) and determine the haematocrit.

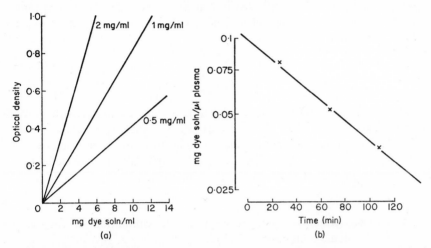

Fig. 12. Determination of plasma volume using the dye dilution technique. (a) Standard curve, optical density against mg dye solution per ml. (b) Concentration/time curve. The logarithm of the concentration is plotted against time and extrapolated to give concentration at the time of injection (zero time).

6. Using a glass knife, with the tube placed horizontally over the edge of a bench, cut off the red cells and discard. Weigh the tube and plasma. Blow out the plasma into a $4 \times 1 \times 1$ cm cuvette containing exactly 3 ml of Ringer solution. Re-weigh the tube. The solutions containing the dye are read against this solution.

7. Take up 150 μl of Evans blue into a 1 ml tuberculin syringe. Weigh the syringe and attached hypodermic needle. Inject the dye into the circulation through the cardiac catheter. Ideally an air bubble should be included in the syringe between the dye solution and plunger. On completion of injection the catheter is rinsed into the circulation by movement of blood in and out of the catheter but not the syringe. After 4 or 5 rinses the blood is forced from the catheter, into the heart, by the air contained in the syringe. The catheter is clamped. Re-weigh the syringe and determine the weight of dye solution injected.

8. After 20–30 min take 150 μl of blood into a sample tube, centrifuge and determine the haematocrit. Discard the red cells. Weigh the tube + plasma

N

and blow out the plasma into 3 ml of Ringer solution contained in a $4 \times 1 \times 1$ cm cuvette. Reweigh the tube. Determine the optical density of this solution (at about 625 mμ) reading against the clear solution from step 6.

9. Repeat this procedure at 20–30 min intervals at least 2–3 times.

Calculation. A known quantity of test substance Wg is introduced into the blood vascular system of volume, V ml, which is to be measured. After the test substance is uniformly distributed in the volume V ml, a sample is taken for the determination of its concentration C. Assuming no losses and even distribution then

$$W = C \times V$$

$$\text{or } V = \frac{W}{C}.$$

It is assumed that W occupies a negligible volume compared with V. With small amphibia this is not so but is partially overcome by injecting a volume of dye solution which is approximately equal to the volume of blood withdrawn when preparing the reference (clear) sample. If this is not done then V must be corrected for the volume of dye injected.

Sample Calculation.

1. Reference (clear) Sample: by approximate calibration of the sample tube total volume removed was 160 μl.
Hct $= 36\cdot5\%$

$$\begin{aligned}
\text{wt of tube} + \text{plasma} &= 0\cdot9642 \text{ g} \\
\text{wt of tube} &= 0\cdot8830 \\
\hline
\text{wt of plasma} &= 0\cdot0812 \text{ g}
\end{aligned}$$

∴Reference sample contains 81·2 mg of plasma in 3 ml of Ringer solution.

2. Injection

$$\begin{aligned}
\text{wt of Syringe} + \text{Evans blue dye soln} &= 14\cdot0153 \text{ g} \\
\text{wt of Syringe after injection} &= 13\cdot8606 \text{ g} \\
\hline
\text{wt of Evans blue dye soln injected} &= 0\cdot1547 \text{ g}
\end{aligned}$$

3. Sample 1:27·5 min post injection
Hct $= 35\cdot5\%$

$$\begin{aligned}
\text{wt of tube} + \text{plasma} &= 0\cdot9750 \text{ g} \\
&= 0\cdot9022 \text{ g} \\
\hline
\text{wt of plasma} &= 0\cdot0728 \text{ g}
\end{aligned}$$

∴ Sample 1 contains 72·8 mg of plasma in 3 ml of Ringer solution
Optical Density (at 625 mμ) $= 0\cdot32$

From the standard curve O.D. of 0·32 represents a concentration of 1·925 mg dye soln/ml.

Density of plasma = 1·012 gm/ml

$\therefore$ 72·8 mg plasma occupies 71·9 μl

$\therefore$ Total volume of liquid in cuvette = 3071·9 ml

Cuvette contains 3·072 × 1·925 mg dye soln = 5·9 mg dye soln.

This was originally contained in 71·9 μl of plasma

$\therefore$ 1 μl of plasma contained $\dfrac{5\cdot9}{71\cdot9} = 0\cdot082$ mg dye soln

4. Repeat this procedure for Samples 2, 3, 4 . . .

5. Construct a curve of concentration against time. It is assumed that the dye stuff disappears exponentially from the fluid compartment. The logarithm of concentration is plotted against time (Fig. 12b) and the linear portion of this curve is extrapolated back to the time of injection (0 min). The intercept on the concentration axis gives the concentration which would have existed assuming no loss. This value is used in the calculation of plasma volume.

$$\text{Wt of dye soln injected} = 154\cdot7 \text{ mg}$$

Concentration of dye soln in 1 μl of plasma at zero time = 0·1 mg

$$\text{Total plasma volume} = \frac{154\cdot7}{0\cdot1} = 1550 \ \mu\text{l}$$

Hematrocrit = 36·0% (average value)

$$\text{Total blood volume} = \frac{100 \times \text{plasma volume}}{100 - \text{Hct}}$$

$$= \frac{100 \times 1550}{64}$$

$$= 2422 \ \mu\text{l}$$

Wet wt of animal = 30·2 g

Total blood volume; % of body weight = 8%

Precautions

1. Various refinements, particularly concerned with the injection of dye solution, can be incorporated to minimize the experimental error. However, the law of diminishing returns makes these in many cases impractical. Only if a systematic study of blood volume alone is being made does this seem worthwhile. The results given by this technique, as it stands, are in good agreement with those obtained by other authors.

2. An animal may make up a proportion of any large fluid loss which it suffers during an experiment. If this occurs it will progressively detract from the accuracy of the concentration against time curve as the "apparent"

loss of dye solution from the circulation will be increased. This error may be reduced by (a) taking samples, after the first one, more quickly than in the above procedure i.e. 20, 30, 40 min and (b) by taking as small a sample as possible, the volume removed in sampling should not exceed 10% of the animal's total blood volume. In general, if the haematocrit of each sample is within 2% of the original haematocrit one can assume that dilution of the dye solution by incorporation of extravascular fluids has not occurred.

Determination of Red Cell Volume

Measurement of red cell volume involves a dilution technique in which red cells, labelled with a radioisotope, are used. Cr^{51} in the form of $Na_2Cr^{51}O_4$ is most commonly used. One of the outstanding advantages of Cr^{51} is that loss of the chromium label is negligible during an experiment so that there is no need for extrapolation. In the description of the technique it is assumed that normal precautions for working with radio-active substances will be known and observed.

1. Tagging red blood cells. The ventricle is cannulated as for the dye-dilution technique and blood is withdrawn into a well-heparinized non-glass syringe with a close fitting plunger. Two to four hundred μl of blood are required. The syringe is inverted, and the end blocked with an occluded hypodermic needle and centrifuged. After centrifugation the supernatant plasma is ejected from the syringe and stored in a refrigerator. The volume is reconstituted with Ringer's solution and the $Na_2Cr^{51}O_4$ solution (in Ringer) is added and mixed. Activities between 40–100 μc/ml of blood are used. The tagging can be allowed to proceed overnight at 15°C.

2. Insert a catheter into the ventricle of a fresh animal and remove exactly 50 μl of blood into a calibrated disposable pipette. Determine the haematocrit.

3. Take a 50 μl sample of incubation mixture (1) into a calibrated disposable pipette and rinse the pipette in 3 ml of distilled water. If desired, at this and at all succeeding stages, the pipette may be broken up and placed in the distilled water. Count I.

4. Centrifuge remaining incubation mixture (3000 rev/min for 5 min) and take a 50 μl sample of the supernatant. Place in 3 ml of distilled water. Count II.

5. Discard remaining supernatant and wash cells with amphibian Ringer solution. Repeat this procedure several times until the count rate of 50 μl of the Ringer wash, in 3 ml of distilled water, is not significantly above background. Count III.

6. Make an injection mixture by diluting the red cells with plasma (stored from (1)) until the haematocrit is close to or preferably identical with the haematocrit of the experimental animal.

7. Take a 50 μl sample of the injection mixture (6) and rinse in 3 ml of distilled water. Count IV.

8. Take a further 50 μl sample of injection mixture (6) and inject it into the animal. If agglutination occurs following injection amphibian ringer may be used instead of plasma in stage (6). Allow the animal's blood to run back and forth in the catheter to rinse out the injection tube. Leave the catheter full of air. Rinse and break up the glass injection pipette in 3 ml of distilled water Count V.

9. Take a 50 μl sample of blood from the animal 20–30 min after injection. Determine the haematocrit. Wash out pipette into 3 ml of distilled water. Count VI.

10. Repeat (9), at suitable intervals, 2–3 times.

Calculation. The background count rate is subtracted from all other count rates to give the net count rate. Counts are usually performed for 1000 sec. A well-type scintillation counter is used. The pulse height analyser is set for peak energy of 0·32 meV. The technique has been so designed that the counting geometry remains virtually constant since all samples of 50 μl are placed in 3 ml of distilled water in more or less identical capped containers. The standard deviation of single observations of N counts is equal to the square root of the number of counts observed, N. With very weak samples N approaches the background count and the accuracy will be correspondingly low. In this case samples must be counted for a longer period of time.

Background Count (Bg) = 9710 (mean of 5 counts)

Count I—incubation mixture = 1 129 360.

The resolving time of the instrument was such that only count rates of under 500/sec were faithfully recorded. Consequently this sample was diluted with 5% potassium dichromate solution to 10 ml and a 3 ml aliquot of the diluted solution recounted.

Count I—3 ml Aliquot of diluted incubation mixture = 366 720

$$\therefore \text{Total counts in original solution} = 366\,720 - Bg \times \frac{10}{3}$$

$$= 1\,190\,033$$

Count II—Supernatant from incubation mixture = 242 380 − Bg
$$= 232\,670$$

Incorporation of Cr^{51} into red blood cells

$$= \frac{\text{Count of Mixture} - \text{Count of Supernatant}}{\text{Count of Mixture}}$$

$$= \frac{\text{Count I} - \text{Count II}}{\text{Count I}}$$

$$\therefore \% \text{Incorporation} = \frac{1\,190\,033 - 232\,670 \times 100}{1\,190\,033}$$

$$= 80\cdot4\%$$

Count III—Saline wash (5th Wash) = 10 000

This value was not significantly above Bg and means that the washing procedure was thorough in that all the Cr^{51} adhering to the surface of the blood cells had been removed. Consequently only that label bound with the cells was injected. It is imperative to check this before injection.

Count IV—Injection Sample = 389 700 − Bg

$$Hct = 10\%$$

Count V—Wash of Injection Syringe = 12 250 × Bg

Count V—Must be subtracted from Count IV to give the activity of the injected blood.

Count VI—Sample 1 (20 min post injection) = 23 470 − Bg

$$Hct = 10\%$$

Count VII—Sample 2 (60 min post injection) = 22 810 − Bg

$$Hct = 9·5\%$$

Wet weight of animal = 12·3 g   Hct = 10%

$$\text{Red blood cell volume} = \frac{\text{Total number of counts injected}}{\text{Count rate post injection/unit volume}}$$

Total number of counts injected = Counts IV–V
$$= 377\ 450$$

Count VI—Blood sample (20 min post injection) = 28 470 − Bg

$$\text{Counts/unit volume of red blood cells} = \frac{100 \times (\text{Count VI} - Bg)}{\text{Hct} \times \text{Sample Volume}}$$

$$\left(\begin{array}{c}\text{Sample Volume} = 50\ \mu l \\ \text{Hct} = 10\%\end{array}\right) \qquad = \frac{100 \times (23\ 470 - 9710)}{10 \times 50}$$

$$= 2740\ \text{counts}/\mu l$$

Count VII—Blood Sample (60 min post injection) = 22 810 − Bg

$$\text{Counts/unit volume of red blood cells} = \frac{13\ 100}{4·75}$$

$$\left(\begin{array}{c}\text{Sample volume} = 50\ \mu l \\ \text{Hct} = 9·5\%\end{array}\right) \qquad = 2757\ \text{counts}/\mu l$$

$$\text{Average counts}/\mu l = 2748$$

(With a series of samples agreement should be within 4%)

$$\text{Red blood cell volume }(\mu l) = \frac{377\ 450}{2748} = 137·3$$

$$\text{Total blood volume} = \frac{137·3}{\text{Hct}} \times 100 = 1373\ \mu l$$

∴ Blood volume (% of body weight) = 11·2%.

Although the technique can be improved by careful attention to detail the major limiting factor appears to be the accuracy with which the haematocrit can be read. Only an estimate of total blood volume can be obtained by using either of these techniques alone. In current experiments plasma and red blood cell volume are being measured simultaneously using Evans blue dye and Cr^{51}. The dilution of red blood cells, to prepare the injection mixture, is made with dye solution in amphibian Ringer instead of plasma. From there on the procedures outlined above are combined.

EXPERIMENTS ON THE ROLE OF THE NERVOUS SYSTEM IN CIRCULATORY AND RESPIRATORY CONTROL

The role of the central and peripheral nervous system in control of circulation and respiration has been investigated in several ways. The role of the autonomic nervous system and the brain has been somewhat tentatively investigated either by ablation or recordings of electrical activity. Some gross stimulation experiments have also been performed. There is some controversy as to the exact path taken by the sympathetic innervation of the heart in amphibia. It seems most likely that the vagus nerve Xth cranial) contains both sympathetic and parasympathetic elements (Gaskell 1884, 1886). However, claims have been made that the sympathetic innervation runs direct from one of the first four sympathetic ganglia.

Most of the work done to date, including my own, has been done on anuran amphibia and consequently descriptions of operative procedures involved in these experiments are only given for anuran amphibians. Furthermore the techniques have been limited to those after which the animal still functions as a physiological entity.

THE PERIPHERAL NERVOUS SYSTEM

Section of the IXth and Xth Cranial Nerves.

Section of the IXth and Xth cranial nerves is best carried out in the angle of the jaw.
1. A latero-ventral skin incision (0·5–1 cm long) is made just posterior to the angle of the jaw.
2. Gently stretch the tissues under the incision to reveal a muscle block running obliquely dorso-ventrally (from the cranium to the scapula).
3. Pulling this muscle ventrally exposes the IXth and Xth nerves. The IXth cranial is closely approximated to the carotid artery and the Xth to the internal jugular vein. Consequently great care must be taken when sectioning the nerves at this point.

Section of the Sympathetic Chain.

Section of the sympathetic chain or removal of sympathetic ganglia is most easily accomplished through an incision in the roof of the buccal cavity.

1. The buccal cavity is propped open by means of a matchstick or piece of perspex rod. The internal carotid arteries can be clearly seen through the mucous membrane of the roof of the buccal cavity before they disappear into the orbits.

2. Make a 0·5 cm incision in the mid line caudal to the entry of the carotids into the orbits.

3. Lifting the cut edge of the mucus membrane exposes the insertion of the *M. levator agnuli scapulae* on the exoccipital.

4. Cut the muscle free from its insertion, working laterally until the connective between the vagus ganglion and the 1st sympathetic ganglion is exposed. The connective may then be sectioned.

5. If removal of sympathetic ganglia is being effected leave the connective intact and trace the sympathetic chain backwards, removing the overlying connective tissue. It is possible to remove the first 4 sympathetic ganglia using this approach (Jones, 1966). With care the sympathetic chain can be removed intact and the ganglia can be counted.

6. The first sympathetic ganglia (and more posterior ganglia) may be removed without cutting through the insertion of the *M. levator anguli scapulae*. However, this approach is not recommended until one is quite familiar with the "look" of the sympathetic chain.

Nerve Recording and Stimulation.

Neil and Zotterman (1950) and Neil *et al.* (1950) have given a very detailed description of the termination of the cardiac and pulmonary branches of the vagus (Xth) and the glossophargyngeal (IXth) nerves on the carotid labyrinth. For exposure of the carotid nerve they suggest removal of the external jugular vein; however with suitable positioning of the recording electrodes it is possible to record from this nerve leaving the vein intact (Jones, in preparation). Ishii *et al.* (1966) have also described a vagal branch which innervates the carotid labyrinth (Fig. 13). Figure 13 also shows the types of afferent activity which can be recorded from these nerves using simple silver wire hook electrodes. Identification of the nature of the recorded activity must be made. Sectioning the nerve above or below the recording electrodes allows assessment of whether activity is afferent or efferent. In the case of afferent mechanoreceptor activity localization of the source of the activity may be made by mechanical stimulation of appropriate regions. More sophisticated techniques can be used to investigate the properties of the receptors when they have been isolated (Ishii *et al.*, 1966).

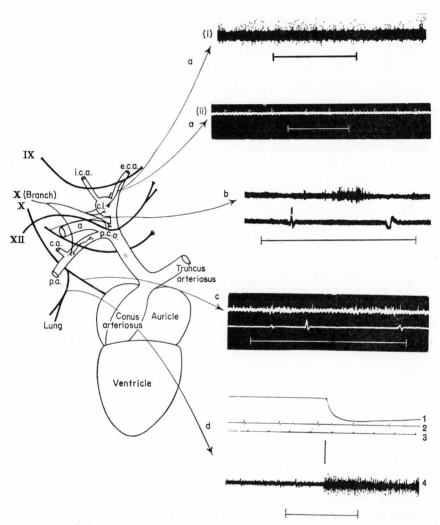

FIG. 13. Innervation of the carotid labyrinth, heart and lungs of amphibians by the IXth and Xth cranial nerves. The position of the vagal branch innervating the carotid labyrinth was copied from Ishii *et al.* (1966). Afferent activity which can be recorded from these nerves by simple hooked wire electrodes is also shown. a. aorta; c.a. cutaneous artery; c.l. carotid labyrinth; e.c.a. external carotid artery; i.c.a. internal carotid artery; p.a. pulmonary artery; p.c.a. pulmocutaneous artery. (a) Carotid nerve (i) Chemoreceptor discharge, time 5 sec (ii) Stretch receptor discharge, time 1 sec. (b) Laryngeal nerve—stretch receptor discharge, time 1 sec. (c) Cardiac vagus—auricular and ventricular stretch receptor discharge, time 1 sec. (d) Pulmonary vagus—stretch receptor discharge. Trace 1, lung volume (down on trace = increase in volume); trace 2, e.c.g.; trace 3, time (sec). Trace 4, selected portion of activity in the pulmonary vagus taken on a different time scale (calibration mark = 1 sec). The vertical line links coincident points in time on the traces (Jones, 1966).

For recording or stimulating, the sympathetic chain is best approached dorsally. (Dale and Mines, 1914).

1. Make a 2–3 cm incision in the skin, mid dorsally, from the hind edge of the cranium back over the vertebral column.

2. Cut the *M. cucullaris*, running from the supra-scapula to the exocipital and turn the supra-scapula backwards and laterally. Ligature the supra-scapula in this position.

3. Cut through the fascia dorsalis—the covering material—in the mid line to expose the *M. longissimus dorsi*.

4. Cut through the insertion of the *M. longissimus dorsi* on the exoccipital and free it from the vertebral column as far back as the first transverse process, turning it outwards and backwards.

5. This exposes muscles running from the pro-otic to the transverse process of the second vertebra (the first vertebra with a transverse process)· These are *M. intertransversarius capitis superior* and *M.i.c. inferior*.

6. Working from the mid line, carefully remove these muscles by tearing free longitudinal strips antero-posteriorly. The connective between the 1st sympathetic ganglion and the vagus ganglion will be exposed after stripping away about half of these muscles.

7. An essentially similar approach can be repeated from transverse process to transverse process to expose the second and succeeding sympathetic ganglia.

THE CENTRAL NERVOUS SYSTEM

Several regions of the brain have been investigated by stimulation, recording or transection to elucidate their role in respiratory and cardio-vascular control. Several methods have been described for holding the brain fixed relative to recording or stimulating electrodes. (Oka, 1958a, b; Ito and Watanabe, 1962; Iriuchijima 1963). The head must be fixed in such a way as to allow respiratory movements to continue normally. A holder which allows recording from the respiratory centre is illustrated in Fig. 14a. The vertebral column is rigidly held by means of two clamps (A and B) fixed just in front of the urostyle and at the posterior border of tympanic membrane.

1. Clamp A consists of two 6mm diameter rods in the ends of which are cut V-shaped notches of a size suitable to fit around the transverse processes of the vertebrae.

2. Clamp B consists of two 4 or 2·5 mm diameter rods with V-shaped notches in the ends to clamp onto the hind edge of the tympanic membrane, fixing to the ring of cartilage around the tympanic membrane where it is attached to the squamosal bone.

3. Both clamps A and B are adjustable so that different sizes of animal may be accommodated.

4. The head clamp C consists of 3 rods of 2·5 mm diameter. Two of the rods are bent as shown and the ends are cut to a L-shaped notch. These rods clamp onto the mandibular and maxillary bones on each side of the head. The third rod which is short is brought down onto the surface of the cranium between the eyes. The head is rigidly fixed but respiratory movements are

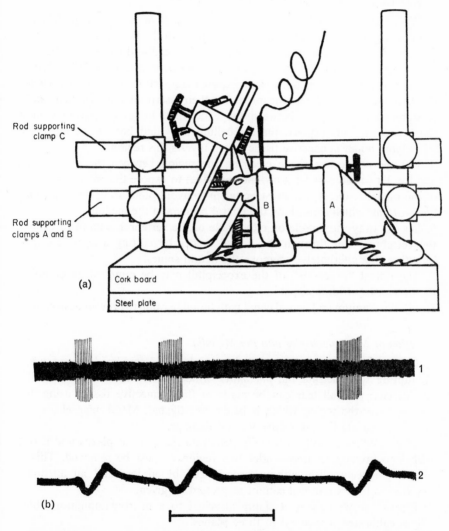

FIG. 14. (a) Clamp for immobilizing anuran amphibians, described in the text. (b) Trace 1, record of nervous activity from the medulla of *B. bufo* (20 g), related to buccal breathing movements (Trace 2). Marker = 1 sec. (Record redrawn from D. R. Jones and B. M. Bush, unpublished.)

not impeded since the floor of the buccal cavity is free. These clamps are adjustable.

5. The holder is fixed to a cork board attached to a steel plate. The animal's limbs may be pinned to the board.

Setting Up the Animal and Exposing the Medulla

1. With the animal held in clamp A, fix clamp B in position and then the head clamp (C). The dissection may be done with the head free if desired.

2. Cut out a triangular piece of skin from the head and trunk. The base of the triangle is just behind the eyes and the apex over the 2nd or 3rd vertebra.

3. Cut through the fascia dorsalis, to expose the insertion of the *M. longissimus dorsi* on the exoccipital. Cut the muscles at their insertions and turn them back.

4. Remove the cartilage between the exoccipital bones by paring with a sharp scalpel. This exposes the cerebellum and hind borders of the optic lobes lying under connective tissue which invests this region.

5. Lift the connective tissue covering the region between the exoccipitals and the 1st vertebra and cut around the edges to expose the anterior portion of the medulla. Great care must be taken to avoid puncturing the *vena spinalis posterior* which runs along the lateral borders of the medulla.

6. Scrape away the muscle on either side of the vertebral column to expose the vertebrae. Cut through the neural arches by cutting a short distance on either side alternately —remove the neural spines.

7. The dorsal "processes" of the exoccipital may be removed by chipping the bone away with a scapel.

8. Fill the cranium and neural canal with liquid paraffin to prevent desiccation.

Insertion of Microelectrodes into the Medulla

1. If glass microelectrodes are being used these may be damaged when attempting to penetrate the *pia mater* which closely invests the medulla. In this case a small tear can be made in the connective tissue, using fine needles, over the region which is being investigated. Metal microelectrodes usually penetrate the *pia mater* without damage.

2. Glass electrodes will not readily penetrate the choroid plexus and if one wishes to investigate areas under this region it must be removed. This is difficult to accomplish without pronounced blood loss and an adequate description for its removal cannot at present be given.

3. Electrodes are held in a clamp attached to a micromanipulator which allows calibrated movement in three planes.

4. Electrodes should be inserted perpendicular to the brain and great care must be taken when lowering to avoid injury discharges. These are easily recognized by their short duration and high frequency. One can expect about

1 in 10 electrode traverses to give potential discharges in rhythm with breathing movements once the "active" regions of the medulla have been localized.
5. Movement artefact may give potential discharges in time with the breathing movements. The most useful criterion for deciding whether activity is "genuine" is the constancy of spike amplitude throughout the discharge.
6. The position of the recording site can be approximately ascertained by measuring from fixed reference points on the surface of the brain by means of the calibrated slides of the manipulator. However, the actual position of the tip of the recording electrodes can be confirmed later by removing the brain and sectioning it. Brains are fixed in 10% formal in Ringer, sections cut at 10 μ and stained in Heidenhain's iron haematoxylin. The electrode tracks are usually discernible in these sections and allow identification of the active region. Correction must be made for shrinkage during fixation. More sophisticated techniques may be used to mark active sites (see Frank and Becker, 1964).
7. The animal should be kept moist throughout the experiment.

EXPERIMENTS ON THE RESPIRATION AND CIRCULATION OF LARVAL AND YOUNG AMPHIBIANS

In many cases the epidermal layers of larval and young amphibians are relatively transparent and such structures as the heart and main blood vessels can be readily observed. The apparatus illustrated in Fig. 15a can be used to measure gaseous exchange and heart rate etc. under varying conditions. A rectangular tank 15 cm × 5 cm × 2 cm is mounted on a perspex frame. An angled mirror is placed under the tank. The tank is divided into small compartments by partitions of 1 mm thick perspex perforated by a

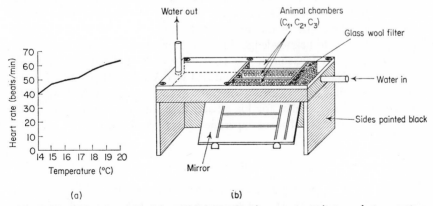

FIG. 15. (a) Heart rate of 1–5 day old Salamanders in response to increase in temperature of the inlet water (Thomas, unpublished). (b) Apparatus suitable for studying circulation and respiration of young or larval amphibians, described in the text.

large number of holes. Water enters and leaves the tank by the inlet in the side and outlet in the lid. If desired glass wool can be placed in front of the small compartments to filter the incoming water. A series of different sized components can be constructed so that animals of varying sizes can be examined. Alternatively adjustable partitions may be used.

1. The tank is filled with water and animals placed in the compartments c_1–c_3.

2. The lid is screwed on and water flow, through the tank, commenced.

3. The ventral surface of the animal is reflected in the mirror and heart rate can be measured with the naked eye. However with very small animals it is easier if the apparatus is illuminated from above and a binocular microscope is used to observe the reflection in the mirror.

4. PO_2 and PCO_2 of the inlet and outlet water can be measured and, providing flow rate is known, oxygen uptake and carbon dioxide production can be calculated. With small animals the dead space of the tank, behind the small compartments, can be reduced by inclusion of a block of perspex.

5. Heart rate under varying conditions of PO_2, PCO_2 and temperature of the inlet water may also be examined (Fig. 15b).

ACKNOWLEDGEMENTS

My thanks are due to the following; George Holeton for the loan of his apparatus which was used to study circulation and respiration of larval amphibians; John Phillips, late of the University of East Anglia, who designed and built the respiratory pump; Mary Mills for advising and helping to determine red blood cell volume using Cr^{51}; Graham Shelton who developed the techniques used to measure cardiac output; Mike Jarman, George Holeton, Brian Bush, Dick Saunders and Jim Dodson for reading and criticizing earlier drafts of this manuscript.

It is a pleasure to acknowledge the help given to me by many technicians, particularly Robin Jackson of the University of East Anglia and Norman Ablett, Philip Garland, John Sharland and Ken Wood of Bristol University.

Finally I would like to express my gratitude to Graham Shelton, of the University of East Anglia, for his advice, help and encouragement during the period when most of these experiments were performed.

REFERENCES

EXPERIMENTS ON THE RESPIRATORY SYSTEM

Chase, A. M., Unwin, D. M. and Brown, R. H. J. (1968). A simple electrolytic respirometer for the continuous recording of oxygen consumption under constant and natural conditions. *J. exp. Biol.*, **48**, 207–15.

Jones, D. R. (1967). Oxygen consumption and heart rate of several species of anuran amphibia during submergence. *Comp. Biochem. Physiol.*, **20**, 691–707.

Jones, D. R. (1968). Specific and seasonal variations in development of diving bradycardia in anuran amphibians. *Comp. Biochem. Physiol.*, **25**, 821–34.

Jones, D. R. and Shelton, G. (1964). Factors influencing submergence and the heart rate in the frog. *J. exp. Biol.*, **41**, 417–31.

Krogh, A. (1904). On the cutaneous and pulmonary respiration of the frog. *Skand. Arch. Physiol.*, **15**, 328–419.

Moore, E. W. (1939). Graphic determination of carbon dioxide and the three forms of alkalinity. *J. Am. Wat. Wks Ass.*, **31**, 51–66.

Oka, K. (1957). The normal respiratory movements of the frog (Japanese). *J. physiol. Soc. Japan*, **19**, 613–20.

Shinkai, K. and Narita, T. (1957). Electromyographical studies on toad's respiratory movements. *Nagoya J. med. Sci.*, **19**, 1–6.

Whitford, W. G. and Hutchison, V. H. (1963). Cutaneous and pulmonary gas exchange in the spotted salamander, *Amphystoma maculatum*. Biol. Bull. mar. biol. Lab., Woods Hole, **124**, 344–54.

Willem, V. (1920). Observations sur la respiration des Amphibiens. *Bull. Acad. r. Belg. Cl. Sci.*, **6**, 298–314.

EXPERIMENTS ON THE CIRCULATORY SYSTEM

Chien, S. and Gregersen, M. I. (1962). Determination of body fluid volumes. *In* "Physical Techniques in Biological Research". Vol. IV (W. L. Nastuk, ed.), Academic Press, New York and London.

De Graaf, A. R. (1957). Investigations into the distribution of blood in the heart and aortic arches of *Xenopus laevis*. *J. exp. Biol.*, **34**, 143–72.

Foxon, G. E. H. (1947). The mode of action of the heart of the frog. *Proc. zool. Soc. Lond.*, **116**, 565–74.

Foxon, G. E. H. (1955). Problems of the double circulation in vertebrates. *Biol. Rev,*. **30**, 196–228.

Johansen, K. (1963). Cardiovascular dynamics in the amphibian *Amphiuma tridactylum*. *Acta. physiol. scand.*, **60**, suppl. 217.

Lockwood, A. P. M. (1961). "Ringer" solutions and some notes on the physiological basis of their ionic composition. *Comp. Biochem. Physiol.*, **2**, 241–289.

McDonald, D. A. (1960). "Blood flow in arteries.". Edward Arnold, London.

Poczopko, P. (1957). Further investigations on the cutaneous vasomotor, reflexes in the edible frog with connexion with the problem of cutaneous respiration in frogs. *Zoologica. Pol.*, **8**, 161–75.

Poczopko, P. (1958). On the seasonal variability of cutaneous vasomotor reflexes in the edible frog (*Rana esculenta* L). *Zoologica Pol.*, **9**, 115–29.

Poczopko, P. (1959). Changes in blood circulation in *Rana esculenta* L. while diving. *Zoologica Pol.*, **10**, 29–43.

Rappaport, M. B., Black, E. H. and Irwin, J. W. (1959). A manometer for measuring dynamic pressures in the microvascular system. *J. appl. Physiol.*, **14**, 651–5.

Shelton, G. and Jones, D. R. (1965a). Central blood pressure and heart output in surfaced and submerged frogs. *J. exp. Biol.*, **42**, 339–57.

Shelton, G. and Jones, D. R. (1965b). Pressure and volume relationships in the the ventricle, conus and arterial arches of the frog heart. *J. exp. Biol.*, **43**, 479–488.

Simons, J. R. (1959). The distribution of the blood from the heart in some amphibia. *Proc. zool. Soc. Lond.*, **132**, 51–64.

Tucker, V. A. (1967). Method for oxygen content and dissociation curves on microlitre blood samples. *J. appl. Physiol.*, **23**, 410–414.

Wiederhielm, C. A., Woodbury, J. W., Kirk, S. and Rushmer, R. F. (1964). Pulsatile pressures in the microcirculation of frog's mesentery. *Am. J. Physiol.*, **207**, 173–176.

Wilson, B., Hansard, S. L. and Cole, B. T. (1960). Total blood volume of the turtle and the frog. *Proc. La. Acad. Sci.*, **23**, 45–52.

EXPERIMENTS ON THE ROLE OF THE NERVOUS SYSTEM IN CIRCULATORY AND RESPIRATORY CONTROL

Dale, D. and Mines, G. R. (1914). The influence of nerve stimulation on the cardiogram. *J. Physiol., Lond.*, **46**, 319–336.

Frank, K. and Becker, M. C. (1964). Microelectrodes for recording and stimulation. *In* "Physical Techniques in Biological Research", Vol. V, (W. L. Nastuk, ed.). Academic Press, New York and London.

Gaskell, W. M. (1884). On the augmentor (acclerator) nerves of the heart of cold-blooded animals. *J. Physiol., Lond.*, **5**, 46–8.

Gaskell, W. M. (1886). The structure, distribution, and function of the nerves which innervate the visceral and vascular system. *J. Physiol., Lond.*, **7**, 1–80

Iriuchijima, J. (1963). Diencephalic cardiovascular controls in toads. *Jap. J. Physiol.*, **13**, 333–40.

Ishii, K., Honda, K. and Ishii, K. (1966). The function of the carotid labyrinth in the toad. *Tohoku J. exp. Med.*, **88**, 103–116.

Ito, F. and Watanabe, S. (1962). Localization and organization of respiratory neurons in the brain-stem of the toad, with reference to the activities of the slow motor system. *Jap. J. Physiol.*, **12**, 611–22.

Jones, D. R. (1966). Factors affecting the recovery from diving bradycardia in the frog. *J. exp. Biol.*, **44**, 397–411.

Niel, E. and Zotterman, Y. (1950). Cardiac vagal afferent fibres in the cat and frog. *Acta. physiol. scand.*, **20**, 160–165.

Niel, E., Strom, L. and Zotterman, Y. (1950). Action potential studies of afferent fibres in the IXth and Xth cranial nerves of the frog. *Acta. physiol. scand.*, **20**, 338–350.

Oka, K. (1958a). The influence of the transection of the brain upon the respiratory movement of the frog (Japanese). *J. physiol. Soc. Japan*, **20**, 513–9.

Oka, K. (1958b). Further studies on the localisation of the respiratory centres of the frog (Japanese). *J. physiol. Soc. Japan*, **20**, 520–4.

APPENDIX

Static and Dynamic Calibration of pressure transducers and blood flowmeters.

In virtually all cases one is interested in calibrating the response not only of the flow or pressure transducer but also of the amplification and recording systems. The descriptions below are given with this in mind.

STATIC CALIBRATION

Pressure Transducers

For static calibration of pressure transducers one requires a vertical column of liquid and a ruler. The liquid column is connected to the transducer and the level of the fluid in the column varied. The deflection produced on the recording device for a given difference in levels is noted. The pressure applied to the transducer is $h\rho g$ (h = difference in levels, cm, ρ = density of fluid, gm/cc, and g = 981 cm sec^{-1} sec^{-1}). However for physiological pressure measurements a zero level must be established. With air filled manometers this is readily achieved by connecting the transducer to the atmosphere. With saline filled manometers the simplest system is to connect the transducer to a vertical column of saline the meniscus of which is at the same level as the tip of any attached catheter. Having established the reference zero the transducer is then connected to either a U-tube manometer (air filled systems) or a further vertical column of saline (saline filled systems). The difference between the fluid in both limbs of the manometer, or between the meniscus in level on the liquid column and that of the zero reference column, is adjusted to encompass the normal range expected during an experiment, i.e. pressures recorded from the respiratory tract will be of the order of 2–10 cm H_2O (air filled transducer); blood pressures 20–60 cm H_2O (saline filled transducer). The set up used by Shelton and Jones (1965, 1968) for blood pressure recording is illustrated in Fig. 8a.

Blood Flowmeter

Basically, calibrating a flowmeter system consists of letting blood or saline flow through an excised artery at various known rates. A flow probe is located around the vessel and the recorder deflections produced are plotted against the different flowrates. This determination is one of probe sensitivity and must be performed with every probe. Most flowmeter manuals give entirely adequate descriptions. Ideally, recorder outputs during laminar and turbulent flow should be investigated. Case *et al.* (1966) have successfully substituted cellulose dialysis tubing for blood vessel segments in electromagnetic flowmeter calibrations. Most authors find some difference in sensitivity between saline and blood of various haematocrits when calibrating electromagnetic blood flowmeters. This difference may be as large as 20% at flow rates of around 200 ml/min. With anuran amphibians maximum flow rates are of the order of 5–10 ml/min and any difference between saline and blood calibrations at these flowrates is well within the noise level of the instrument.

An alternative method of determining probe sensitivity is to record flow through the blood vessel *in situ*.

1. At the end of the experiment the vessel is cannulated downstream of the flow transducer.

2. A screw clip is placed on the cannula so that outflow can be varied and the cannula is closed off with a pair of haemostats.

3. A 1 ml tuberculin syringe (minus plunger) is attached to the end of the cannula. The haemostats are removed and the time taken for 1 ml (or less) of blood to flow into the syringe barrel is noted. The recorder deflection is plotted against flow rate. The blood is injected back into the animal so that a large number of determinations can be made, at various flow rates.

DYNAMIC CALIBRATION

Pressure Transducer

The ideal method of calibrating manometric systems is to apply as oscillating pressure of constant amplitude and progressively increasing frequency to the end of the catheter. Several devices for applying known forced vibrations to manometers have been described (Yanof *et al.* 1963). Both amplitude and phase of the vibration must be recorded with reasonable accuracy. Since heart rates of amphibia are low (30–60 beats/min) accurate recording of arterial pulse waves is not normally required above 5–10 cyc/sec (> 87% of the variance of the arterial pulse wave is represented by 3 harmonics). For accurate recording of amplitude and phase up to this limit, the natural frequency of the manometer should be 5–10 times this frequency and the damping less than 0·1 of critical damping. (McDonald, 1960). In many cases the damping is inherently greater than this (Shelton and Jones, 1968) and the optimum under these conditions is between 0·6–0·8 of critical since phase distortion increases almost linearly with frequency and therefore can easily be allowed for (McDonald, 1960). Consequently the need for accurate calibration of the manometer with respect to the frequency range being investigated is apparent.

The easiest method of assessing the dynamic characteristics of a manometric system is to subject it to a sudden pressure change and study its free vibrations (providing damping is less than critical). A thick walled rubber or polythene tube, closed at one end, filled with saline may be used to generate the sudden pressure change. The catheter is introduced through the wall of the tube. Slight suction is applied orally to the end of the tube which is then blocked by the tongue. Rapid removal of the tongue causes an immediate restoration of pressure and if damping is

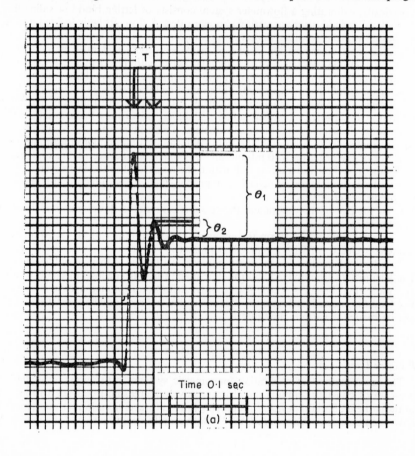

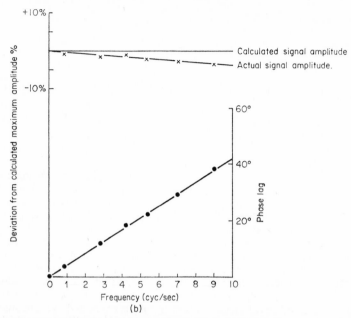

FIG. 16. Dynamic calibration of pressure transducers and blood flowmeters. (a) Response of a saline filled electro-manometer and catheter to a sudden change in pressure at the catheter tip. (b) Frequency response of a pulsed-logic electromagnetic blood flowmeter showing amplitude (above) and phase (below) frequency dependence. The flow signal was compared to piston displacement. Records were analysed numerically and resolved into sine and cosine coefficients by the method of Fourier. Signal amplitude is expressed as percentage charge from the calculated value. Phase lag is in degrees.

less than critical there is first an overshoot followed by oscillations dying away exponentially (Fig. 16a). Figure 16a will be used to illustrate the calculation.

The period of one complete oscillation $= T = 0 \cdot 025$ sec.
Deflection from final equilibrium position:

$$\text{at end of first cycle} \qquad = \theta_1 = 10 \cdot 75 \text{ mm}$$
$$\text{at end of second cycle} \qquad = \theta^2 = 2 \cdot 25 \text{ mm}$$

Then: Damping (as a proportion of critical damping)

$$= \frac{\ln \theta_1 - \ln \theta_2}{\sqrt{4\pi^2 + (\ln \theta_1 - \ln \theta_2)^2}}$$

when ln is a natural logarithm i.e. to base e.

$$= \frac{1 \cdot 56}{6 \cdot 47} = 0 \cdot 24$$

$\therefore$ Damping is 24% of critical.

Natural frequency (cyc/sec)

$$= \frac{\sqrt{4\pi^2 + (\ln \theta_1 - \ln \theta_2)^2}}{2\pi T}$$

$$= \frac{6\cdot 47}{0\cdot 157} = 41\cdot 2$$

$\therefore$ Frequency response is $41\cdot 2$ cyc/sec.

As an approximation: frequency response $= 1/T$ cyc/sec.

Flowmeters

Dynamic calibration of flowmeters can be performed either by passing a known sinusoidal flow, generated by a pump, through an arterial segment around which is a flow probe, or by using an electrically generated analogue of a sinusoidal flow signal (Grassner and Berger 1964; Goodman, 1966). Pulsatile flow can also be generated manually. (Inouye and Kuga 1954).

Sinusoidal flow can be generated by a pump similar to that described by Taylor (1957). The pump generates almost a perfect sinusoidal flow and the flowmeter output may be analysed with a harmonic resolver (Taylor, 1957; O'Rourke, 1965). Alternatively movement of the piston may be monitored with either a velocity or displacement recorder. The pump is connected by rigid tapering tubes (perspex or lead) to the blood vessel segment which in turn is connected to a pressure reservoir. The pressure reservoir consists of a large bottle of saline, into which air is pumped over the surface of the saline, until the pressure is between 30–60 mm Hg.

Comparing flowmeter output with piston movement provides a quick and fairly adequate means of analysis. Doubling the frequency of the pump will double flowmeter output providing that the amplitude response is frequency independent. Similarly phase relationships can be assessed by comparing piston velocity to flowmeter output at such times as maximum flow velocity or zero flow. Alternatively the flow signal may be resolved into the sine and cosine components of the fundamental oscillation (first harmonic) using, for instance, piston displacement as a reference signal. The sine and cosine coefficients (A and B, respectively, if the piston movement is of sine form; B and A, if of cosine form) are related to the amplitude and phase by

$$M^2 = A^2 + B^2 \text{ and } \tan \theta = B/A.$$

The phase lag and ratio of modulus to calculated maximum velocity (V max $= 2 \times$ frequency of piston $\times$ piston area $\times \frac{1}{2}$ piston stroke) are plotted against frequency (O'Rourke, 1965). Resolution of flow signal into sine and cosine components can be performed arithmetically, (Cole, 1945) but this introduces measurement errors in the analysis of records and an harmonic resolver (Taylor 1957, O'Rourke, 1965) is preferable.

REFERENCES

STATIC AND DYNAMIC CALIBRATION OF PRESSURE TRANSDUCERS AND BLOOD FLOWMETERS

Case, R. B., Roselle, H. A. and Nassar, M. E. (1966). Simplified method for calibration of electromagnetic flowmeters. *Med. Res. Eng.*, **5**, 38–40.
Cole, L. S. (1945). Graphical analysis of complex waves. *Electronics*, **18**, 142–5.

Goodman, A. H. (1966). Electronic dynamic calibration of electromagnetic flow-meters. *J. appl. Physiol.*, **21**, 933–7.

Grassner, U. and Berger, D. (1964). Frequency response of electromagnetic flow-meters. *J. appl. Physiol.*, **19**, 1209–11.

Inouye, A. and Kuga, H. (1954). On the applicability of the electromagnetic flow-meter for the measurement of blood flow rate. Studies on the flow pattern in the peripheral artery 1. *Jap. J. Physiol.*, **4**, 205–20.

O'Rourke, M. F. (1965). Dynamic accuracy of the electromagnetic flowmeter. *J. appl. Physiol.*, **20**, 142–7.

Shelton, G. and Jones, D. R. (1968). A comparative study of central blood pressure in five amphibians. *J. exp. Biol.* (In press).

Taylor, M. G. (1957). An approach to an analysis of the arterial pulse wave. II. Fluid oscillations in an elastic pipe. *Physics Med. Biol.*, **1**, 321–9.

Yanof, H. M., Rosen, A. L., McDonald, N. M. and McDonald, D. M. (1963). A critical study of the response of manometers to forced oscillations. *Physics Med. Biol.*, **8**, 407–22.

Exp. in Physiol. and Biochem. (1970). 3, 295–332.

9 | Two Experiments Using the Dog Lung Apparatus:* Study of Deterioration of Preparation and Prolonged Veno-venous Perfusion

JACK L. RATLIFF

Naval Hospital, National Naval Medical Center, Bethesda, Maryland, U.S.A.

EXPERIMENT I: GENERAL PRINCIPLES THAT THE EXPERIMENTS AND METHODS WILL ILLUSTRATE

The isolated lung apparatus can effectively contribute to respiratory support (Ratliff, 1968a).

In Experiment I: Isolated dog lung apparatus; study of its deterioration, we are evaluating the isolated lung apparatus as it deteriorates with time.

In Experiment II: Prolonged veno-venous perfusion experiment; serial homologous lungs used in the study of a system of chronic pulmonary support we are evaluating the effects of interaction of this lung apparatus and an animal that it is supporting through veno-venous circuitry.

This work was undertaken to evaluate the possible use of heterogeneous lungs as gas exchange units for supporting human respiration.

ISOLATED DOG LUNG APPARATUS; STUDY OF ITS DETERIORATION

APPARATUS

Chest Lung Container

This is described in detail (design and construction) by the author in a previous publication (Ratliff, 1968b). The container is vinyl plastic, made in the same general proportions as a dog's thorax. The empty container can be cleaned, packaged, sterilized and stored easily. The lung can be sealed within it and the unit can be handled for storage under refrigeration, or inserted into the perfusion system. The lightweight apparatus can be easily tilted during the experiment to prevent atelectasis. The sterile shell provides support for the delicate lung tissue and prevents axial rotation of the lobes. It is inexpensive and only one is required for a perfusion. The shell can be made in any size, can be sterilized by gas and is reusable.

* Please see note on page ix concerning vivisection and guiding principles in the care and use of animals.

Environmental Chamber

The environmental chamber is used to enclose the pump, the vinyl lung container, the flow line and the regulatory devices. The chamber is maintained at a controlled temperature. It should be mainly transparent and should have portholes that enable viewing and easy manipulation of the contents (Ratliff, 1968b).

One Ventilator

This will be used for the isolated lung. We use a Bird Mark VIII ventilator driven by compressed air. Any clinical respirator, or a Harvard respirator, would suffice.

One Blood Pump

For the perfusion, we employ a Sarnes No. 3500 roller pump but any other relatively atraumatic blood pump would suffice. Optimally, the pump should afford manual pumping when desired and should allow easy insertion of the flow line without threading it through the pump, a maneuver that makes maintenance of sterile technique awkward.

One Perfusion Line

The perfusion line should be seamless and of Silastic or other pliable material that would withstand the autoclave, to facilitate cleaning and sterilizing (see *Experimental Details*).

Two Three-way Stopcocks

These are for the perfusion line.

Two U-shaped Manometers

These are for determination of mercurial or of saline pressure in the perfusion line and in the airway, respectively.

One Laboratory Thermometer

This is to monitor the temperature in the environmental chamber.

Laboratory Equipment and Reagents

Those appropriate to perform routine blood chemistry and blood–gas determinations, routine hematologic studies, serum protein electrophoresis, serum-free hemoglobin determination, animal X-rays, electrocardiograms and bacteriologic studies.

Surgical Support Facilities

These should include the necessary tables, "drapes", gloves, gowns, instruments, autoclave, gas sterilizer and refrigerator.

One young healthy dog without heart worms, for each perfusion.

CHEMICAL SOLUTIONS

1. Antiseptic solution for skin preparation (Betadine [povodine-iodine]), one liter.
2. Heparin sodium 10 mg/cc for intravenous use. Two 10 cc vials.
3. Nembutal sodium (pentobarbital sodium), 5 mg/cc, 50 cc.
4. Sterile lactated Ringer's solution, 2 l.

DETAILS OF EXPERIMENT

The Lung Apparatus

1. Dogs to provide the lungs for the perfusions are screened for heart worms (*Dirofilaria immitis*) with two thick smears drawn late in the afternoon. (Counts of microfilaria are higher in the afternoon, therefore, specimens taken at that time lend to greater diagnostic accuracy.) Heart worm infestations obstruct the pulmonary artery and adversely affect these studies. During long perfusions the microfilariae may die and their toxic products, or the bacteria within them, may alter the expected results of these perfusions. The dogs should be in good general health. We have noted that even the healthiest dogs have low serum albumin levels, which increases their tendency to develop pulmonary edema (Guyton and Lindsey, 1959). The younger and generally healthier dogs tend to have higher albumin levels. Small dogs (10 to 15 kg) are usually used because they cost less.

2. The dog is heavily sedated, restrained in the supine position, and intubated by way of the trachea. The dog is ventilated mechanically. The ventilation is important because occasionally a dog succumbs to hypoxia before it can be exsanguinated and its untimely death does not allow the collection of sufficient blood for the perfusion experiment. Hypoxemia also adds to the blood waste products. During exsanguination, balanced salt solution is administered to keep the tissue perfused and to wash out a sufficient quantity of blood for the experiment before the release of the toxic agents that develop in large quantities in the shock state.

3. Heparin sodium (2·0 mg/kg) is given intravenously. The dog's femoral artery is cannulated aseptically. The blood is collected in a sterile container. The dog's femoral vein is similarly cannulated to enable rapid crystalloid infusion. The dog is rapidly exsanguinated, from the femoral artery, until the blood flow diminishes, at which time one liter of Ringer's lactate solution is infused rapidly by the femoral vein. The blood is collected in 500 cc aliquots. This blood must be numbered in the order collected. Blood from the first

bottle must be used in the perfusion, for it has the highest albumin and hemo-globin content and the lowest level of the toxic agents liberated in the agonal state. This flushing solution should be administered cold (0°C to 10°C) in order to maintain and preserve the lung tissue in a physiological state until the perfusion is begun.

4. As the washout return declines, the dog's chest is opened down the midline, with sterile technique, taking care to clamp the caval system as soon as possible lest air be sucked into it from torn mediastinal vessels and thus compromise the preparation (Fig. 1). The caval and azygous veins are ligated

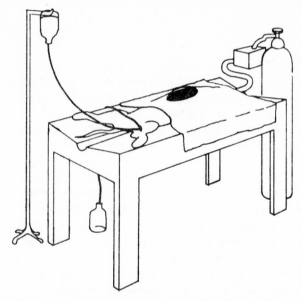

FIG. 1. Donor dog properly cannulated for the sterile excision of heart and lungs.

and transected first. The aortic arch is then transected at the level of the great vessels, without clamping, because air can be evacuated from the left side of the heart easily. The heart and lungs are dissected from the diaphragm, remaining attached only to the trachea. The esophagus is left in place in the thorax and care is taken not to enter it, in order to maintain sterile technique. The lungs are inflated. The trachea is clamped and transected high above the clamp, in the base of the neck, leaving the lungs inflated.

5. The heart and lungs are cannulated (Fig. 2). Separating the pulmonary artery from the aorta is a meticulous procedure since the pulmonary artery is friable and can very easily be lacerated. The aorta is ligated with a stout tie at the level of the sinuses of Valsalva, to occlude the coronary ostia and to prevent air or bacteria from entering the blood stream. The pulmonary artery

is clamped, to prevent air from entering it and the pulmonary outflow tract is opened. The right atrium, right ventricle, and the proximal pulmonary artery and the pulmonary arterial cannula are filled with Ringer's lactate solution.

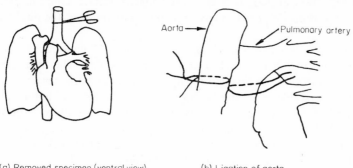

(a) Removed specimen (ventral view)   (b) Ligation of aorta

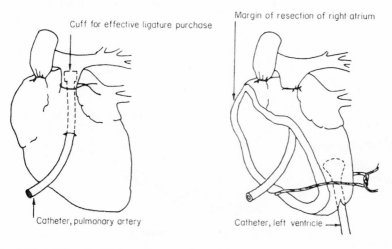

(c) Cannulation of pulmonary artery   (d) Cannulation for closed venous return

FIG. 2. Cannulation of the heart and the lungs.

As the pulmonary artery is unclamped and the heart is gently massaged to express any air, the cannula is advanced into and affixed around, the proximal pulmonary artery. The cannula must be clamped at this point in time to prevent air from entering the pulmonary vascular bed. The right atrium, the right ventricle and any vestige of the parietal pericardium are excised.
6. The left ventricle is stabbed at its apex and the funnel-shaped catheter is inserted and tied in place with umbilical tape around the ventricle. Even

though the ventricle has become firm from the cold flushing during exsanguination and from hypocalcemic tetany, the tie will tear through the ventricle and will ruin the apparatus if anything other than wide tape is used. The left ventricle, now elevated, is filled with Ringer's lactate solution. While the atrium and ventricle are massaged to express any bubbles, the outflow line is clamped.

7. The lung is fitted into the lung container and the endotracheal tubing is tied in place within the trachea and clamped outside. The other tubes are threaded to the outside through the apertures in the container and the entire container is sealed with sterile tape. A small catheter is left in an extra aperture and its entrance is plugged with cotton. This allows aspiration of any hilar lymph, of pleural effusion, or of condensation during the process of perfusion. It also enables balancing of air pressure around the lung with the atmosphere during ventilation, in sterile fashion.

8. Care is taken to avoid rotating a lung or a lobe about its hilar attachment. The ends of the cannulae are covered to maintain sterility if there is a delay in performing the perfusion. It now can be handled without gloves (Fig. 3).

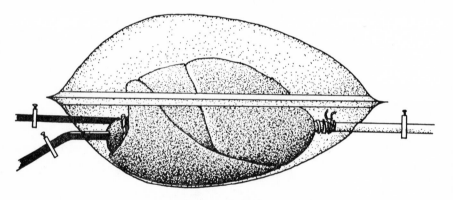

FIG. 3. Sealed lung preparation.

9. In many descriptions of isolated lung preparations in the literature, sterile technique is not emphasized. Because we plan ultimately to use these isolated lungs as gas exchange units in human veno-venous perfusion circuits, sterile technique is important. The lung can be maintained frequently for six or more hours in this apparatus. Over this time span even minimal contamination at the beginning of the perfusion would permit massive bacterial overgrowth and resultant metabolic toxicity with alterations in the physiology. Such toxic effects are well demonstrated in the standardized gram negative shock preparations.

Circuitry for Perfusion

10. Exclusive of the lung apparatus described, the circuit consists of a withdrawal reservoir and a blood pump. It is a one piece, hand fabricated unit which prevents the entrance of air or of bacteria into the system. The system itself is made of Silastic and its joints are sealed with Medical Adhesive Silicone Type A (Dow Corning) (Fig. 4). This system can easily be cleansed with chemicals and sterilized by heat. It is durable during multiple perfusions.

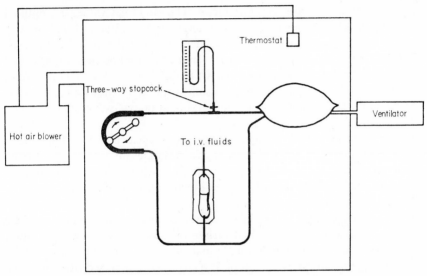

FIG. 4. Silastic circuitry with lung preparation, pump and environmental chamber.

11. The vertical collapsible reservoir is placed lower than the lung preparation in order to siphon blood from the left side of the heart and to avoid increased left atrial pressure, which would promote pulmonary edema (Guyton and Lindsey, 1959). This reservoir is necessary to keep the system filled and to act as a warning if the pump rate should exceed the return of blood from the lung preparation. The reservoir must hold a range of one to five times the stroke volume of the pump, depending on the sophistication of the monitoring system for the pump rate. Additional fluids may be easily added to the system through the top of the reservoir. The construction of this reservoir enables the system to be without an air-fluid interface. The reservoir acts effectively as a flutter valve to prevent the catastrophic entrance of air into the system. Representative samples of blood may be taken from the stopcock in the return line from which the pressure is also monitored. This stopcock remains under positive pressure, an arrangement that eliminates the risk of air or of bacteria entering the system.

12. The entire circuit is enclosed in an environmental chamber (Ratliff, 1968b) which regulates the temperature of the circuit easily. This chamber prevents the risks of thermal protein denaturation, of coagulation and of bacterial multiplication that would occur in areas of stagnant flow often found in heat exchangers. The chamber also prevents increased priming volume required by the conventional heat exchangers.

Beginning the Perfusion

13. In this study, we are recycling blood. The blood gas values are optimal after one passage through the gas exchanger and respiratory alkalosis will rapidly follow. Any other form of isolated circuitry also has its problems. Optimally, the lung should be in a veno-venous circuit of perfusion that would constantly supply it with normal venous blood. Such a veno-venous circuit carries with it such problems as perfusion of the lung with nonautogenous blood and the interaction of the tissue antigen-antibody systems of the support animal and of the lung itself.

14. The most nearly physiological system to recycle blood within a lung preparation would be one which serially incorporates an artificial membrane blood–gas exchange device. With the membrane exchanger most of the oxygen could be deleted from the arterialized blood and carbon dioxide could be added.

15. By serially cycling two lung preparations and ventilating one with air and the other with a nitrogen and carbon dioxide mixture, one preparation could be maintained in a condition approximating the physiological state. The lung selected to deplete the circuit of oxygen could be perfused either forward or backwards through its vascular bed. By using two lungs in a circuit of this nature the tissue antigen-antibody problems would again be introduced and also the possible aberrations would be produced by perfusing the oxygen extracting preparation with arterialized blood. This would defeat our purpose, for this is why we are using the extra lung.

16. The circuit is filled from the first-drawn 500 cc of blood collected during exsanguination. The donor's blood only, is used. The reservoir is filled to the 200 cc mark with this blood, which has been warmed to 37°C. Baseline blood samples are drawn. The pump is begun slowly (100 to 200 cc/min, initially) to allow the lung to warm, and to allow hemoconcentration throughout the pulmonary capillary bed. During the next 5 min the pump is accelerated gradually to the level described in the experimenter's protocol.

17. One-sixth to one-seventh of the total volume of an animal's blood is continuously present in its pulmonary vascular bed under baseline conditions (Lindsey *et al.*, 1957). The quantity of blood required to fill the perfused lung is provided by the full reservoir during the first few minutes of the perfusion. The level of the reservoir drops as the pump is accelerated but usually

stabilizes with the addition of a minimal volume of blood to the reservoir. We have found that the weight of the lungs increases by the weight of the blood drawn from the reservoir as the perfusion commences and as it stabilizes, until pulmonary edema develops. At that time, more blood is required to fill the reservoir and the lung preparation gets heavier. Also, the compliance and the ability of the lung to extract oxygen deteriorate just prior to the development of overt pulmonary edema.

18. Pulmonary edema develops eventually and does so from one or two lobes at a time. This can be shown by clamping the affected lobe at its hilum. The tracheal froth will cease immediately and the rest of the lung will function well for some time before developing pulmonary edema. The edematous lobe usually looks more consolidated and more hemorrhagic and will have been the most dependent lobe throughout the perfusion. It is interesting to note that the production of tracheal froth is accelerated when positive pressure ventilation is stopped, even if perfusion has been stopped.

19. We prefer to have the reservoir nearly empty during the perfusion to avoid having an area of stagnation that favors multiplication of bacteria and the formation of thrombi. Such an area also provides a space wherein levels of metabolites differ from those of the effective circulating blood volume. To avoid diluting or concentrating the perfusate, we prefer to have a leakproof system which does not require the addition of fresh blood to maintain volume. The reclaiming and reinjection of fluid dissipated into the cavity of the vinyl chest shell would be practical were it not for the problem of maintaining sterile technique.

20. As we begin the perfusion we are alert for lacerations unwittingly made of the pulmonary vessels and for congenital defects which require repair or discarding of the preparation. Sterile technique must be adhered to any time the vinyl shell is opened. Patent ducti or small septal defects can be repaired easily whereas most other defects cannot. These problems are often first noted as the vinyl shell fills with blood at the beginning of the experiment.

Maintenance of Perfusion

21. Our purpose is not to maintain the lung but to study various parameters of its function as it deteriorates within this system. During the perfusion we add nothing to the system but 10 mg of heparin per hour. The preparation is ventilated with air. It is tilted from side to side for an hour each, keeping its trachea dependent, to promote drainage.

22. Regardless of the degree of sophistication of the monitoring system, human surveillance is necessary, lest leaks in the system, or other unforeseen events, occur.

23. Blood samples may be drawn during this perfusion at any time. Histological studies may be performed terminally but serial biopsies taken of the

lung make for air leaks, an event that muddles the compliance studies. Bacteriologic, arteriographic and plastic injection casting studies may be performed.

24. We assume that the baseline cardiac output for dogs is 100 cc/kg/min. After perfusion has stabilized, at the beginning and every hour, drop the rate of perfusion to 25% of the predicted cardiac output of the donor dog and record the pulmonary arterial pressure. Increase the perfusion rate by 25% increments and record pressures at each increment. Take readings to 200% of the dog's cardiac output and perfuse at its cardiac output for the interval between each group of determinations.

25. Initially and hourly, allow the lung to collapse for 5 min; clamp the trachea and make a reading of static pressure. Add air by increments of 100 cc. Allow 15 sec for equilibration before recording static pressures from the airway, with each addition of 100 cc. Continue inflation until the pressure exceeds 50 cm of water or until the lung appears to be inflated normally. With the same sequence of volumes and time lapses for equilibration, deflate the lung and record pressures. Between the determinations ventilate the lung to what appears to be normal volume, usually requiring no more than 15 cm of water pressure at peak of inflation. Every 15 min, sigh the lungs by inflation to 40 cm of water pressure to maintain optimal surfactant activity.

26. Maintain the perfusions until they have run 6 h, or until overt edema develops.

SAMPLE RESULTS

Included are sample results from a perfusion in which overt pulmonary edema occurred at 3 h and 15 min. No carbon clearance studies were attempted on this preparation. The lung apparatus was not weighed. Ours was a study of the pulmonary vascular resistance at varying rates of perfusion and of the lung's compliance curve, all recorded at intervals in the deterioration of the preparation, with time. Histologic studies were made of samples of the lung tissue after edema developed (Figs 5, 6, 7).

The author has presented a method for perfusing isolated lung preparations. This experiment was set up to study such a preparation as it deteriorated with time. Several parameters of lung function: vascular resistance, compliance and histologic change, are evaluated in this study. Various other methods of perfusing lungs are discussed. They are: by a serial circuit of two such lung preparations, by one lung and one membrane gas exchanger, and by one lung preparation in a veno-venous perfusion circuit.

In the particular perfusion recorded, the lung continued to function 3 h and 15 min, as mentioned. Its vascular resistance remained linear with flow and did not change significantly as the lung deteriorated. Pulmonary compliance, however, rose sharply as pulmonary edema developed. The histology of the pulmonary parenchyma at the termination of the perfusion revealed large areas of edema, atelectasis, emphysema, and interstitial and inter- alveolar hemorrhage similar to those changes described by Veith *et al.* (1967) and said to be characteristic of lung lesions seen in: hemorrhagic shock, post- perfusion lung syndrome, gram negative shock and others.

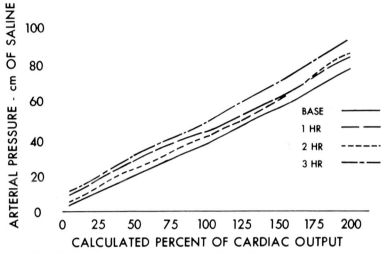

FIG. 5. Vascular resistance curves from isolated lung perfusion study.

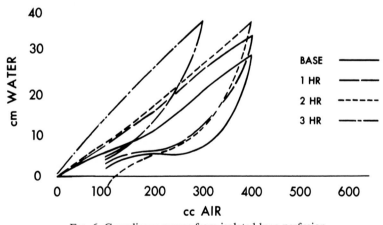

FIG. 6. Compliance curves from isolated lung perfusion.

TROUBLESHOOTING

The lung apparatus is dependable. It must be prepared without lacerating the vascular, or the tracheo-bronchial, tree of the heart and lungs. Congenital anomalies have been mentioned earlier. They can usually be corrected as the

o

perfusion is begun, without discarding the lung. As stated in Details of Experiment (20), sterile technique must be adhered to when the vinyl chest shell is opened.

The preparation should be inclined and propped, first to one side, and then to the other, every hour, and the trachea must be slanted downward to promote its drainage. The lungs must be occasionally deep-sighed to make the surfactant function more effectively. We have not encountered a hemorrhagic diathesis except in lung preparations that were stored in a refrigerator for

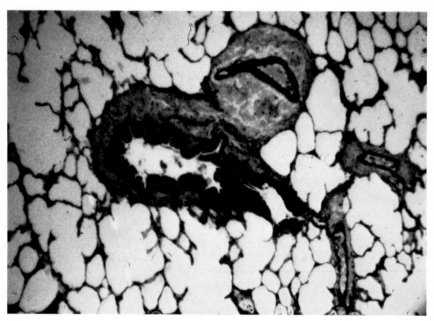

FIG. 7. Microscopic section of bronchiole and pulmonary arteriole, showing interstitial hemorrhage. (H & E) ×315.

prolonged periods (more than one day); however, theoretically, if the donor dog had gross defects in its coagulation system or if a noticeable deficiency of platelets developed during the perfusion, a hemorrhagic diathesis could occur and could destroy the preparation.

Pulmonary edema that develops prematurely because of occlusion of outflow from kinked lines, or because the pump rate is excessive for a moment and line collapse develops, can be reversed and can be gradually alleviated to a near normal functional state. Reversal of pulmonary edema takes 15 to 30 min and probably is an indication to discard the lung, for edema will muddle the results.

The author's limited experience with perfusions at over twice the calculated cardiac output for the donor dog and at perfusion temperatures of over 40°C suggest that these conditions jeopardize the survival time of the lung. Although we have not specifically evaluated the effects of sepsis on the isolated lung apparatus, we do know that the duration of many of these perfusions extend into time ranges compatible with heavy bacterial overgrowth. On theoretical grounds we feel that alterations of the vascular dynamics and cellular metabolism of the lung are likely to result from bacterial toxins and therefore, again, the maintenance of sterile technique is requisite.

PROJECTED EXPERIMENTS USING THIS EQUIPMENT

The relative merits of this perfusion apparatus compared to such an apparatus in a veno-venous perfusion circuit, or in a series with a biological or artificial membrane deoxygenator, have been discussed briefly in the Beginning the Perfusion section; these other systems each have merit. An application of the most complex of them, veno-venous perfusion, constitutes the second experiment, to be described in this text.

The chief disadvantage of this perfusion circuit is the alkalosis and the abnormal gas relationship that develops for lack of a deoxygenator. This could be circumvented by ventilating the lung apparatus with a variable gas mixture that would keep the oxygen and carbon dioxide concentrations in a range between those of normal arterial and venous blood. Deviations in pH could be corrected by the addition of appropriate buffers. Such a modification of this system has not been worked out to our knowledge, but may be worthwhile.

Alveolar absorptive and excretory functions and various other phases of the lung's physiology are amenable to a study with this apparatus. This apparatus would help to illuminate some of the problems encountered in the storage and transplantation of organs. The application of xenon[133] scanning or of light microscopic study of the pulmonary circulation of this system would have practical uses.

Recent work described by Belzer et al. (1968) and Eiseman (1968) suggests that all isolated organ perfusions should be conducted with cell-free lipoprotein extracted perfusate. We have not used this approach as yet, but it appears to have promise.

EXPERIMENT II: GENERAL PRINCIPLES THAT THE EXPERIMENTS AND METHODS WILL ILLUSTRATE

The isolated lung apparatus can effectively contribute to respiratory support in a veno-venous perfusion system (Ratliff, 1968a).

In Experiment I: Isolated dog lung apparatus; study of its deterioration, we evaluate the isolated lung apparatus as it deteriorates with time.

In Experiment II: Prolonged veno-venous perfusion experiment; serial homologous lungs used in the study of a system of chronic pulmonary support, we examine the effects of the interaction of this lung apparatus and an animal that it is supporting through veno-venous circuitry.

This work was undertaken to evaluate the possible use of heterogeneous lungs as gas exchange units in the support of human respiratory insufficiency.

PROLONGED VENO-VENOUS PERFUSION EXPERIMENT; SERIAL HOMOLOGOUS LUNGS USED IN THE STUDY OF A SYSTEM OF CHRONIC PULMONARY SUPPORT

APPARATUS

Operating Table

This table allows for placing and restraining the patient dog in any position. It is so designed that operations on the neck, chest, abdomen, or groin can be performed. The table must allow rotation to the side or to the prone position without disturbing the perfusion cannulae. It cannot restrict respiration or access to the airway and must be tolerated by the conscious dog for prolonged periods. It must allow, in all positions, for feeding and for collecting body wastes. (Discussed further, under Experimental Details.)

Work Table

This is for the lung preparation. Its height is adjustable. It is portable and should have storage space and electrical outlets sufficient to support the experiment. It must be so designed that it can be placed effectively against the operating table.

Chest Lung Container

This is described in detail (design and construction) by the author in a previous publication (Ratliff, 1968b). The container is vinyl plastic, made in the same general proportions as a dog's thorax. The empty container can be cleaned, packaged, sterilized and stored easily. The lung can be sealed within it and the unit can be handled for storage under refrigeration, or inserted into the perfusion system. The lightweight apparatus can be easily tilted during the experiment, to prevent atelectasis. The sterile shell provides support for the delicate lung tissue and prevents axial rotation of the lobes. It is inexpensive and only one is required for each lung preparation. The shell can be made in any size, can be sterilized by gas, and is reusable.

Environmental Chamber

The environmental chamber is used to enclose the pump, the vinyl lung container, the flow line and the regulatory devices. The chamber is maintained at a controlled temperature. It should be mainly transparent and should have portholes that enable viewing and easy manipulation of the contents.

One Ventilator

We use a Bird Mark VIII ventilator driven by compressed air for the isolated lung. Any clinical respirator, or a Harvard respirator, would suffice.

One Blood Pump

We employ a Sarnes No. 3500 roller pump, but any other relatively atraumatic blood pump would suffice for the perfusion. Optimally, the pump should afford manual pumping when desired and should allow easy insertion of the flow line without threading it through the pump, a maneuver that makes maintenance of sterile technique awkward.

One Perfusion Line

This should be seamless and should be of Silastic or other pliable material that would withstand the autoclave to facilitate cleaning and sterilizing (see Experimental Details).

Vacuum Source

200 mm mercury with regulator and flexible tubing.

A Vacuum Chamber

This is for the withdrawal reservoir (see Experimental Details).

Withdrawal Catheters

A set of vinyl Bardic catheters for vascular cannulation, ranging from French size No. 20 to 40.

Return Catheters

We use thin-walled Teflon tubing of varying sizes, obtained from V. Meuller and Co., Atlanta, Georgia, U.S.A., which we cut into 6 cm lengths and wire to adapters for the return line. Caps, or stoppers, should be available, to enable the sealing of these adapters.

Arterial Cannulae

Two disposable arterial catheters to monitor the arterial pressure.

Four Three-way Stopcocks

These are for the perfusion line.

Two U-shaped Manometers

These are for determination of mercurial or of saline pressure in the perfusion line and in the airway, respectively.

Two Laboratory Thermometers or Two Thermocouples

These are to monitor the temperature in the environmental chamber and of the patient dog.

Cardiac Defibrillator

This is for external defibrillation, should respiratory or vascular accidents occur, requiring resuscitation.

Laboratory Equipment and Reagents

Those appropriate to perform: blood chemistry and blood-gas determinations, hematologic studies, serum protein electrophoresis, serum-free hemoglobin determination, X-rays, electrocardiograms and bacteriologic studies.

Surgical Support Facilities

These should include the necessary tables, "drapes", gloves, gowns, instruments, autoclave, gas sterilizer and refrigerator.

ANIMALS

Young healthy dogs without heart worms, cross-matched, weighing 10–25 kg. Two dogs are required for beginning the perfusion, and others are required, one for each 6 h of perfusion.

CHEMICAL SOLUTIONS

1. Antiseptic solution for skin preparation (Betadine [povodine-iodine]), one liter.
2. Heparin sodium 10 mg/cc for intravenous use. Twenty vials of 10 cc each.
3. Nembutal sodium (pentobarbital sodium), 5 mg/cc, 500 cc.
4. Lactated Ringer's solution for intravenous use, 20 l.
5. Dextrose, 5% in water, for intravenous use, 20 l.
6. Local anesthetic, 30 to 50 cc, Xylocaine (lidocaine) 1%.
7. Sodium cephalothin (Keflin), 1 g vials for intravenous use, 20 vials.
8. Digoxin (Lanoxin), 0·5 mg vials for intravenous use, 10 vials.
9. Methylprednisolone sodium succinate (Solu-Medrol), 40 mg, 5 vials.
10. Mineral oil, sterile, to lubricate cannulae, 1 oz.

DETAILS OF EXPERIMENT

The Patient Dog

1. Systematically condition the dogs to be used in this prolonged perfusion experiment. Too much time and equipment are invested in these perfusions to allow the dog's poor condition to invalidate an entire experiment. Anaphylaxis secondary to transfusion from a donor with heart worms; contamination from the use of dogs with pneumonia; or anemia from intestinal parasites, etc. are preventable; they invalidate results, and are factors that must be eliminated.

2. Dogs with long hair are used. Mosquitoes, which carry heart worms, cannot penetrate a heavy coat of hair, thus, long-haired dogs have a lower incidence of heart worms than short-haired dogs. Since we detect and eliminate dogs with heart worms by the findings of blood tests, we can decrease the number of dogs that must be examined, by using those with long hair. All animals are vaccinated against distemper and hepatitis. They are screened twice for heart worms, by examining thick preparations of blood smears taken in the afternoon. (Counts of microfilaria are higher in the afternoon, therefore, specimens taken at that time lend to greater diagnostic accuracy.) The animals are rid of cutaneous and intestinal parasites and fed and housed for at least three weeks before the experiment. No dogs are used if they have a hemoglobin concentration of less than $12 \cdot 0$ g %, white blood cell counts of more than 15 000, or if they are not young and in good health.

3. All of the potential lung donors are cross-matched with the patient dog. Do not feed the patient dog 24 h before the perfusion. By this, hyperlipemia, which increases the "pump trauma" to the blood is reduced and defecation by the animal at the beginning of the perfusion, when sterile technique is so critical, is also reduced. Only bitches are used as the patient dog because they run less risk of contaminating the operative field about the groin, should they void during cannulation.

4. The patient dog is given Nembutal for sedation, to the point of tolerating an endotracheal tube. We routinely insert an endotracheal tube in all heavily sedated dogs to prevent the loss of animals from hypoventilation, aspiration or obstruction of the airway. We feel that not only does mild to moderate hypoxia, so induced, occasionally threaten the life of these animals, but it also alters the vital signs by which we monitor our dogs at the beginning of the perfusion.

5. Immobilization of the upper extremities is done because otherwise, the dogs can free themselves partially or completely from this restraint. Threaded Kirschner wires are inserted horizontally through the distal humeri just proximal to the flair of the condyles. Well padded casts of plaster of Paris and felt are applied to all four extremities, immobilizing the elbow and knee joints. The casts are so applied that the knee and elbow joints are in 90° of

flexion. This lessens the likelihood of pulling out of a cast. Care is taken to incorporate the Kirschner wires firmly in the casts around the forelegs (Fig. 8).

6. Infection at the sites of the Kirschner wires has not been a problem for up to one week at a time. Shave the hair at the point where the wire goes into the skin and insert the wire with sterile technique. We cover the wounds with sterile gauze, and pad and cast the extremity for the duration of the experiment.

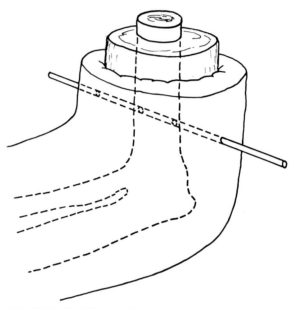

FIG. 8. Detail of K-wire through the humerus and the cast.

7. Place the patient dog on its back, upon the support device (Fig. 9) and affix the extremities to the frame of the device by means of additional plaster wrappings over their casts. While the dog is supine or on its side, insert supporting padded slats between the extremities and the frame for creature comfort. A padded breast plate suspended from the support device makes the prone position, when used, more tolerable. The head support, padded and positioned at the level of the ears, provides adequate and comfortable support. All points of pressure on the animal are well padded and periodically examined. It is important to position the elbow to wrist part of the forelegs and the knee-to-ankle part of the hind legs parallel to the floor because it is on the knee and the elbow joints, as well as on these broad surfaces that the animal's weight rests. The paws will become edematous and possibly gangrenous from stasis unless elastic wrappings are placed over them. The elastic

wrappings must be removed and the paws massaged two or three times daily to prevent pressure sores from the wrappings themselves.

8. It is generally known that dogs that are restrained in a supine position for prolonged periods die. We have assessed this phenomenon and have found that sedation and respiratory fatigue are the major causes of their death. Heavy sedation is required to prevent pain, but it suppresses the dog's respiratory center, also. The forced spread of the dog's forelegs immobilizes its thorax and causes hypoxia from respiratory fatigue and cardiac arrest in

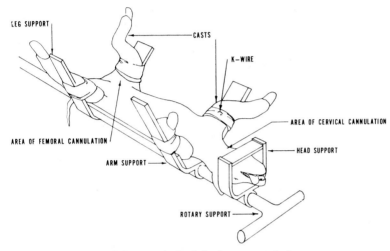

FIG. 9. Dog on its back in the support device.

24 to 48 h. Sedation should be withheld if possible and the forelegs should not be widely spread. We have found that in this device, dogs tolerate 7 days of restraint, without difficulty. Thus restrained, they seldom whine or bark and they usually eat, drink and eliminate readily. The dogs we have worked with have not shown any gross behavioral abnormalities as a result of such confinement.

9. Insert superior and inferior caval catheters and an arterial pressure line (Fig. 10). All cannulae are inserted on the side of the dog opposite the position intended for the support system. When the dog is rotated to the prone position, these cannulae exit on the side of the support system, and tubing length can be kept to a minimum.

10. To insert the femoral catheters, make a 3 cm incision parallel to the femoral artery and extend it distal from the inguinal ligament (Fig. 11). The skin incision should be kept small, however inconvenient, for this represents a major source of hemorrhage and infection during perfusion. Once

the skin incision has been made, the remainder of the procedure is carried out with blunt dissection to decrease wound bleeding during the perfusion. A significant medial arterial branch can usually be found 2 to 4 cm distal to the inguinal ligament. Isolate the arterial branch with ties. Isolate the femoral vein. Rather than cleaning off the vein, isolate it by dissecting outside the adventitia. Enter the femoral arterial sheath lateral to the vein and dissect to the floor of the femoral canal and then medially well free of the vein,

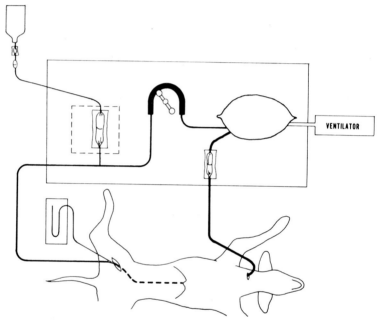

FIG. 10. Cannula positions and flow circuit.

before passing the ties. Trauma directly to the adventitia of the vein produces spasm and often reduces the diameter of the catheter that can be passed, from 2 to 4 catheter sizes. Even so, we have not found a significant difference in the amount of blood that can be withdrawn from the cava. The increased resistance encountered with the smaller cannulae is overcome by the pressure gradient that we use across the withdrawal catheter.

11. Identify the external jugular vein on the same side by applying pressure to the supraclavicular area. Administer local anesthesia and make a 1 cm incision over and at right angles to the long axis of the vein. By blunt dissection entirely, deliver the vein through the wound and place ties about it. As was the case of the femoral vein, the external jugular vein is not stripped of its adventitia for fear of producing spasm, and it is even more important with this vein, than in the femoral area. Unlike the withdrawal suction, the return

pressure gradient is smaller; it is desirable to insert as large a cannula as possible in the external jugular vein to minimize resistance.

12. Give the dog heparin (3·0 mg/kg) intravenously. Spray additional local anesthetic forcefully over the jugular and the femoral veins to block the nerves and to decrease the likelihood of spasm. Insert the cannula into the arterial tributary, tie it in place and anchor the tie to the skin. Fill the catheter before insertion, with a diluent solution of heparin in Ringer's lactate solution and connect it to a mercurial manometer, for continuous monitoring of pressure.

13. Partially transect the femoral vein above the saphenous tributaries.

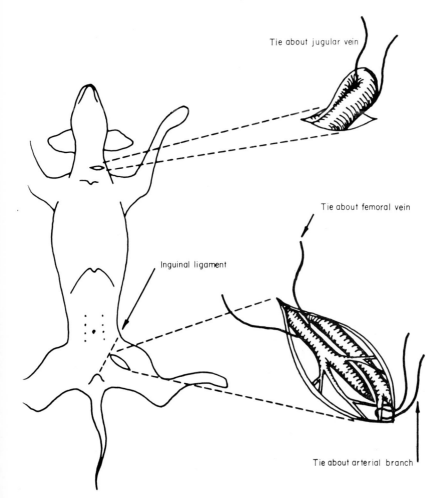

Tie about jugular vein

Tie about femoral vein

Inguinal ligament

Tie about arterial branch

FIG. 11. Detail of femoral and jugular dissections.

Control the opened vein with a bulldog clamp until you have accomplished three point fixation with small hemostats. Fill the catheter with Ringer's lactate solution, cap it and pass it rapidly to the desired level in the cava when the vein clamp is removed. The first "pass" is the easiest one, for once manipulated, the vein goes into spasm and will not accommodate any but small catheters. Pass the well-oiled catheter up into the inferior vena cava to the level of the xyphoid process. Mineral oil is satisfactory for this purpose. By doing so, you are assured that the catheter is advanced into the caval system. If the catheter is passed further toward the diaphragm, the risk of passing it into the atrium would be introduced. This would facilitate recirculation of part of the superior vena caval return. Secure the catheter firmly in place and insert the jugular catheter. It is important to pass the catheter in the external jugular vein beneath the clavicle and into the thorax to prevent kinking of the vein when the dog moves his head, which would occlude the tip. This catheter must be well secured, also.

14. Ligate the distal ends of all cannulated vessels. Paint the wounds with an antiseptic solution (povidone-iodine) and close the wound snugly about the catheters. Pack Betadine-soaked pledgets against the incisions and tape them in place. Turn the animal to the prone position, for its comfort, while awaiting the beginning of the perfusion.

The Lung Apparatus

15. The lung donors are chosen and prepared in the same manner as the patient dog, except that their sex is not important. Sedate the dog, restrain it in the supine position and insert an endotracheal tube. Mechanically ventilate the dog. Ventilation is important because occasionally a dog succumbs to hypoxia before it can be exsanguinated and its untimely death does not allow flushing of its pulmonary vascular bed. Hypoxemia also adds to the blood waste products. During exsanguination, balanced salt solution is administered to maintain circulation volume and to wash out a sufficient quantity of blood for the experiment before the release of the toxic factors that develop in the shock state.

16. Give heparin sodium (2·0 mg/kg) intravenously. Cannulate the dog's femoral artery and vein aseptically. Collect the arterial blood in a sterile container. Rapidly exsanguinate the dog, from the femoral artery, until the blood flow diminishes, at which time, infuse one liter of Ringer's lactate solution rapidly by the femoral vein. Collect the blood in aliquots of 500 cc. Number these blood bottles in the order collected. The flushing solution should be administered cold (0°C to 10°C) in order to maintain and preserve the lung tissue in a physiological state until the perfusion is begun.

17. As the washout return declines, open the dog's chest down the midline, with sterile technique, taking care to clamp the caval system as soon as

possible lest air be sucked into it from torn mediastinal vessels and thus compromise the preparation (Fig. 1). Ligate and transect the cavae and the azygous vein next. Transect the aortic arch at the level of the great vessels, without clamping, because air can easily be evacuated from the left side of the heart. Dissect the heart and lungs from the diaphragm and the posterior chest wall, leaving only the trachea attached. The esophagus is left in place in the thorax and care is taken not to enter it, in order to maintain sterile technique. Inflate the lungs. Clamp the trachea and transect it high above the clamp, in the base of the neck, leaving the lungs inflated.

18. The process of inserting cannulae into the heart and the lungs is begun (Fig. 2). Separate the pulmonary artery from the aorta. The procedure is meticulous since the pulmonary artery is friable and can very easily be lacerated. Ligate the aorta with a stout tie at the level of the sinuses of Valsalva, to occlude the coronary ostia and to prevent air or bacteria from entering the blood stream. Clamp the pulmonary artery, to prevent air from entering it; open the pulmonary outflow tract. Fill the right atrium, the right ventricle, the proximal pulmonary artery and the clamped pulmonary arterial cannula with Ringer's lactate solution. As the pulmonary artery is unclamped, massage the heart gently to express any air, and advance the cannula into, and affix it within the proximal pulmonary artery. Excise the right atrium and the right ventricle and any remnant of the parietal pericardium.

19. Stab the left ventricle at its apex and insert the funnel-shaped glass catheter. Tie it with umbilical tape around the ventricle. Even though the ventricle has become firm from the cold flushing during exsanguination, the tie will tear through the ventricle and will ruin the apparatus if anything other than wide tape is used. Fill the now elevated left ventricle with Ringer's lactate solution, massage the atrium and the ventricle to express any bubbles and simultaneously clamp the outflow line.

20. Fit the lung into the lung container, tie the endotracheal tubing within the trachea, and clamp it outside the container. Take care to avoid rotating a lung or a lobe about its hilar attachment. Thread the other tubes to the outside through the apertures in the container and seal the entire container with sterile tape. Leave a small catheter in an extra aperture and plug its entrance with cotton. The catheter allows aspiration of any hilar lymph, of pleural effusion, or of condensation during the process of perfusion. The cotton plug enables the balancing of air pressure around the lung with the atmosphere during ventilation, in sterile fashion.

21. Cover the ends of the cannulae to maintain sterility if there is a delay in performing the perfusion. This lung preparation is then ready for rapid incorporation within the system when needed. It can be refrigerated if desired, at 0°C to 4°C for up to 6 h without affecting its function. When sealed, the lung preparation can be handled without gloves, sterile technique, etc. (Fig. 3).

The Circuitry for Perfusion

22. The perfusion circuit is so constructed that blood is withdrawn from the inferior vena cava by way of the femoral vein, is sucked into a reservoir and is pumped through the lung preparation from the reservoir. The blood returns by gravity to the patient dog and enters the superior vena cava by the jugular vein (Fig. 10).

23. The withdrawal line must have a sturdy wall and narrow lumen. The large pressure gradient across its walls will collapse the walls if they are not sturdy. This same pressure gradient makes the effect of resistance to flow negligible through this narrow channel and such a small lumen allows a

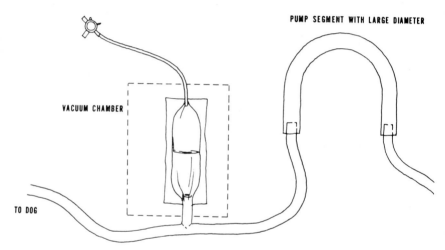

Fig. 12. Withdrawal line with reservoir, vacuum chamber and pump segment.

decreased priming volume. A vertical, collapsible reservoir is placed in the withdrawal line proximal to the pump (Fig. 12). The reservoir is a safeguard against an excessive pump rate, which causes the vena cava to collapse against the catheter tip and to erode the cava. Erosion of the cava may give way to perforation. Overpumping also flattens the withdrawal line between the dog and the pump. When this happens, the operator has to stop the pump and interrupt the perfusion to wait for the line to refill. The reservoir holds 1 to 5 times the stroke volume of the pump, depending on the sophistication of the pump monitoring system. The level within the reservoir can be used to trigger autoregulatory systems that control the pump rate, by either photoelectric or weight sensing devices.

24. Intravenous fluids, drugs and transfusions are all given through the top of the reservoir. They flush the reservoir to prevent stagnation of its contents with the multiplication of bacteria and the formation of clots. Administering

fluids through this reservoir allows the lung preparation to filter everything that is added to the system and lessens the dangers of particulate, air, or microbial emboli inherent with any such preparation. Because the reservoir is collapsible, there is no need for an air–fluid level, which has toxic effects on the blood.

25. We have encased the withdrawal reservoir in a vacuum chamber so that it does not have to be lowered to the floor for adequate suction by gravity. This promotes a compact apparatus, shortens the circuit and facilitates monitoring the volume of blood in this reservoir. This vacuum chamber is lightweight, transparent and is clamped easily over the reservoir to facilitate maintenance. The negative pressure within the chamber requires that a flutter valve be inserted in the line between the top of the reservoir and any fluids that are being infused into it, lest they be exhausted and lest an air embolus suddenly destroy the lung preparation (Fig. 13).

26. The entire tubing used in the perfusion is silicone plastic. It can be easily cleaned chemically and rapidly sterilized with heat. Its jointless construction keeps air or bacteria out of the system. This is not so in the systems which have multiple line couplings and large pressure gradients throughout. The trauma to the blood associated with a roller pump is partially related to its stroke volume. Insert a segment of large bore Silastic tubing in the position occupied by the pump to increase its stroke volume.

27. The vinyl chest shell aforementioned and described in an earlier publication (Lindsey et al., 1957) is sterilized easily by gas and is packaged easily, including the appropriate connecting tubing, ligatures and sterile tape required for its assembly. The shell is inexpensive and easy to make. It is practical to have an ample supply of them sterilized and packaged in various sizes.

28. The return line is constructed similarly to the withdrawal line (Fig. 14). There is no return pump. Return flow is by gravity. Elevate the entire preparation to maintain an adequate return flow rate. The return reservoir is incorporated with the return line just beyond the lung preparation. At least a 6 cm drop must be maintained between the left atrium and this reservoir to ensure that no elevation of the pulmonary venous pressure occurs and jeopardizes the function of the preparation. The return reservoir is situated immediately beyond this zone of suction. Its function is to be a monitoring chamber to warn of any increased resistance in the return line that would elevate the pulmonary venous pressure. Its diameter can be that of the return line, making it a small reservoir. A small silastic tube sealed in the upper end of the reservoir facilitates the drawing of blood samples and the removal of small quantities of air that may enter the system with each fresh lung preparation.

29. The diameter of the return line should be larger than that of the withdrawal line because the lower return pressure gradient accentuates the effect

of resistance in this line. With any increased flow rate or resistance at the return catheter tip, elevate the entire preparation to avoid increases in the left atrial pressure of the lung preparation. Keep the length of tubing between the environmental chamber and the patient dog at a minimum to avoid heat loss.
30. The entire system beginning about one foot from the patient dog and including all reservoirs, the pump, the lung preparation, the vacuum chamber and any flow-sensing or flow-regulating devices are enclosed in an environmental chamber (Ratliff, 1968b). With the more popular heat exchangers blood is run through a low volume, high surface area unit across which there is a high thermal gradient. The design of these exchangers usually allows areas

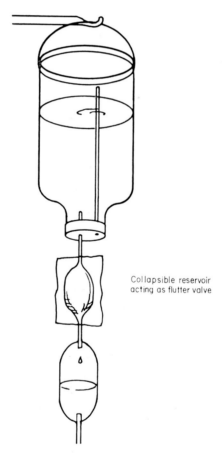

Collapsible reservoir
acting as flutter valve

To vacuum reservoir

FIG. 13. Detail of reservoir valve.

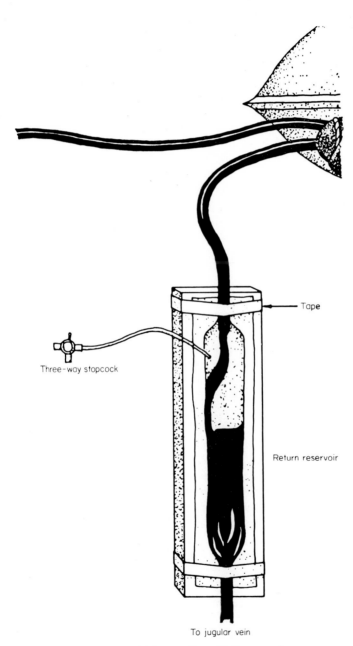

FIG. 14. Return line with its reservoir.

of relative stagnation. Stagnation promotes thrombus formation and bacterial multiplication as well as increases the priming volume with a device that is difficult to clean. This thermal gradient surely promotes protein denaturation, the cumulative effect of which must be significant with prolonged perfusion. With this environmental chamber the entire system can be kept at a physiological temperature without the foregoing hazards.

Beginning the Perfusion

31. Begin the perfusion with all the lines, including the withdrawal reservoir, filled with Ringer's lactate solution. Start the pump at a slow speed to allow gradual admixing of the blood and crystalloid. The initial flow rate is 200 to 300 cc/min. Increase the rate over the first 5 min to full flow rate, depending on the protocol of the experiment. Gradual admixture is necessary to allow the temperature and the colloidal osmotic pressure within the lung preparation to rise before exposure to the full perfusion pressure. Rapid flows of protein-free fluid threaten the preparation with pulmonary edema.

32. The maximal perfusion rate is largely dependent on the amount of blood in the central venous pool. The perfusion can be run at a higher bypass flow rate when the patient animal is maintained in a hypervolemic state. The disadvantages of hypervolemia are significant, however. The closer the dog's condition is to congestive failure from fluid overload, the less well its own lungs will perform. The more fluid there is in the system, the greater will be the danger of developing anasarca. The aberrations of central venous flow inherent in this preparation make monitoring the central venous pressure less meaningful. The benefits derived by increasing bypass flow with fluid overload are partially cancelled because of the decreased percentage of the cardiac return that this flow then represents. Fluid overload should increase, also, the risk of recirculation before the heart can pump the arterialized venous blood. Last, this increase in flow also means more pump trauma and more homologous blood with its proven hazards.

33. One-sixth to one-seventh of the total volume of an animal's blood is continuously present in its pulmonary vascular bed under baseline conditions (Lindsey et al., 1957). The quantity of blood required to fill the perfused lung is provided by the full withdrawal reservoir during the first few minutes of the perfusion. The fluid level in the reservoir drops as the pump is accelerated, but usually it stabilizes with the addition of a minimal volume of blood to the reservoir. We have found that the weight of the lungs increases by the weight of the blood drawn from the reservoir as the perfusion commences and stabilizes, until pulmonary edema develops. At that time, more blood is required to fill the reservoir and the lung preparation gets heavier. Also, the compliance and the ability of the lung to extract oxygen deteriorate just prior to the development of overt pulmonary edema.

34. Pulmonary edema develops eventually and does so from one or two lobes at a time. This can be shown by clamping the affected lobe at its hilum. The tracheal froth will cease immediately and the rest of the lung will function well for some time before developing pulmonary edema also. The edematous lobe usually looks more consolidated and more hemorrhagic and will have been the most dependent lobe throughout the perfusion. It is interesting to note that the production of tracheal froth is accelerated when positive pressure ventilation is stopped, even if perfusion has been stopped.

35. We prefer to have the reservoir nearly empty during the perfusion to avoid having an area of stagnation that favors multiplication of bacteria and the formation of thrombi. The reclaiming and reinjection of fluid dissipated into the cavity of the vinyl chest shell would be practical were it not for the problem of maintaining sterile technique.

36. As we begin the perfusion we are alert for lacerations unwittingly made of the pulmonary vessels and for congenital defects that require repair or discarding of the preparation. Sterile technique must be adhered to any time the vinyl shell is opened. Patent ducti or small septal defects can be repaired easily whereas most other defects cannot. Often these problems are first noted as the vinyl shell fills with blood at the beginning of the experiment.

37. Isolated lung preparations similarly perfused often function well for 6 h, but in this perfusion circuit, lung preparations usually function well for over 12 h. In our experience, because the pulmonary vascular resistance remains stable while the lung function remains adequate, we do not monitor the pulmonary arterial pressure.

38. A central venous pressure probe would be of value in this preparation in monitoring the relative blood volume. The radically disturbed hemodynamics in the caval system would make such a catheter accurate only in the right atrium. The maintenance of this position in prolonged perfusions could be accomplished only by direct atrial cannulation but we have not found this necessary.

Maintenance of the Perfusion

39. Before the inauguration of perfusion, evaluate certain baseline parameters, depending on the protocol of the experiment. Determine, as applicable: weight of patient dog and of each lung donor; temperature; blood pressure; electrocardiogram; hemoglobin and hematocrit values; pulmonary compliance; cardiac output; serum protein, by electrophoresis and precipitation methods; calcium, phosphate, sodium, chlorine, potassium and carbon dioxide combining power; platelet count; white blood and differential counts; PO_2, PCO_2 and pH; base excess and serum-free hemoglobin.

40. At the start of the perfusion, the dog's vital signs and the levels in the

reservoirs must be monitored continuously but as the preparation stabilizes, these values may be determined periodically.

41. Change lung preparations every 6 h, as a deterrent to bacterial overgrowth in the lung preparation and resultant contamination of the system. Determine the following values before each lung change: hemoglobin and hematocrit; serum protein and electrolyte levels; platelet count; white blood cell and differential counts; and serum free hemoglobin concentration.

Take representative biopsies for histologic study from various areas of the lung preparation. Obtain blood and lung biopsy cultures when there has been evidence of sepsis.

42. Measure blood gas levels, etc. proximal to and distal to the lung preparation in the bypass circuit and from the patient dog's arterial system every 24 h. Record electrocardiograms at 24 h intervals.

43. Position changes are not necessary for the restraint of the animals in the apparatus for as long as a week at a time. The cutdown sites and various catheters must be periodically inspected to make sure that all skin entrances are kept clean and protected. The paws must be unwrapped and massaged alternately 3 or 4 times a day to prevent edema.

44. Blood and fluids are given as indicated by clinical and laboratory parameters. When indicated, relatively fresh lung donor blood is used. The first bottle of 500 cc from the exsanguination procedure is used. As exsanguination proceeds and the crystalloid flush is begun, the formed elements and proteins become diluted. Very high levels of vasoactive hormones and probably other agents too, are released in an attempt to compensate for, or as a result of, the profound state of shock. Ventilate the lung preparation with air. It is tilted from side to side for an hour each, keeping its trachea dependent, to promote drainage.

45. The patient dog is alert throughout most of the procedure and is eating and drinking normally. Her thirst perception will keep her in optimal hydration and although the lung preparation is somewhat dehydrating, no maintenance or insensible fluid losses need be given. Should she be uncooperative and refuse to eat or drink, as the occasional hostile animal will do, hydration must be supplied intravenously. An estimate of the volume is made clinically and with the help of the laboratory and monitoring parameters outlined.

46. Maintain a continuous slow drip of heparin and Keflin (sodium cephalothin) into the withdrawal reservoir. The heparin sodium is given at 0·5 mg/kg/h and the Keflin is given at 1·0 gm/6 h. No more than 100 cc of fluid should be required to deliver these agents per 6 h. If an open sidearm is provided in the arterial pressure line and dilute heparin is infused very slowly, this line will stay open without difficulty. We prefer, however, to flush it periodically if it becomes occluded and to let this occlusion warn us of the need for increasing the heparin dosage.

Change of the Lung Preparation

47. Every 6 h, or at any time that contamination, massive air embolus or edema develop, the perfusion pump may be turned off. Unless contamination has occurred, allow the lung to empty into the return line and allow the withdrawal reservoir to fill by vacuum. This will not significantly alter the blood volume of the patient dog. Clamp the withdrawal line proximal to the withdrawal reservoir, manually evacuate the reservoir through the lung preparation, refill the reservoir with Ringer's lactate solution and flush this in turn through the lung preparation. By so doing, only a minimal amount of the dog's blood will be lost with each lung change.

48. Isolate the *old* lung preparation with clamps across the lines entering and leaving it. Paint these joints with Betadine and disconnect. Connect the new preparation after the open connections are flushed with saline to prevent air entering the system. Remove the clamps. Withdraw any bubbles in the return line through the vent in its reservoir. Gloves, "drapes", etc. are not required for lung changes.

49. The procedure for beginning each perfusion is the same. The regular perfusion rate should be re-established within 5 min. Procure the next lung preparation as soon as the *new* lung preparation is functioning well. Refrigerate and store this additional lung preparation, should an untimely lung deterioration or accident occur, requiring early replacement of the preparation in use.

Termination of the Perfusion

50. To complete the perfusion, stop the pump and remove the segment of tubing going through it. The lung may be flushed if desired, as described in (47). Break the vacuum on the withdrawal reservoir and disconnect the lung preparation. This is done so that the blood in the circuitry will flow by gravity into the dog. The return reservoir will act as a flutter valve unless a small vent is advanced through it from above. Turn the dog onto its back and remove the catheters. If a terminal cardiac output should be desired, it should be obtained before the catheters in the venous tree are removed, for they facilitate the placement of central catheters. Remove the catheters and pack the wounds open after ligating the vessels with chromic ligatures. Remove the dog from the support device and take off the casts, together with the Kirschner wires.

51. Studies performed at the termination of the perfusion are a duplication of the initial studies with the addition of a chest X-ray. Follow-up care will depend on the condition of the animal and the protocol of the study.

SAMPLE RESULTS

Sample results are included from a 48 h and 30 min run performed in 3 days (Figs 15 through 19) (Table I). The patient dog weighed 28·2 kg at the beginning, and 31·0 kg at the end of the perfusion. The eight lung donors ranged in weight from 10·5 to 22·7 kg. Neither the time required to change the lung donors nor that involved in the occasional interruptions in perfusion to correct minor problems was counted in this 48½ h. In this particular study we did not measure the pulmonary compliance of the patient dog or the lung preparations. The dog was in excellent condition at the end of the perfusion. Electively it was sacrificed while still in good condition five months after the perfusion. This particular dog did develop pressure ulcers on its extremities from the casts.

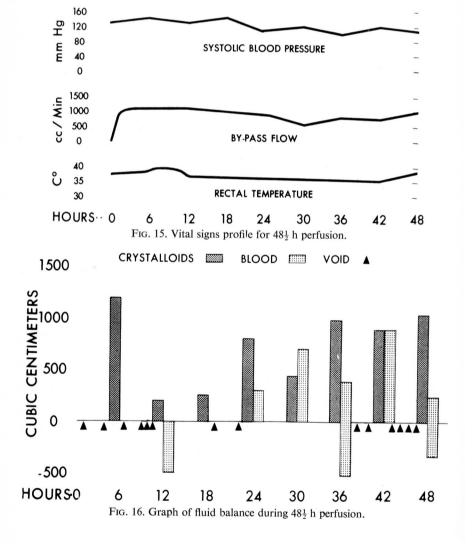

FIG. 15. Vital signs profile for 48½ h perfusion.

FIG. 16. Graph of fluid balance during 48½ h perfusion.

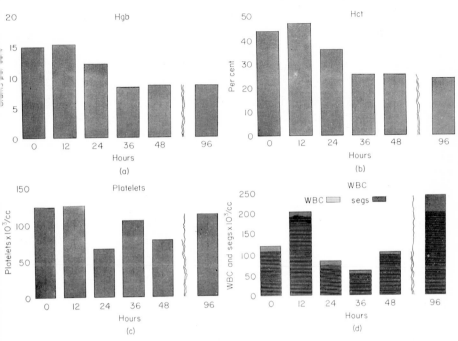

FIG. 17. Serial hematology studies during Experiment II.

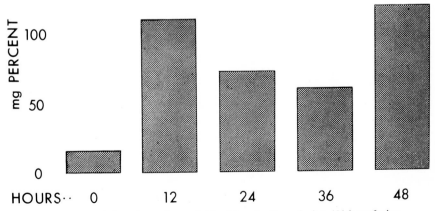

FIG. 18. Serial free plasma hemoglobin determinations during 48½ h perfusion.

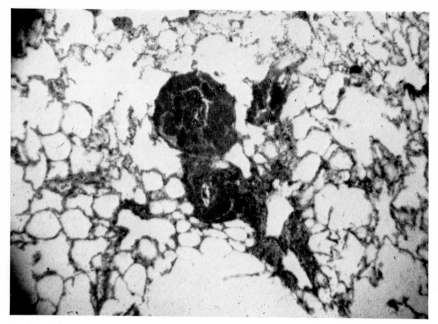

Fig. 19. Photomicrograph of support lung in Experiment II, showing emphysema and perivascular hemorrhage. (H & E) × 70.

TROUBLESHOOTING

The support device is very dependable, but occasionally a dog will work the cast loose from each support arm, and its weight then hangs down and fatigues the dog, compromising its respiration or pulling on another extremity and causing a pressure ulcer. She may work out a catheter with her tail. Also, growling or barking, because of discomfort, elevates the intra-thoracic pressure, and causes the hepatic return to flow caudad. The bypass withdrawal pool is increased with retrograde caval flow which potentiates the recirculation of already bypassed blood. The head of resistance against which the return line must flow is increased likewise and threatens the lung preparation with an increase in its pulmonary venous pressure. For the foregoing, and other, complications, constant surveillance is necessary.

The bony pelvis is well-supported by the leg casts. The pectoral girdle is not rigidly supported by the vertebral column or the chest, and in the prone position the dog will become fatigued, and will be suspended as if it were shrugging its shoulders. This compromises its respiratory function and is uncomfortable for the animal. This can be relieved by a well-padded sternal plate, which is tied over the horizontal support bar. When lying on her back or side, the patient dog tends to roll off the support bar or to sag to the dependent side and this, too, is uncomfortable and compromises respiration. This can be relieved with padded slats which convert the support device into a trough in which the dog lies comfortably. All pressure points must be well-padded.

The tongue may obstruct the airway in the sedated supine animal. The stirrup-shaped head rack may compress the airway in the prone animal. For

TABLE I

Serial blood gas and chemistry studies

Study	Units	Baseline	24 h	48 h
Blood gases				
pH	—	7·37	7·24	7·29
pO_2	mm Hg	90	—	80
pCO_2	mm Hg	37·5	41·0	34
Base excess	mEq/l blood	−6·5	−9·6	−5·0
Chemistries				
Calcium	mEq/l	4·8	4·4	4·1
Phosphorus	mg %	3·2	3·6	4·1
Sodium	mEq/l	149	125	122
Chloride	mEq/l	118	102	97
CO_2 CP	mEq/l	23	22	17
Potassium	mEq/l	4·4	3·2	3·0
Miscellaneous				
Protein	g %	5·7	3·6	3·0
Albumin	g %	1·7	1·0	0·9
Glucose	mg %	102	450	347
BUN	mg %	16	12	17
Amylase	60 to 160 = normal for human being	—	688	918
Serum Osmol.	mOsm/l	311	275	291

sedated dogs we insert an oral endotracheal tube that is cuffed to prevent aspiration and to allow the option of intermittent positive pressure ventilation in any position.

Narrowing of the pulse pressure usually means that the anticoagulation is insufficient and that the arterial cannula is clotting. This can be managed by flushing the cannula with heparin sodium (0·5 mg/kg). Decreases in the systolic or mean blood pressure usually signify sepsis or hypovolemia and should be managed as indicated.

When fever, tachycardia, hypotension or the sudden inability to perfuse at or near a previously established flow rate develop, septicemia is suspected. Septicemia usually originates from the lung preparation, therefore, change it for another. If the *new* lung does not function for a full 6 h without recurrence of symptoms of sepsis, stop the perfusion and quickly remove the tubing. Clean, autoclave and connect it again with a fresh lung preparation. Hemorrhagic shock and dehydration must be ruled out before the above measures are taken. Obtain cultures with each lung preparation that is removed by taking blood samples from the withdrawal reservoir, the return reservoir, the lung and the chest cage.

Blood loss from the system may be occult. We have had the inferior caval catheter erode through the cava when excessive suction allowed the withdrawal line to collapse repeatedly. This was manifested by repeated decreases in the maximal perfusion rate and blood pressure drops that responded only temporarily to transfusion. Gastrointestinal hemorrhage from over-anticoagulation has not been a problem but bleeding from the intestine in the face of septicemia has been seen. We give our animals neomycin by mouth when it does develop, to prevent the hemorrhagic lesion described in dogs in shock. Bleeding from the cut-down sites is reduced by making very small incisions and blunt dissection with ligation of all apparent bleeders. We do occasionally have to re-explore these wounds to stop persistent oozing from them.

Apparent hypothermia usually means that the dog has expelled the rectal probe, although it is sutured into the skin of the anus, or that the environmental chamber is too cool for proper heat exchange. Hyperthermia usually means that the environmental chamber is too warm or that the dog is septic. The shivering of barbiturate-sedated animals, as they are aroused should not be confused with a response to cold.

The lung preparation usually requires only minimal maintenance. Occasionally a patent ductus will require ligation, or preparations with septal defects must be discarded if they cannot be rapidly oversewn. Lacerations of the pulmonary artery or trachea during the procurement of the preparation occur occasionally, but usually can be repaired. These lungs gradually exude plasma, pleural effusion and hilar lymph which should not be allowed to accumulate in the trough beside the lung. They are excellent "pabulum" for bacterial growth and this hastens the contamination of the system. Antiseptic agents cannot be added to this container, for they will be rapidly absorbed through the pleural surface into the system. This fluid can easily be siphoned off periodically with the catheter left in the chest shell for this purpose. The chest shell and lung therein should be tilted alternately from side to side, but the trachea must be kept in such a position that it drains toward the reservoir in the ventilator tube. The lung lobes must not be allowed to rotate about their hilar attachment, for they will strangle. The lung preparation must be occasionally "sighed" to maintain surfactant efficiency.

We have been able to incriminate hyperthermia, depletion of carbohydrate, high perfusion rates, neglect in changing position and lack of deep-sighing as factors which accelerate the deterioration of lung preparations. Most of these factors were documented in isolated lung preparations and some do not apply in the situation described in this experiment but the others should be kept in mind. Any manipulation within the chest cage must be accomplished aseptically.

The design of the return reservoir makes it especially prone to kink and to occlude at either end. We find it advisable to tape this reservoir to a firm support (Fig. 14). Other kinks in the system must be diligently watched for. They usually occur while the system is being raised or lowered and the flow line is being payed out of, or returned to, the environmental chamber. Should this occur and the lung become edematous, the edema will clear and the lung will again be functional but this process requires 30 min of slow perfusion and gentle handling. A new lung can usually be inserted faster. The return reservoir should be high enough above the patient dog so that no blood stands in it. Any elevation above this leaves excessive line outside the environmental chamber and requires greater effort to prevent heat loss from this portion of the system.

Projected Experiments Using this Equipment

This equipment could be used to study the dialysis of anesthetics and other volatile agents, either into or out of, animals. It could be used to differentiate the pulmonary parenchymal toxicity from the systemic toxicity of various agents. Perfusion could be performed intermittently by capping the cannulae and leaving them in the dog and leaving the dog in the support device. This equipment could be used to evaluate lung function *in vitro* and to study the lung transplant during rejection. By perfusing a different lobe of the same dog's lung in the same patient dog at various intervals, early lung rejection could be studied under differing phases in the evolution of antibody response. By occasionally perfusing the lung preparation and alternately refrigerating it, the period of safe extracorporeal xenobanking might be prolonged. This preparation may be the prototype for an applicable chronic respiratory support system in the care of patients.

Acknowledgement

The author acknowledges with appreciation the tireless inspiration and technical suggestions of James D. Hardy and the assistance of Frances H. Atkinson in technical editing.

This study was supported by the John A. Hartford Foundation, Inc. and the Southern Medical Association.

The opinions or assertions contained herein do not necessarily reflect the views of the Bureau of Medicine and Surgery of the Navy Department of the United States of America, or the naval service at large.

REFERENCES

Belzer, F. O., Ashby, B. S., Huang, Josephine S. and Dunphy, J. E., (1968). Etiology of Rising Perfusion Pressure in Isolated Organ Perfusion. *Ann. Surg.*, **168** : 382–390

Eiseman, B. (1968). *In* discussion following presentation of paper, "Etiology of Rising Perfusion Pressure in Isolated organ." Belzer, F. O. *et al.*, (1968) *op sit.*

Guyton, A. C. and Lindsey, A. W. (1959). Effect of Elevated Left Atrial Pressure and Decreased Plasma Protein Concentration on Development of Pulmonary Edema. *Circulation Res.*, **7** : 649–657.

Lindsey, A. W., Banahan, B. F., Cannon, R. A. and Guyton, A. C. (1957). Pulmonary Blood Volume of the Dog and Its Changes in Acute Heart Failure. *Am. J. Physiol.*, **190** : 45–48.

Ratliff, J. L. (1968a). Extracorporeal Biologic Oxygenation for Prolonged Total Respiratory Support. *J. thorac. cardiovasc. Surg.*, **55** : 686–690.

Ratliff, J. L. (1968b). A New Mode of Support for the Isolated Lung Preparation. *Appl. Physiol.*, **24** : 600–601.

Veith, F. J., Hagstrom, J. W. C., Nehlsen, Sandra L., Karl, R. C. and Deysine, M. (1967). Functional, Hemodynamic and Anatomic Changes in Isolated Perfused Dog Lungs: The Importance of Perfusate Characteristics. *Ann. Surg.*, **165** : 267–278.

Exp. in Physiol. and Biochem. (1970). **3**, 333–340.

10 | Base Ratio Analysis of Small Samples of RNA

J. P. MONJARDINO

*Department of Molecular Virology, The Imperial Cancer
Research Fund, London, England*

INTRODUCTION

RNA base ratio analysis is one of the standard techniques for characterization of RNA. In order to perform it RNA is hydrolysed to its constitutive "units"—nucleotides, nucleosides or bases depending on the conditions used —and these are separated from each other and individually estimated. The use of the appropriate extinction coefficients makes it then possible to calculate the molar composition of the sample.

METHOD

The method described here for the base analysis of small samples of RNA (Monjardino, 1967) is essentially a modification of the method described by Smith and Markham (1950). The use of thin layers of cellulose for the chromatographic separation of the hydrolysate makes it possible for microgram amounts of RNA to be analysed and allows for the separation to be completed in 2·5–3 h instead of the 48 h of the original method. Other advantages of the method as described here are the sharpness of resolution and its overall simplicity and reproducibility.

APPARATUS

1. Pointed spin tubes (10 ml capacity) with glass stoppers.
2. Covered boiling-water bath.
3. A DESAGA thin layer chromatography set comprising spreader, board, storage rack, desiccator and a number of 5 × 20 cm glass plates.
4. DESAGA cylindrical glass jars with glass lids for developing the plates.
5. A spectrophotometer for reading both in the visible and UV ranges of the spectrum.
6. A heat lamp (Phillips 250 w).

7. An oven thermostatically controlled for temperatures up to 100°C.
8. Balance suitable for weighing 0·1–2 mg.
9. Measuring pipettes of various sizes including 1 ml.
10. One liter polythene bottle for storing the solvent.
11. Capillary bores made by drawing Pasteur pipettes.
12. Magnetic stirrer and small magnetized followers of the appropriate size for a 100 ml beaker.
13. One hundred ml glass beakers and general laboratory glassware.
14. DESAGA "UVIS" lamp.
15. One-edged razor blades.

REAGENTS

1. Tert-butanol freshly redistilled.
2. Concentrated HCl.
3. 1N HCl.
4. 0·1N HCl.
5. Glass distilled water.
6. TLC cellulose (MN 300, Macherey, Nagel).

PREPARATION OF THIN LAYER CHROMATOGRAPHY SOLVENT

The solvent used is 70% (v/v) tert-butanol containing 0·8N HCl and water. Concentrated HCl is made up to about 6N, boiled gently for 30 min and allowed to cool down. To 700 ml of pure tert-butanol (at 26°C) 132 ml of HCl are added and the final volume made up to one liter at 20°C. The solvent is kept in a one liter polythene bottle at room temperature and is well shaken prior to use.

PREPARATION OF THE TLC PLATES

The glass plates are thoroughly washed first with hot water and detergent, dried, and then cleaned with ether before being coated with the absorbent. The absorbent (cellulose MN 300, Macherey, Nagel) was suspended in water (15 g to 90 ml of water) and mixed by stirring in a 100 ml beaker on a magnetic stirrer for at least 3 h. The use of a 100 ml beaker ensures that all the absorbent is suspended whereas the use of larger capacity beakers causes particles of cellulose to stick to the walls of the beaker and eventually to be washed with the slurry into the spreader causing the streaking of the plates. Then the slurry is poured into the spreader and the plates coated 250 μ thick, dried in the oven at 100°C for 20 min and stored in a desiccator.

The RNA samples used were cytoplasmic and nuclear pig pituitary RNAs prepared in our laboratory by a modification of the method described by Cline (1966) and commercial yeast RNA (SIGMA Type XI).

ISOLATION OF RNA

EXTRA APPARATUS AND REAGENTS REQUIRED FOR RNA ISOLATION

Apparatus

1. One Potter-Elvehjem Teflon-glass homogenizer.
2. One refrigerated centrifuge with a super speed attachment capable of generating a centrifugal force of $9000 \times g$. The alternative is a preparative ultracentrifuge.
3. Dialysis tubing.
4. One glass desiccator.

Reagents

1. Medium A-0·25M sucrose made in buffer A (0·001M Tris-HCl buffer pH 7·6 containing 0·0015 MgSO$_4$).
2. 2·5% bentonite aqueous solution.
3. 0·2% citric acid.
4. Redistilled water-saturated phenol containing 0·1% of 8-hydroxyquinoline. Phenol is redistilled into a pre-weighed container. One-tenth of the weight is added in de-ionized water to the liquid phenol and the mixture allowed to cool down to room temperature. The mixture is then transferred to a separating funnel, shaken with de-ionized water and allowed to stand overnight. The phenolic phase is separated and 8-hydroxyquinoline is added to make the final concentration 0·1%.
5. 5% sodium dodecyl sulphate aqueous solution.
6. Buffer B (0·001M Tris-HCl buffer, pH 9·0 containing 0·0015M MgSO$_4$).
7. Buffer C (0·01M Tris-HCl buffer, pH 7·5 containing 0·001M MgCl$_2$).
8. Buffer D (0·01M sodium acetate buffer, pH 5·2, containing 0·05M NaCl and 0·001M MgCl$_2$).
9. Deoxyribonuclease I (ribonuclease-free from "WORTHINGTON").
10. 95% Ethanol ("ANALAR" GRADE, "B.D.H.").
11. Ether.
12. Nitrogen cylinder. A rubber tube to which a pasteur pipette was attached was connected to the cylinder allowing nitrogen to be bubbled gently into the RNA solution contained in a small tube.
13. KOH pellets.

ISOLATION OF RNA

All operations were carried out at 4°C unless specifically stated.

Preparation of the tissue homogenate and of nuclear and cytoplasmic fractions

1. The tissue was weighed in a pre-cooled beaker and for each gram of tissue 2 ml of medium A (0·25M sucrose, 0·0015M $MgSO_4$, 0·001M Tris-HCl, pH 7·6) were added. 0·5 ml of 2·5% bentonite solution was added for each 5 ml of buffer A.

2. The tissue is finely minced with scissors and homogenized with five strokes of a tight pestle of a Teflon-glass Potter-Elvehjem homogenizer. The homogenate is then squeezed through four layers of gauze and constitutes the preparation used for extraction of total RNA.

3. When preparing nuclear and cytoplasmic fractions the homogenate is spun at $600 \times g$ for 10 min. The top two-thirds of the supernatant are removed and constitute the cytoplasmic fraction and the remaining one-third is discarded. The pellet is washed once in medium A (resuspended in medium A and centrifuged at $600 \times g$ for 10 min) and then suspended in 0·2% citric acid (10 ml for 5–10 g of tissue) and stirred for 30 min. The nuclei are spun down at $1650 \times g$ for 10 min and the pellet resuspended in medium A (about 2 ml for each gram of tissue). This constituted the nuclear fraction.

Extraction of RNA (based on the method described by Cline (1966))

To each 5 ml of homogenate 5 ml of freshly redistilled water-saturated phenol were added. 5% sodium dodecyl sulphate was added to make the final concentration 0·4%. The mixture was shaken for 15 min and then centrifuged at $5000 \times g$ for 10 min. The aqueous layer was removed and twice more extracted in the same way with equal volumes of phenol. The final aqueous layer was saved. To the phenol and interphase layers from the first extraction an equal volume of buffer B (0·001M Tris-HCl buffer, pH 9·0 containing 0·0015 $MgSO_4$) was added. The mixture was shaken at 60°C for 3 min, rapidly cooled in ice and spun at $5000 \times g$ for 10 min; the supernatant was removed and twice more extracted with cold phenol in the same way as the pH 7·6 extract. The final aqueous phase was saved.

The RNA was precipitated from the final aqueous extracts by the addition of 0·1 ml of 2% bentonite, 1/10 vol. of 20% potassium acetate and 2 vol. of 95% ethanol and by allowing the mixture to stand in the cold (− 20°C) overnight. The RNA precipitate is collected by centrifugation at $1500 \times g$ for 10 min and dissolved in buffer C (0·01M Tris-HCl buffer pH 7·5 containing 0·001M $MgCl_2$). The volume used to resuspend the pellet was approximately 2·0 ml for each gram of starting tissue. After addition of 1–2 μg of deoxyribonuclease I (ribonuclease-free) for each 4–5 ml of solution the mixture was incubated at 37°C for 5 min and the reaction stopped by rapidly cooling in ice. The bentonite was removed by centrifugation at 9000 × g for 10 min.

The RNA was reprecipitated as before, omitting the bentonite and the RNA precipitate dissolved in buffer D (0·01M sodium acetate pH 5·2, containing 0·05M NaCl and 0·001M MgCl₂) using about 1·5 ml for each gram of starting tissue; the solution was then dialysed for 18 h against 200–800 vol. of buffer D. The RNA was finally reprecipitated as before and dissolved in 0·3–0·6 ml of buffer D; the phenol was extracted with ether which subsequently was removed in a stream of nitrogen. The final preparation was either stored at − 20°C or else reprecipitated, rinsed once with 95% Ethanol, dried "*in vacuo*" over KOH and stored at − 20°C.

BASE RATIO ANALYSIS

DESCRIPTION OF THE PROCEDURE

Hydrolysis of the Sample

The sample was weighed and 1N HCl added to give a final concentration of about 1–2 μg/μl. The tube is placed in a boiling-water bath for 5 min and then stoppered. Hydrolysis is carried out for 1 h. The tube is taken out of the bath and allowed to cool at room temperature before spotting the plates.

Spotting

The hydrolysate is directly spotted onto the plate. Capillary bores (made from Pasteur pipettes drawn over a Bunsen flame) were used for spotting and the diameter of the spot kept under 3 mm. The spots were applied 1·5–2·0 cm from the edge of the plate and 4 or 5 spots could be applied per plate.

Development

The solvent was shaken before use and poured into the jar to a level of approximately 1 cm. Care was taken that the spots were never drowned by the solvent. The plate was then placed in a jar (resting against the sidewall) the lid applied and development allowed to take place for 2·5–3 h at room temperature.

Elution and Estimation

After development had been completed the plate was taken out and dried under (about 20 cm away from the lamp) a heat lamp for 10 min. The spots were located under a UV lamp and pencilled round. A similar area of cellulose was used for a blank. The spots (and blank) were scraped off with a razor blade after making sure that the front spot lies quite clear of the solvent front,

P

transferred to polystyrene tubes containing 0·4 ml of 0·1N HCl and left to elute overnight. The absorbent was centrifuged for 10 min in a bench centrifuge (approx. 600 × g) and the supernatant transferred to microcuvets for measurement of the optical density at the appropriate wavelengths (Uvispek spectrophotometer): guanine 250 mμ; adenine 260 mμ; cytidylic acid 280 mμ and uridylic acid 260 mμ. Conversion to moles of nucleotides used the following coefficients: guanine, $d_{250} = 10\cdot6$; adenine, $d_{260} = 13\cdot0$; cytidylic acid, $d_{280} = 12\cdot95$; uridylic acid, $d_{260} = 9\cdot89$. (The density d is for a cell 1 cm thick, the subscript referring to the wavelength in mμ. The concentration is 10^{-3} M.) A correction factor of 5% has to be added to the final amounts of UMP and CMP to account for partial degradation to the nucleosides (Wyatt, 1955).

Results

Good separation of the hydrolysate mixture into four distinct spots is achieved using the present method. (When the spots are "streaky" the plates should be activated in an oven at 100°C for 15 min and allowed to cool before being spotted.) The four spots were identified by their UV spectra as being guanine, adenine, cytidylic acid and uridylic acid, respectively, from the baseline (Fig. 1). The R_f values calculated under these conditions were: G = 0·26, A = 0·36, CMP = 0·55 and UMP = 0·82.

The base compositions of the RNA samples analysed are in good agreement with previous reports (Table I). Recoveries of about 91% of the materials spotted were obtained using 3–4 μg of each of the nucleotides and bases (commercial preparations). With elementary care good separations and accurate analyses were performed with amounts of hydrolysate corresponding to as little as 8 μg of original RNA.

Suggestions for Further Experiments

No significant differences in total RNA base composition have been found when preparations of different animals are analysed (Magasanik, 1955; Wyatt, 1955). This finding can be confirmed easily by analysing liver RNA from two different animals (for example rat and rabbit). Similarly base composition does not seem to be organ-specific. The analysis of preparations of two different organs from the same animal (calf liver and spleen for example) can easily be performed and is not expected to show significant differences. Pancreas should be handled with care if chosen for this experiment as degradation by pancreatic ribonuclease might take place during the preparation of RNA giving rise to a degradation product with high guanine and low pyrimidine content.

Significant differences in base composition can be observed however if mammalian and yeast preparations are compared (as shown in this article).

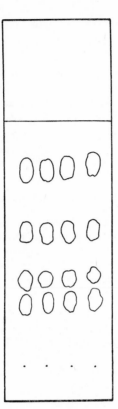

FIG. 1. Chromatogram of a hydrolysate of yeast ribonucleic acid. The hydrolysate was run on a thin layer of cellulose in 70% (v/v) tert-butanol containing 0·8N HCl and water. The spots in ascending order are: (a) guanine, (b) adenine, (c) cytidylic acid, (d) uridylic acid.

TABLE I

Base composition of pig pituitary and yeast RNAs by TLC
(molar percentages)

	No. of det.	G	A	C	U
Pig pituitary Cytoplasm	4	34·1 ±0·41	17·2 ±0·60	27·8 ±0·54	20·9 ±0·75
Pig pituitary Nuclei	5	34·3 ±1·03	18·8 ±1·23	26·0 ±0·8	20·9 ±0·53
Yeast	14	30·1 ±1·1	25·3 ±1·0	20·5 ±1·2	24·1 ±1·2

This comparative study can easily be carried out using the more readily available rat liver instead of pig pituitaries.

Lower animals (earth worms, for example) also can be chosen for RNA extraction and analysis and their total RNA base composition compared with that of higher animals. Plants and plant seeds in particular (because they are rich in RNA) are another readily accessible source of RNA which can be analysed by the methods reported in this article provided the tissue is not too hard and is amenable to homogenization in the way described.

REFERENCES

Cline, M. J. (1966). "Isolation and characterization of RNA from Human Leukocytes". *J. Lab. clin. Med.*, **68**, 33.

Magasanik, B. (1955). *In* "The Nucleic Acids" (E. Chargaff and E. N. Davidson, eds), **1**. Chap. 11, "Isolation and Composition of the Pentose Nucleic Acids and of the Corresponding Nucleoproteins", 406. Academic Press, New York and London.

Monjardino, J. P. (1967). "A Simple Thin-Layer Chromatography Method for Base Ratio Analysis of Small Samples of RNA". *Analyt. Biochem.*, **21**, 308–312.

Smith, J. D. and Markham, R. (1950). "Chromatographic Studies on Nucleic Acids. 2. The Quantitative analysis of Ribonucleic Acids". *Biochem. J.*, **46**, 509–513.

Wyatt, G. R. (1955). *In* "The Nucleic Acids" (E. Chargaff and E. N. Davidson, eds), **1**, Chap. 7, "Separation of Nucleic Acid Components by Chromatography on Filter Paper", 260. Academic Press, New York and London.

Exp. in Physiol. and Biochem. (1970). 3, 341–350

11

A. The Push–Pull Cannula (PPC)
B. Bioassay of Acetylcholine on Leech Muscle Suspended in a Microbath

J. D. DUDAR AND J. C. SZERB

Department of Physiology and Biophysics, Dalhousie University, Halifax, Nova Scotia, Canada

A. The Push–Pull Cannula (PPC)

Gaddum (1961) described a simple device, the push–pull cannula (PPC), for the estimation of diffusible substances in tissues *in vivo*. It has proved to be especially valuable in measuring the release in the brain of suspected transmitters such as acetylcholine and dopamine (Mitchell and Szerb, 1962; McLennan, 1964; McKenzie and Szerb, 1968).

The push-pull cannula consists of two concentric tubes, the inner one protruding beyond the outer tube (Fig. 1). Physiological saline is driven through the inside tube and removed through the outside by slight suction. The saline solution passing through the PPC is exposed to the tissue when it flows from the inside to the outside tube within a small cavity created by the PPC.

CONSTRUCTION OF THE PPC

In order to avoid excessive tissue damage, the diameter of the PPC has to be as small as possible. The PPCs constructed in the manner described below have been successfully used on the brain of cats.

MATERIALS

1. Stainless steel hypodermic needles
No. 27 (0·41 mm o.d.) 2·5 in. long
No. 18 (1·26 mm o.d.) 2·5 in. long or a similar length of No. 18 stainless steel tubing
2. Polyethylene tubing
PE 90 (0·96 mm i.d., 1·27 mm o.d.)
PE 200 (1·40 mm i.d., 1·90 mm o.d.)
3. Epoxy resin.

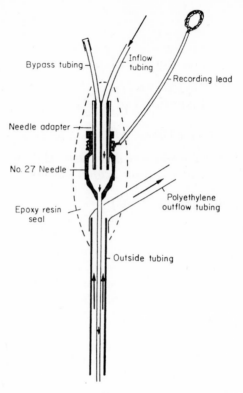

Bypass tubing

Inflow tubing

Recording lead

Needle adapter

No. 27 Needle

Epoxy resin seal

Polyethylene outflow tubing

Outside tubing

FIG. 1.

METHOD OF CONSTRUCTION

The entire No. 27 needle is used for the inner, inflow tubing while the shaft of the No. 18 needle forms the outside of the cannula. The bevels are ground off both needles, leaving the ends square and the hub is ground off the No. 18 needle. The resulting No. 18 tubing should be at least 5 mm shorter than the shaft of the No. 27 needle. The ground ends are highly polished to remove nicks and burrs.

To assemble the PPC, force one end of a 2 ft piece of PE 90 polyethylene tubing over one end of the No. 18 tubing. The PE 90 tubing is then bent slightly with respect to the No. 18 tubing and a small hole is made in it 2–3 mm beyond the end of the steel tubing so that the No. 27 needle can be forced through the polyethylene and down the No. 18 tubing (see Fig. 1). The final bend in the PE 90 tubing should not be too sharp, otherwise flow is impeded. The No. 27 needle is adjusted inside the No. 18 tubing so that it protrudes 0·75 mm.

Two pieces of PE 200 tubing are cemented into a nylon needle adapter or other suitable connector in order to make a tight connection with the No. 27 needle. One serves as the inflow tubing from the perfusion pump, and the other, usually shorter, serves as a bypass for clearing the dead space of the inflow tubing. The bypass tubing is kept closed with a tight fitting cap. The needle adapter is securely fitted into the needle hub, the protrusion of the No. 27 needle is checked and all connections are encased in epoxy resin. The resin is allowed to dry thoroughly before the PPC is used.

If the PPC is to be used for electrical recording or if there is a possibility of a chemical reaction between the perfusate and the stainless steel, the tubing must be varnished before the PPC is assembled. A lead for recording should be soldered on to the hub of the No. 27 needle, before it is varnished, using a pellet of zinc in about 10 ml of concentrated HCl as a flux.

Materials for Model Experiments

1. Perfusion pump.
2. Quinine sulphate.
3. Agar.
4. Turner fluorometer filters—811, 813.

Experiment (Szerb, 1967)

Dissolve 1 mg quinine sulphate in 100 ml distilled water. Add 1 g agar powder and dissolve it by heating in a 250 ml beaker. Allow it to gel at room temperature.

Mount the PPC in a holder with a rack and pinion and connect the PPC to the perfusion pump which contains distilled water. Fill the outflow tube and the outer needle with distilled water and leave the syringe and needle at the end of the outflow tubing connected. Start the infusion at the rate of 0·1 ml/min with the PPC in the air. Make sure that no more air is coming through the inside needle. With the perfusion pump going and the outside needle filled, lower the PPC into the agar gel about 1 in. below the surface, then withdraw the PPC by about 0·5 mm. After removing the needle and syringe from the outflow tubing, the end of which should be slightly lower than the tip of the PPC to form a small siphon, there should be fluid continuously dropping from the outflow. Collect the outflow in centrifuge tubes graduated to 0·1 ml for 10 min. Each sample should contain 1 ml, the same amount as the inflow if the perfusion technique is correct. Collect three 10 min samples, then double the rate of infusion and again collect 1 ml samples, which now should take 5 min. Estimate the quinine sulphate content of the samples by adding 2 ml 0·2N

H_2SO_4, mixing thoroughly, and reading the fluorescence against a standard quinine sulphate fluorescence curve ranging from 20–200 ng quinine sulphate.

Samples obtained with an inflow rate of 0·1 ml/min should contain about 100 ng quinine sulphate, while samples with the same volume obtained with a perfusion rate of 0·2 ml/min should contain only 50 ng. This shows that the amount extracted by the PPC does not depend on the rate of perfusion but on the duration of extraction.

The PPC so constructed can be mounted on an electrode holder of a stereotaxic instrument and used in animal experiments. Knowing the extraction characteristics of the PPC and the content of the substance to be estimated in a given area of the brain, it is possible to calculate the fraction of the substance that is diffusible and available for extraction.

REFERENCES

Gaddum, J. H. (1961). Push-pull cannulae. *J. Physiol., Lond.*, **155**, 1P.
McKenzie, G. M. and Szerb, J. C. (1968). The effect of dihydroxyphenylalanine, pheniprazine and dextroamphetamine on the *in vivo* release of dopamine from the caudate nucleus. *J. Pharmac. exp. Ther.*, **102**, 302–308.
McLennan, H. (1964). The release of acetylcholine 3-hydroxytyramine from the caudate nucleus. *J. Physiol., Lond.*, **174**, 152–161.
Mitchell, J. F. and Szerb, J. C. (1962). The spontaneous and evoked release of acetylcholine from the caudate nucleus. *Abst. XXII Int. physiol. Congr.*, No. 819.
Szerb, J. C. (1967). Model experiments with Gaddum's push-pull cannulas. *Can. J. Physiol. Pharmac.*, **45**, 613–620.

B. Bioassay of Acetylcholine on Leech Muscle Suspended in a Microbath

Biological assay procedures can be improved by increasing their sensitivity and the rate at which the assay can be performed. The longitudinal dorsal muscle of the leech has been utilized for the assay of acetylcholine since the muscle is sensitive to as little as 1 or 2 ng/ml of acetylcholine in the bath fluid. Furthermore, extraneous substances are less likely to affect the nicotinic action of ACh on the leech muscle than they are the muscarinic effects of ACh on other tissues. However, both the contraction produced by the application of ACh and the relaxation after its removal are slow in the leech muscle, so that only a limited number of samples can be assayed.

Gaddum and Szerb (1961) and Szerb (1961) described a method by which both the sensitivity and the rapidity of the ACh assay on the leech muscle could be improved by suspending a thin strip of muscle in a bath having a very small volume (0·05 ml). This method speeds up the diffusion of ACh between bath fluid and muscle and reduces the amount of ACh that can be assayed. However, this procedure requires a special bath and recording techniques, which are described below.

CONSTRUCTION OF THE MICROBATH

MATERIAL

1. Perspex block 1 in. sq. (25 mm²) ¾ in. (19 mm) thick.
2. Twist Drills

No.	Inch (o.d.)	mm (o.d.)	Fig. 2
50	0·070	1·78	A
63	0·037	0·94	B
14	0·182	4·62	C
75	0·021	0·53	D
59	0·041	1·04	E
31	0·120	3·05	F

METHODS OF CONSTRUCTION

A ¾ × ¼ in. (19 × 6 mm) section is cut from one corner of the 1 in. sq. face of the Perspex block, and the resulting L-shaped block should resemble Fig. 2. The block is polished using Brasso. The essential components are the bath itself (A), the reservoir (C) and the connection between the two (B). They must

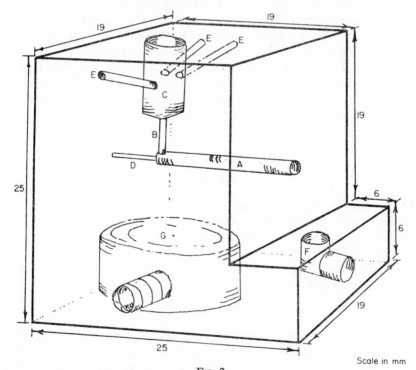

Scale in mm

FIG. 2.

be carefully drilled, with hole B perpendicular to and centred at the end of hole A. Hole A is drilled 15 mm deep, with a centre on the midline of the front face and 13·5 mm from the top. Drill hole D either from a similar point on the back of the block or as an extension of hole A. It should be in the centre of hole A. On the top of the block, hole C is drilled 8·5 mm deep, with a centre 18·5 mm from the front edge along its midline. Drill hole B as an extension of C, with the same centre. The inlet holes E now can be drilled, slanting slightly into hole C and entering about 4 mm from the top. Three holes are included so that three different bathing solutions can be used without changing perfusion systems, but one is sufficient for most purposes. The holes are polished with Brasso, using cotton wool or paper tissue, so that the muscle and fluid levels can be seen. Two other holes are F, a drain which is connected to tubing to take away the bath outflow, and G, drilled to take a $\frac{3}{8}$ in. rod for mounting and provided with a small tapped hole for a set screw. The microbath is attached to a heavy support stand using three racks and pinions for movement in all three planes and the bath is mounted so that it is level.

The bath is perfused from a reservoir with a flow rate of approximately 1 ml/min which is regulated by the pressure head of the reservoir and by a suitable length of capillary-bore glass tubing. This tubing is connected to the bath with a short piece of rubber tubing and then to polyethylene tubing drawn out at one end to fit into one of the inlet holes (E). The outflow from the bath is adjusted with a small wick, made from paper tissue, positioned below hole A, so that during perfusion there is a meniscus $\frac{1}{4}$ to $\frac{1}{3}$ of the way up hole C, and when the perfusion is stopped, the meniscus drops to the top of hole B. It is suggested that the bath and perfusion apparatus be set up and thoroughly rinsed with distilled water before any muscle preparations are used in order to wash out possible contaminants.

RECORDING

MATERIALS

1. Perspex disc 30 mm diameter, 10 mm thick.
2. Pivot shaft and yoke from muscle lever.
3. Linear variable differential transformer.
4. Demodulator.
5. Direct current pen recorder.
6. Light, relatively stiff spring.

ASSEMBLY (FIG. 3)

The apparatus for measuring the movements of the muscle has been described by Szerb (1964). A lightweight double pulley is machined from the Perspex disc; one wheel with a diameter of 26·5 mm and the other with a

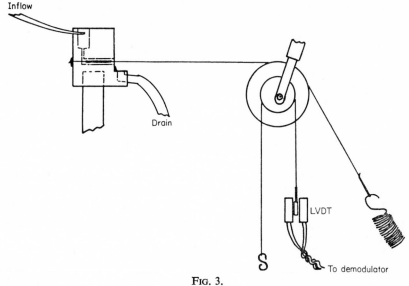

FIG. 3.

diameter of 15·0 mm. They are 3 mm thick, separated from one another by 4 mm and grooved to take a thread. The pulley is fixed on the pivot shaft and mounted in the yoke from the muscle lever attached to the same support stand as the bath. The core of the linear variable differential transformer (LVDT 010MS-L, Schaevitz Engineering) is precisely balanced and suspended over the smaller wheel of the pulley. The body of the transformer is attached below the pulley with a rack and pinion on the same support stand. The pulley is positioned about 3 in. in front of the bath and the top of the large wheel is aligned by eye with the centre of hole A. The body of the transformer is then adjusted so that the suspended core moves freely within it. A demodulator (DMP5-3, Schaevitz Engineering) provides exciting current for the transformer and rectifies the output for the direct current pen recorder. This system can give a linear amplification up to 3000. The spring is attached to the support stand behind the pulley and below it with a rack and pinion. With this arrangement, a light thread attached to the leech muscle passes over the large wheel of the pulley and down to the spring so that movements of the muscle are converted to DC signals by the demodulator.

EXPERIMENT

MATERIALS

1. Leech, *Hirudo medicinalis.*
2. Fine scissors, fine forceps, pins, cork dissecting board, dissecting microscope.

3. Fine needle to pass through hole D of bath.

4. Two feet of fine, unravelled terylene thread.

5. Small pipettes drawn from 4 mm o.d. glass tubing.

6. Greased 0·25 ml syringe with 0·01 gradations; tipped with short piece of rubber tubing to take drawn pipettes for applying samples to microbath.

7. Plasticine.

8. 200 and 400 mg weight.

9. Stopwatch.

SOLUTIONS

1. Locke's solution

NaCl 4·5 g, dextrose 0·5 g, NaHCO$_3$ 0·25 g, KCl 0·21 g, CaCl$_2$ 0·12 g, MgCl$_2$.6H$_2$O 0·125 g, distilled water to 500 ml; pH 7·4.

2. Diluted Locke's solution

1 volume diluted to 1·8 volumes with distilled water (300 ml Locke's solution + 240 ml water).

3. Echothiophate iodide (phospholine iodide) solution

0·1 mg/ml in diluted Locke's solution (25 ml). Some other organophosphate cholinesterase inhibitor may be substituted.

4. Acetylcholine chloride standard solutions

1 to 10 ng/ml in diluted Locke's solution (5 ml of each).

PREPARATION OF THE LEECH MUSCLE

The leech is stretched out and pinned to a paper-covered cork board, dorsal side (dark side with stripes) down, by a pin in each sucker. A small segment (about 10–15 mm long) of the oral end, denoted by the smaller sucker, is pinned out flat with four pins. The rest of the leech is cut off, as is the oral sucker. The ventral muscle wall (green portion) is removed and the remaining dorsal muscle wall is cleared of adhering fascia and other material. The fine needle is threaded with the terylene thread, and 12–15 in. of thread are tied in the centre of one end and 4–5 in. of thread are tied to the centre of the other end of the longitudinal muscles. The threads are fastened down with plasticine and pulled to put the muscle under slight tension. A thin strip of longitudinal muscle is then cut from the stretched muscle, with the threads attached to both ends. Experience has shown that the best preparations come from strips about 10 mm long, when lightly stretched and 1 mm wide. By using a dissecting microscope and by keeping the muscle under light tension, the skin and adhering fascia are removed and the muscle strip is trimmed down to be as uniform as possible, about 0·5 mm wide. The muscle is kept covered by a large drop of Locke's solution during the dissection to prevent it from drying out and care is taken not to overstretch it.

The muscle is mounted in the microbath (hole A) by drawing the shorter piece of thread out through hole D with the needle, and fastening the thread and filling the hole with a bit of plasticine. The longer thread coming from the free end of the muscle is led over the large wheel of the double pulley and gently attached to a weight of 200 or 400 mg depending on the thickness of the muscle. A properly mounted muscle is freely suspended in the bath and the position of the bath is adjusted until this is achieved.

The bath is perfused with Locke's solution until the muscle begins to relax. At this point, the perfusion fluid is changed to Locke's solution, diluted 1 vol. to 1·8 vol. with water, which usually produces a contraction of the muscle followed by its relaxation. When the muscle has relaxed to a constant length, the perfusion fluid is changed to one containing echothiophate iodide, 0·1 mg/ml in dilute Locke's solution. This solution is perfused for 15 min to inhibit cholinesterase and then replaced by dilute Locke's solution. If the muscle has relaxed completely, the echothiophate iodide solution has little effect, but if the muscle is not sufficiently relaxed, a contraction followed by a slow relaxation may result. After replacement of this solution with dilute Locke's solution, the muscle is allowed to relax to its previous length and the hanging weight is replaced by the relatively stiff spring for an approximately isometric record (Szerb, 1964). The spring is adjusted until the muscle reaches its relaxed length.

ASSAY PROCEDURE

The perfusion of the bath is stopped by clamping the rubber tubing of the inflow tubing with a hemostat and the bath reservoir (C) is allowed to empty. A 0·05 ml sample containing 5 ng/ml ACh is then introduced into the reservoir which displaces the bath fluid. Leave it in the bath for 30 sec before resuming perfusion of the bath. The response should be a contraction of the muscle followed by a spontaneous relaxation, but the relaxation might not be complete. If not, use this new level as the baseline for all subsequent samples. If there is no response to the ACh sample, assess the tension of the muscle. A muscle which is stretched too tightly or is without sufficient tension will not respond. If this does not appear to be the problem, check to see that the muscle is not touching the sides of the bath, that the pulley moves freely and that the suspended transformer core moves freely.

Repeat the procedure with the same concentration and for the same length of time. The response should be a contraction followed by a relaxation to about the same baseline. Relaxation is usually spontaneous but occasionally the muscle has to be helped to relax by tapping the bath apparatus with a forefinger. Tapping should be avoided as much as possible since it can change the tension of the muscle and hence the response to ACh. Samples are tested every 2·5 to 3 min depending on the rate of relaxation. Try the same concentration again, only vary the length of time it remains in the bath, then try smaller concentrations and vary the time for these as well. Note that the strength of the contraction is dependent on the amount of ACh present and on the length of time that it is present in the bath. The assay procedure requires the time to be constant for all samples. Have several unknown samples of ACh prepared in the ng/ml range and attempt to estimate the amount of ACh present in them. All samples of unknown or standard amounts of ACh must be made up in dilute Locke's solution or be diluted to the same tonicity with water. The ACh content of each unknown sample is estimated by bracketing the response between standard ACh solutions at least twice. An attempt should be made to suitably dilute unknown samples with dilute Locke's solution to give a response between that of 4 and 7 ng/ml ACh, as this is the range in which most preparations respond well and there is good separation between responses.

This microbath technique can also be used for other assay procedures which utilize small pieces of tissue at room temperature.

REFERENCES

Gaddum, J. H. and Szerb, J. C. (1961). The assay of substance P on goldfish intestine in a microbath. *Br. J. Pharmac. Chemother.*, **17**, 451–463.
Szerb, J. C. (1961). The estimation of acetylcholine, using leech muscle in a microbath. *J. Physiol., Lond.*, **158**, 8–9.
Szerb, J. C. (1964). The effect of tertiary and quaternary atropine on cortical acetylcholine output and on the electroencephalogram in cats. *Can. J. Physiol. Pharmac.*, **42**, 303–314.

Exp. in Physiol. and Biochem. (1970). 3, 351–364.

12 | The Spider Heart

ROBERT G. SHERMAN and RALPH A. PAX

Department of Zoology, Michigan State University, East Lansing, Michigan, U.S.A.

ANIMALS

Spiders are present almost everywhere and can be collected easily. Locations and procedures for collecting spiders can be obtained by consulting field guides to the spiders such as Kaston and Kaston (1953) and Levi and Levi (1968). Certain species of spiders may also be obtained from biological supply houses.

Spiders are maintained easily in the laboratory for extended periods of time. Methods for the laboratory care of spiders are given by Baerg (1937). Our experience in keeping spiders in the laboratory has been confined entirely to the tarantula *Eurypelma marxi* Simon and the burrowing wolf spider *Geolycosa missouriensis* Banks. The spiders are kept individually in large, two to three liter glass jars at room temperature. The containers are kept covered but they should not be air tight. Each jar is filled partially with sand and water is supplied two or three times a week by soaking pieces of sponge and placing one in each container. Though almost any small arthropod may serve as food, in our laboratory we feed the wolf spiders wax moth larvae (*Galleria* sp.) and the tarantulas cockroach nymphs (*Blaberus* sp.). One or two larvae or nymphs each month is sufficient.

EXPERIMENT 1.—HEART RATES IN INTACT SPIDERS

MATERIALS AND APPARATUS

The experiments described here require no specialized apparatus. For recording of heart rates from restrained spiders some sort of restraining method is necessary. We accomplished this by placing the spider on a small block of wood and then taping a piece of cotton gauze securely over both spider and wood block.

EXPERIMENTAL PROCEDURES

The purpose of this experiment is the determination of the heart rate of spiders disturbed as little as possible and a determination of how spider heart rates can change under various experimental conditions.

Heart rates of the unrestrained spider

Because of the location and anatomical arrangement around the spider heart, it is possible to determine heart rate without manipulating the spider in any way. The heart lies just below the abdominal exoskeleton in a mid-dorsal position. It extends from the anterior of the abdomen posteriorly for about half the total length of the abdomen. The heart itself is attached to the dorsal exoskeleton by a series of suspensory ligaments. See Petrunkevitch (1933) or Millot (1949) for an account of the general anatomy of the spider circulatory system. The abdomen is covered with hairs and since the suspensory ligaments attach to the exoskeleton, the hairs can be seen to pulsate with each contraction of the heart. Because of this one can determine the heart rate by simply counting the pulsations of the abdominal hairs.

To determine heart rate by this method, place the container in which the spider is normally kept in the laboratory under a dissecting microscope. Using a microscope illuminator, direct a beam of light on the dorsal surface of the spider's abdomen. The light should be kept at a minimum to avoid heating effects and it should be shone only on the abdomen. Now adjust the microscope so that the tips of some of the hairs on the abdominal surface overlying the heart are in focus. With a little practice one can usually find at least some hairs that are pulsating in rhythm with the heart.

With the spiders we have studied, this procedure usually works quite well. However for reasons unknown to us, we find that it is not always possible to count the hair pulsations on every spider we examine. This procedure also may prove to be unsuccessful in attempting to determine heart rates in some of the more heavily armored spiders where the exoskeleton is less readily moved by the contractions of the heart.

In such cases other procedures are possible. In some spiders the abdominal hairs overlying the heart may be shaved away. This will expose the exoskeleton and the outline of the heart beneath will be visible. The heart rate can then be determined by watching the movements of the heart. We have had success using this method on the tarantula. Wilson (1967) has made the heart visible and the contractions observed easily by painting the surface of the abdominal exoskeleton with immersion oil and directing the light laterally toward the heart.

Regardless of the method used for obtaining the heart rate, some precautions are necessary if one is to obtain a true resting rate. Spiders generally remain motionless for long periods of time and rates should only be taken from spiders which have not moved for at least ten minutes. Loud noises, vibrations, sudden movements and bright lights are factors which may affect the heart rate.

Once a measure of the resting rate has been obtained from a spider determine how various factors will change this rate. One method of obtaining elevated heart rates which we find convenient is to force the spider to run in its container for about a minute. The rate should then be measured as soon as possible after the spider ceases to run and also at intervals after this, to see how quickly the rate drops with time after exercise. A variety of other factors such as vibrations, puffs of air, noises and bright light may also be tested.

Heart rate of the restrained spider

In most animals it is necessary to employ some sort of restraint on the animal in order to measure heart rates. To determine what effect restraint has on the spider heart rate, take a piece of cotton gauze and tape two adjacent edges to a piece of wood about 5 cm². Place the spider under the cotton gauze and draw the cloth over the spider. Tape the remaining two edges of the gauze to the wood. We use long forceps placed on one of the spider's legs to position the spider on the wood block. The gauze should be fairly tightly drawn over the spider so that only slight struggling movements are allowed. Holes in the gauze allow some of the abdominal hairs to protrude unhampered, thus permitting them to pulsate.

After the spider has stopped struggling allow at least ten minutes to elapse and then measure the heart rate as before. Determine the rate over a period of several minutes and compare these values to those for the resting unrestrained spiders.

RESULTS

There appears to be no characteristic heart rate for spiders in general, the rate varying markedly from species to species and also for a given species under different conditions. Table I gives some representative examples of rates which have been reported. The first four rates given probably represent true resting rates in undisturbed spiders but the last four rates given were obtained from spiders restrained to varying extents. Mikulska (1961) gives a number of other heart rates but these were obtained from very young spiders (3–4 days old).

A variety of extrinsic factors aside from restraint are capable of producing elevated heart rates. Forced exercise typically results in a transient three to seven-fold increase in heart rate (Bristowe, 1932; Sherman and Pax, 1968). Figure 1 shows the pattern of heart rate changes observed as a result of exercise in the tarantula and the wolf spider. Temperature (Mikulska, 1961) and bright light shone on the prosoma (Mikulska and Kokociński, 1965) also produce elevated heart rates.

R

TABLE I

Species	Rate (beats/min)	Source
Liphistius desultor	26	Bristowe, 1932
Eurypelma marxi	37	Wenk, 1967 (unpublished)
Geolycosa missouriensis	48	Sherman and Pax, 1968
Micrommata virescens	54	Bristowe, 1932
Tegenaria atrica	59	Mikulska and Kokociński, 1965
Heteropoda venatoria	70	Wilson, 1967
Pholcis phalangioides	134	Willem, 1917
Epeira diademata	139	Willem, 1917

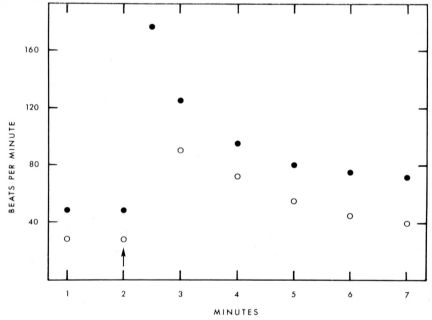

FIG. 1. Spider heart rates before and after forced exercise. ● represents the mean heart rate for *Geolycosa missouriensis* (5 animals). ○ represents the mean heart rate for *Eurypelma marxi* (5 animals). The arrow denotes the time at which the spiders were forced to run.

EXPERIMENT 2—THE ISOLATED HEART

MATERIALS AND APPARATUS

The spider saline

The saline to be used for the isolated heart is that described by Rathmayer (1965) for a leg nerve-muscle preparation of the spider *Eurypelma hentzi* Girard. The composition of the saline is listed in Table II. The calcium chloride

TABLE II

Salt	g/1	$mM/1$
NaCl	12·70	217·0
KCl	0·37	5·0
CaCl$_2$.2H$_2$O	0·59	4·0
MgCl$_2$.6H$_2$O	0·22	1·1
NaHCO$_3$	0·25	3·0

should be added after all of the other constituents have dissolved, since it otherwise tends to precipitate. Generally one liter of saline is sufficient for the experiment.

Dissection materials

To dissect out the heart it is advantageous to use fine forceps, scissors and small insect pins, since spider hearts are quite small (less than 15 mm). A small glass dish partially filled with paraffin can be used to hold the heart and the saline.

Recording apparatus

A number of different mechano-transducers can be used to monitor contractions of the isolated heart as long as they are sensitive enough to respond to the heart contractions. In experiments conducted in our laboratory we use the E and M Instrument Co. (Houston, Texas 77071, U.S.A.) Model F-50 microdisplacement transducer. This transducer has a maximum sensitivity of 0·1 g/cm of displacement and is adequate for use on both the wolf spider and the tarantula heart. Fine thread with a small hook attached at one end can be used to attach the mechano-transducer to the heart.

EXPERIMENTAL PROCEDURES

Isolation of the spider heart

Place a spider in a refrigerator or cold room at 5°C for 15–30 min. When the spider appears to be acting "sluggish" remove its legs by cutting them off close to their origins. This will completely immobilize the animal (see Fig. 2). The abdomen is joined to the cephalothorax by the narrow pedicel. With scissors cut completely through the pedicel as near the cephalothorax as possible. Place the abdomen ventral-side-up in a glass dish which has been partially filled with paraffin. Cover the abdomen with saline. Beginning just dorsal to the spinnerets make a cut along the lateral margin of one side of the abdomen to the pedicel. Stop cutting just short of the pedicel and just ventral to it. Make a similar cut along the other side of the abdomen. Using large

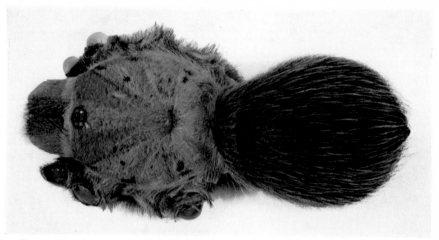

FIG. 2. Dorsal view of the tarantula *Eurypelma marxi* with its legs removed. The spider is 50 mm in length.

insect pins, pin the posterior end of the abdomen to the paraffin and position the abdomen so that its posterior is toward you.

Draw the ventral exoskeleton up and forward to a point in front of the rest of the abdomen and carefully complete the cuts that you have previously made (see Fig. 3). The ventral portion of the abdomen then can be removed completely and discarded. Pin each side of the dorsal abdomen to the paraffin at a point mid-way along each lateral margin. Now with forceps lift the viscera at the posterior and pull them up and forward while gently teasing them away from around the heart. With practice nearly all of the viscera can be removed *en masse* in a single operation. The heart now should be visible in its mid-dorsal position still attached to the dorsal exoskeleton (see Fig. 4). Carefully remove any remaining viscera from around the heart. During these procedures the saline should be changed several times. The isolation procedures can best be done under a dissecting microscope.

At this point the heart will have been exposed sufficiently for some experiments. However the procedures outlined above do not expose the cardiac ganglion which is situated on the dorsal external surface of the heart. To accomplish this, take forceps and lift the heart at its posterior and working anteriorly, progressively cut the suspensory ligaments. Some of the pericardial lining also may have to be removed along with the ligaments. Continue in this way until the heart can be completely lifted free of the exoskeleton. Be careful to avoid stretching the heart and do not place forceps on the mid-dorsal surface of the heart. This is where the cardiac ganglion is located and if it is damaged the heart may stop beating. After the heart is completely free place

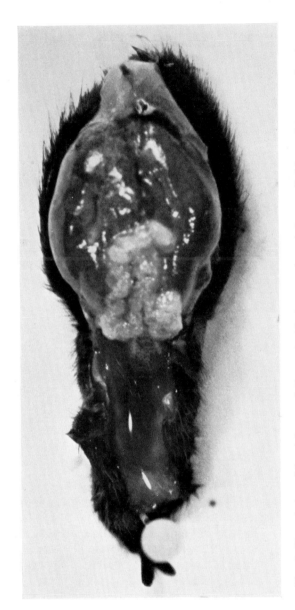

FIG. 3. Ventral view of the abdomen of *E. marxi* with the ventral exoskeleton pulled forward to expose the viscera. Anterior is to the left.

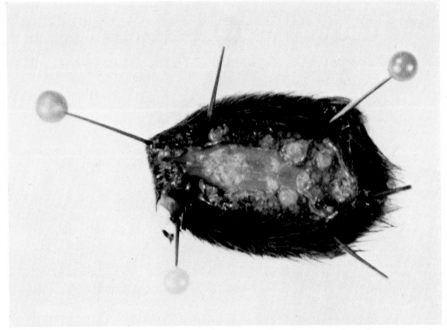

FIG. 4. Ventral view of the abdomen of *E. marxi* after the viscera have been removed. The heart can be seen still attached to the dorsal exoskeleton. On either side of the heart one can see the cut stumps of the large abdominal dorso-ventral muscles. Anterior is to the left.

it dorsal-side-up in the paraffin filled dish and pin it at both ends with fine insect pins to the paraffin (see Fig. 5). Make sure that any debris left in the dish is discarded. The heart can be cannulated, but for our purposes it is only necessary that the saline be changed periodically (every 2–3 min is sufficient).

Continuous recording of the mechanical activity of the heart

Once the spider heart has been isolated it is a simple matter to measure the heart rate by counting the number of contractions over a particular period of time. However in conducting experiments on isolated hearts it is usually advantageous to continuously monitor the heart rate by other means. This can be done with a variety of mechano-transducers which are sufficiently sensitive to respond to the mechanical contractions of the heart.

Using small insect pins, pin the heart laterally near the ostial opening which is located at the region of greatest movement of the heart upon contraction. The heart should already be placed dorsal-side-up in the dish and pinned at both ends. All pins should be placed at the extreme ends and margins

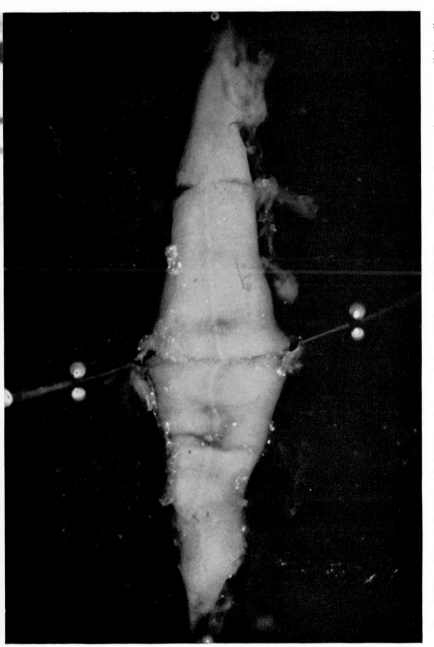

FIG. 5. Dorsal view of the isolated heart of *E. marxi*. Anterior is to the left. The cardiac ganglion can be seen as a lighter line along the mid-dorsal heart surface. The transverse darker slits near the posterior of the heart are ostia.

of the heart in order to avoid damage to the heart musculature. When pinning out the heart maintain its normal shape and avoid stretching of the heart musculature. Bend a small piece of insect pin into a hook and attach the pin to a short length of fine thread. One method for making this attachment is to use a small drop of melted paraffin which upon hardening will hold the pin to the thread. After the thread has been attached to the mechano-transducer, attach the hooked end of the insect pin to the lateral margin of the heart at a point opposite the insect pin already holding one side of the heart to the paraffin. All pins should be inserted carefully and care taken that the myocardium is not seriously damaged.

Removal of the cardiac ganglion

The cardiac ganglion is responsible for initiating contractions of the spider heart, i.e., the heartbeat is neurogenic. With fine forceps tease the ganglion from the heart beginning posteriorly and working forward. Take care not to damage the muscle cells of the heart. Notice what happens to the heart contractions as the ganglion is removed. Regions of the heart in which the ganglion is still attached continue to beat while those no longer innervated by the ganglion no longer contract. When the ganglion has been completely removed, all regions of the heart will remain quiet.

RESULTS

After isolation, the hearts of both the tarantula and the wolf spider show a progressive decline in heart rate, but in the first several minutes the rate of beating of the isolated heart will probably be somewhat higher than the rates for the resting intact spiders. For the wolf spider, the heart rate in the first minute after isolation averages 60 beats/min about 10 beats/min higher than that recorded for the resting intact spider. The initial rate of beating of the isolated tarantula heart averages 41 beats/min, 4 beats/min higher than recorded for the resting intact tarantula. Though the initial rate after isolation may be a little higher than that recorded from intact resting spiders, it is never as high as that recorded from "excited" or restrained intact spiders. Also in contrast to the heart in the intact animal, there are no large rate changes and a general lack of variability is seen in the isolated heart rates.

EXPERIMENT 3—ELECTRICAL ACTIVITY OF THE SPIDER HEART
MATERIALS AND APPARATUS

For recording of electrocardiograms from intact spiders and for extra-cellular recording from isolated hearts, stainless steel electrodes made from small insulated insect pins (size 000) are satisfactory. These electrodes are connected through a capacitance-coupled preamplifier to an oscilloscope. Positioning of the electrodes is accomplished by means of manipulators stationed along each side of the heart. In our laboratory we use a Tektronix 502A oscilloscope, Grass P5 or P8 preamplifiers and Narashige manipulators.

For intracellular recordings from heart muscle cells, we use glass micro-electrodes filled with 3M KCl. Procedures for the preparation of such electrodes and the experimental set-up for making intracellular electrical recordings are given in Volume 1 of this series.

EXPERIMENTAL PROCEDURES

Electrocardiogram of the intact spider

Restrain a spider using the procedure already described in Experiment 1. Make sure that the spider cannot move appreciably or the electrodes may injure the animal. Position the recording electrodes above the mid-dorsal surface of the abdomen, one near the pedicel, the other several millimeters to the posterior. Slowly and carefully lower the electrodes on to the abdomen until indentations occur in the exoskeleton beneath them. Do not penetrate the abdomen with the electrodes.

In most cases this procedure will allow you to record the electrocardiogram. If no electrical activity can be recorded there may not be sufficient electrical contact between the electrodes and the surface of the abdomen. If this is the case, we find that a small piece of cotton moistened with saline and wrapped around each electrode tip will usually give good recordings. If by this method sufficient electrical contact is still not achieved, it may be necessary to shave the abdomen to remove the hairs on the mid-dorsal abdominal surface.

Electrical activity of the spider cardiac ganglion

Isolate a heart and pin it to a paraffin filled dish as previously described. Recordings from the ganglion may be made from the whole heart. However to reduce movement artifacts, the ganglion, along with a strip of muscle on either side of the ganglion, can be removed from the rest of the heart and the recordings taken from this. With fine scissors cut the heart along each side of the ganglion as close to it as possible. Keep the ganglion covered with saline.

Insulated electrodes of the type used for recording the electrocardiogram may be used and they should be placed directly on the surface of the ganglion. The electrodes must be well insulated except for a small area at the tip or else the saline level in the dish must be lowered temporarily while the recordings are being made. If this is done, make sure that the ganglion is kept moist, for it will dry-out quite rapidly.

Microelectrode recording from cardiac muscle cells

Isolate a spider heart in the manner described in Experiment 2. However do not pin the heart to the paraffin. By not pinning, the heart movement with each contraction will be considerably reduced. This is desirable for it is rather difficult to maintain an electrode in a cell that is moving a great deal. The heart will continue to beat for hours by allowing it to lie on one side completely free of any restraint. Muscle cells in the middle region of the heart are the ones most easily penetrated.

RESULTS

The electrocardiogram

The electrocardiogram is a representation of the sum of the electrical activity associated with the heartbeat of an animal. In forms in which detailed information is lacking the electrocardiogram serves as an indication as to the origin of the heartbeat. The pattern of the electrocardiogram of myogenic hearts usually is quite different from that of neurogenic ones. In forms having a neurogenic heartbeat the pattern consists of a series of rapid potentials. In animals where the heartbeat is myogenic the pattern consists of a few simple slow electrical potentials.

The electrocardiogram of the spider shows the oscillatory pattern characteristic of neurogenic hearts. A typical electrocardiogram is shown in Fig. 6. The pattern consists of a series of bursts of electrical potentials, each burst corresponding to one contraction of the heart.

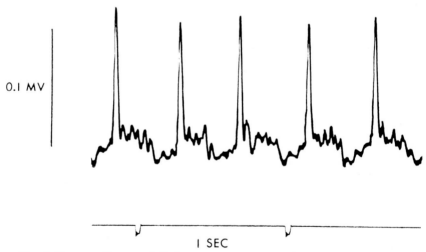

0.1 MV

I SEC

Fig. 6. Electrocardiogram of *Geolycosa missouriensis*. Five bursts of electrical potentials are shown, each one corresponding to a contraction of the heart. Note the oscillatory nature of the electrocardiogram.

Cardiac ganglion electrical activity

The cardiac ganglion electrical activity consists of a series of bursts of electrical potentials, each burst corresponding to a contraction of the heart. In *G. missouriensis*, the number of potentials in the burst is variable and may range from 10 to 40. The burst duration is also variable and may be as long as 650 msec or as brief as 150 msec. Figure 7 shows an example of the cardiac ganglion electrical activity.

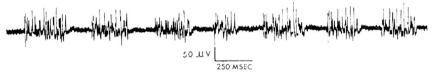

50 µV

250 MSEC

FIG. 7. Electrical activity recorded from the surface of the cardiac ganglion of an isolated *G. missouriensis* heart. Seven bursts of electrical potentials are shown, each one corresponding to a heartbeat (from Sherman and Pax, 1968).

Intracellularly recorded electrical activity of the heart muscle

In *G. missouriensis*, the resting potentials of the heart muscle cells average −45 mV with a range from −30 to −60 mV. With each contraction of the heart there occurs a rapid depolarization followed by a lesser maintained oscillatory depolarization about 75% the size of the initial depolarization. The initial depolarization ranges from 10 to 40 mV. Superimposed on the maintained depolarization is a series of potentials numbering anywhere from 5 to 15. The duration of the electrical activity ranges from 150 to 650 msec.

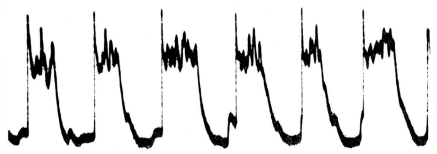

FIG. 8. Electrical activity recorded from within a cardiac muscle cell of *G. missouriensis* during six contractions of the heart. The time between successive beats is approximately 500 msec and the maximum depolarization averages about 30 mV. Resting potential: −50 mV (from Sherman and Pax, 1969).

The rise time of the initial depolarization, i.e., the time for the depolarization to become maximum, ranges from 15 to 35 msec. Figure 8 shows an example of the type of electrical activity recorded from within the muscle cells.

BIBLIOGRAPHY

Baerg, W. J. (1937). Laboratory care of tarantulas. *In* "Culture Methods for Invertebrate Animals" (J. H. Needham, ed.), 243–244. Dover Publications, New York, U.S.A.

Bristowe, W. S. (1932). The liphistid spiders. With an appendix on their internal anatomy by J. Millot. *Proc. zool. Soc. Lond.*, **103**, 1015–1057.

KASTON, B. J. (1948). Spiders of Connecticut. *St. Geol. Nat. Hist. Surv., Bull.* No. 70, Hartford, Conn., U.S.A.

Kaston, B. J. and Kaston, E. (1953). "How to Know the Spiders". W. C. Brown, Dubuque, Iowa, U.S.A.

Legendre, R. (1968). Sur la présence d'un nerf cardiaque chez les araignées orthognathes. *C.r. hebd. Séanc. Acad. Sci., Paris*, **267**, 84–86.

Levi, H. and Levi, L. (1968). "Spiders and their Kin." Golden Press, New York, U.S.A.

Mikulska, I. (1961). Changes in heart rate in spiders effected by increased temperature. *Zoologica Pol.*, **12**, 149–160.

Mikulska, I. and Kokociński, W. (1965). Le rythme du coeur dans l'abdomen isolé de l'araignée. *Bull. Acad. pol. Sci. Cl. II Sér. Sci. biol.*, **13**, 533–537.

Millot, J. (1949). Ordre des Araneides. *In* "Traite de Zoologie" (P. Grasse, ed.), 639–646. Masson et Cie, Paris.

Petrunkevitch, A. (1933). An inquiry into the natural classification of spiders based on a study of their internal anatomy. *Conn. Acad. Arts Sci.*, **31**, 299–389.

Rathmayer, W. (1965). Neuromuscular transmission in a spider and the effect of calcium. *Comp. Biochem. Physiol.*, **14**. 673–687.

Sherman, R. G. and Pax, R. A. (1968). The heartbeat of the spider, *Geolycosa missouriensis. Comp. Biochem. Physiol.*, **26**, 529–536.

Sherman, R. G. and Pax, R. A. (1969). Electrical activity in single muscle cells of a spider heart. *Comp. Biochem. Physiol.*, **28**, 487–489.

Sherman, R. G., Bursey, C. R., Fourtner, C. R. and Pax, R. A. (1969). Cardiac ganglia in spiders (Arachnida : Araneae). *Experientia* (in press).

Willem, V. (1917). Observations sur la circulation sanguine et la respiration pulmonaire chez les araignées. *Archs néerl. Physiol.*, **1**, 226–256.

Wilson, R. S. (1967). The heartbeat of the spider *Heteropoda venatoria. J. Insect Physiol.*, **13**, 1309–1326.

Exp. in Physiol. and Biochem. (1970). **3**, 365–415.

13

A. Techniques for Maintaining a Stock of the Blowfly *Phormia regina*

B. The Non-glycogen Carbohydrates of the Hemolymph and Fat Body during Larval Development of *Phormia regina*

C. Glycogen Changes during Metamorphosis of *Phormia regina*

D. Lipid Composition of the Fat Body during Third-instar Development of *Phormia regina*

L. T. WIMER, R. H. LUMB* and L. G. TATE

Department of Biology, University of South Carolina, Columbia, South Carolina, U.S.A.

A. Techniques for Maintaining a Stock of the Blowfly *Phormia regina*

PRINCIPLE OF EXPERIMENT

A wide variety of experiments use blowflies to investigate basic problems in physiology and biochemistry. *Calliphora*, *Phormia*, and *Lucilia* are three of the most frequently used genera. Blowflies are especially good experimental animals for the following reasons: (1) they are inexpensive and easy to rear; (2) they can be maintained under constant environmental conditions in the laboratory, thus diminishing variability in larval growth and metamorphosis and consequently producing more consistent results; (3) the larvae can be reared aseptically on diets of known chemical composition providing an essential requirement for nutritional studies in addition to reducing undesirable odors from diets such as fresh meat; (4) they complete a life cycle in $2\frac{1}{2}$–$3\frac{1}{2}$ weeks, thus facilitating studies in developmental physiology and biochemistry; and (5) the individual insects, or isolated organs, with the aid of recently developed microtechniques, are adaptable to experimentation.

The purpose of this experiment is to familiarize the investigator with the materials and procedures required to maintain a stock of *Phormia regina*, with particular emphasis placed on rearing and selecting larvae for developmental studies. Terms used in describing the events and stages during the life cycle of *Phormia regina* also are defined.

* Present address: Western Carolina University, Cullowhee, North Carolina, U.S.A.

ANIMALS

The stock culture of *Phormia regina* has been maintained continuously in our laboratory for seven years. The original stock was acquired from the strain at the Department of Biology, Johns Hopkins University, Baltimore, Maryland, U.S.A.

MATERIALS

MATERIALS FOR PREPARING CULTURE MEDIUM*

1. Ingredients of culture medium.

(a) Cholesterol (Nutritional Biochemicals Corporation NBCo., Cleveland, Ohio 44128, U.S.A.) 5 g.

(b) Salt mixture M-D No. 185 (NBCo.) 5 g.

Components of salt mixture

Calcium lactate . $5H_2O$	$35 \cdot 19 \%$	NaCl	$4 \cdot 67 \%$
Ca $(H_2PO_4)_2 . H_2O$	$14 \cdot 60 \%$	$MgSO_4$ (anhydrous)	$7 \cdot 19 \%$
KH_2PO_4	$25 \cdot 78 \%$	Ferric citrate	$3 \cdot 19 \%$
NaH_2PO_4	$9 \cdot 38 \%$		

(c) Methyl p-hydroxybenzoate, mold inhibitor (Eastman Organic Chemicals) 11 g.

(d) Brewer's yeast (NBCo.) 50 g.

(e) Agar, granulated (NBCo.) 20 g.

(f) Casein, purified high nitrogen (NBCo.) 500 g.

(g) Distilled water, 1350 ml.

2. Balance with a minimum capacity of 1 kg.

3. Beakers, 1 liter (1) and 200 ml (2) for weighing casein, yeast and agar.

4. Weighing papers.

5. Spatulas.

6. Materials for mixing and boiling medium

(a) 3 liter flask.

(b) Powder funnel.

(c) Large stirring rod 18 in. long.

(d) Gas burner with tubing.

(e) Tripod.

(f) Matches.

(g) Wire gauze with asbestos center.

(h) Asbestos gloves.

7. Pint jars (tapered, wide mouth, graduated in ounces, Ball canning jars No. 66, Ball Brothers Co., Muncie, Indiana 47302, U.S.A.).

8. Aluminum foil.

9. Autoclave.

* All items are listed in the order used. Some items may be required for more than one part of the experiment: however, they are listed only once.

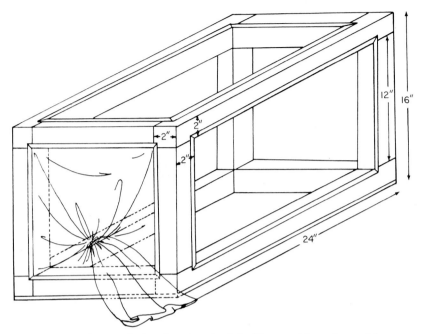

Fig. 1. Screen wire cage for housing *Phormia* adults. The top, sides and rear of the cage are covered with 18–14 copper mesh screen wire fixed in place with $\frac{1}{4}$ in. $\times$ $\frac{3}{8}$ in. molding. The bottom of the cage consists of $\frac{1}{4}$ in. plywood. The front of the cage is covered with bedsheeting material held in place with $\frac{1}{4}$ in. $\times$ $\frac{3}{8}$ in. molding.

MATERIALS FOR MAINTAINING ADULTS

Screen wire cage (Fig. 1).
Petri dishes, 100 $\times$ 15 mm.
Sucrose, block or granulated.

Filter paper, 9 cm.
Water bottle, 4 oz. wide mouth.

MATERIALS FOR COLLECTING AND PROCESSING EGGS

Pork or beef liver (may be stored frozen in about 3 oz. packages).
Forceps (2).
Watch glass, Syracuse type.
NaOH, 2 g/100 ml.
Distilled water, 100 ml.
Aluminum foil discs cut with a cork borer, about 1·7 mm in diameter.
Balance, analytical.

Pasteur-type disposable transfer pipettes (Fig. 2), 3 ml rubber bulbs and triangular file.
Disposable paper tissue.
Dissecting microscope and lamp.
Aluminum foil squares, 3 $\times$ 3 cm.
Incubator set at 28·5°C.
Squares of bedsheeting material, 14 $\times$ 14 cm.

Wood shavings, preferably untreated pine.
Aluminum foil cups, laboratory-made for weighing larvae.
Tank of carbon dioxide with pressure regulator.

EXPERIMENTAL PROCEDURES

PREPARATION OF CULTURE MEDIUM

Water (1350 ml) is brought to boiling in a 3 liter flask and allowed to cool for several minutes. Ingredients are then added in the order listed in the Materials section; and flask contents are mixed after the addition of each substance (use a large stirring rod or swirl the flask by hand using asbestos gloves). The contents of the flask should be boiling gently as the agar and casein are added. Cap the flask with aluminum foil and autoclave at 15 pounds pressure and 121°C for 20 min. The autoclaved medium is mixed by swirling (use asbestos gloves) before it is poured. Approximately 5 oz. of medium are poured into each jar; one batch will yield about 12 jars of medium. The jars are capped immediately and stored in a refrigerator, where they may be kept for as long as two months.

MAINTENANCE OF ADULTS, COLLECTING AND PROCESSING EGGS

The adults are housed in a screen wire cage (Fig. 1) and maintained on sucrose and water. Sucrose, either the granulated or block form, is supplied in a Petri dish; use of the block form reduces the frequency of cage cleaning. Water is supplied by inverting a 4 oz. bottle of water in a Petri dish containing a disc of filter paper.

A Petri dish containing about 3 oz. of pork liver (and a few ml of water) is introduced into the cage to stimulate egg production. The liver should be obtained directly from the slaughter house since some food preservatives may interfere with egg production. When females are newly emerged, liver should be fed to the adults immediately following emergence (day 1), and good egg production will be attained on the morning of the fifth day. It is best to remove the liver on the fourth day and supply fresh liver in the early morning of the fifth day. However, when females have oviposited previously, eggs are generally obtained from 2–24 h after the addition of pork liver. The females are allowed to oviposit for a period of 3 h after the appearance of the first eggs.

The eggs are laid on the liver, usually in one or two large clusters. Remove the egg clusters from the liver with forceps and place in a Syracuse watch glass containing 2% sodium hydroxide. Separation of the eggs is facilitated by stirring gently with forceps; then remove the NaOH and wash the separated eggs with three changes of distilled water. The sodium hydroxide solution and water

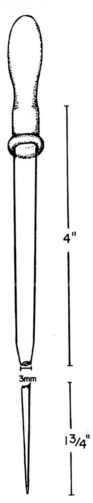

FIG. 2. Pasteur-type disposable transfer pipette for approximating the number of eggs. The tip is removed after making an etch mark with a triangular file. If the outside diameter of the tip is about 3 mm, two drops of packed eggs will deliver about 600 eggs.

may be removed from the Syracuse watch glass by gently tilting the vessel to a vertical position. The eggs are transferred in water, using a transfer pipette which has 1¾ in. of the tip removed (Fig. 2), to a *tared* aluminum foil disc (1·7 mm in diameter). After the eggs have settled to the tip of the pipette, two drops will deliver about 600 eggs. The excess water is removed from the eggs by making a small hole with forceps in the foil disc which is on a piece of paper tissue. Spread the eggs evenly over the foil disc with forceps while viewing with a dissecting microscope. The eggs are air dried until they begin to adhere to each other. This is noted by probing the eggs gently with forceps. The foil disc and eggs are weighed to estimate the number of eggs placed on the foil disc. The average weight of a single egg (0·068 mg) has been ascertained by weighing a known number of eggs.

Sample calculation of number of eggs placed on the aluminum foil disc

weight of foil disc and eggs	50·00 mg
weight of foil disc	−10·00 mg
weight of eggs placed on foil disc	40·00 mg

wt. of eggs on foil disc ÷ wt. of single egg = no. of eggs on foil disc

$$40\!\cdot\!00 \text{ mg} \div 0\!\cdot\!068 \text{ mg} = 588.$$

The weight of eggs placed on the foil disc should be in the range of 36–44 mg to obtain optimum population size. After weighing, the foil disc and eggs are placed on a square piece of foil and placed together in a jar of culture medium. The foil square prevents the eggs from being drawn onto the medium by the surface liquid. The culture medium should be at 28·5°C and excess fluid poured off before placing the eggs in the jar.

To prevent desiccation of the eggs, the metal lid should be placed on the jar until hatching begins (hatching is observed with the dissecting microscope). When maintained at 28·5°C, the eggs begin to hatch about 12–14 h after the end of the collecting period. As hatching begins, the flat part of the metal lid should be replaced with a piece of bedsheeting material. This reduces the humidity and "drives" the larvae off the foil disc and onto the medium. Since the eggs are collected over a 3 h period, almost all the viable eggs hatch within a period of 3 h. Four hours after hatching begins, the foil disc with the unhatched eggs and empty egg cases is removed from the jar, air dried as before, and weighed. Since the weights of a single egg (0·068 mg) and egg case (0·002 mg) are known, it is possible to estimate the number of hatched eggs.

Sample calculation of number of hatched eggs

weight of foil disc and eggs before hatching	50·00 mg
weight of foil disc, unhatched eggs and empty egg cases after hatching	−26·00 mg
weight loss due to hatched eggs	24·00 mg

wt. loss due to hatched eggs ÷ (wt. of single egg − wt. of single egg case)

= no. of hatched eggs

$$24\!\cdot\!00 \div (0\!\cdot\!068 \text{ mg} - 0\!\cdot\!002 \text{ mg})$$

$$= 364$$

By knowing the number of hatched eggs (364) and the number placed on the foil disc (588), one may calculate the percentage of hatched eggs. In this example 61·9% of the eggs hatched.

The percentage of hatched eggs ranged from 35% to 83% when eggs from five different collecting periods were compared. The reason for this variation is not known, although one contributing factor may be the tendency of older females to produce fewer viable eggs. When comparing the percentage hatched among six different samples from a single egg collection, the variation was only 7%. Because of the variation in percentage of hatched eggs and the number placed on the foil disc, the larval populations may range from 150 to 550 larvae. Larval cultures with too few larvae appear to have difficulty in feeding, while larvae in overpopulated cultures do not attain optimum size. More consistent growth is noted in those cultures containing 250–400 larvae.

REARING LARVAE

The larval cultures are maintained at 28·5°C. During the first day of larval life, the jars are covered with bedsheeting material. This prevents the larvae from gathering around the top of the jar and insures feeding. On the second day, wood shavings are placed in the jars to a depth of about two inches. The shavings serve a dual purpose: to prevent excessive medium desiccation and to keep the larvae on the medium.

OBSERVATIONS

Larval growth

Larval growth is measured from the mean time of hatching ($\pm$ 1·5 h) to puparium formation (Fig. 3). It appears that within a single larval culture, at any given time, most of the larvae are approximately the same size, although there will always be exceptions. In measuring larval growth, care must be taken to select only those larvae which are not of obviously extreme sizes. In preparing the larval growth curve, ten larvae are removed at selected times from each culture jar, weighed in an aluminum cup and discarded. The growth curve in Fig. 3 represents data from 32 different jars of larvae.

During growth, the larvae increased in weight from about 0·066 mg at hatching to 50·1 mg just prior to day six. The decline in weight at puparium formation is due to a loss of water.

Larval ecdysis and puparium formation

The larvae of *Phormia regina* pass through three instars during their development. The first instar consists of larvae emerging from the egg cases. During much of the first day, these larvae wander aimlessly over the surface of

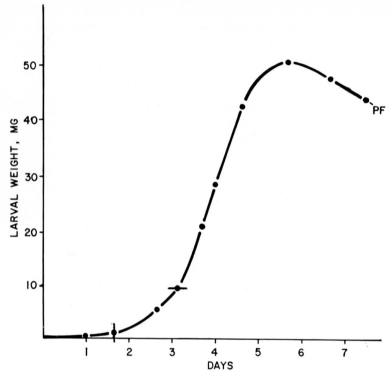

FIG. 3. Larval growth curve of *Phormia regina*. ⬦, ecdysis to the second instar. -•-, ecdysis to the third instar. PF, puparium formation.

the medium. Toward the end of the first day, almost all of the larvae cluster on the surface of the medium where it comes in contact with the side of the jar. Such clustering appears to be associated with moulting; hence the first larval moult (moult to the second instar) occurs during the second day (Fig. 3).

Ecdysis and moulting generally are used synonymously; although some investigators consider them two separate processes. Therefore, sometimes a distinction between ecdysis and moulting is made (Snodgrass, 1954; Imms, 1964). This distinction designates moulting as the separation of the old cuticle from the hypodermis; while referring to ecdysis as the subsequent rupture and casting off of the old cuticle. Moulting marks the initiation of the next instar. Hence the second larval instar is contained within the first larval cuticle for a short time, during which the second larval instar is known as the pharate instar (Hinton, 1946).

The size of the mouthparts (black "dots" at the anterior end of the larvae) may be observed visually through the side of the jar and used to identify each instar. Because mouthparts' size is used as the criterion to distinguish different instars, the following observations refer to the time of ecdysis. The ecdysial period is taken as the time interval during which 80% of the larvae complete ecdysis. The beginning of the period is ascertained by noting the time when about 10% of the larvae have completed ecdysis, while the period ends when only 10% of the larvae have not undergone ecdysis. While a few larvae undergo ecdysis sporadically during the initial and terminal phases of the ecdysial period, most larvae complete ecdysis within a well-defined period.

Observations of the first larval ecdysis (ecdysis to the second instar)

Number of larvae in jar	300 (100%)
Time at which about 10% of the larvae have completed ecdysis to the second instar is 35 h after the mean hatching time	−30 (10%)
Time at which only 10% of the larvae have not undergone ecdysis to the second instar is 40 h	−30 (10%)
Time period during which 80% of the larvae have completed ecdysis to the second instar is 35–40 h	240 (80%)

Observations of the second larval ecdysis (ecdysis to the third instar)

Number of larvae in jar	300 (100%)
Time at which about 10% of the larvae have completed ecdysis to the third instar is 68 h after the mean hatching time	−30 (10%)
Time at which only 10% of the larvae have not undergone ecdysis to the third instar is 76 h	−30 (10%)
Time period during which 80% of the larvae have completed ecdysis to the third instar is 68–76 h	240 (80%)

Therefore, the period of ecdysis to the second instar is 35–40 h, while the period of ecdysis to the third instar is 68–76 h. These ecdysial periods represent mean values obtained from 32 jars of larvae. Among the different larval cultures, variation in the time of ecdysis occurs. In the larval culture with the slowest developmental rate, the first and second ecdysial periods terminated at 46 and 81 h, respectively. In the larval culture with the fastest developmental rate, the first and second ecdysial periods terminated at 35 and 69 h, respectively. Since the third-instar larvae initially increases in weight at the rate of about 1 mg/h, two larvae which differ in age by 12 h may differ in weight by 12 mg. If it is desirable to obtain larvae in similar stages of development, the period of ecdysis may be used as the reference time for selection of larvae.

Near the end of third-instar development, the larvae migrate into the wood shavings where puparium formation occurs. At about 130 h after hatching, the wet wood shavings should be replaced with fresh shavings to minimize time variability in puparium formation. The term prepupa is used frequently to refer to the third-instar larva at the onset of puparium formation (when the larva shortens and becomes motionless but before it begins to darken). If it is desirable to obtain insects in similar stages of metamorphosis, puparium formation serves as a convenient reference point for selection of animals. As puparium formation occurs, the insects may be removed from the wood shavings and placed in a Petri dish. The time of puparium formation has been observed in 4055 larvae.

Observations on the time of puparium formation

Days after hatching	Number of insects forming a puparium at each time interval	% of total insects
6·5–7·0	414	10·2%
7·0–7·5	1589	39·2%
7·5–8·0	1295	31·9%
8·0–8·5	757	18·7%

These observations show that about one-half of the larvae initiate puparium formation from 6·5–7·5 days after hatching, while the other half do so from 7·5–8·5 days.

Metamorphosis

The type of metamorphosis in Diptera is termed holometabolous, which typically refers to the extensive reorganizational processes in the transformation of the larva into the imago or adult insect. Puparium formation may be considered the beginning of metamorphosis, while eclosion (emergence of the adult from the puparium or pupal case) terminates metamorphosis. The time interval between puparium formation and eclosion of the adult is about 118 h at 28·5°C.

The number of moults in the Cyclorrhaphan Diptera has been investigated by Fraenkel (1938). As previously noted, there are three larval instars and two larval moults. Near the end of larval development, the cuticle of the third-instar larva gives rise to the puparium. Three moults occur during metamorphosis with the formation of three additional cuticles within the puparium. The three moults and cuticles are termed prepupal, pupal, and adult. The pupa denotes the insect's development from the pupal moult to eclosion. Following the adult moult, the adult in its own cuticle, actually is contained within three additional cuticles and should be termed the pharate adult (Hinton, 1946) while in this stage (2½–3 days).

COLLECTING ADULTS

Adults may be collected directly from the cage by moving the mouth of a pint jar over the inside screen surface and periodically tilting the jar slightly to permit the insects to enter the jar; then cap the jar. Or the insects may remain in the culture jar during metamorphosis and collected at eclosion. If older adults are required, eclosion serves as a convenient starting time for designating the age of the adult. For experimentation, the adults are anesthetized with CO_2.

OTHER EXPERIMENTS USING BLOWFLIES

Blowflies have been used frequently for experiments in physiology and bio-chemistry. Experiments B, C, and D of this series use *Phormia regina* for investigating the carbohydrate and lipid changes during development. In Volume I of *Experiments in Physiology and Biochemistry*, Experiments 3, 11, and 23 mention the use of blowflies. The potential experimental use of *Phormia* is immeasurable.

The flesh fly, *Sarcophaga bullata*, may be substituted for blowflies in many experiments. *Sarcophaga* is obtained from Carolina Biological Supply Company, Burlington, North Carolina 27215, U.S.A. The materials and procedures described for maintaining a stock of *Phormia regina* may be used for maintaining *Sarcophaga bullata*, with minor alterations. *Sarcophaga* is larviporous (the adult female deposits live first-instar larvae and not eggs). The newly emerged female requires up to 10 days before larvae are deposited. About 125 larvae are transferred with forceps from the surface of the pork liver to a jar of medium. The medium is prepared using 10 g of agar, instead of 20 g as used in the *Phormia* medium.

BIBLIOGRAPHY

Brust, M. and Fraenkel, G. (1955). The nutritional requirements of the larvae of a blowfly, *Phormia regina* (Meig.). *Physiol. Zööl.*, **28**, 186–204.

Fraenkel, G. (1938). The number of moults in the cyclorrhaphous flies (Diptera). *Proc. R. ent. Soc. Lond.*, **13**, 158–160.

Hill, D. L., Bell, V. E. and Chadwick, L. E. (1947). Rearing of the blowfly, *Phormia regina* Meigen, on a sterile synthetic diet. *Ann. ent. Soc. Am.*, **40**, 213–216.

Hinton, H. E. (1946). Concealed phases in the metamorphosis of insects. *Nature, Lond.*, **157**, 552–553.

Imms, A. D. (1964). "A General Textbook of Entomology", 9th ed. Methuen and Co., London.

Snodgrass, R. E. (1954). Insect metamorphosis. *Smithson. misc. Collns.*, **122**, No. 9, 1–124.

B. The Non-glycogen Carbohydrates of the Hemolymph and Fat Body during Larval Development of *Phormia regina*

Principle of Experiment

The occurrence of trehalose in various insect orders was initially demonstrated by Wyatt and Kalf (1957), who also established its presence in larval, pupal and adult stages. The principal location of trehalose within the insect is considered generally to be the hemolymph, although small amounts have been observed in the fat body. The importance of trehalose as a metabolic substrate during flight was demonstrated in *Phormia regina* (Clegg and Evans, 1961; Sacktor and Wormser-Shavit, 1966), while its significance during larval development and metamorphosis remains unclear.

Although trehalose is frequently recognized as the predominant blood sugar of insects, larval Diptera may be an exception. Fructose was the predominant blood sugar of larval *Gastrophilus intestinalis* (Levenbook, 1950), while glucose predominated in the larval hemolymph of *Agria affinis* (Barlow and House, 1960) and *Phormia regina* (Evans and Dethier, 1957). Nevertheless, trehalose was detected chromatographically in whole larvae of *Aedes aegypti* and *Drosophila repleta* (Wyatt and Kalf, 1957), thus introducing the possibility that this disaccharide is located at some site other than the hemolymph. Since the fat body is known to be important in the synthesis and storage of carbohydrate, it is of interest to compare quantitatively the non-glycogen carbohydrates of the hemolymph and fat body during larval development.

This analysis of non-glycogen carbohydrates involves four basic steps: (1) extracting non-glycogen carbohydrates with 70% ethanol; (2) deionizing the sample with ion exchange resins; (3) separating and identifying the sugars by thin-layer chromatography (TLC); and (4) quantitating the sugars directly on the TLC plate by photodensitometry. The technique of thin-layer densitometry is very sensitive, requiring as little as 1·2 µg of each sugar for quantitation. Since this is a relatively new quantitative method, another objective of this experiment is to acquaint investigators with the specificity and versatility of thin-layer densitometry of carbohydrates.

Animals

Larvae of *Phormia regina* are obtained by following the procedures in Experiment A. These experiments have been performed on larvae at five periods during third-instar development. However, any number of convenient ages in third-instar larvae could be used.

MATERIALS FOR OBTAINING HEMOLYMPH AND FAT BODIES, AND EXTRACTION OF NON-GLYCOGEN CARBOHYDRATES

1. *Microscope slides with concavity (2).
2. *Micropipettes, 25 μl, manufactured to deliver with 5 μl subdivisions (8).
3. Balance, analytical.
4. Aluminum foil weighing cups for larvae, laboratory made.
5. Insect Ringer, 7·5 g of NaCl (Merck No. 74073), 0·35 g of KCl, and 0·21 g of anhydrous CaCl$_2$/liter.
6. Fine microdissecting scissors (1).
7. Fine microdissecting forceps (2).
8. Test tube racks.
9. Centrifuge tubes, 15 ml Corex, 17 mm o.d. (Corning No. 8441); 3/hemolymph and 3/fat body sample.
10. Ethanol, 250 ml of 70%.
11. Pipettes, measuring, 0·2, 5 and 10 ml.
12. Stoppers for centrifuge tubes covered with aluminum foil.
13. Temperature block heater for 15 ml centrifuge tubes.
14. Centrifuge, refrigerated which develops an RCF of about 14 000 g and with rubber adapters to hold 15 ml centrifuge tubes.
15. Apparatus to deliver a stream of air for evaporating solvent.
(a) Rubber tubing.
(b) Pasteur-type disposable transfer pipettes.
(c) Ring stand.
(d) Three-prong clamps.
(e) Y connectors.
16. Cation and anion exchange resins, Dowex 50W-X8 (hydrogen form) and Dowex 1-X8 (formate form), 20–50 mesh (Bioradlabs, New York 10014, U.S.A.).
17. Microspatulas.
18. Pasteur-type disposable transfer pipettes and rubber bulbs.
19. Distilled water, 100 ml.
20. Disposable paper tissue.
21. †Dissecting microscope and lamp.
22. †Dissecting dish (Syracuse watch glass half-filled with a layer of black wax, Carolina Biological Supply Co., Burlington, North Carolina 27215, U.S.A.).
23. †Aluminum foil squares, 2 × 2 cm.
24. †Petri dishes.

---

* These items are used only for the hemolymph experiment.
† These items are used only for the fat body experiment. All other items are required for both experiments.

25. †Carbon dioxide, solid block.

26. †Lyophilizing apparatus (vacuum desiccator, vacuum pump and vacuum rubber tubing).

27. †Tissue grinders, 13 × 100 mm (5).

28. †Separatory funnels with Teflon stopcock, 60 ml (5).

29. †Diethyl ether, 100 ml.

MATERIALS FOR THIN-LAYER CHROMATOGRAPHY (TLC) AND PHOTODENSITOMETRY

1. Automatic plate leveller and spreader (Quickfit Inc., Fairfield, New Jersey 07006, U.S.A.).

2. Glass carrier plates, 200 × 200 mm.

3. Glass carrier plates, 200 × 50 mm, 2 only.

4. Adsorbosil 3 (Applied Science Lab. Inc., State College, Pennsylvania 16801, U.S.A.).

5. Balance, general laboratory for weighing 50 g of Adsorbosil.

6. Distilled water.

7. Erlenmeyer flask, 250 ml.

8. Graduated cylinder, 100 ml.

9. Plate racks.

10. Drying oven, must heat to 150°C.

11. Spotting template.

12. Dissecting needle.

13. Carbohydrate standards (see Appendix); anhydrous glucose, maltose monohydrate and trehalose dihydrate; 20 ml screw cap vials (5).

14. Micropipettes, calibrated to 10 μl in the laboratory (see Appendix); glass tubing (minimum of 10 feet) for making micropipettes (precision capillary tubing of Pyrex, 1 mm o.d., 0·8 mm i.d., tolerance 0·01 mm, Drummond Scientific Co., Broomall, Pennsylvania 19008, U.S.A.); Livingston micropipette puller with 2 heaters and special transformer (Otto K. Hebel, Scientific Instruments, Rutledge, Pennsylvania 19070, U.S.A.) or an alcohol lamp; micropipette, 25 μl, manufactured to deliver with 5 μl subdivisions; dissecting microscope and lamp; India ink.

15. Chromatogram spot dryer (forced air heat).

16. Developing tanks to hold 200 × 200 mm plates.

17. Solvent system, absolute ethanol-ethyl acetate-water (50 : 40 : 13), freshly prepared.

18. Sulfuric acid, 10% v/v, add 3 ml concentrated H_2SO_4 (36N) to 27 ml H_2O, freshly prepared.

19. Universal aerosol spray kit (Nutritional Biochemicals Co., Cleveland, Ohio 44128, U.S.A.).

20. Fume hood.

21. Aluminum foil.

22. Disposable paper tissue.

23. Photovolt densitometry system consisting of photometer-multiplier, TLC stage assembly with special 0·1 mm × 15 mm slit aperture, light source unit, motor drive and recorder (Scientific Products, Evanston, Illinois 60201, U.S.A.).

PROCEDURES FOR OBTAINING HEMOLYMPH AND FAT BODIES AND EXTRACTION OF NON-GLYCOGEN CARBOHYDRATES

The hemolymph and fat bodies are obtained from larvae at five periods: 28, 44, 60 and 84 h after the second larval ecdysis and from the stage at puparium formation. To eliminate larvae of extreme sizes, obtain the fresh weight of each insect and use only those within a 6 mg weight range. After the larvae are selected, rinse them in Ringer solution before using.

HEMOLYMPH PROCEDURES (see Table I)

1. Collect hemolymph from two larvae simultaneously by placing them on the concavity of a microscope slide and making several superficial slits in the dorsal body wall with microdissecting scissors (Fig. 4, part A). Caution must be taken in making the slits. If the wound is too deep, the gut may be severed, thus contaminating the hemolymph. The gut contents give a cloudy appearance to the hemolymph and such a sample should be discarded. However, hemolymph from insects at puparium formation normally may be cloudy due to histolysis of larval tissues.

2. Transfer the hemolymph with 25 μl pipettes (Fig. 4, part B) to a centrifuge tube containing 10 ml of 70% ethanol and record the exact hemolymph volume. Stopper the tubes and mix by inversion.

3. Heat the ethanol-hemolymph sample to boiling (about 85°C) to facilitate precipitation of protein and glycogen.

4. Centrifuge at about 14 000 g and 0°C for 30 min.

5. Decant the supernatant into another centrifuge tube and evaporate to about 2 ml at 60°C under a stream of air.

6. Deionize the sample by adding a volume of about 1 ml of Dowex 1-X8 (formate form) and 1 ml of Dowex 50W-X8 (hydrogen form) with a microspatula. Mix the contents thoroughly and allow to remain for 8–12 h, with occasional shaking.

7. Centrifuge the sample for 5 min at about 1000 g and room temperature.

8. Remove the supernatant with a disposable transfer pipette and place in another centrifuge tube.

9. Wash the resins twice with 2 ml portions of distilled water and add the supernatants to the original in part 8.

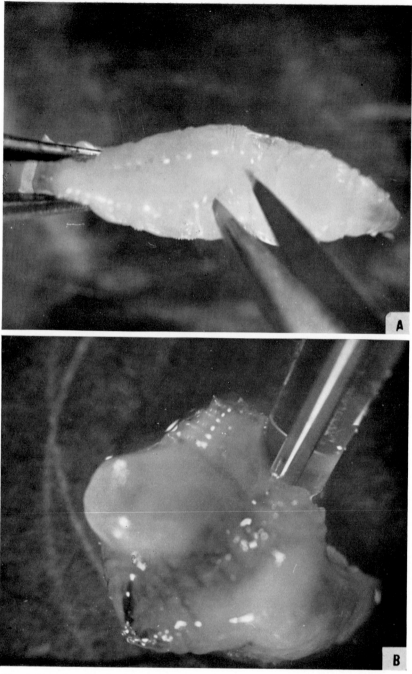

Fig. 4. Hemolymph collection. A. The larva is held at the posterior end with forceps while making superficial slits in the dorsal body wall. B. The tip of the micropipette is inserted underneath the larvae (two) to obtain the hemolymph. (Photographs by G. T. Cowley.)

10. Evaporate the sample to dryness at 60°C under a stream of air.

11. Dissolve the dried sample in an appropriate volume of distilled water (see Table I) and stopper the tube immediately. After shaking, the sample is ready to be spotted on a TLC plate.

TABLE I

Data pertinent to the hemolymph experiment

Hours after ecdysis to third instar	Mean fresh wt. of larva (mg)	Total hemolymph collected (μl)	Volume (ml) sample dissolved in for TLC
28	37 *(8)	40	0·20
44	48 (8)	80	0·30
60	51 (8)	70	0·12
84	52 (8)	60	0·12
Puparium formation†	49 (10)	50	0·12

* ( ) Number of animals used.
† This stage is collected at 96–108 h.

FAT BODY PROCEDURES (see Table II)

1. Three larvae usually are dissected simultaneously and fat bodies processed in groups of threes. The larvae are dissected in a Syracuse watch glass, half-filled with black wax and containing insect Ringer.

2. Sacrifice the larva by cutting entirely through the body just behind the anterior end (Fig. 5). The two parts of the larva are turned inside-out to expose the fat body. This is accomplished by: (a) moving closed forceps underneath the body wall to the end of the larva; (b) opening the forceps and taking hold of the inside of the body wall; (c) taking hold of the severed surface of the body wall with a second pair of forceps; and (d) moving the two pairs of forceps toward, then past, each other. The fat body is recognized as whitish sheets of tissue, one cell layer thick, interspersed among the other visceral organs.

3. Dissect the fat body away from other body tissues and transfer with forceps to squares of aluminum foil. To remove the residual Ringer solution, transfer the clump of fat bodies three or four times to new spots on the foil square.

4. Place the foil square containing the fat bodies in a chilled Petri dish which is on a block of solid carbon dioxide.

5. Lyophilize the fat bodies for about 2 h in a vacuum desiccator.

6. Obtain the dry weight of the fat bodies, then transfer to a tissue grinder containing 3 ml of 70% ethanol.

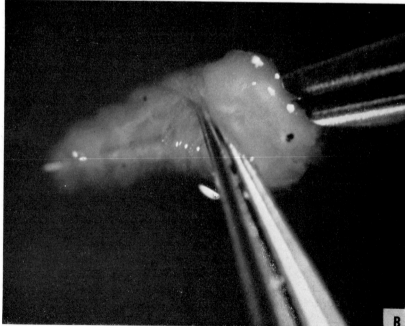

Fɪɢ. 5. Fat body dissection. A. The larva is held with forceps at the posterior end while cutting through the entire insect. B. Position of forceps to turn the larva inside-out. (Photographs by G. T. Cowley.)

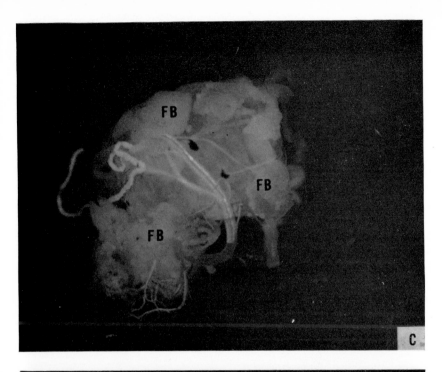

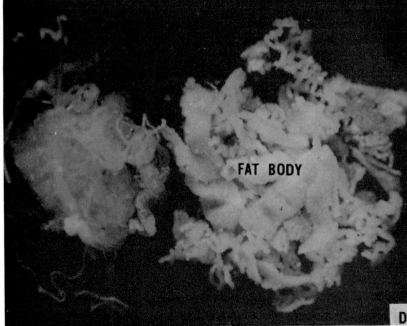

FIG. 5. Fat body dissection. C. Larva turned inside-out exposing the fat body (FB). D. Fat body dissected away from other body tissues. (Photographs by G. T. Cowley.)

7. Homogenize the fat bodies and pour the homogenate into a Corex centrifuge tube.

8. Wash the tissue grinder twice with 3 ml portions of 70% ethanol and combine with the homogenate in 7.

9. Heat the homogenate until boiling (about 85°C), then centrifuge at 14 000 *g* and 0°C for 30 min.

10. Decant the supernatant into a separatory funnel and evaporate with a stream of air to about 5 ml.

11. Add 10 ml of diethyl ether to the separatory funnel and shake vigorously. Let stand 8–12 h, then drain the lower phase into a centrifuge tube. Remove the upper phase, which contains lipid contaminants, with a disposable pipette and discard. To rinse the separatory funnel, add 2 ml of distilled water and 4 ml diethyl ether, shake vigorously, and let stand until the two phases separate. Drain the lower phase and combine with the original.

12. Deionize and process the sample following steps 6–11 as described previously for hemolymph samples. The volume of water each sample is dissolved in for TLC is shown in Table II.

TABLE II

Data pertinent to the fat body experiment

Hours after ecdysis to third instar	Mean fresh wt. of larva (mg)	Mean fat body dry wt. (mg)	Volume (ml) sample dissolved in for TLC
28	34 *(16)	1·22	0·08
44	47 (20)	2·50	0·15
60	53 (16)	3·77	0·18
84	51 (12)	4·86	0·30
Puparium formation†	45 (12)	5·51	0·30

* ( ) Number of fat bodies obtained.
† This stage is collected at 96–108 h.

THIN-LAYER CHROMATOGRAPHY AND PHOTODENSITOMETRY OF HEMOLYMPH AND FAT BODY NON-GLYCOGEN CARBOHYDRATES

Perhaps the most important aspect of thin-layer densitometry is a uniform thickness of adsorbent on the TLC plates (see TROUBLE-SHOOTING). The TLC apparatus of Quickfit Inc. has proved to be very satisfactory in this respect. In addition, it is recommended that a machinist add adjustable legs to the automatic plate leveller so that it may be levelled.

The TLC plates are 200 × 200 mm and the adsorbent is Adsorbosil 3. A slurry is prepared by adding 75 ml of distilled water to a flask containing

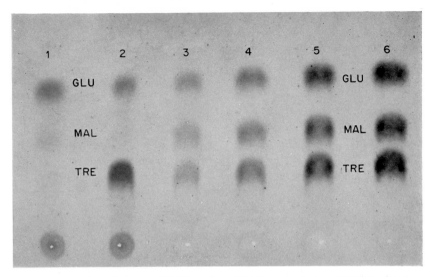

FiG. 6. Separation of glucose (GLU), maltose (MAL) and trehalose (TRE) by thin-layer chromatography. Column 1, hemolymph sample at the 60 h period; column 2, fat body sample at the 60 h period; columns 3, 4, 5 and 6, 1·2 μg, 2·4 μg, 3·6 μg and 4·8 μg of each sugar, respectively. The adsorbent is Adsorbosil 3 and the solvent system is absolute ethanol–ethyl acetate–water (50 : 40 : 13). (Photograph in transmitted light by G. T. Cowley.)

50 g of Adsorbosil and mixing with a swirling motion for 1 min. The slurry is spread onto five plates to a thickness of 0·5 mm. The coated plates are allowed to air dry for about 2 h, then stored on a plate rack up to 1 week. Each plate is activated immediately before use by heating at 110°C for 30 min, then allowed to air cool at room temperature for 30 min. Using a spotting template, mark up to 8 origin spots with a dissecting needle. The spots should be 1·8 cm from the bottom of the plate and 2 cm apart. A line drawn 9 cm from the origin serves as the front. The specific sample applied to an origin spot may be indicated by making etch marks in the Adsorbosil above the front line.

Place four unknown samples and four standards containing 1·2 μg, 2·4 μg, 3·6 μg and 4·8 μg of each sugar on each TLC plate. To apply the standards, it is necessary to use the following amounts: for the 1·2 μg standard, use 10 μl of standard 2; for the 2·4 μg standard, use 10 μl of standard 1; for the 3·6 μg standard, use 10 μl of standard 1 and 10 μl of standard 2; for the 4·8 μg standard, use 20 μl of standard 1. In all hemolymph and fat body samples, 10 μl are deposited on each spot. To consistently regulate the size of the spots, apply about 5, 3 and 2 μl in that order. A forced hot air dryer is used after each application to dry the spot. After spotting, the plate is introduced into a developing tank containing about 0·8 cm of solvent. The solvent system is absolute ethanol–ethyl acetate–water (50 : 40 : 13). The solvent should be

s

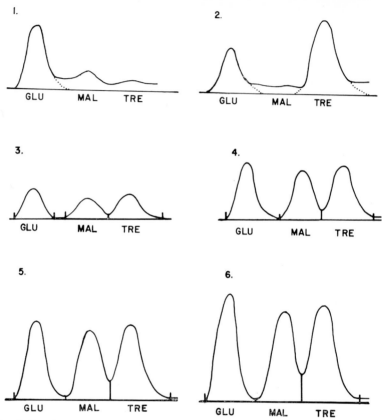

Fig. 7. Densitometer tracings of the chromatogram in Fig. 6 showing glucose (GLU), maltose (MAL) and trehalose (TRE) curves. 1, hemolymph sample at the 60 h period; 2, fat body sample at the 60 h period; 3, 4, 5 and 6, 1·2 μg, 2·4 μg, 3·6 μg and 4·8 μg standards, respectively. The baselines are drawn as straight lines. The hemolymph and fat body tracings do not return to the baseline after the trehalose curve, and this is partially due to the presence of a small amount of charred materials. The baseline is not reached in the 4, 5 and 6 standard tracings after the trehalose curve. This is due to a slight baseline shift and/or tailing of trehalose. The vertical lines denote the points of separation of the standards and consequently delimit the areas under the curves.

freshly prepared and placed in the tank immediately before the plate. Plate development should take about 70 min at 28°C. After development, the plate is thoroughly dried with the forced hot air dryer, then sprayed in a fume hood with about 20–25 ml of freshly prepared 10% H_2SO_4 (v/v). The plate is sprayed while the 10% acid is still warm. Spraying is a very critical step. If the plate is not saturated with sulfuric acid, charring is poor; however, if too much acid is sprayed, the adsorbent will be eluted from the plate and ruin it. The plate is placed immediately on a sheet of aluminum foil in an oven preheated to 150°C, and left for 30 min. The sugars appear as charred black spots (Fig. 6). The

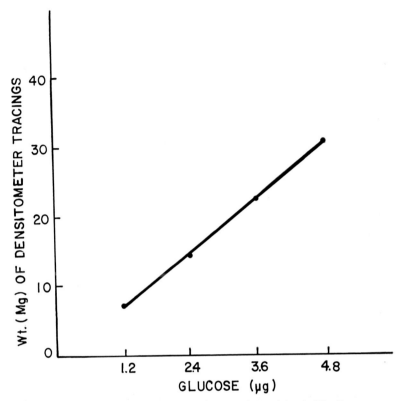

FIG. 8. Standard glucose curve from tracing weights in Fig. 7.

plate is allowed to cool for a few minutes, then the back of it is wiped clean with a moist piece of paper tissue.

A graphic recording of the migration path of each standard and unknown sample is obtained with the densitometer (Fig. 7). Densitometer settings of 3 on the range switch of the multiplier-photometer and 3 on the response control of the recorder are used. The relative area under each curve is obtained by cutting out the area and weighing. Standard curves are constructed for glucose, maltose and trehalose by plotting the weights of densitometer tracings versus micrograms of standard (Figs 8, 9 and 10). The μg values for the unknown sugars are read directly from the standard curves. Because of the variation in the degree of charring, each plate is quantitated independently.

Sample calculation of hemolymph glucose for the 60 h period

$$\text{mg of glucose/100 ml of hemolymph} = \frac{3{\cdot}1 \ \mu\text{g} \times 12}{70 \ \mu\text{l}} \times 100 = 53{\cdot}1 \ \text{mg} \ \%$$

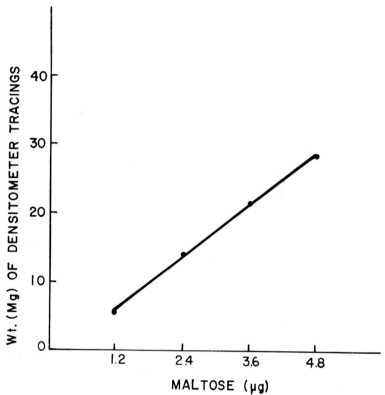

FIG. 9. Standard maltose curve from tracing weights in Fig. 7.

3·1 μg   Amount of glucose from standard curve (Fig. 8) for a tracing weight of 19·1 mg (Fig. 7, part 1).

12   Factor to account for aliquot of sample spotted on TLC (used 10 of 120 μl).

70 μl   Total amount of hemolymph collected.

100   To convert mg/ml to mg/100 ml.

RESULTS

HEMOLYMPH NON-GLYCOGEN CARBOHYDRATES

Glucose is the predominant blood sugar in the first four periods of third-instar development (Fig. 11); but at puparium formation, glucose (61·5 mg %) is slightly exceeded by maltose (65 mg %). A comparison of maltose and trehalose is shown in Table III. A chromatogram of the 60 h period is given in Fig. 6, column 1, and a chromatogram of the stage at puparium formation is shown in Fig. 12, column 1.

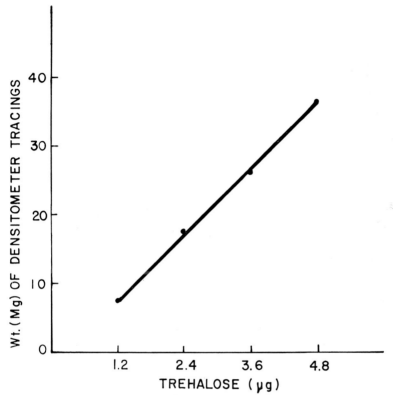

FIG. 10. Standard trehalose curve from tracing weights in Fig. 7.

TABLE III

Comparison of hemolymph maltose and trehalose during third-instar development of Phormia regina

Hours after ecdysis to third instar	Maltose	Trehalose
28	Trace	Undetectable
44	Trace	Minimum detectable
60	20 mg %	Present, but too low to measure accurately
84	37 mg %	25 mg %
Puparium formation*	65 mg %	40 mg %

* This stage is collected at 96–108 h.

FAT BODY NON-GLYCOGEN CARBOHYDRATES

Trehalose and glucose are identified in the fat body at all five periods of third-instar development, with trehalose predominating (Fig. 13). A substance thought to be a glycoside is present in trace amounts at the 84 h period and increases at puparium formation. The unknown substance is anthrone positive, negative for reducing sugar and fluorescent in shortwave U.V. light. These observations were made using: (1) an anthrone spray (90 parts of absolute ethanol saturated with anthrone and 10 parts concentrated H_2SO_4, freshly prepared); (2) a reducing sugar spray (2 g of NaOH and 2 g of 2, 3, 5 triphenyl-tetrazolium chloride/100 ml of methanol, freshly prepared); and (3) Adsorbosil (200 parts) mixed with a fluorescent dye (1 part, duPont No. 609 luminescent chemical) under U.V. light. The plates sprayed with anthrone, or reducing reagent, must be heated for 5–10 min at 110°C.

TROUBLE-SHOOTING

One of the most troublesome aspects of this experiment is thin-layer chromatography. The TLC carrier plates must be absolutely spotless because any residue on the plate will affect the light beam of the densitometer as it passes through the plate. An Adsorbosil thickness of 0·5 mm gives a more uniform layer than does the traditional 0·25 mm. Spraying the plate with 10% H_2SO_4 is a very critical step. The 10% acid must be prepared within a few

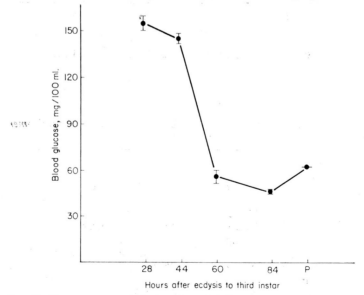

FIG. 11. Glucose content of the hemolymph during third-instar development of *Phormia regina*. Mean and range of duplicate samples. P, puparium formation.

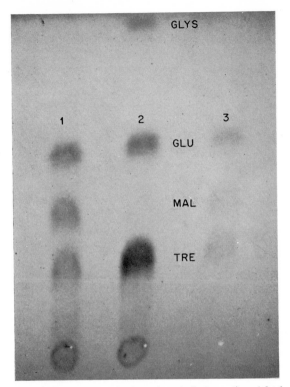

FIG. 12. Thin-layer chromatogram of a hemolymph (column 1) and fat body (column 2) sample at puparium formation. Glycoside (GLYS), glucose (GLU), maltose (MAL) and trehalose (TRE); column 3, 1·2 μg standards. (Photograph by G. T. Cowley.)

minutes before spraying. To obtain uniform charring of the sugars, extreme care must be taken when spraying. The spray must saturate all areas of the plate below the front line; yet too much acid will cause streaks to appear on the plate, rendering it unusable. It is advisable to practice by first spraying several blank plates. The most pronounced charring is obtained when the plate is placed in an oven (preheated to 150°C) within 15 sec after spraying.

Another troublesome spot in this experiment lies in photodensitometry. The accuracy of photodensitometry is dependent upon the uniformity in the thickness of the adsorbent layer and the degree of separation of sugars by TLC. The apparatus described in the Procedures section works satisfactorily for spreading the adsorbent on the carrier plates. However, when coating the plates it is difficult to prevent the spreader from oscillating. Best results have been obtained by holding the spreader as shown in Fig. 14. The spreader must be pulled with a smooth motion or else uneven areas will appear in the adsorbent. Despite all of these precautions some plates will not have a uniform layer.

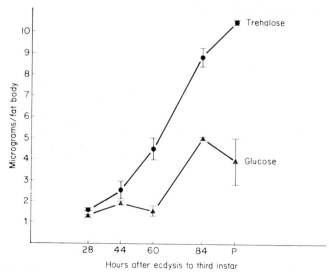

FIG. 13. Trehalose and glucose content of the fat body during third-instar development of *Phormia regina*. Mean and range of duplicate samples. P, puparium formation.

When viewing the coated plates in transmitted light, large uneven areas are visible. Smaller, uneven areas that cannot be seen with the naked eye are detectable with the densitometer. If the thickness of the adsorbent varies over the migration path of the sample, it is impossible to obtain a straight baseline with the densitometer; thus error will be introduced into the measurements. It is, therefore, advisable to monitor the plates by scanning the prospective migration paths *before* the samples are applied. If the baselines vary more than ± 1 unit on the graph paper, the plate should be discarded.

Adsorbosil 3 has been used very successfully to separate glucose, maltose and trehalose. However, the lots of Adsorbosil 3 vary; so maltose and trehalose may not separate by as great a distance as shown in Fig. 6. As of this writing the supplier (Applied Science Lab. Inc., State College, Pennsylvania 16801, U.S.A.) has been unable to correct this variability. It is advisable to obtain and test a sample of Adsorbosil 3, then use only that lot number.

FURTHER EXPERIMENTS

In this experiment the technique of thin-layer densitometry is utilized to quantitate amounts as small as $1 \cdot 2$ μg of specific sugars. The sensitivity and versatility of this method renders it adaptable for measuring the mono- and disaccharide content of the hemolymph and body tissue of other insects. For example, the hemolymph of adult Diptera is known to contain large concentrations of trehalose (1–3 g/100 ml), thus requiring only 2–3 μl of hemolymph

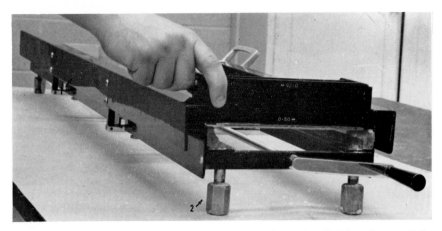

FIG. 14. Demonstration of automatic plate leveller and spreader. (1) It is easier to pull the spreader if the handle is removed. (2) Adjustable levelling legs. The spreader is held with the thumb and index finger of one hand only and, while applying slight pressure downward and toward yourself, pull the spreader over the plates. Coating the side member of the plate leveller with a thin film of glycerine allows the spreader to slide more easily.

for measurement. Furthermore, this technique is suitable for use on other invertebrate or vertebrate materials.

In developmental studies, it is frequently relevant to compare the changes in non-glycogen carbohydrates with the changes in glycogen. Such an experiment may be performed by combining the procedures in this experiment with the procedures in Experiment C of this series. The insect material is first extracted with 70% ethanol to remove the non-glycogen carbohydrates; then glycogen is extracted, isolated and quantitated from the remaining residue following the procedures in Experiment C.

APPENDIX

CALIBRATION OF THE LABORATORY-MADE MICROPIPETTE

About 12–15 laboratory-made micropipettes are needed for the entire experiment. The micropipettes are made using precision capillary tubing and the micropipette puller. If the latter item is unavailable, the micropipettes may be pulled by hand using an alcohol lamp. The micropipettes should be about 5 in. long and the very fine part of the tip removed with forceps. The lab-made micropipette is calibrated to 10 μl, using a 25 μl manufactured micropipette (TD) with 5 μl subdivisions. Calibration is accomplished by bringing the apertures of the delivery ends of the two pipettes together in a horizontal position, then tilting both slightly so that exactly 10 μl of water is transferred to the lab-made micropipette. The reproducibility of transferring

10 μl has been ascertained by weighing the lab-made micropipette before and after five independent transfers, and is within 1 %.

The 10 μl level on the lab-made micropipette is marked using India ink while viewing with a dissecting microscope. The reproducibility of drawing water up to the 10 μl mark has been examined by weighing the pipette before and after the water is drawn in five independent observations, and is within 1 %.

PREPARATION OF STANDARDS FOR THIN-LAYER CHROMATOGRAPHY

In preparing standard solutions, it is sometimes difficult to weigh and transfer accurately an exact quantity of material. Therefore, it is easier to weigh an unspecified, but known, amount of standard and obtain the desired concentration by adding an appropriate volume of water. Since a composite standard containing 3 sugars is required, it is simpler to prepare 3 separate standards, at 3 × the desired concentration, and combine equal volumes.

Place 10–15 mg of anhydrous glucose, 10–15 mg of maltose monohydrate and 10–15 mg of trehalose dihydrate into *separate tared* 20 ml screw cap vials. Obtain the precise weight of each sugar. Water is added to each vial giving a concentration of 7·2 μg/10 μl of anhydrous glucose, 7·58 μg/10 μl of maltose monohydrate and 7·96 μg/10 μl of trehalose dihydrate (the volume change due to the sugar is considered negligible). The maltose and trehalose standards contain 7·2 μg of sugar/10 μl, but a larger amount is needed to account for the monohydrate form of maltose and the dihydrate form of trehalose. Add 5 ml of each sugar solution to a single vial. The composite standard contains 2·4 μg of each sugar/10 μl and this is termed standard 1. Standard 2, containing 1·2 μg of each sugar/10 μl, is prepared by diluting a 5 ml aliquot of standard 1 with an equal volume of water.

BIBLIOGRAPHY

Barlow, J. S. and House, H. L. (1960). Effects of dietary glucose on haemolymph carbohydrates of *Agria affinis* (Fall.). *J. Insect Physiol.*, **5**, 181–189.

Clegg, J. S. and Evans, D. R. (1961). The physiology of blood trehalose and its function during flight in the blowfly. *J. exp. Biol.*, **38**, 771–792.

Crompton, M. and Birt, L. M. (1967). Changes in the amounts of carbohydrates, phosphagen, and related compounds during the metamorphosis of the blowfly, *Lucilia cuprina*. *J. Insect Physiol.*, **73**, 1575–1592.

Evans, D. R. and Dethier, V. G. (1957). The regulation of taste thresholds for sugars in the blowfly. *J. Insect Physiol.*, **1**, 3–17.

Levenbook, L. (1950). The composition of horse bot fly (*Gastrophilus intestinalis*) larva blood. *Biochem. J.*, **47**, 336–346.

Randerath, K. (1964). "Thin-layer Chromatography." Academic Press, New York and London.

Sacktor, B. and Wormser-Shavit, E. (1966). Regulation of metabolism in working muscle *in vivo*—I. Concentrations of some glycolytic, tricarboxylic acid cycle, and amino acid intermediates in insect flight muscle during flight. *J. biol. Chem.*, **241**, 624–631.

Stahl, E. (1965). "Thin-layer Chromatography: A Laboratory Handbook" (E. Stahl, ed.). Academic Press, New York and London.

Wimer, L. T. (1969). A comparison of the carbohydrate composition of the hemo-lymph and fat body of *Phormia regina* during larval development. *Comp. Biochem. Physiol.*, **29**, 1055–1062.

Wyatt, G. R. and Kalf, G. F. (1957). The chemistry of insect hemolymph—II. Trehalose and other carbohydrates. *J. gen. Physiol.*, **40**, 833–847.

C. Glycogen Changes during Metamorphosis of *Phormia regina*

PRINCIPLE OF EXPERIMENT

Insect tissues, like other animal tissues, store carbohydrate in the form of glycogen. The insect fat body is considered to be the chief site of glycogen synthesis and storage. In holometabolous insects, glycogen accumulates during larval development and a large amount is utilized during metamorphosis. The principal fate of glycogen during metamorphosis is thought to be in the formation of chitin; while minor amounts are used as an energy source or converted to other substances such as trehalose. The purpose of this experiment is to analyse the glycogen content of individual insects at six periods during metamorphosis of *Phormia regina*.

In this experiment glycogen is extracted in hot alkali, isolated by precipitating in ethanol and quantitated using anthrone reagent. Glycogen in insects, as well as other animal materials, frequently has been reported as both "free" and "fixed" glycogen. If such a distinction is made, trichloroacetic acid extracts only the "free" glycogen, while hot alkali extracts both "free" and "fixed" glycogen. This distinction between the two types of glycogen has been discounted by Roe *et al.* (1961), by attributing the incomplete extraction of glycogen with trichloroacetic acid to inadequate homogenization. Since there seems to be general agreement that hot alkali solubilizes all the glycogen, the use of this extractant is recommended for this experiment.

ANIMALS

This experiment is performed on *Phormia regina* at 24 h intervals during metamorphosis. The insects are obtained at six different periods, the initial stage marked by puparium formation and the terminal stage distinguished by the newly emerged adult. The materials and procedures for rearing *Phormia regina* are given in Experiment A of this series.

Materials for Processing Insects*

1. Forceps (2).
2. Insect Ringer, 7·5 g of NaCl (Merck No. 74073), 0·35 g of KCl and 0·21 g of anhydrous $CaCl_2$/liter.
3. Paper tissue.
4. Balance, analytical.
5. Petri dishes.
6. Incubator set at 28·5°C.
7. Aluminum foil.
8. Carbon dioxide, solid block.
9. Scissors, dissecting (1).
10. Lyophilizing apparatus (vacuum desiccator, vacuum pump and vacuum rubber tubing).
11. Test tube racks.
12. Centrifuge tubes, 15 ml Corex, 17 mm o.d. (Corning No. 8441), 2/sample.
13. Stirring rods, 0·5 × 15 cm.

Materials for Extracting Glycogen

1. Pipettes, measuring, 0·1, 1, 2 and 5 ml.
2. Sodium hydroxide, 4 g/100 ml.
3. Glass bubbles, 1/sample (Tudor Scientific Glass Co., Belvedere, South Carolina 29841, U.S.A.).
4. Boiling water bath (large enough to hold a test tube rack) and marble chips.
5. 1N perchloric acid (84·8 ml of 71% perchloric acid/liter).
6. Distilled water.
7. Centrifuge, refrigerated which develops an RCF of about 14 000 g and with rubber adapters to hold 15 ml centrifuge tubes.
8. Pasteur-type disposable transfer pipettes and 3 ml rubber bulbs.
9. Test tubes, 13 × 100 mm, 2/sample.
10. Absolute ethanol saturated with NaCl (200 ml).
11. Stoppers for centrifuge tubes.

Materials for Quantitating Glycogen

1. Cuvettes, 1/sample.
2. Glucose standard, 10 mg of anhydrous glucose/100 ml (stored under refrigeration).

* All items are listed in the order used. Some items may be required for more than one part of the experiment; however, they are listed only once.

3. Anthrone reagent, 0·16 g anthrone/100 ml of 80% H_2SO_4 (v/v), may be used for several days (see TROUBLE-SHOOTING).

4. Spectrophotometer set at 620 mμ.

METHODS FOR SELECTING AND PROCESSING INSECTS

In the experiments reported here, eight insects are analysed individually for glycogen content at each of the six periods during metamorphosis. Due to possible mortality during metamorphosis, about 70 insects should be collected at the stage of puparium formation. The insects are washed in Ringer solution, blotted dry with tissue paper and weighed. Weight is used as the criterion for initially selecting the insects at puparium formation and should not vary more than 3 mg (for example 44–47 mg). Eight weighed insects are immediately sacrificed and serve as the first stage. The remainder of the insects are placed in a Petri dish and incubated at 28·5°C. Then 8 insects are weighed and sacrificed at 24 h intervals through the 96 h period. When collecting the insects, it is assumed that they are alive; however, mortality does occur during metamorphosis. This is detected by noting the weight of the insect, because water is rapidly lost after death. If the wet weight of an insect deviates markedly from the others, it should be discarded. Note, however, that an insect normally loses 6–8 mg of water during the initial 24 h of metamorphosis (Table IV).

The adults usually emerge from the puparium at about 118 h. Each insect must be isolated prior to emergence because the weight of each adult must be combined with the weight of its puparium. This is essential in order to compare the wet and dry weights of the adult with the other stages.

A Petri dish containing aluminum foil squares (2 × 2 cm) is chilled on a solid block of CO_2. Each insect is individually sacrificed by placing it on the foil square and cutting it in half. The frozen insects are lyophilized for 3–4 h. The dry weight of each insect is obtained by weighing the aluminum foil with the insect, then weighing the foil square after the insect has been transferred to a centrifuge tube. The insect is pulverized in the centrifuge tube with a glass stirring rod, facilitating digestion and glycogen extraction.

The insects must *not* be stored in the frozen condition because glycogen may be hydrolysed during storage. If it is necessary to store the samples, they may be kept at −20°C after step 2 of METHOD FOR GLYCOGEN EXTRACTION.

METHOD FOR GLYCOGEN EXTRACTION

The extraction of glycogen follows the basic procedure of Roe and Dailey (1966).

1. Add 1·5 ml of 4% NaOH to each tube containing a crushed insect. Cover the tubes with glass bubbles to prevent evaporation during heating.

2. Heat the samples in a boiling water bath for 45 min with occasional

shaking to facilitate complete digestion. Remove the tubes and cool to room temperature.

3. Add 3 ml of 1N perchloric acid and 0·5 ml of distilled water to each tube, giving a final volume of 5 ml. Thoroughly mix the contents and let stand for 15 min to precipitate protein.

4. Centrifuge the tubes at about 14 000 g and 0°C for 30 min. The supernatant is difficult to transfer because the protein pellet is fragile and a thin film covers the supernatant surface. It is easier, therefore, to transfer about one-half of the supernatant with a disposable transfer pipette to a test tube and obtain an aliquot of this to isolate glycogen.

5. Transfer a 1 ml aliquot of the supernatant to a centrifuge tube. Since the total volume was 5 ml, only 20% of the supernatant is used to isolate glycogen.

6. Precipitate glycogen in 70% ethanol by adding 2·3 ml of absolute ethanol saturated with NaCl. Mix the contents thoroughly, stopper the tubes and let stand 8–12 h.

7. Isolate the glycogen by centrifuging at about 14 000 g and 0°C for 30 min. Decant the supernatant and leave the tubes inverted until the glycogen pellet dries.

8. Dissolve the glycogen pellet in 4 ml of distilled water and use a 1 ml aliquot (25%) for quantitation of all glycogen samples. After this step the fraction of sample used for glycogen analysis represents only 5% of the total (25% of 20%).

Method for Glycogen Quantitation

Glycogen is quantitated using a modification of the anthrone method of Roe (1955). A standard glucose curve is constructed and the unknown values are read directly from it.

Preparation of standard glucose curve

μg of standard glucose	ml of standard glucose		ml of distilled water added
10	0·10	+	0·90
25	0·25	+	0·75
40	0·40	+	0·60
55	0·55	+	0·45
70	0·70	+	0·30

The final volume of all standards and unknowns is 1 ml. A reagent blank consisting of 1 ml of distilled water is required to set the absorbance of the spectrophotometer at zero. Color development can occur directly in cuvettes, or in ordinary test tubes, and the contents transferred to cuvettes. Add 4 ml of

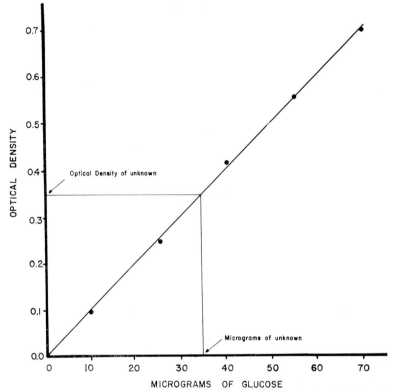

FIG. 15. Standard glucose curve. An unknown with an optical density of 0·35 (ordinate) contains 35 μg of glucose (abscissa).

anthrone reagent carefully down the side of each tube: the standard, the unknown and the reagent blank tubes. Mix the contents thoroughly by stirring with a clean glass rod. Cover the tubes with glass bubbles, transfer immediately to a boiling water bath, and heat for 15 min. Remove the tubes and cool in tap water. Read the optical density (absorbance) in a spectrophotometer at a wavelength of 620 mμ.

A standard curve is prepared by plotting the optical density of the glucose standards versus micrograms of glucose (Fig. 15). Heating glycogen in strong acid hydrolyses it to glucose, and anthrone detects the amount of glucose present. As a result, the unknown values read from the curve are actually glucose values. To convert these values to glycogen it is necessary to divide by 1·11 (Hassid and Abraham, 1957). Also since only 5% of the sample actually is used for glycogen analysis, the μg of unknown must be divided by 0·05.

Calculation of glycogen content of an insect 48 h after puparium formation

μg of glycogen/insect

$$= \frac{\mu\text{g of unknown from curve}}{\text{conversion factor of glucose to} \atop \text{glycogen} \times \text{fraction of sample used for} \atop \text{analysis}}$$

$$\text{or } \frac{35 \cdot 0}{1 \cdot 11 \times 0 \cdot 05} = 631 \; \mu\text{g}.$$

RESULTS

During metamorphosis, glycogen declines from a high of 1006 μg at puparium formation to 374 μg in the newly emerged adult (Table IV). This represents a decrease of about 63 % of the glycogen. The largest decline occurs during the initial 24 h period when 38 % of the total glycogen is utilized. At puparium formation, glycogen accounts for 6·8 % of the insect's dry weight; while in the adult, glycogen accounts for only 2·7 % (based on dry weight of adult plus the puparium). The principal fate of glycogen during metamorphosis is thought to be in the formation of chitin (Crompton and Birt, 1967), with minor amounts converted to other substances such as trehalose or utilized as an energy source.

TABLE IV

Glycogen changes during metamorphosis of Phormia regina

Hours after puparium formation	Fresh wt. mg/insect*	Dry wt. mg/insect	Glycogen μg/insect	Glycogen % of dry wt.
0	45·4±0·5†	14·87±0·39	1006±43	6·8
24	38·3±0·5	14·16±0·20	621±47	4·4
48	38·3±0·6	13·93±0·21	657±84	4·7
72	37·9±0·6	13·71±0·19	558±34	4·1
96	37·0±0·5	13·27±0·08	497±31	3·7
118 (adult)	36·7±0·4‡	14·02±0·23‡	374±56¶	2·7
	4·0±0·2§	3·37±0·12§		

* Fresh weights are obtained immediately before sacrificing.

† All values represent the mean ± one standard error.

‡ Adults are obtained immediately after emergence. The adults were collected several weeks after the other five stages, and were on the upper end of the weight range giving a dry weight slightly larger than the previous stage. Adult plus puparium.

§ Puparium only. The puparium does not contain significant amounts of glycogen.

¶ Adult only.

FURTHER EXPERIMENTS

This experiment is concerned only with the glycogen content; however, the corresponding changes in non-glycogen carbohydrates during metamorphosis are equally important. An experiment could be designed to measure the non-glycogen carbohydrates and glycogen of the same insect. The non-glycogen carbohydrates are extracted and quantitated first, following the procedures in Experiment B. After the extraction of the non-glycogen carbohydrates, the remaining residue is analysed for glycogen following the procedures in this experiment. This type of experiment permits a correlation between the changes in glycogen and the changes in non-glycogen carbohydrates. These experiments can also be used for analysing the carbohydrate content of various larval and adult tissues.

TROUBLE-SHOOTING

Since this is a quantitative procedure, all glassware must be absolutely immaculate. In preparing the anthrone reagent, the acid should be added to cold distilled water with extreme caution. The solution should not be allowed to heat above 90°C. The anthrone is added to the 80% H_2SO_4 and will dissolve readily if the solution is 80°C, but do *not* overheat. The anthrone reagent must have a yellow color; if any color change is noted, the reagent is contaminated and must be prepared again. After the anthrone reagent is added to the unknown and standard tubes, if the contents are not thoroughly mixed, color development will be inconsistent. During color development in the boiling water bath, water must be prevented from splashing into the tubes. If water gets into the tubes, the top of the solution will appear cloudy (anthrone is insoluble in water), rendering the sample unusable.

BIBLIOGRAPHY

Crompton, M. and Birt, L. M. (1967). Changes in the amounts of carbohydrates, phosphagen, and related compounds during the metamorphosis of the blowfly, *Lucilia cuprina. J. Insect Physiol.*, **13**, 1575–1592.

Hassid, W. Z. and Abraham, S. (1957). Determination of glycogen with anthrone reagent. *In* "Methods in Enzymology" (S. P. Colowick and N. O. Kaplan, eds), **3**, 35–36. Academic Press, New York and London.

Lindh, N. O. (1967). Some characteristics of glycogen from a fly pupa (*Calliphora erythrocephala* Meig.). *Comp. Biochem. Physiol.*, **20**, 209–216.

Roe, J. H. (1955). The determination of sugar in blood and spinal fluid with anthrone reagent. *J. biol. Chem.*, **212**, 335–343.

Roe, J. H., Bailey, J. M., Gray, R. R. and Robinson, J. N. (1961). Complete removal of glycogen from tissues by extraction with cold trichloroacetic acid solution. *J. biol. Chem.*, **236**, 1244–1246.

Roe, J. H. and Dailey, D. E. (1966). Determination of glycogen with the anthrone reagent. *Analyt. Biochem.*, **15**, 245–250.

T

Wimer, L. T. (1969). A comparison of the carbohydrate composition of the hemo-lymph and fat body of *Phormia regina* during larval development. *Comp. Biochem. Physiol.*, **29**, 1055–1062.

D. Lipid Composition of the Fat Body during Third-instar Development of *Phormia regina*

PRINCIPLE OF EXPERIMENT

An important characteristic of holometabolous insects is the accumulation of lipid during larval development. The chief site of lipid synthesis and storage has long been considered to be the fat body, but only recently has emphasis been placed on the fat body rather than whole insects. Since the fat body is an active site of lipid metabolism, it constitutes an extremely valuable system for *in vivo* and *in vitro* studies of the control mechanisms of lipid metabolism during development. A comprehensive analysis of the lipid constituents of the fat body at different developmental stages is preliminary to these investigations. This experiment utilizes the combined techniques of thin-layer and gas-liquid chromatography for such an analysis.

ANIMALS

Larvae of *Phormia regina* are obtained following the procedures in Experiment A of this series. The experiments described herein have been performed on larvae at five periods during third-instar development, with the last period being the stage at puparium formation. However, third-instar larvae of any number of convenient ages may be used.

MATERIALS FOR OBTAINING FAT BODIES AND EXTRACTION OF LIPIDS*

1. Balance, analytical.
2. Aluminum foil weighing cups for larvae, laboratory made.
3. Insect Ringer, 7·5 g of NaCl (Merck No. 74073), 0·35 g of KCl and 0·21 g of anhydrous $CaCl_2$/liter.
4. Fine microdissecting scissors (1).
5. Fine microdissecting forceps (2).
6. Dissecting microscope and lamp.
7. Dissecting dish (Syracuse watch glass half-filled with a layer of black wax, Carolina Biological Supply Co., Burlington, North Carolina 27215, U.S.A.).
8. Aluminum foil squares, 2 × 2 cm.
9. Petri dishes.
10. Carbon dioxide, solid block.
11. Lyophilizing apparatus (vacuum desiccator, vacuum pump and vacuum rubber tubing).

* All items are listed in the order used. Some items may be required for more than one part of the experiment; however, they are listed only once.

12. Centrifuge tubes, 15 ml Corex, 17 mm o.d. (Corning No. 8441).
13. Test tube racks.
14. Glass stirring rods.
15. Chloroform : methanol, 2 : 1 (v/v), 500 ml.
16. Pipettes, measuring, 1, 2, 5 and 10 ml.
17. Apparatus to deliver a stream of nitrogen (nitrogen cylinder, pressure regulator, rubber tubing, Pasteur-type disposable transfer pipettes, ring stand, three-prong clamps).
18. Cork stoppers covered with aluminum foil for 15 ml centrifuge tubes.
19. Centrifuge, refrigerated which develops an RCF of about 14 000 g and with rubber adapters to hold 15 ml centrifuge tubes.
20. Separatory funnels with Teflon stopcock, 60 ml.
21. Salt solution, 0·40 g $CaCl_2$, 0·34 g $MgCl_2$, and 5·8 g NaCl/100 ml.
22. Culture tubes with Teflon-lined screw cap, 20 × 150 mm.
23. Pasteur-type disposable transfer pipettes and rubber bulbs.
24. Volumetric flasks, 10 and 25 ml.
25. Weighing vessels to contain up to 12·5 ml.

MATERIALS FOR THIN-LAYER CHROMATOGRAPHY OF LIPIDS

1. Automatic plate leveller and spreader (Quickfit Inc., Fairfield, New Jersey 07006, U.S.A.).
2. Glass carrier plates, 200 × 200 mm.
3. Glass carrier plates, 200 × 50 mm, 2 only.
4. Silica gel H (acc. to Stahl).
5. Balance, general laboratory for weighing 30 g of silica gel.
6. Erlenmeyer flask, 250 ml.
7. Graduated cylinders, 25 and 100 ml.
8. Distilled water.
9. Plate racks.
10. Drying oven set at 110°C.
11. Developing tanks to hold 200 × 200 mm plates.
12. Methanol : concentrated HCl (37%), 9 : 1 (v/v), 200 ml.
13. Desiccator to hold plate rack and plates.
14. Micropipettes, laboratory made using capillary tubing and alcohol lamp.
15. Spotting template.
16. Dissecting needle.
17. Centrifuge tubes, 3 ml.
18. Micropipettes, 50 μl.
19. Hexane : diethyl ether : glacial acetic acid, 85 : 15 : 1 (v/v/v), 100 ml freshly prepared.

20. Filter paper sheets, Whatman No. 1.
21. Iodine crystals and small beaker.
22. Hot plate.
23. Fume hood.
24. Single-edge razor blades.
25. Diethyl ether, 100 ml.
26. Methanol, 250 ml.
27. Chloroform, 100 ml.

Materials for Gas-liquid Chromatography (GLC) of Fatty Acids

1. Evaporator, vacuum type, 100 ml boiling flasks.
2. 0·5N NaOH, 2 g/100 ml of methanol.
3. 0·5N HCl, 4·2 ml of concentrated HCl (37%)/100 ml.
4. Hexane, 100 ml.
5. $MgSO_4$, anhydrous.
6. Hamilton microliter syringe, 10 μl.
7. Fatty acid standards.
8. Gas–liquid chromatograph, Barber-Colman Model 10, dual column with tritium and strontium ionization detector systems; two hairpin columns containing 5% diethylene glycol succinate on 100/120 mesh Chromasorb W inert support.

Procedures for Obtaining Fat Bodies and Extraction of Lipids

Fat bodies are obtained from larvae at 28, 44, 60 and 84 h after the second larval ecdysis and from the stage at puparium formation; the number of larvae dissected at each period is 21, 18, 15, 12 and 12, respectively. Obtain the fresh weight of each insect and use only those within a 6 mg weight range.

1. Rinse the larvae with Ringer solution before dissecting. Dissect three larvae simultaneously, and process the fat bodies in groups of threes. The larvae are dissected in a Syracuse watch glass, containing insect Ringer and half-filled with black wax.

2. Sacrifice the larva by cutting through the entire body behind the anterior end (the larval dissection is illustrated in Fig. 5, Experiment B of this series). Both parts of the larva are turned inside-out to expose the fat body. This is accomplished by: (a) moving closed forceps underneath the body wall to the end of the larva; (b) opening the forceps and taking hold of the inside of the body wall; (c) taking hold of the severed surface of the body wall with a second pair of forceps; and (d) moving the two pairs of forceps toward, then past, each other. The fat body is recognized as whitish sheets of tissue, one cell layer thick, interspersed among the other visceral organs.

3. Dissect the fat body away from other body tissues and transfer with forceps to squares of aluminum foil. To remove the residual Ringer solution, transfer the clump of fat bodies three or four times to new spots on the foil square.

4. Place the foil square containing the fat bodies in a chilled Petri dish situated on a block of solid CO_2.

5. Lyophilize the fat bodies for about 2 h in a vacuum desiccator.

6. Obtain the dry weight of the fat bodies, then transfer to a 15 ml centrifuge tube.

7. Pulverize the fat bodies with a glass stirring rod and add 10 ml of chloroform : methanol (2 : 1, v/v). Flush the tube with nitrogen, stopper, and let stand 8–12 h with occasional shaking.

8. Centrifuge the sample at about 14 000 g and 0°C for 30 min.

9. Decant the supernatant into a separatory funnel. Wash the residue with 10 ml of chloroform/methanol, recentrifuge as before and add the supernatant to the original.

10. Add 4 ml of salt solution (0·40 % $CaCl_2$, 0·34 % $MgCl_2$, and 5·8 % NaCl) to the separatory funnel and shake vigorously (Folch *et al.*, 1957). When two clear phases appear, the lower phase (containing the lipid) is drained into a culture tube.

11. Evaporate the sample under a stream of nitrogen to about 2 ml, then transfer with a disposable pipette to a 10 ml volumetric flask. Using chloroform/methanol, rinse the tube several times; add the rinses to the volumetric flask, adjust the volume to 10 ml and mix.

12. Remove a 2 ml aliquot of the crude lipid sample and place in a *tared* weighing vessel. Evaporate to dryness and weigh. The weight of the lipid multiplied by 5 gives the total amount of crude lipid extracted from the fat bodies. The remaining 8 ml of crude lipid is used for TLC.

Sample calculation of amount of total crude lipid, mg of lipid/fat body, and lipid as a percent of total fat body dry weight

weight of crude lipid in 2 ml aliquot   4·27 mg
$\times$ 5
_____

total amount of crude lipid in 10 ml sample   21·35 mg

mg of total lipid (21·35) ÷ No. of fat bodies (18) = mg of lipid/fat body (1·19)

[mg of lipid/fat body (1·19) ÷ mg dry wt./fat body (2·42)] × 100 = percentage of lipid (49·2 %)

Procedures for Thin-layer Chromatography (TLC) of Lipids

The automatic plate leveller and spreader of Quickfit Inc. is satisfactory for preparing TLC plates. The glass carrier plates (200 × 200 mm) must be washed thoroughly and rinsed in distilled water. The adsorbent is silica gel H (acc. to Stahl). A slurry is prepared by adding 70 ml of distilled water to a flask containing 30 g of silica gel, then mixing with a swirling motion for 1 min. Spread the slurry to a thickness of 0·25 mm on 5 plates. After allowing the coated plates to air dry for 10 min, place in a plate rack. The plates are heated at 110°C for 30 min, then cooled to room temperature. Place the plates in a developing tank containing methanol/concentrated HCl (9 : 1, v/v) (Randerath, 1964). When the solvent front has travelled to the top of the plates, the plates are air dried for 10 min and then activated for 30 min at 110°C. The plates are stored in a desiccator and should be used within 12–72 h.

Micropipettes are made in the laboratory to use in spotting the lipid sample on the TLC plate. Using an alcohol lamp, draw thin-walled capillary tubing out to a fine point and break to yield a small opening. Using a spotting template and dissecting needle, etch 18–20 columns on a TLC plate (Fig. 16), mark origin spots 3 cm from the bottom of the plate and draw a solvent front line 10 cm from the origin.

The 8 ml crude lipid sample is transferred in small amounts to a 3 ml centrifuge tube, while evaporating to near dryness under a stream of nitrogen. Rinse the flask with a small volume of chloroform/methanol, add the rinse to the centrifuge tube and evaporate as before. The lipid is dissolved in about 50 μl of chloroform/methanol and spotted on the 18–20 origin marks of the TLC plate. Care must be taken to limit the spot size (Fig. 16) by working slowly and allowing only a small amount of fluid to flow onto each spot at a time. To speed drying of the solvent and hence the spotting operation, direct a gentle stream of nitrogen on the spot. Do not use forced air, which may cause peroxidation of the lipid, or breath, which may cause inactivation of the silica gel, to aid solvent drying. To completely remove the lipid from the centrifuge tube, rinse the tube twice with 50 μl portions of chloroform/methanol and spot the rinses on the plate.

The plate is placed in a developing tank containing hexane : diethyl ether : acetic acid, 85 : 15 : 1 and lined with Whatman No. 1 filter paper. The solvent front is allowed to travel to the 10 cm line, then the plate is removed from the tank. The triglyceride area may be seen on the plate by using the following method. Place iodine crystals in a small beaker and heat on a hot plate in a fume hood until they vaporize. Partially cover the top of the beaker with a glass plate so that only a small opening remains. The 10 cm line of the plate is held over the iodine vapors and the plate is then moved so that the vapors come in contact with areas closer to the origin. The first spot (Fig. 17) encountered is triglyceride which stains yellow. At this point the plate must be

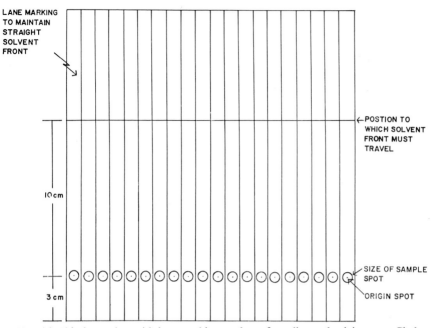

LANE MARKING
TO MAINTAIN
STRAIGHT
SOLVENT
FRONT

←POSTION TO
WHICH SOLVENT
FRONT MUST
TRAVEL

10 cm

SIZE OF SAMPLE
SPOT

ORIGIN SPOT

3 cm

FIG. 16. Thin-layer plate with lane markings, solvent front line and origin spots. Circles around the origin spots (not etch marks) denote the sample spot size.

removed from the iodine vapors; *no other fractions should be exposed to iodine vapors* as this will inhibit their migration in a second solvent which is described below. Use no more iodine than is absolutely necessary. The fraction may be seen by staining only one or two columns. Mark the bottom of the triglyceride area. Then a line is etched across the plate at the bottom mark and a second line is etched 4 cm above this (Fig. 18). The band of silica gel between the two lines contains the triglyceride fraction. This band is scraped into a 15 ml centrifuge tube with a clean razor blade. To facilitate scraping the triglyceride area, first remove the silica gel above it (Fig. 18). Chloroform/methanol (8 ml) is added immediately to the centrifuge tube.

The plate is placed in another developing tank, lined with filter paper, containing only diethyl ether. The solvent front is allowed to travel within a few mm of the top of the remaining silica gel (Fig. 18). A partial glyceride fraction is collected by drawing a line 2 cm down from the top of the silica gel and scraping the band into a centrifuge tube. Lines drawn 1 cm above and 1 cm below the origin delimit the phospholipid fraction and this band is scraped into a centrifuge tube. Add 8 ml of chloroform/methanol to each of these tubes. The contents of each of the three tubes are mixed thoroughly, and the tubes centrifuged at 14 000 *g* and 0°C for 30 min. Decant the supernatants into

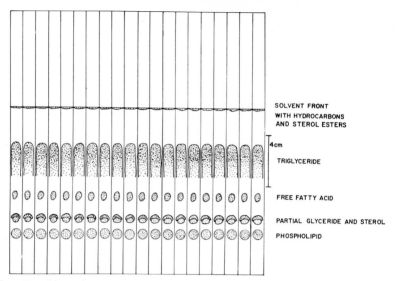

SOLVENT FRONT
WITH HYDROCARBONS
AND STEROL ESTERS

4cm

TRIGLYCERIDE

FREE FATTY ACID

PARTIAL GLYCERIDE AND STEROL

PHOSPHOLIPID

FIG. 17. Thin-layer chromatogram after the plate has developed in hexane : diethyl ether : acetic acid (85 : 15 : 1). The different lipid classes may be visualized by spraying with phosphomolybdic acid (5 g of acid/100 ml of 95 % ethanol) and heating at 85°C for 5–10 min, however, such a plate is unusable for lipid quantitation.

25 ml volumetric flasks with extreme care to prevent silica gel from entering the flasks. Another 8 ml portion of chloroform/methanol is added. The tubes are mixed and centrifuged and the supernatants added to the originals. Add methanol (8 ml) to the tubes, mix, allow to stand 12 h, and centrifuge. Then add the supernatants to the originals. The volumes of the flasks are adjusted to 25 ml with chloroform. Mix the contents thoroughly, and let stand undisturbed for several hours to allow any silica gel to settle out.

The weight of each fraction is ascertained using a 5 ml aliquot. This amount is pipetted off the top of the sample, transferred to a *tared* weighing vessel and evaporated using a stream of nitrogen. The sample is placed in a vacuum desiccator and must be weighed immediately upon removal to prevent any moisture absorption. Since only one-fifth of the sample is taken for gravimetric analysis the total quantity of each fraction is obtained by multiplying by 5. The remaining 20 ml is used for fatty acid analysis.

Even though the coated plates have been washed with methanol/HCl, a small amount of material in the silica gel is still soluble in the solvents it is exposed to. To correct for the contaminants, it is necessary to follow the procedures described for lipid samples using two TLC plates which do not contain a lipid sample. These "blank" plates are run in the same two solvent systems, and three bands of silica gel are obtained from the same areas of the plate used to collect the three lipid fractions. The three "blank" silica gel samples are washed and processed following the exact procedures described for lipid samples. About 15 ml of each "blank" is poured into graduated cylinders and 12·5 ml (12·5 is one-half so must multiply by 2) obtained for gravimetric analysis. The average weight of contaminant in each "blank fraction" is subtracted from the weight of the corresponding lipid fraction.

Sample calculation of triglyceride, partial glyceride and phospholipid

	Triglyceride	Partial glyceride	Phospholipid
Weight of 5 ml aliquot	3·06 mg	0·38 mg	0·48 mg
	× 5	× 5	× 5
Total amount (in 25 ml)	15·30 mg	1·90 mg	2·40 mg
Weight of contaminant	− 1·50 mg	− 0·76 mg	− 0·68 mg
Actual amount in 80% of sample (used 8 or 10 ml for TLC)	13·80 mg ÷ 0·8	1·14 mg ÷ 0·8	1·72 mg ÷ 0·8
Total amount extracted from 18 fat bodies	17·25 mg ÷ 18	1·43 mg ÷ 18	2·15 mg ÷ 18
Amount of each fraction/ fat body	0·96 mg	0·08 mg	0·12 mg
Total amount of crude lipid/fat body	÷ 1·19 mg	÷ 1·19 mg	÷ 1·19 mg
	0·807 × 100	0·067 × 100	0·101 × 100
Percentage of each fraction of total lipid	80·7%	6·7%	10·1%

Sum of percentages = % recovery 80·7% + 6·7% + 10·1% = 97·5%

GAS-LIQUID CHROMATOGRAPHY OF TRIGLYCERIDE, PARTIAL GLYCERIDE AND PHOSPHOLIPID FATTY ACIDS

The remaining 20 ml samples of triglyceride, partial glyceride and phospholipid are analysed for their fatty acid content. Transfer the 20 ml sample to a boiling flask and evaporate to near dryness under reduced pressure. Using

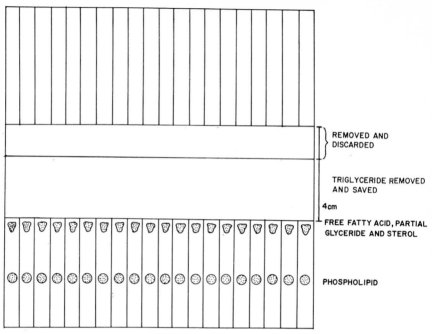

Fig. 18. Thin-layer chromatogram after the triglyceride area is removed, and after the plate has developed in diethyl ether.

chloroform/methanol, transfer the sample to a culture tube with a Teflon-lined screw cap. The solvent is evaporated to near dryness with nitrogen and 0·5 ml of chloroform is added.

Methylation is accomplished according to the method of Morgan *et al.* (1963). Methanolic NaOH (5 ml of 0·5N) is added to the sample and allowed to remain, with occasional shaking, for 40 min at room temperature. Then HCl (5 ml of 0·5N) is added, followed immediately with 5 ml of cold distilled water and 5 ml of hexane. Shake the tube vigorously and allow to stand until two phases appear. The upper hexane phase, containing the fatty acid methyl esters, is transferred to a culture tube. The remaining lower phase is washed twice with 5 ml portions of hexane and these are combined with the original. To remove the water soluble contaminants from the hexane sample, add 1 ml of distilled water, shake vigorously, let stand until two phases appear and then remove the lower water phase. Evaporate about 4 ml of the hexane sample and transfer the remainder to a 15 ml centrifuge tube. Add about 1 g of anhydrous $MgSO_4$ (to remove any residual water) and centrifuge. The supernatant is decanted into another 15 ml centrifuge tube, evaporated to about 2 ml with nitrogen and then transferred to a 3 ml centrifuge tube. Evaporate the sample to near dryness with nitrogen and add 20 μl of hexane.

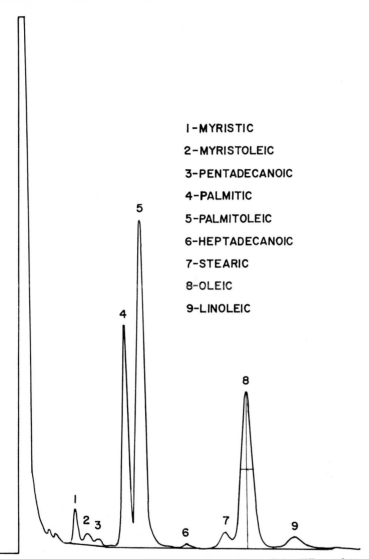

FIG. 19. Gas–liquid chromatogram illustrating the position of the different fatty acid peaks. Lines denoting the height and width at one-half height are shown on the oleic acid peak.

The quantity of sample injected onto the column of the gas chromatograph depends upon the amount of fatty acid methyl esters in the sample and the sensitivity of the gas chromatography itself. In our system, about 1 μl of the triglyceride fraction was injected, whereas up to 10 μl was used for the partial glyceride and phospholipid fractions.

The analysis of fatty acids was accomplished using a Barber-Colman Model 10 Gas Chromatograph. This instrument has two 6 ft. $\times \frac{1}{4}$ in. glass hairpin columns, one equipped with tritium and the other with a strontium ionization detector system. The chromatograph columns contain 5% diethylene glycol succinate coated on 100–120 mesh acid-washed Chromasorb W. The columns are maintained at 180°C and the detector cells at about 25°C higher than the column. Argon serves as the carrier gas and the flow rate is maintained at about 60 ml/min.

A typical recording from the gas chromatograph is shown in Fig. 19. The analysis of a chromatogram involves calculating the area under each fatty acid curve, obtaining the sum of all areas, then calculating the percentage of each fatty acid proportional to the total fatty acids. Calculation of a peak area is done by triangulation, which involves multiplying the height of the peak by the width of the peak at one-half height (Fig. 19).

Results

During the investigated duration of development, the total lipid content of the fat body increases about 4-fold (Table V). The percentage values (Table VI) show that lipid constitutes an increasing proportion of the total fat body except at puparium formation. The percentage decrease at this period does not result from a net decline in lipid (Table V), but rather from a proportional increase in protein. Triglyceride is the major storage form of lipid and constitutes a greater percentage of the total lipid during development. The increasing proportion of triglyceride results in a concomitant decrease in the percentage of partial glycerides and phospholipid. Although the percentage values decline for these two fractions, net synthesis during development did occur (Table V). The percentage recovery from TLC ranged from 96·7% to 103·0%. These values do not include about 1% sterol ester and hydrocarbon previously measured by column chromatography.

Fatty acid analyses of the three lipid fractions reveal palmitoleic (C16 : 1) and oleic (C18 : 1) as the major unsaturated fatty acids and palmitic (C16 : 0) as the major saturate (Table VII). These three fatty acids account for 81·6%–96·8% of the total (lowest in 84 h triglyceride and highest in 84 h phospholipid). Myristic (C14 : 0), myristoleic (C14 : 1) and stearic (C18 : 0) are considered minor components with traces of lauric (C12 : 0) and linoleic acids (C18 : 2).

The pattern of distribution of fatty acids in the three fractions at a given time period and the change in the distribution of fatty acids during development may be summarized as follows. (1) The distribution of fatty acids usually is   palmitoleic > oleic > palmitic > myristic > stearic > myristoleic.   (2)

Phospholipid and partial glycerides more frequently exhibit a greater percentage of palmitoleic and oleic acids than does triglyceride, with the exception of puparium formation when the pattern is reversed. The change in the distribution of fatty acids at puparium formation results chiefly from a decline in the percentage of palmitoleic and oleic acids, and a concomitant increase in palmitic acid, in both the phospholipid and partial glyceride fractions. In the phospholipid fraction, oleic acid shows an increasing trend until puparium formation. (3) Palmitic, myristic, stearic, and myristoleic acids are usually higher in triglyceride than in phospholipid or partial glycerides.

TABLE V

Content of total lipid and different lipid classes of the fat body during third-instar development of Phormia regina

Hours after ecdysis to third instar	Fat body (mg dry wt.)†	Total lipid (mg/fat body)	Triglyceride (mg/fat body)	Partial glycerides (mg/fat body)	Phospholipid (mg/fat body)
28	1·59	0·63	0·46	0·09	0·10
44	2·42	1·19	0·97	0·09	0·12
60	3·75	1·97	1·70	0·11	0·10
84	4·31	2·25	1·99	0·16	0·13
Puparium formation*	5·82	2·59	2·31	0·12	0·15

* This stage is collected at 96–108 h.
† All values represent the average of duplicate samples.

TABLE VI

Total lipid as a percentage of fat body dry weight and lipid classes as a percentage of total fat body lipid

Hours after ecdysis to third instar	Total lipid (% of fat body dry wt.)†	Triglyceride (% of total lipid)	Partial glycerides (% of total lipid)	Phospholipid (% of total lipid)	Amount recovered (%)
28	39·5	72·8	13·8	16·4	103·0
44	49·0	81·9	7·3	10·1	99·3
60	52·6	86·1	5·8	4·8	96·7
84	52·3	88·5	7·0	5·8	101·3
Puparium formation*	44·6	88·9	4·5	5·9	99·3

* This stage is collected at 96–108 h.
† All values represent the average of duplicate samples.

TABLE VII

Fatty acid composition of fat body triglyceride, partial glycerides and phospholipid during third-instar development of Phormia regina

	C16 : 1	C18 : 1	C16 : 0	C14 : 0	C18 : 0	C14 : 1	Others*
28 hours†							
Triglyceride	31·6	26·4	25·9	6·8	3·2	2·7	3·4
Partial glycerides	39·8	29·3	20·7	4·4	1·3	2·3	2·2
Phospholipid	38·0	29·3	24·0	3·9	0·9	1·0	2·9
44 hours							
Triglyceride	30·6	29·8	24·1	5·6	3·0	2·5	4·4
Partial glycerides	33·7	31·4	26·1	3·4	1·4	1·5	2·5
Phospholipid	42·5	35·4	18·5	1·3	0·1	0·4	1·8
60 hours							
Triglyceride	32·3	27·6	25·6	5·4	3·6	2·1	3·4
Partial glycerides	36·6	32·3	21·2	3·6	1·5	2·2	2·6
Phospholipid	37·5	38·2	19·4	1·4	0·5	0·4	2·6
84 hours							
Triglyceride	27·7	30·7	23·2	7·0	4·7	2·6	4·1
Partial glycerides	37·1	29·1	21·6	3·2	2·0	1·8	5·2
Phospholipid	37·5	39·2	20·1	0·8	0·3	0·3	1·8
Puparium formation‡							
Triglyceride	32·9	29·1	27·4	4·3	2·6	1·3	2·4
Partial glycerides	27·4	27·2	30·7	3·3	4·8	0·9	5·7
Phospholipid	30·2	28·7	28·5	2·3	0·5	1·9	7·9

* Lauric, pentadecanoic, linoleic and several unidentified fatty acids.
† Hours after ecdysis to third-instar.
‡ This stage is collected at 96–108 h.

TROUBLE-SHOOTING

The presence of contaminants in the silica gel and the procedure used to correct for these contaminants has been mentioned previously. If this correction is not made, values of 110%–130% recovery will be obtained. Even when this correction is made, occasionally the percentage recovered from TLC will be greater than 100%. This probably is due to the presence of a small amount of silica gel in the weighed sample. Therefore, it is advisable to perform the gravimetric analysis of the triglyceride, partial glyceride and phospholipid fraction, and calculate the percentage recovered before using the remaining 20 ml samples for GLC. Then, if recovery percentages are high, the 20 ml sample is allowed to remain for several hours and a new 5 ml aliquot removed from the top of the sample.

As the fat bodies are collected, it is best to lyophilize and extract them with chloroform/methanol immediately. Storage of frozen insect tissues for prolonged periods may result in production of larger amounts of free fatty acids at the expense of glycerides.

FURTHER EXPERIMENTS

The techniques of thin-layer and gas-liquid chromatography are used in this experiment to analyse the lipid components of the larval fat body of *Phormia regina*. TLC is used to quantitate lipid classes (triglyceride, partial glycerides and phospholipid), while GLC is used to analyse the fatty acids of the different lipid classes. Similar experiments could be performed on other insect tissues or whole insects, if they are very small. This experiment also could be extended for use on other invertebrate or vertebrate materials.

BIBLIOGRAPHY

Barlow, J. S. (1964). Fatty acids in some insect and spider fats. *Can. J. Biochem.*, **42**, 1365–1374.

Fast, P. G. (1964). Insect lipids: A review. *Mem. ent. Soc. Can.*, No. 37, 1–50.

Folch, J., Lees, M. and Sloane, S. G. H. (1957). A simple method for the isolation and purification of total lipids from animal tissues. *J. biol. Chem.*, **226**, 497–509.

Morgan, T. E., Hanahan, P. J. and Ekholm, J. (1963). A rapid method for deacylation of phospholipids and neutral lipids. *Fedn Proc. Fedn Am. Socs exp. Biol.*, **22**, 419.

Randerath, K. (1964). "Thin-layer Chromatography." Academic Press, New York and London.

Wimer, L. T. and Lumb, R. H. (1967). Lipid composition of the developing larval fat body of *Phormia regina*. *J. Insect Physiol.*, **13**, 889–898.

Exp. in Physiol. and Biochem. (1970). **3**, 417–484.

14 | The Use of Sephadex® in the Separation, Purification and Characterization of Biological Materials

JOHN CURLING

Pharmacia Fine Chemicals AB, Uppsala, Sweden

PRINCIPLES OF GEL CHROMATOGRAPHY

CHROMATOGRAPHY: SOME GENERAL CONSIDERATIONS

Gel chromatography, as its name implies, is a chromatographic technique. It is, therefore, worthwhile considering some of the more fundamental aspects of chromatography since these will lead to a better understanding of the principles of gel chromatography.

The aim of chromatography is to separate: if separation is not obtained then the technique has failed. We must, therefore, look closely at the way in which separation is achieved. All chromatographic techniques have one feature in common, the use of two phases, one stationary, the other mobile. The stationary phase is the basis of a chromatographic bed. Separation is achieved by the migration of substances at different rates through the bed. Migration is produced by the flow of the mobile phase.

The stationary phase in the form of finely divided particles is packed into a column or spread as a thin layer on a solid support. The mobile phase is made to flow through the bed. Substances to be separated are applied as a zone at the top of the column or as a spot on a thin layer. The substances are carried through the bed by the mobile phase and are more or less retarded by the stationary phase. They are, therefore, separated and eluted from the column or migrate different distances on the thin layer.

Chromatographic techniques differ in the nature of stationary and mobile phases and therefore in the way in which substances are retarded by the stationary phase. If retardation is due to the interaction of substances with the surface of the bed material the technique is known as "adsorption" chromatography. If the retardation is due to the interaction of substances with the bulk of the bed material the technique is known as "partition" chromatography.

GEL CHROMATOGRAPHY

In gel chromatography substances are retarded by the bulk of the stationary phase and we can consider gel chromatography to be a form of partition chromatography. The feature which differentiates gel chromatography from all other chromatographic techniques is that the stationary phase is a gel swollen in the liquid used as the mobile phase. Since the mobile phase serves only to transport the substances through the gel bed, it is of greater interest and more instructive to look at the stationary phase and the way in which it selectively retards different substances. In the next section we shall consider the special properties of the bed material "Sephadex®" but here we will consider only the mechanism of gel chromatography.

The gel is prepared for use by allowing it to swell in an excess of eluant. In this process the dry gel grains take up water because of the presence of hydrophilic groups (e.g. hydroxyl) in the gel matrix. By introducing lipophilic groups into the gel matrix the gel can be made to swell in organic solvents. The swollen gel is packed into a column and the gel bed stabilized by running eluant through the column. A simple separation is shown in Fig. 1.

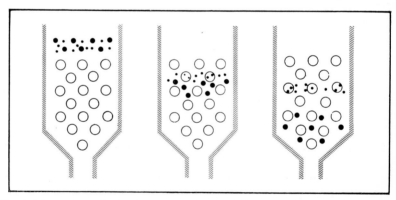

FIG. 1. Three stages of a simple separation on a Sephadex bed. The open circles represent the Sephadex beads, the large dots represent the large molecules, the small dots the small molecules. (From "Sephadex—Gel Filtration in Theory and Practice", Pharmacia Fine Chemicals AB, Uppsala, Sweden.)

When a sample containing, let us say, high and low molecular weight solutes is applied to the top of the bed the following will occur. Molecules larger than the largest pores of the gel will be excluded from the gel grains and will be able to exist only in liquid surrounding the gel particles. Small molecules, however, will be able to penetrate the gel grains and may exist in both the gel grains and the liquid surrounding them. For small molecules, therefore, there is always a dynamic equilibrium set up between the molecules entering and leaving the gel grains. As soon as a molecule leaves a gel particle

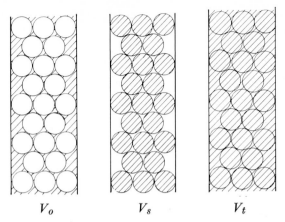

$$V_o \qquad\qquad V_s \qquad\qquad V_t$$

Fig. 2. Variables used to characterize the bed: V_o, V_s and V_t. (From "An introduction to gel chromatography", Fischer, L., in "Laboratory Techniques in Biochemistry and Molecular Biology" (T. S. Work and E. Work, eds), North-Holland Publishing Co., Amsterdam, 1969: with the kind permission of the author and the publisher).

it is carried by the mobile phase further down the column until it again penetrates a gel particle. These small molecules are, therefore, sterically hindered by the gel matrix and are thus retarded by the stationary phase. This mechanism gives a separation according to molecular size, large molecules being eluted first, small molecules last. Molecules intermediate between these extremes are, of course, more or less retarded by their molecular size depending on the extent to which the gel is available to them.

This is an ideal picture since we have not considered the possibility of interactions, other than sterical, with the gel matrix. Interactions such as ion exchange, ion exclusion and aromatic adsorption do occur and lead to deviations from ideality. They can, however, be used to advantage to separate molecular species of similar molecular size but of different chemical nature.

Let us now return to the idea of gel chromatography as a form of partition chromatography in order to construct a more quantitative picture.

We can define V_s as the volume of the stationary phase and V_o as the volume of the mobile phase; in gel chromatography V_o is known as the "void volume". The volumes V_s, V_o and V_t are illustrated in Fig. 2.

Let V_e be the volume taken to elute a given solute and K be the partition coefficient of the solute between the stationary and mobile phases.

Now,
$$K = \frac{c_s}{c_m} \tag{1}$$

where c_m and c_s are the concentrations of solute in the mobile and stationary phases, respectively.

Let F be the fraction of solute in the mobile phase; then $(1-F)$ is the fraction of solute in the stationary phase.

Now
$$F = c_m V_o$$

and
$$(1 - F) = c_s V_s.$$

The ratio of solute in the mobile phase to that in stationary phase can be expressed as

$$\frac{F}{(1 - F)} = \frac{c_m V_o}{c_s V_s}. \tag{2}$$

But
$$\frac{c_s}{c_m} = K.$$

Therefore
$$\frac{F}{(1 - F)} = \frac{V_o}{K V_s}. \tag{3}$$

Solving for F, the fraction of solute in the mobile phase, we have

$$F = \frac{V_o}{V_o + K V_s}. \tag{4}$$

Now, the migration rate of the solute through the bed is proportional to the fraction of solute in the mobile phase.

i.e. Migration rate $\quad \alpha \quad \dfrac{V_o}{V_o + K V_s}. \tag{5}$

The elution volume, V_e is inversely proportional to the migration rate so that

$$V_e \, \alpha \, \frac{V_o + K V_s}{V_o}. \tag{6}$$

or

$$V_e = \text{const.} \, \frac{(V_o + K V_s)}{V_o}. \tag{7}$$

Now, if the solute were present only in the mobile phase we should have

$$V_e = V_o \text{ and } K = 0.$$

Substituting these values in Equation (7) we obtain, $V_o = \text{const.}$

and
$$V_e = V_o + K V_s. \tag{8}$$

Rearranging for K we obtain

$$K = \frac{V_e - V_o}{V_s}. \tag{9}$$

The partition coefficient K is the parameter used to characterize the behaviour of solutes in partition chromatography. In gel chromatography K has two forms depending on what is taken as the stationary phase.

If we regard the stationary phase as being the liquid imbibed by the gel we have

$$K_d = \frac{V_e - V_o}{V_i} \qquad (10)$$

where V_i is the volume of imbibed liquid.

If we regard the stationary phase as being the gel matrix volume plus the imbibed liquid we have

$$V_s = V_t - V_o \qquad (11)$$

where V_t is the total volume of the gel bed.

Therefore
$$K_{av} = \frac{V_e - V_o}{V_t - V_o}. \qquad (12)$$

Let us now consider the measurable variables and the results obtainable from an experiment, although the practical aspects of these measurements will be dealt with later.

V_e, V_o and V_t are all directly measurable. It is, therefore, easy to calculate an elution volume relative to the void volume or total volume, i.e. V_e/V_o or V_e/V_t. These relative elution volumes were used in early gel chromatographic studies to characterize the behaviour of solutes but they have been superseded by the K_{av} and K_d values since, although they are independent of column volume they are dependent on the column packing.

K_d, as defined in Equation (10) and K_{av}, defined in Equation (12) are both independent of the column volume and the packing. For the calculation of K_d, however, it is necessary to calculate V_i from one of the following equations:

$$V_i = (V_t - V_o) - 0 \cdot 6\, m_g \qquad (13)$$

or
$$V_i = \frac{W_r.d}{(W_r+1)} (V_t - V_o) \qquad (14)$$

where m_g is the weight of dry gel used, W_r is the "water regain" value of the gel (expressed as the number of grams of water imbibed by 1 gram of gel) and d is the wet density of the gel. In Equation (13) $0 \cdot 6$ is the partial specific volume of the gel. There is a considerable measure of uncertainty in both equations since they are dependent on the accurate determination of W_r and d.

It is preferable, therefore, to use the K_{av} value to characterize the behaviour of a solute on a gel. Ideally, K_{av} values should range between 0 and 1. If a substance is excluded totally from a gel then $V_e = V_o$ and $K_{av} = 0$; if the whole of the imbibed liquid is available to a solute then $V_e = V_t$ (approximately) and $K_{av} = 1$. K_{av} values greater than 1 indicate interactions, such as aromatic adsorption, with the gel matrix.

For a given gel we can define a "fractionation range" and an "exclusion limit". The fractionation range is the range in which a change of molecular size or weight gives a change in elution volume. The upper limit of this range is the exclusion limit. The fractionation range and therefore the exclusion limit is dependent on the density of the gel. Above the exclusion limit substances have K_{av} values equal to zero, within the fractionation range K_{av} values lie between 0 and 1 and below the range K_{av} values equal one.

THE BED MATERIAL, SEPHADEX®

Sephadex is the registered trade mark of the dextran gel manufactured by Pharmacia Fine Chemicals AB, Uppsala, Sweden. Dextran is an anhydro-glucose polymer produced in sucrose-containing solutions by numerous strains of *Leuconostoc*. Sephadex is prepared by cross-linking selected dextran fractions with epichlorohydrin. The reaction is carried out in an organic solvent in the presence of emulsifying and stabilizing agents and results in a bead-formed, insoluble product. Because of the high content of hydroxyl groups in the polysaccharide chains Sephadex is strongly hydrophilic and thus swells in water and electrolyte solutions.

The degree of swelling, which is controlled by the concentration of dextran and degree of cross-linking, is one of the most important characteristics of the gel. The "water regain" value is used to characterize the gel with respect to its ability to swell: water regain, W_r, is expressed as ml H_2O/g dry Sephadex. Different Sephadex types are denoted G-10, G-15, G-25, etc., where the numbers refer approximately to the water regain value; thus G-10 has a water regain $= 1$ and G-25 a water regain $= 2.5$. Doubling the W_r value gives an approximate value of the volume of gel obtainable from 1 g dry Sephadex. The physical data, including fractionation ranges, for Sephadex G-types is given in Table I.

Sephadex is available in different particle size grades. A guide to the uses of the different grades are given in Table II.

The Sephadex G-types, described above, swell not only in aqueous solutions but also in dimethylsulphoxide, formamide and glycol. Sephadex G-10 and G-15 also swell in dimethylformamide. In addition to these solvents aqueous mixtures of lower alcohols may be used.   •

For work in organic solvents, however, a modified gel, Sephadex LH-20 is available. Sephadex LH-20 is prepared by hydroxypropylation of Sephadex G-25. The gel obtained swells both in aqueous and polar organic solvents and

TABLE I

Physical properties of Sephadex types
(From "Sephadex-gel filtration in theory and practice", Pharmacia
Fine Chemicals AB, Uppsala, Sweden)

Sephadex type	Particle diameter μ	Bed volume ml/g dry Sephadex	Fractionatian range for peptides and globular proteins MW	dextrans MW
Sephadex G-10	40–120	2–3	–700	–700
Sephadex G-15	40–120	2·5–3·5	–1500	–1500
Sephadex G-25 Coarse	100–300	4–6	1000–5000	100–5000
Sephadex G-25 Medium	50–150	4–6	1000–5000	100–5000
Sephadex G-25 Fine	20–80	4–6	1000–5000	100–5000
Sephadex G-25 Superfine	10–40	4–6	1000–5000	100–5000
Sephadex G-50 Coarse	100–300	9–11	1500–30 000	500–10 000
Sephadex G-50 Medium	50–150	9–11	1500–30 000	500–10 000
Sephadex G-50 Fine	20–80	9–11	1500–30 000	500–10 000
Sephadex G-50 Superfine	10–40	9–11	1500–30 000	500–10 000
Sephadex G-75	40–120	12–15	3000–70 000	1000–50 000
Sephadex G-75 Superfine	10–40	12–15	3000–70 000	1000–50 000
Sephadex G-100	40–120	15–20	4000–150 000	1000–100 000
Sephadex G-100 Superfine	10–40	15–20	4000–150 000	1000–100 000
Sephadex G-150	40–120	20–30	5000–400 000	1000–150 000
Sephadex G-150 Superfine	10–40	18–22	5000–400 000	1000–150 000
Sephadex G-200	40–120	30–40	5000–800 000	1000–200 000
Sephadex G-200 Superfine	10–40	20–25	5000–800 000	1000–200 000

TABLE II

Recommended uses of the different grades of Sephadex

Grade of Sephadex	Recommended use
Superfine	Thin-layer and high resolution column gel chromatography
Fine	Preparative and analytical gel chromatography with good flow rate and resolution
Medium Coarse	Preparative and industrial gel chromatography at high flow rates. Concentration (batch procedure, Coarse grade)

TABLE III

Solvent regain for Sephadex LH-20 in different solvents

Solvent	Approx. solvent regain ml solvent/g dry gel	Approx. bed volume ml/g dry gel
Dimethylformamide	2·2	4·0–4·5
Water	2·1	4·0–4·5
Methanol	1·9	3·9–4·3
Chloroform*	1·8	3·8–4·1
Ethanol†	1·8	3·6–3·9
n-Butanol	1·6	3·5–3·8
Tetrahydrofurane	1·4	3·3–3·6
Dioxane	1·4	3·2–3·5
Acetone	0·8	2·4–2·6
Ethyl acetate	0·4	1·7–1·8
Toluene	0·2	1·5–1·6

* Containing 1 % ethanol.
† Containing 1 % benzene.

as indicated in Table III it is necessary to specify a "solvent regain" for each solvent.

In addition to the Sephadex types described above there are four ion exchangers based on the dextran matrix. Since ion exchange chromatography is a special subject it will be treated as such in a following section.

EXPERIMENTAL TECHNIQUE IN COLUMN GEL CHROMATOGRAPHY
PREPARING THE SEPHADEX

Weigh out the required amount of Sephadex (given in the instructions for each experiment) and stir it into an excess volume of eluant. The gels should be allowed to swell for at least the times given in Table IV: swelling may be accelerated by placing the gel slurry on a boiling water bath. This not only reduces the swelling time to 1 h but it also causes deaeration of the slurry and partial sterilization. If time and equipment permit the gel slurry should be

TABLE IV

Swelling times for Sephadex types

Type of Sephadex	Minimum swelling time at room temperature	on boiling water bath
G-10, G-15, G-25, G-50	3 h	1 h
G-75	24 h	3 h
G-100, G-150, G-200	3 days	5 h
LH-20	3 h	—

deaerated under vacuum before packing to avoid the risk of air bubble formation in the gel bed.

PACKING THE COLUMN

If the gel has been swollen on a water bath make sure that it has reached room temperature before packing it in the column. Allow the gel to settle and decant the excess eluant (containing fines). Resuspend the gel in excess eluant and when it has settled decant the supernatant until a volume of not more than 30% of the gel volume remains above the gel. Stir to a uniform slurry and without trapping air bubbles pour into the column either down a glass rod held against the side of the tube or down the wall of the tube—tilting the column slightly makes this easier. All the gel intended for the experiment should be poured at one time: with the soft gel types (Sephadex G-75 to G-200) it may be necessary to fix an extension tube or small funnel to the top of the column. Check with a spirit level or plumb line that the column is mounted vertically.

Fill the column to the top with eluant and connect it to an eluant reservoir (Mariotte flask—see the Section on Elution). Position the outlet tubing so that the operating pressure does not exceed the value given in Table V. Ten to twenty minutes after pouring the column the outlet should be opened and the column allowed to run until stabilized (when 2–3 column volumes have passed through the gel bed). If the column is to be left to run overnight or without attention a safety loop arrangement should be used (see the Section on Elution). Before applying samples the bed surface should be protected either with a sample applicator cup, a flow adaptor or a filter paper disc. Run a zone of Blue dextran 2000 through the bed to check the packing: irregularities are easily seen and if they occur the bed must be repacked. Running a Blue dextran 2000 sample serves both as a check of the packing and as a void volume determination.

TABLE V

Recommended optimum operating pressures for Sephadex types

Sephadex type	Recommended optimum operating pressure, % of bed height
G-10 to G-75	100
G-100	30
G-150	15
G-200	10

COLUMN SAMPLE APPLICATION

Preferences in the method of sample application vary. Essentially, there are three different ways.

(a) Drain off excess eluant from above the bed surface, either by letting eluant drain from the column, pipetting off the excess or sucking it off with a syringe. Make sure that the column outlet is closed. Pipette the sample onto the drained surface and open the column outlet. When all the sample has entered the gel wash the top of the column with small aliquots of eluant and then connect the column for elution. A slight modification of this procedure is to use a graduated pipette with a small "bead valve" attached: this is easily made by lodging a glass bead in a piece of silicon tubing attached to the pipette. By pressing the tubing against the glass bead the flow can be very carefully controlled.

(b) Leave the excess eluant on top of the gel. Attach some very thin capillary tubing to a syringe and flare the end of the tubing by heating it gently. Fill the syringe with sample and layer the sample on top of the gel surface by arranging the end of the tubing just above the gel surface and slowly pressing out the required amount of sample. Note that, if this method is used the sample must be denser than the eluant or made denser by the addition of, for instance, sucrose.

(c) Using a flow adaptor, samples can be applied extremely reproducibly. If possible connect the flow adaptor to a three-way valve (see the Section on Elution). Connect sample and eluant reservoirs to the valve. Apply the sample by simply switching from eluant to sample and back again. If a valve is not available the adaptor is normally connected to the eluant reservoir. To apply the sample, close the column outlet, take the tubing from the eluant and put into a graduated sample reservoir. Open the column outlet and allow the sample to flow to the column, being careful not to trap an air bubble between the eluant and the sample. When the required sample volume has been applied, close the column and replace the tubing in the eluant reservoir and start the elution.

ELUTION

After sample application the column should be filled with eluant and connected to a Mariotte flask. A simple construction of a Mariotte flask is shown in Fig. 3.

Note that the operating pressure is measured from the bottom of the inner glass tube to the end of the outlet tubing. Using this device the operating pressure is constant, not varying with the level of eluant in the flask. The operating pressure is defined in Fig. 4.

The optimum operating pressures given under the Section "Packing the

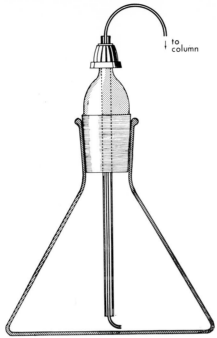

to
column

FIG. 3. Simple construction of a Mariotte Flask. (Source as Fig. 2.)

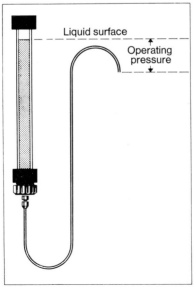

Liquid surface

Operating
pressure

FIG. 4. Column packing and definition of operating pressure. (Source as Fig. 1.)

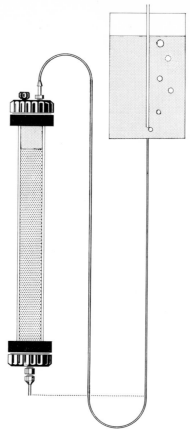

Fig. 5. Safety loop arrangement for running columns overnight or without attention.
(Source as Fig. 2.)

Column" should not be exceeded: this is especially important for the gels with
high water-regain values.

If elution is to be carried out over night it is wise to set up the column with
a safety loop so that there is no chance of it running dry. Use the set-up
shown in Fig. 5.

For semi-automatic sample application and elution the scheme shown in
Fig. 6 is useful. This set-up should be used, for example, for the skim-milk
desalting experiment.

In the following section "Packing Sephadex LH-20 in Chloroform" it is
mentioned that it may be necessary to run the column under increased
hydrostatic pressure to avoid air-bubble formation. Figure 7 shows the set-up
for running under increased hydrostatic pressure.

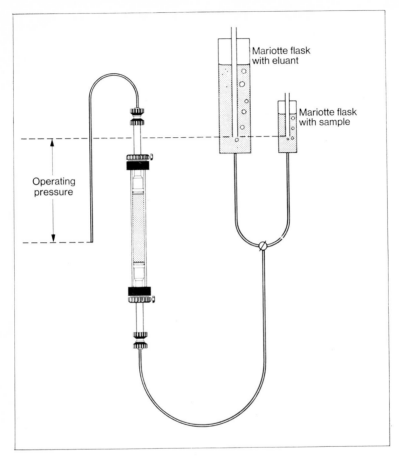

Fig. 6. Experimental set-up for semi-automatic gel chromatography. (Source as Fig. 1.)

PACKING SEPHADEX LH-20 IN CHLOROFORM

Sephadex LH-20 floats in chloroform. A somewhat different packing procedure must therefore be adopted. Firstly, a solvent resistant column fitted
with two flow adaptors should be used. Set up the column in the normal way
and pour in the gel slurry to the top of the column. Open the column outlet
and allow the gel to pack downwards under the flow. When there is enough
space in the top of the column to insert the top flow adaptor stop the flow
and wash the top of the column with chloroform. Insert the flow adaptor and
run the column upwards: this will cause the gel to pack against the top flow

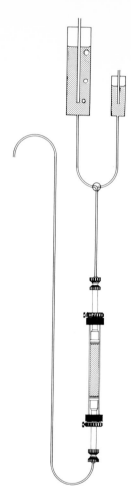

F IG. 7. Experimental set-up for running under increased hydrostatic pressure. (Source as Fig. 2.)

adaptor leaving a dead space between the gel and the bottom adaptor. Adjust the position of the bottom flow adaptor until it is in contact with the gel.

Due to the high vapour density of chloroform there is a tendency for bubbles to form in the gel bed and it is advisable, therefore, to run the column under increased hydrostatic pressure (see the Section on Elution).

EXPERIMENTAL TECHNIQUE IN THIN-LAYER GEL CHROMATOGRAPHY
APPARATUS FOR THIN-LAYER GEL CHROMATOGRAPHY

A simple apparatus is shown in Fig. 8 (p. 432). It consists of a glass plate lodged between two solvent reservoirs. The gel layer is connected to eluting solvent by means of filter paper wicks. The gel layer is covered by a plastic lid to prevent evaporation from the layer. The angle of the plate is determined by the positions of the two reservoirs.

Figure 9 (p. 432) shows a somewhat more sophisticated apparatus. The glass plate rests in a shallow box fitted with reservoirs at each end. The lid of the box has a slit near the top through which samples can be applied. During runs the slit is covered with tape. The whole assembly is mounted so that it can be tilted to any angle between 0° and 30°.

Both types of apparatus can be made to take standard thin-layer plates 20 × 20 cm, 20 × 30 cm or 20 × 40 cm.

PREPARING THIN-LAYER PLATES

Prepare a suspension of the required grade of "Superfine" Sephadex. Having allowed the gel to sediment decant all the supernatant above the gel layer. Thoroughly clean a glass plate and then be careful not to finger the surface on to which the gel is to be spread.

The gel layer can be spread using any commercial spreading device but a simple (and cheap) method is with a stainless steel rod with collars at each end. The rod may be machined so that the collar diameter is 1–2 mm larger than the rod diameter: the distance between the collars should be about 18 cm and the overall rod length about 24 cm. An even simpler modification is to wrap insulating tape round each end of a 1 cm diameter rod until the tape thickness is 0·5–1 mm.

Spread some gel on to the plate with a spatula and attempt to spread a layer by moving the rod back and forth over the plate. Do not rotate the rod. End with one even stroke taking excess gel off the plate. If the gel runs off the plate then the slurry is too thin and must be filtered to obtain a thicker suspension. If the Sephadex will not adhere to the plate but sticks to the spreading rod it is too thick and more eluant must be added to the slurry.

EQUILIBRATING THE PLATE

Place the plate in the thin-layer chamber and connect the gel to the eluant reservoirs with pre-soaked filter paper. Ensure that the filter paper wicks are perpendicular to the length of the plate. If they are not, uneven flow will ensue. Place the lid on the chamber and equilibrate the plate by running it overnight at an angle of 10°–15°. Very much shorter equilibration times may be used if reproducibility is not important.

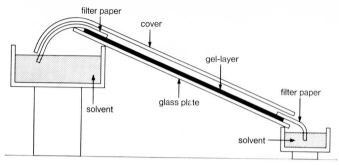

FIG. 8. Experimental set-up for thin-layer gel chromatography: "Sandwich" chamber apparatus. (Source as Fig. 1.)

FIG. 9. Experimental set-up for thin-layer gel chromatography: thin-layer box.

APPLYING SAMPLES

Put the thin-layer box horizontal and remove the tape from the slit or the whole lid if necessary. Apply approximately $5 \mu l$ samples with a syringe, micropipette, from a glass rod or capillary tube. It should not be necessary to touch the gel layer with the application tool if a drop is formed at the end of it. Samples of 5–10 μl can be applied using the short side of a microscope slide as the application tool. A rectangular zone is formed, the migration distance of which is more accurately measurable than that of a spot. Take care not to apply samples too near to the edge of the layer since flow may be uneven at the edges of the plate. Make marks on each side of the plate to show the starting line. Reseal the box.

ELUTING SAMPLES

A marker substance should be applied at each side of the plate. This marker will show the progress of the elution and if applied at each side of the plate will show if the flow rate varies across it. Suitable substances are cytochrome c, haemoglobin, fluorescein isothiocyanate or lissamine rhodamine isothiocyanate conjugated proteins. Elution can be carried out at an angle of 10°–20° depending on the flow rate required or the time available. As in column gel filtration low flow rates give the best results.

IDENTIFICATION OF PROTEINS ON THE CHROMATOGRAM

It is possible to dry the gel layer after the run and thereafter stain for proteins. The method, however, has serious practical difficulties and takes far longer than the "replica" method described below.

After the marker substances have migrated sufficiently, the elution should be stopped, the thin-layer chamber laid horizontal and the thin-layer plate removed.

Cut a piece of Whatman 3 MM filter paper to the same size as the plate and lay it on the gel layer: start from one end of the plate taking care not to trap air bubbles between the paper and the plate or to push the gel to one end of the plate. The paper need be in contact with the gel layer only one or two minutes before it is removed and stained in the normal way for proteins.

Lay the paper in methanol for 1–2 min and then transfer it to a stain bath. Any of the following staining solutions can be used: Bromophenol blue, 0·1 % in acetic acid/methanol (1 : 9, v/v), Amidoblack, 0·06 % in methanol/ acetic acid/water (9 : 2 : 9, v/v/v), Coomassie brilliant blue R 250, 0·25 % in acetic acid/methanol (1 : 9, v/v).

One minute in the stain bath is sufficient. Background stain can be washed out with 5 % acetic acid in the case of Bromophenol blue but it is necessary to use an acetic acid/water/methanol rinse for the Amidoblack and Coomassie blue stains.

All the experiments described here have been carried out using Bromo-phenol blue with a 1 min methanol "fixer", 1 min stain and 10–15 min rinse.

U

SEPHADEX ION EXCHANGERS
ION EXCHANGE CHROMATOGRAPHY: SOME GENERAL CONSIDERATIONS

Before looking at the special properties of Sephadex ion exchangers let us consider some of the general properties of ion exchangers and the mechanism of ion exchange.

An ion exchanger is an insoluble material containing fixed charged groups and mobile counterions which are exchangeable with similarly charged ions. Anion exchangers carry positively charged groups and therefore exchange negatively charged ions. Cation exchangers are negatively charged and therefore exchange positive ions. The presence of charged substituents is, therefore, a fundamental property of the ion exchanger. The type and strength of the ion exchanger is determined by the substituents. An ion exchanger has three basic characteristics: (i) chemical and mechanical stability, (ii) resistance to flow of eluant, (iii) exchange capacity.

The first of these is determined largely by the nature of the matrix carrying the charged groups. The resistance to flow is determined by the form and rigidity of the ion exchanger. The capacity can be expressed in two ways and is dependent on a number of factors. The *total capacity* is a theoretical constant of the ion exchanger calculated from the number of functional groups per unit dry weight of the material. The *available capacity* which is of more practical importance, is the real capacity obtained for specified compounds under specified experimental conditions. The available capacity is dependent on: (i) the number of accessible functional groups, (ii) the ionic strength of the eluant, (iii) the nature of the counter ions, (iv) the pH of the eluant, (v) temperature and (vi) non-specific adsorption.

The mechanism binding proteins to ion exchangers

Substances are bound to ion exchangers if they have a charge opposite to that of the ion exchanger: the binding is electrostatic and is reversible.

Proteins are amphoteric polyelectrolytes. Since they carry both negative, for example carboxyl, and positive, for example amino, groups their net charge is dependent on pH. At low pH the charge is positive, at high pH it is negative. The point of zero charge is called the isoelectric point and at this pH the protein is not bound to either anion or cation exchangers. The binding of protein to ion exchangers is illustrated in Fig. 10.

At pH below their isoelectric points, proteins are bound to cation exchangers and at pH above their isoelectric points to anion exchangers. The binding is also dependent on the amount of charge carried by the protein. The greater the charge, the greater is the binding. The ionic strength of the environment has a pronounced influence on the binding. An increase in ionic strength of the eluant means increased competition for the binding sites of the ion exchanger:

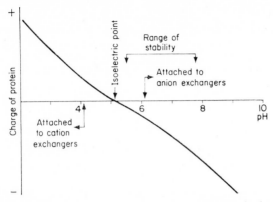

FIG. 10. Illustration of the binding of a model protein, stable within the pH range 5 to 8, to ion-exchangers. The range of stability determines the pH range usable and therefore the choice of an anion exchanger in this case. (From "Sephadex Ion exchangers", Pharmacia Fine Chemicals AB, Uppsala, Sweden.

the electrical properties of the eluant are also changed, decreasing the electrostatic interaction between the ion exchanger and the counter ions. These combine to produce a reduced binding strength with the ion exchanger.

The porosity of the ion exchanger does not influence the binding mechanism but influences the capacity since much of the ion exchanger may be unavailable to large molecules.

SEPHADEX ION EXCHANGERS

Sephadex ion exchangers are prepared by the introduction of charged groups into the dextran matrix. High capacities are attained because of the high degree of substitution which can be achieved without breakdown of the matrix. Sephadex G-25 and G-50 are used as starting materials:

The following types are available:

QAE-Sephadex A-25   QAE-Sephadex A-50.
DEAE-Sephadex A-25   DEAE-Sephadex A-50
CM-Sephadex C-25   CM-Sephadex C-50
SE-Sephadex C-25   SE-Sephadex C-50

The prefixes signify:

QAE, the quaternary amino group; DEAE, the diethyl aminoethyl group; CM, the carboxymethyl group; SE, the sulphoethyl group.

The suffixes signify:

A, anion exchanger   25, Sephadex G-25 matrix
C, cation exchanger   50, Sephadex G-50 matrix.

Cation exchangers are supplied in their sodium forms, anion exchangers in their chloride forms.

Technical data for Sephadex ion exchangers are summarized in Table VI.

TABLE VI

Physical properties of Sephadex Ion Exchangers
(From "Sephadex Ion Exchangers", Pharmacia Fine Chemicals AB, Uppsala, Sweden)

Sephadex type	Ionic group	Form (counter-ions)	Total capacity g/g	Haemoglobin capacity*
QAE A-25 QAE A-50	$-C_2H_4-N^+-CH_2-CH$ with C_2H_5, C_2H_5, OH, CH_3	Chloride	$3\cdot0\pm0\cdot4$	$0\cdot3$ 6
DEAE A-25 DEAE A-50	$-C_2H_4-N^+-H$ with C_2H_5, C_2H_5	Chloride	$3\cdot5\pm0\cdot5$	$0\cdot5$ 6
CM C-25 CM C-50	$-CH_2-COO^-$	Sodium	$4\cdot5\pm0\cdot5$	$0\cdot4$ 7
SE C-25 SE C-50	$-C_2H_4SO_3^-$	Sodium	$2\cdot3\pm0\cdot3$	$0\cdot2$ 3

* The haemoglobin capacity is the amount of this protein (MW = 69 000) bound by one gram of dry ion exchanger. The values are approximate. The capacities were measured for QAE-Sephadex in Tris-HCl buffer pH 8·0, I = 0·01, for DEAE-Sephadex in Tris-HCl pH 8·8, I = 0·01, for CM- and SE-Sephadex in phosphate buffer pH 6·5, I = 0·05.

The dependence of available capacity on the accessibility of charged groups and other factors has already been pointed out. As in gel filtration the inner volume of the gel is more or less available to different molecules depending on their size in comparison with the porosity of the gel. The porosities of the two types (-25 and -50) are naturally different but the porosity is also determined by the nature of the counter-ions, the environmental pH and ionic strength since these factors influence the swelling of the ion exchanger.

Although an ion exchanger with a given functional group may have the same total capacity for both -25 and -50 types its capacity for a given molecular species is dependent on the porosity. -50 type ion exchangers are

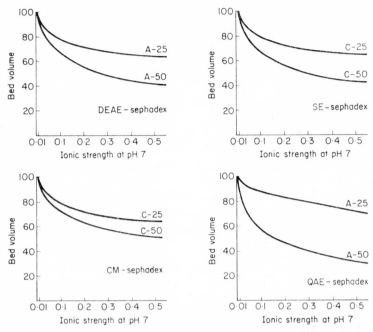

Fig. 11. Contraction of ion-exchange beds caused by increasing ionic strength. The contraction of DEAE- and QAE-Sephadex types was measured in Tris-HCl buffer pH 7·6: contraction of CM- and SE-Sephadex types was measured in acetate buffer pH 4·3. (Source as Fig. 10.)

thus more effective in the molecular weight range 30 000–200 000 whilst the -25 types are most effective for molecular weights under 30 000. Over 200 000 the -25 types are also preferable since neither the inner volume of the -25 nor that of the -50 type ion exchangers is available to such large molecules. The -25 type is preferable because of its greater rigidity and hence better flow properties.

The available capacity of an ion exchanger has a maximum value in the pH range where all its functional groups are dissociated. Optimum pH ranges can be deduced from titration curves (see booklet "Sephadex Ion Exchangers", Pharmacia Fine Chemicals). CM-Sephadex has its maximum capacity above pH 6, SE-Sephadex above pH 3·5 and DEAE-Sephadex below pH 9·5. QAE-Sephadex is a sufficiently strong ion exchanger to be usable in any pH range.

The swelling properties of Sephadex ion exchangers have been mentioned already. The dependence of swelling on pH and ionic strength is shown in Figs 11 and 12. Contraction of anion exchangers with increasing ionic strength and pH need not cause problems if experimental conditions are

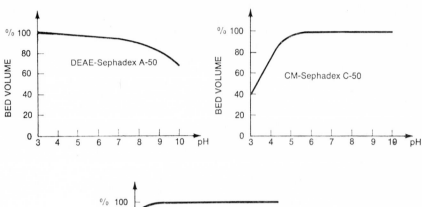

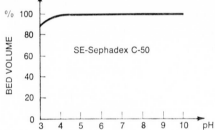

FIG. 12. Contraction of ion-exchange beds caused by alterations in pH. Investigations were carried out with buffers of 0·05 ionic strength. (Source as Fig. 10.)

correctly chosen. It should be noted that the swelling of QAE-Sephadex is particularly independent of changes in pH.

PRACTICAL CONSIDERATIONS IN ION EXCHANGE CHROMATOGRAPHY ON SEPHADEX ION EXCHANGERS

There are two basic problems in ion exchange chromatography of proteins. The first is how to adsorb the proteins on the ion exchanger; the second is how to remove them, separated from one another.

The solution to the first problem lies in the choice of ion exchanger (anion or cation), the type of ion exchanger (-25 or -50 type), the choice of buffer and the choice of buffer ionic strength and pH.

An immediate choice of ion exchanger can be made only when the iso-electric points of the proteins to be chromatographed are known. If these are known the net charges on the proteins can be adjusted to be either negative or positive by adjustment of the buffer pH. The choice of pH is, however, limited by the lability of protein structures to a pH or pH range(s) in which the secondary, tertiary and quaternary structures are unaffected and biological activity preserved. Once the appropriate buffer pH has been chosen, the actual buffer can be decided and the choice of ion exchanger made.

We can draw the following guide lines for the above mentioned choices.

1. If the protein is biologically active and not subject to denaturation at pH below its isoelectric point it should be chromatographed on CATION exchangers (CM or SE-Sephadex).

2. If the protein is biologically active and not subject to denaturation at pH above its isoelectric point it should be chromatographed on ANION exchangers (DEAE or QAE-Sephadex).

The differences between -25 and -50 type ion exchangers have already been discussed. The choice is summarized in Table VII.

TABLE VII

Choice of ion-exchanger type according to size of proteins

MW of protein	Preferable type of ion exchanger
Low MW < 30 000	A-25, C-25
Medium MW 30 000–200 000	A-50, C-50
High MW > 200 000	A-25, C-25

The operating pH and the ion exchanger to be used will have been decided already but it must be kept in mind that the ion exchangers have maximum capacities in certain pH ranges. These are given in Table VIII.

TABLE VIII

Optimum pH ranges for Sephadex ion exchangers

Ion exchanger	Recommended pH range
QAE-Sephadex	all pH
DEAE-Sephadex	below pH 9·5
CM-Sephadex	above pH 6
SE-Sephadex	above pH 3·5

Cationic buffers should be used with anion exchangers whereas anionic buffers should be used with cation exchangers. Some examples are given in Table IX.

When cationic buffers are used with anion exchangers the buffering ions are not bound to the ion exchanger: the same is true for anionic buffers with cation exchangers. If, however, a cationic buffer is used with a cation exchanger

TABLE IX

Recommended buffers for use with Sephadex ion-exchangers

Ion exchanger	Buffer	Buffer pH-
Anion exchanger	CATIONIC, e.g. alkylamines, amino-ethyl alcohol, ammonia, ethylene diamine, imidazole, tris, pyridine, barbital	1 pH unit above isoelectric point of protein
Cation exchanger	ANIONIC, e.g. acetate, barbital citrate, glycine, phosphate	1 pH unit below isoelectric point of protein

the buffering ions compete for binding sites on the ion exchanger, disturbing the buffering equilibrium and creating a pH difference between the inside of the ion exchanger and the surrounding solution. The same is true when anionic buffers are used with anion exchangers. It is, however, not impossible to use such systems, although they should be avoided.

Ionic strength: the effect of ionic strength has been mentioned previously. The starting buffer ionic strength should be as low as possible but it must be borne in mind that the buffering capacity of a buffer is low at low ionic strength. At low ionic strengths the swelling of the ion exchangers is rather ionic strength dependent and ionic strengths below 0·02 should be avoided.

In the final choice of the system to be used the elution of the bound substances must be considered. The pH should be chosen so that interesting substances are bound to the ion exchanger, and if a pH gradient elution is to be used, at a pH about 1 unit above the pI of the protein for anion exchangers and 1 unit below the pI of the protein for cation exchangers.

The amount of substances in the sample will also influence the choice of ion exchanger and buffer. If a mixture of two proteins A and B in which the concentration of A greatly exceeds that of B is to be chromatographed conditions should be chosen so that B is bound to the ion exchanger. In this way a much smaller amount of ion exchanger is needed than if A were to be bound.

Overloading of columns should be avoided: no more than 10–20 % of the capacity of the ion exchanger should be used. The actual sample size is of less importance since conditions are chosen where most or all of the proteins are bound to the ion exchanger. This means that relatively large volumes of dilute protein solutions can be applied.

We can now set about solving the problems of removing the bound substances. It has been noted above that the binding of proteins to ion exchangers is dependent on both pH and ionic strength and therefore alterations of pH or ionic strength can be used to elute bound substances.

pH or ionic strength changes may be made stepwise or continuously. Stepwise elution is probably simpler from a technical viewpoint but has serious disadvantages. All substances released by a change of buffer are eluted together. Although peaks have sharp fronts, pronounced tailing occurs which may lead to false peaks because of overlapping if a buffer change is introduced too quickly.

Continuous gradient elution: a simple apparatus for producing a continuous gradient is shown in Fig. 13. In continuous gradient elution peaks are eluted symmetrically. The eluant volume should be large compared to the volume of the ion exchanger bed. For instance, a bed 1·5 cm × about 20 cm requires about 200 ml in each buffer reservoir.

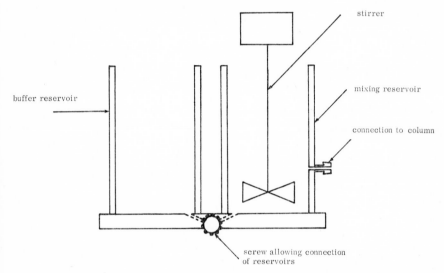

FIG. 13. Simple apparatus for production of linear ionic strength gradients.

Gradients can be produced by changing pH or ionic strength. If a pH gradient is used it should be towards the isoelectric points of the attached proteins. Gradients of increasing pH should be used with cation exchangers and conversely, decreasing gradients with anion exchangers. Linear pH gradients, however, are not produced by the apparatus shown in Fig. 13. Ionic strength gradients should correspond to increasing ionic strength and are produced most easily by increasing the concentration of a neutral salt, e.g. NaCl. A linear change of the volume ratio between the buffers produces a linear ionic strength gradient.

The flow characteristics, swelling and shrinking of Sephadex ion exchangers have been discussed. Shrinkage causes uneven flow if gravity feed is used for elution. The use of a pump connected to the outlet side of the column is therefore recommended.

Preparing ion exchangers for use

The gels should be swollen in a large excess of eluant which should be decanted and replaced several times over a 24 h period. After the column has been packed it should be equilibrated overnight and then the ionic strength and pH of the eluant entering and leaving the column compared.

Column packing

Ion exchangers should be packed in the same way as the neutral Sephadex types. Low hydrostatic pressure should be used when packing. The bed surface is best protected by a layer (0·5–1·0 cm) of Sephadex G-25 Coarse swollen in the eluting buffer.

Regeneration

Regenerating Sephadex ion exchangers is generally not profitable since such small amounts are needed for column experiments. If, however, regeneration is necessary the following procedure may be followed. Remove the gel from the column and wash it with a salt solution—ionic strength up to about 2. Wash the gel with water until free from salt and re-equilibrate with starting buffer. Treatment with NaOH and HCl may be necessary to remove trace amounts of impurities.

EXPERIMENTS

The following experimental section is divided into three parts:
1. Experiments illustrating the principles of gel chromatography.
2. Experiments illustrating the choice of gel type, grade, sample size, etc.
3. Experiments illustrating desalting, fractionation and molecular weight determination.

Only experimental details are given since the technique is the same in each experiment and has been described already.

All the experiments described here have been performed using apparatus from Pharmacia Fine Chemicals. Column gel filtration has been carried out in columns 2·5 cm × 45 cm (Code K 25/45 and SR 25/45 in the case of Experiment 21). Ion exchange experiments were carried out in columns 1·5 cm × 30 cm (Code, K 15/30). Reservoirs for packing and elution R 25 and R 15 were used for columns K 25/45 and K 15/30, respectively. In some experiments, Flow Adaptors (to fit K 25/45) were used. Thin-layer apparatus was made in the laboratory workshop.

A list of suppliers of auxilliary equipment, chemicals, biochemicals, etc. is given at the end of the experimental section.

EXPERIMENTS ILLUSTRATING THE PRINCIPLES OF GEL CHROMATOGRAPHY

EXPERIMENT 1

Separation of Blue dextran 2000, vitamin B_{12} and potassium chromate on Sephadex G-25 Fine.

Apparatus and chemicals

1. Chromatographic column, 2·5 cm i.d. × 45 cm.
2. Mariotte flask, 300 ml.
3. Graduated cylinder, 250 ml.
4. Pipette, 2 ml.
5. Sephadex G-25 Fine, 35 g in 300 ml NaCl solution.
6. NaCl solution, 9 g/litre.
7. Sample solution, 2 ml containing Blue dextran 2000 (2 mg/ml), vitamin B_{12} (0·3 mg/ml), potassium chromate (2 mg/ml).

Experimental details

Prepare the column as described in the Section "Preparing the Sephadex". Adjust the flow rate to about 2 ml/min and allow the bed to stabilize. Apply the sample (2 ml) and start collecting the column effluent in the graduated cylinder. Note the volumes at which the three sample components begin to be eluted from the column.

Results

Observe the immediate separation of the sample components. The Blue dextran is eluted first (in the void volume) followed by the red, vitamin B_{12} (mol. wt. = 1357) and the potassium chromate which marks the volume of the column available to a solute which is able to penetrate the entire inner volume of the gel. Note that the components are eluted in order of decreasing molecular weight.

EXPERIMENT 2

Separation of Blue dextran 2000, cytochrome c and potassium chromate on Sephadex G-50 Fine.

Apparatus and chemicals

1. Chromatographic column, 2·5 cm i.d. × 45 cm.
2. Mariotte flask, 300 ml.
3. Graduated cylinder, 250 ml.
4. Pipette, 2 ml.

5. Sephadex G-50 Fine, 15 g in 300 ml NaCl solution.
6. NaCl solution, 9 g/litre.
7. Sample solution, 2 ml containing Blue dextran 2000 (2 mg/ml), cyto-chrome c (3 mg/ml), potassium chromate (2 mg/ml).

Experimental details

See Experiment 1.

Results

Observe the immediate separation of the sample components into blue, brown-red and yellow zones. Blue dextran 2000 marks the void volume and is followed by cytochrome c (mol. wt. = 13 000) and potassium chromate. The components are eluted in order of decreasing molecular weight.

EXPERIMENT 3

Separation of fluorescent labelled serum proteins on Sephadex G-200 Superfine.

Apparatus and chemicals

1. Chromatographic column, 2·5 cm i.d. × 45 cm.
2. Mariotte flask, 300 ml.
3. Pipette, 2 ml.
4. Sephadex G-200 Superfine, 7 g in 300 ml NaCl solution.
5. NaCl solution, 9 g/litre.
6. Sample solution, fluorescein isothiocyanate (FITC) labelled serum proteins (approx. 10 mg/ml) (see Experiment 10).

Experimental details

Pack the Sephadex G-200 Superfine under a hydrostatic pressure not exceeding 10–15 cm water. Equilibrate the column overnight. Apply the sample and start the elution—with the same hydrostatic pressure used for equilibration.

Results

After 3–4 h many fluorescent zones can be seen—even in daylight but the effect is better if the column is viewed in UV light. The serum is separated into three main zones, in order of elution—19S γ-globulins, 7 S γ-globulins and albumin. Two more zones can be seen—low molecular weight serum compounds and excess FITC which is strongly retarded on the column.

Demonstration of the reaction sequence: methaemoglobin → haemoglobin → oxyhaemoglobin on Sephadex G-25 Fine.

Apparatus and chemicals

1. Chromatographic column, 2·5 cm i.d. × 45 cm.
2. Mariotte flask, 300 ml.
3. Pipettes, 0·5 ml, 2 ml.
4. Sephadex G-25 Fine, 35 g in 300 ml phosphate buffer.
5. Phosphate buffer (0·02M, pH 7).
6. Sample solutions, sodium dithionite, 0·5 ml containing 10 mg/ml; methaemoglobin solution prepared as directed below.

Experimental details

Prepare the column as described in the section "Preparing the Sephadex". Adjust the flow rate to about 2 ml/min and allow the bed to stabilize. Apply 0·2 ml freshly prepared sodium dithionite solution and wash it into the column with approximately 3 ml buffer. Methaemoglobin solution is prepared by diluting 0·2 ml whole blood to 2 ml with the phosphate buffer and adding 10 mg potassium ferricyanide. Apply the methaemoglobin and start the elution.

Results

This experiment demonstrates not only the principle of gel chromatography but also the application of the method to removal of a reaction product from biproducts of a reaction carried out in a column.

Sodium dithionite is a low molecular weight salt: it is applied as a narrow zone at the top of the column. Methaemoglobin, a high molecular weight substance, is excluded from Sephadex G-25 and travels in the void volume. Methaemoglobin migrates faster than the sodium dithionite and potassium ferricyanide (which is present in excess). The following changes can be seen.

Methaemoglobin (brown zone) separates from excess potassium ferricyanide (yellow zone) and changes to purple haemoglobin as it is reduced by the dithionite. The haemoglobin leaves the dithionite zone as a purple band but is quickly turned to scarlet oxy-haemoglobin by reaction with dissolved

---

* This experiment is based on one used in the practical classes of the Department of Biochemistry, Cambridge University, developed from Dixon, H. B. F. and McIntosh, R., *Nature, Lond.*, **213** (1967), 399.

oxygen in the eluant. These changes can be summarized:

Haemoglobin + $K_3Fe(CN)_6$ $\xrightarrow{\text{oxidation}}$ Methaemoglobin (sample)

Methaemoglobin + $Na_2S_2O_4$ $\xrightarrow{\text{reduction}}$ Haemoglobin

Haemoglobin + O_2 $\xrightarrow{\text{oxygenation}}$ Oxyhaemoglobin

Experiment—Determination of column parameters (i) calibration of the chromatographic tube

Apparatus.
1. Chromatographic column.
2. Graduated cylinder.
3. Cm ruler.

Experimental details. Fill the tube almost completely with water and measure the height of the water column from a reference point low on the tube. Open the outlet and run about 25 ml of water out of the column: record this volume and measure the height of the water in the tube. Repeat this operation until the water reaches the level of the bed support. Record the total volume of water run out of the column.

Determine also the dead volume, i.e. the volume from the bed support net to the outlet.

Calculations. If the total volume of water run out of the column $= T$ ml, and the volumes run out at each step are x_1, x_2, x_3, etc., then the total volumes of water in the column, at each distance y_1, y_2, y_3 from the reference point, are $T - x_1$, $T - (x_1 + x_2)$, $T - (x_1 + x_2 + x_3)$, etc. Plot these values against the distances y.

Results. From the graph obtained it is possible to read off, directly, the column volume for any distance from the reference point.

Knowledge of the dead volume allows corrections to be made to the elution volumes, since the measured elution volumes are too large by an amount equal to the dead volume.

(ii) Determination of the void volume (V_o) and total volume (V_t)

Apparatus and chemicals.
1. Chromatographic column.
2. Measuring cylinder (and/or Uvicord).
3. Gel.

Sample, Blue dextran 2000, 2 mg/ml; volume, approximately 2% of column volume.

Experimental details. Pack and stabilize the column by running at least 1 or 2 column volumes through the gel bed. Apply the Blue dextran 2000 sample and start collecting the column effluent in a measuring cylinder. Note the volume at which the Blue dextran first appears. Note the distance from the reference point on the column to the surface of the gel bed.

V_t can also be determined in non-calibrated columns by marking the position of the bed height, taking the gel out of the column, filling to the mark with water and then running this water into a measuring cylinder.

Results. The elution volume, V_e of the Blue dextran corresponds to the "outer" or void volume, V_o of the column. From the graph plotted in Experiment (1) one can deduce the "total" volume, V_t of the gel bed.

EXPERIMENTS ILLUSTRATING THE CHOICE OF GEL TYPE, GRADE, THE SAMPLE SIZE AND THE INFLUENCE OF SAMPLE VISCOSITY AND FLOW RATE ON THE SEPARATION RESULT

EXPERIMENT 5

Choice of Sephadex type.

Apparatus and chemicals

1. Three chromatographic columns, 2·5 cm i.d. × 45 cm.
2. Three Mariotte flasks, 300 ml.
3. Test tubes—calibrated for 5 ml*.
4. Pipettes, 2 ml.
5. Sephadex G-25 Fine, 35 g in 300 ml NaCl solution.
6. Sephadex G-50 Fine, 15 g in 300 ml NaCl solution.
7. Sephadex G-75, 12 g in 300 ml NaCl solution.
8. NaCl solution, 9 g/litre.
9. Sample solution, 6 ml solution containing 2 mg/ml Blue dextran 2000, 3 mg/ml cytochrome c, 2 mg/ml potassium chromate.
10. One set of standard dilutions concentrations (given in mg/ml).
   Blue dextran 2000: 1·0, 0·5, 0·2, 0·1, 0·05.
   Cytochrome c: 1·0, 0·5, 0·2, 0·1, 0·05.
   Potassium chromate: 0·5, 0·2, 0·1, 0·05, 0·01.

* If an automatic fraction collector is unavailable the column effluent can be collected in precalibrated test tubes. Ordinary glass or plastic test or centrifuge tubes can be marked at a given distance from one end. Volume variations from tube to tube are not taken into account and need not be if plastic centrifuge tubes are used.

Experimental details

Three columns should be packed with Sephadex G-25, G-50 and G-75, respectively. The columns should be properly equilibrated and the flow rates adjusted to between 1 and 2 ml/min. The flow rates in each of the three columns should be about the same. Apply a 2 ml sample to each column and start collecting column effluent from the moment of sample application. If an automatic fraction collector is available arrange for fractions to be about 5 ml. If a Uvicord or similar continuous recording spectrophotometer is available this can be used instead of the standard dilutions for determining the elution volumes of the components. The recorder should have a paper speed of about 60 mm/h. Otherwise direct spectrophotometric measurements may be made on fractions at 254 nm and an elution curve obtained from the extinction values. Determine the total volume of the column.

Determination of elution volumes

(*i*) *By comparison with standard dilutions.* Determine the concentration of Blue dextran, cytochrome c or potassium chromate by direct comparison with the standard dilutions. Construct an elution diagram (histogram) by plotting component concentration (mg/ml) against elution volume. Take the centre of the fraction with the highest concentration as the elution volume for that component.

(*ii*) *From continuous recording instrument.* Convert the mm scale on the recorder paper to elution volume using the elution rate. Take the maximum of each peak as the elution volume.

(*iii*) *From spectrophotometric measurements.* Plot extinction versus elution volume (calculated from fraction number) and take the maximum of each peak as the elution volume.

Calculations

Calculate the K_{av} values for the eluted components using the experimentally determined elution volume, void volume and total volume.

Use the equation $$K_{av} = \frac{V_e - V_o}{V_t - V_o}$$

(see the Section on Gel Chromatography) Sample results and calculations are given in Table X and Fig. 14.

Conclusions

Compare the elution curves obtained on each of the three gels. Note that Sephadex G-25 has an exclusion limit below the molecular weight of cytochrome

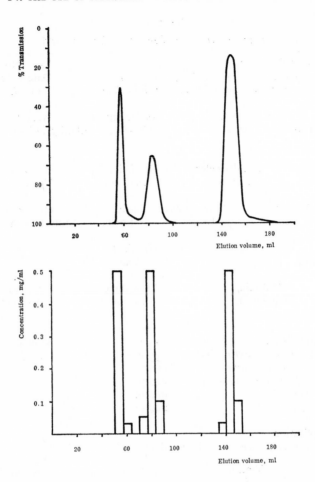

FIG. 14. Elution of Blue dextran 2000, cytochrome c and potassium chromate from Sephadex G-50 Fine. Comparison of block and UV absorption diagrams.

c and that on this gel both Blue dextran and cytochrome c are eluted together. The molecular weight of cytochrome c lies within the fraction range of both Sephadex G-50 and G-75 and thus all three components are separated on both these gels. Sephadex G-50, however, is preferable since the cytochrome c is eluted earlier than on Sephadex G-75. Sephadex G-50 has also somewhat better flow properties.

w

TABLE X

Experimental data and results of Experiment 5

Title *Choice of Sephadex type*			Expt. No. *5*
Separation of Blue dextran 2000, cytochrome c			Date *6.12.68*
and potassium chromate of Sephadex G-50 Fine			Name *J. M. Curling*

Gel type	Lot No.	Water regain	Weight
Sephadex G-50 Fine	*5556*	$W_r = 5 \pm 0.3$ ml/g	*15* g

Column type	Int. diameter	Bed height	Bed volume
K 25/45	*2.5* cm	*31.5* cm	$V_t = 155$ ml

Sample applicator	Flow adaptor *None*		Other bed surface
Yes	Upper	Lower	protection *None*

Eluant	Gradient
0.9% NaCl	*None*

Flow rate	*1.3* ml/min	Flow direction	Flow control
	16 ml/cm² h	*Downward*	*Hydrostatic pressure*

Sample composition			Sample volume
Component I *Blue Dextran 2000*	*2* mg/ml		*2* ml
II *Cytochrome c*	*3* mg/ml		
III *Potassium chromate*	*2* mg/ml		
IV	mg/ml		
V	mg/ml		

Sample application			
Drained bed surface *Yes*	Flow adaptor *No*		Under eluant *No*

Fractions	Time interval	Volume	Fraction collector
	5 min	*6.5* ml	*Automatic*

Monitor	Type	Paper speed
	Uvicord	*60 mm/h*

Detection
    Uvicord and visual by comparison of fractions with standard dilutions

Notes
    Parallel experiments should be performed on Sephadex G-25 Fine and Sephadex G-75 and comparisons made.

Results and calculations	Expt. No. *5*
Void vol.=Elution vol. of Blue Dextran 2000=*58.5* ml	$V_o =$ *58.5* ml
	$V_t =$ *155* ml
	$V_t - V_o =$ *96.5* ml

Fraction No.	Component concentration		Elution volumes (ml)
8	<0.05	⎫	I 58.5
9	0.5	⎬ Blue dextran 2000	II 83
10	0.05	⎭	III 149
11	<0.05	⎫	
12	0.1	⎬ Cytochrome c	
13	0.5		
14	0.2	⎭	
15	—		
20	—		
21	<0.01	⎫	
22	0.05	⎪	
23	0.5	⎬ Potassium chromate	
24	0.2	⎪	
25	<0.01	⎭	
26	—		

V_e (ml)	$V_e - V_o$ (ml)	$V_e - V_o / V_t - V_o$	K_{av} values
I 58.5	$58.5 - 58.5$	0	I 0
II 83	$83 - 58.5$	$24.5/96.5$	II 0.25
III 149	$149 - 58.5$	$90.5/96.5$	III 0.94

Notes

K_{av} values of cytochrome c and potassium chromate were found to be 0.25 and 0.94, resp.

EXPERIMENT 6

Choice of grade of Sephadex.

Apparatus and chemicals

1. Three chromatographic columns 2·5 cm i.d. $\times$ 45 cm.

2. Three Mariotte flasks, 300 ml.

3. Test tubes—calibrated for 5 ml (see footnote to Experiment 5).

4. Pipettes, 2 ml.

5. Sephadex G-50 Superfine, 15 g in 300 ml NaCl solution.

6. Sephadex G-50 Medium, 15 g in 300 ml NaCl solution.

7. Sephadex G-50 Coarse, 15 g in 300 ml NaCl solution.

8. NaCl solution, 9 g/litre.

9. Sample solution, 6 ml containing 2 mg/ml Blue dextran 2000, 3 mg/ml cytochrome c, 2 mg/ml potassium chromate.

10. One set of standard dilutions (see Experiment 5).

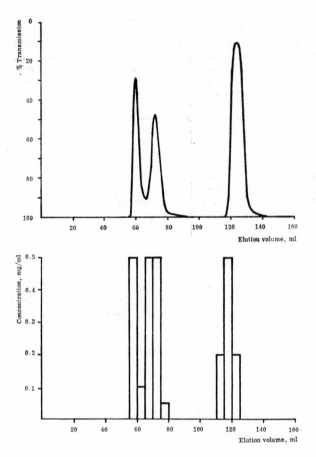

Fɪɢ. 15 (i). Elution of Blue dextran 2000, cytochrome c and potassium chromate from Sephadex G-50 Superfine. Comparison of block and UV absorption diagrams.

Experimental details

This experiment should be carried out in exactly the same way as Experiment 5. In addition, the volume in which each component is eluted should be noted.

Calculations

Calculate K_{av} values and the dilution factors for each component.

$$\text{Dilution factor} = \frac{\text{total volume of eluted component (ml)}}{\text{sample volume (ml)}}.$$

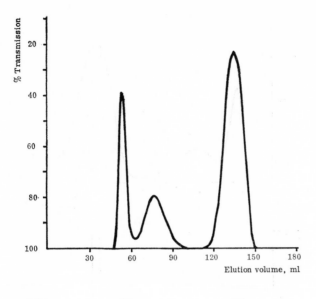

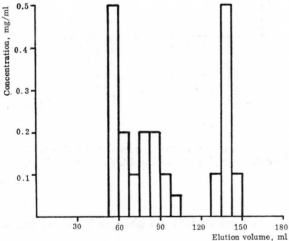

FIG. 15 (ii). Elution of Blue dextran 2000, cytochrome c and potassium chromate from Sephadex G-50 Medium. Comparison of block and UV absorption diagrams.

The dilution factor is a measure of zone spreading. It will be immediately noticed that zone spreading is greater on the coarse gel than on the fine. The zone spreading naturally affects the efficiency of the column as regards the resolution obtainable.

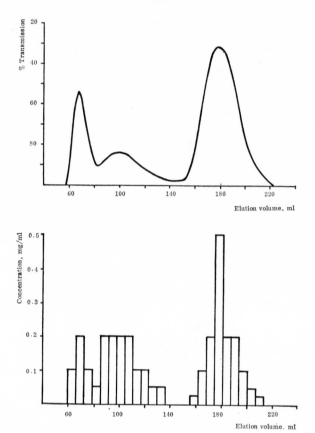

FIG. 15 (iii). Elution of Blue dextran 2000, cytochrome c and potassium chromate from Sephadex G-50 Coarse. Comparison of block and UV absorption diagrams.

Sample results and calculations are given in Table XI (i), (ii), (iii) and Fig. 15 (i), (ii), (iii).

Conclusions

From the elution curves on the three different grades of Sephadex it is evident that Sephadex G-50 Superfine is most efficient.

Sephadex G-50 Fine gives the best all-round performance with regard to both resolution and flow rate.

The medium and coarse grades, however, can be used when resolution is unimportant compared with flow rate.

TABLE XI
Experimental data and results of Experiment 6
(i)

Title *Influence of Grade of Sephadex* *Separation on G-50 Superfine*			Expt. No. *6 (i)* Date *12.12.68* Name *J. M. Curling*
Gel type *Sephadex G-50* *Superfine*	**Lot No.** *5739*	**Water regain** $W_r = 5 \cdot 0 \pm 0 \cdot 3$ ml/g	**Weight** *15* g
Column type *K 25/45*	**Int. diameter** *2·5* cm	**Bed height** *27·2* cm	**Bed volume** $V_t = 140$ ml
Sample applicator *Yes*	**Flow adaptor** *None* Upper	Lower	**Other bed surface** protection *None*
Eluant *0·9% NaCl*		**Gradient** *None*	
Flow rate *1·0* ml/min *12·3* ml/cm² h		**Flow direction** *Downward*	**Flow control** *Hydrostatic* *pressure*

Sample composition   **Sample volume**

Component	I	*Blue dextran 2000*	*2* mg/ml	*2* ml
	II	*Cytochrome c*	*3* mg/ml	
	III	*Potassium chromate*	*2* mg/ml	
	IV		mg/ml	
	V		mg/ml	

Sample application
Drained bed surface *Yes*   Flow adaptor   Under eluant

Fractions	**Time interval** *5* min	**Volume** *5* ml	**Fraction collector** *Automatic*

Monitor	**Type** *Uvicord*	**Paper speed** *60 mm/h*

Detection
Uvicord and visual (see Expt. 5)

Notes
Compare with Expt. 5 and Expt. 6 (ii) and (iii).

Results and calculations	**Exp. No.** *6 (i)*

Void vol.=Elution vol. of Blue Dextran 2000=*60* ml	$V_0 = 60$ ml $V_t = 140$ ml $V_t - V_0 = 80$ ml

Fraction No.	Component concentration		Elution volumes (ml)
12	0·5	⎫	I 60
13	0·1	⎬ Blue dextran 2000	II 72
14	0·5	⎭	III 124
15	0·5	⎫ Cytochrome c	
16	0·05	⎬	
23	0·2	⎫	
24	0·5	⎬ Potassium chromate	
25	0·2	⎭	

V_e (ml)	$V_e - V_0$ (ml)	$V_e - V_0 / V_t - V_0$	K_{av} values
I 60	60–60	0	I 0
II 72	72–60	12/80	II 0·15
III 124	124–60	64/80	III 0·8

Notes

Compare results with those obtained in Expt. 5 and Expt. 6 (ii) and (iii).

(ii)

Title *Influence of Grade of Sephadex Separation on Sephadex G-50 Medium*	Exp. No. *6 (ii)* Date *12.12.68* Name *J. M. Curling*

Gel type	Lot No.	Water regain	Weight
Sephadex G-50	*6701*	$W_r = 5·0 \pm 0·3$ ml/g	*15 g*

Column type	Int. diameter	Bed height	Bed volume
K 25/45	*2·5* cm	*33·5* cm	$V_t = 166$ ml

Sample applicator	Flow adaptor *None*		Other bed surface
Yes	Upper	Lower	protection *None*

Eluant	Gradient
0·9% NaCl	*None*

Flow rate *1·5* ml/min *18·4* ml/cm² h	Flow direction *Downward*	Flow control *Hydrostatic Pressure*

Sample composition

Component				Sample volume
	I	*Blue dextran 2000*	2 mg/ml	2 ml
	II	*Cytochrome c*	3 mg/ml	
	III	*Potassium chromate*	2 mg/ml	
	IV		mg/ml	
	V		mg/ml	

Sample application
Drained bed surface   *Yes*   Flow adaptor *No*   Under eluant *No*

Fractions	Time interval 5 min	Volume 7·5 ml	Fraction collector *Automatic*

Monitor	Type *Uvicord*	Paper speed *60 mm/h*

Detection
Uvicord and Visual (see Expt. 5)

Notes
Compare with Expt. 5 and Expt. 6 (i) and (iii).

(ii)

Results and calculations	Expt. No. 6 (ii)

Void vol.=Elution vol. of Blue Dextran 2000=54 ml	$V_o = 54$ ml $V_t = 166$ ml $V_t{-}V_o = 112$ ml

Fraction No.	Component concentration		Elution volumes (ml)
8	0·5		I 54
9	0·2		II 78
10	0·1		III 142
11	0·2		
12	0·2		
13	0·1		
14	0·05		
15	—		
16	—		
17	—		
18	0·1		
19	0·5		
20	0·1		

V_e (ml)	$V_e{-}V_o$ (ml)	$V_e{-}V_o/V_t{-}V_o$	K_{av} values
I 54	54–54	0	I 0
II 78	78–54	24/112	II 0·22
III 142	142–54	88/112	III 0·8

Notes
Compare with Expt. 5 and Expt. 6 (i) and (iii).

(iii)

Title			Expt. No. 6 (iii)
Influence of Grade of Sephadex			Date *12.12.68*
Separation on G-50 Coarse			Name *J. M. Curling*

Gel type	Lot No.	Water regain	Weight
Sephadex G-50 Coarse	*8146*	$W_r = 5 \cdot 0 \pm 0 \cdot 3$ ml/g	*15* g

Column type	Int. diameter	Bed height	Bed volume
K 25/45	*2·5* cm	*34·3* cm	$V_t = 168$ ml

Sample applicator	Flow adaptor	*None*	Other bed surface
Yes	Upper	Lower	protection *None*

Eluant	Gradient
0·9% NaCl	*None*

Flow rate	*1·3* ml/min	Flow direction	Flow control
	16 ml/cm² h	*Downward*	*Hydrostatic Pressure*

Sample composition			Sample volume
Component I	*Blue dextran 2000*	2 mg/ml	2 ml
II	*Cytochrome c*	3 mg/ml	
III	*Potassium chromate*	2 mg/ml	
IV		mg/ml	
V		mg/ml	

Sample application			
Drained bed surface *Yes*	Flow adaptor *No*		Under eluant *No*

Fractions	Time interval	Volume	Fraction collector
	5 min	*6·5* ml	*Automatic*

Monitor	Type	Paper speed
	Uvicord	*60 mm/h*

Detection
Uvicord and visually (see Expt. 5)

Notes
Compare with Expt. 5 and Expt. 6 (i) and (ii).

(iii)

Results and calculations	Expt. No. 6 (iii)

Void vol.=Elution vol. of Blue Dextran 2000=*75·5* ml	$V_0 = 75 \cdot 5$ ml
	$V_t = 168$ ml
	$V_t - V_0 = 92 \cdot 5$ ml

Fraction No.	Component concentration				Elution volumes (ml)
11	0·1 ⎫	Blue	26	0·01	
12	0·2 ⎬	Dextran	27	0·1	
13	0·1 ⎭	2000	28	0·2	I 75·5
14	0·05		29	0·5	II 105
15	0·2		30	0·2	III 185
16	0·2		31	0·2	IV
17	0·2		32	0·1	V
18	0·2		33	0·05	
19	0·1		34	0·01	
20	0·1		35	—	
21	0·05		36	—	
22	0·05				
23	<0·05				
24	<0·05				
25	—				

Cytochrome c (labels the 14–24 column); *Potassium chromate* (labels the 28–34 column)

	V_e (ml)	$V_e–V_o$ (ml)	$V_e–V_o/V_t–V_o$	K_{av} values
I	75·5	75·5–75·5	0	I 0
II	105	105–75·5	29·5/92·5	II 0·32
III	185	185–75·5	109·5/92·5	III 1·2

Notes

Compare with Expt. 5 and Expt. 6 (i) and (ii).

EXPERIMENT 7

Influence of sample viscosity on the separation result.

Apparatus and chemicals

1. Chromatographic column 2·5 cm i.d. × 45 cm.

2. Mariotte flask, 300 ml.

3. Pipette, 2 ml.

4. Sephadex G-25 Fine, 35 g in 300 ml NaCl solution.

5. NaCl solution, 9 g/litre.

6. Sample solutions, (i) Blue dextran 2000 (2 mg/ml) and potassium chromate (2 mg/ml) dissolved in 2 ml NaCl solution. (ii) as (i) but dissolved in 2·5% Dextran T 250. (iii) as (i) but dissolved in 5% Dextran T 250.

7. Standard dilutions of Blue dextran 2000 and potassium chromate (see Experiment 5).

TABLE XII

Experimental data for Experiment 7

Title   *Influence of Sample Viscosity on the Separation Result*   Expt. No. *7*
                                                                  Date   *16.12.68*
                                                                  Name *J. M. Curling*

Gel type	Lot No.	Water regain	Weight
Sephadex G-25	*2300*	$W_r = 2 \cdot 5 \pm 0 \cdot 2$ ml/g	*35* g
Fine			

Column type	Int. diameter	Bed height	Bed volume
K 25/45	*2·5* cm	*30* cm	$V_t = 147$ ml

Sample applicator	Flow adaptor	*None*	Other bed surface
Yes	Upper	Lower	protection *None*

Eluant	Gradient
0·9% NaCl	*None*

Flow rate *1·3* ml/min	Flow direction	Flow control
16 ml/cm² h	*Downward*	*Hydrostatic*
		Pressure

Sample composition*   Sample volume

Component	I	*Blue dextran 2000*	*2* mg/ml	2 ml
	II	*Potassium chromate*	*2* mg/ml	
	III		mg/ml	
	IV		mg/ml	
	V		mg/ml	

Sample application

Drained bed surface *Yes*	Flow adaptor *No*	Under eluant *No*

Fractions	Time interval	Volume	Fraction collector
None	min	ml	

Monitor	Type	Paper speed
	Uvicord	*60 mm/h*

Detection
   Uvicord and Visual

Notes

   * *Three samples should be applied:*
   1. *The sample given above dissolved in 0·9% NaCl.*
   2. *Sample dissolved in 0·9% NaCl and 2·5% Dextran T 250.*
   3. *Sample dissolved in 0·9% NaCl and 5% Dextran T 250.*
   Results—see Uvicord Curves: compare resolution obtained.

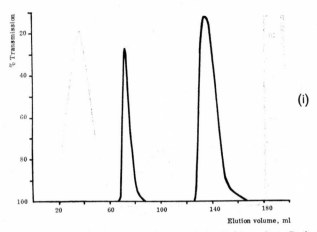

Fig. 16 (i). Elution of Blue dextran 2000 and potassium chromate from Sephadex G-25 Fine. Sample dissolved in eluant.

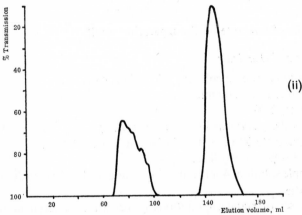

Fig. 16 (ii). Elution of Blue dextran 2000 and potassium chromate from Sephadex G-25 Fine. Sample viscosity increased by the addition of Dextran T 250 (2·5%).

Experimental details

Prepare the column as described in the section "Packing the Column". Adjust the flow rate to about 2 ml/min and stabilize the bed. Apply sample (i) and collect 5 ml fractions as described in Experiment 5. Construct an elution diagram. Repeat the experiment using samples (ii) and (iii).

Results and conclusions

Observe the effect of increasing viscosity (increasing dextran concentration in sample) on zone broadening and mixing and deviation from linear partition isotherms shown by zone assymmetry.

Sample results are given in Fig. 16 (i), (ii), (iii) and Table XII.

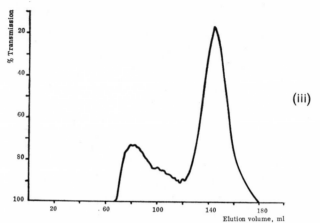

FIG. 16 (iii). Elution of Blue dextran 2000 and potassium chromate from Sephadex G-25 Fine. Sample viscosity increased by the addition of Dextran T 250 (5%).

EXPERIMENT 8

Influence of flow rate on the separation result.

Apparatus and chemicals

1. Chromatographic column, 2·5 cm i.d. × 45 cm.
2. Mariotte flask, 300 ml.
3. Pipette, 2 ml.
4. Test tubes, calibrated (see Experiment 5).
5. Sephadex G-50 Fine, 15 g in 300 ml NaCl solution.
6. NaCl solution, 9 g/litre.
7. Sample solution, 4 ml containing 2 mg/ml Blue dextran 2000, 0·3 mg/ml. Vitamin B_{12}.
8. One set of standard dilutions (concentrations given in mg/ml). Blue dextran 2000: 1·0, 0·5, 0·2, 0·1, 0·05, Vitamin B_{12}: 0·2, 0·1, 0·05, 0·025, 0·001.

Experimental details

Prepare the column as described in the Section "Packing the Column". Adjust the flow rate to about 2 ml/min and stabilize the bed. Measure the bed height. Apply 2 ml of the sample solution and elute. Collect approximately 5 ml fractions. Construct an elution diagram as described in Experiment 5. Re-adjust the flow rate to about 6 ml/min and stabilize the bed. Note any change in bed height. Repeat the elution of a new sample.

Results and calculations

Calculate K_{av} and dilution factors for the two components in each experiment.

Conclusions

Observe the zone broadening effect of increasing the flow rate.

EXPERIMENT 9

Choice of sample size.

Apparatus and chemicals (see Experiment 8)

1. Sample solution, 50 ml solution containing 2 mg/ml Blue dextran 2000, 0·3 mg/ml Vitamin B_{12}.

2. Standard dilutions (concentrations in mg/ml): Blue dextran 2000, 2·0, 1·0, 0·5, 0·2, 0·1; Vitamin B_{12}, 0·3, 0·2, 0·1, 0·05, 0·025.

Experimental details

The column prepared in Experiment 8 can be used in this experiment with the flow rate adjusted to about 1·5 ml/min. Apply a sample with a volume of 35–40% of the total column volume. Collect fractions and construct an elution diagram.

Calculations and results

Calculate the K_{av} values for Vitamin B_{12} using the point of inflexion on the front of the peak as the elution volume. Calculate the dilution factors for both Blue dextran 2000 and Vitamin B_{12}. Compare these results with those obtained under similar conditions with a 2 ml sample (Experiment 8).

Sample results are given in Fig. 17 and Table XIII.

Conclusions

In Experiment 8 it can be seen that there is a large separation volume (difference in elution volumes) between Blue dextran and the Vitamin B_{12}.

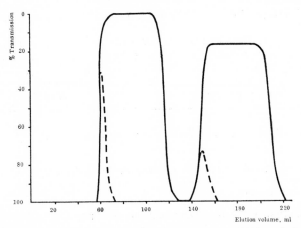

FIG. 17. Elution of 50 ml and 2 ml samples of Blue dextran 2000 and vitamin B_{12} from Sephadex G-50 Fine.

TABLE XIII

Experimental data and results of Experiment 9

Title	*Choice of Sample Size*		Expt. No. *9*
			Date *6.12.68*
			Name *J. M. Curling*

Gel type	Lot No.	Water regain	Weight
Sephadex G-50 Fine	*5556*	$W_r = 5 \cdot 0 \pm 0 \cdot 3$ ml/g	*15* g

Column type	Int. diameter	Bed height	Bed volume
K 25/45	*2·5* cm	*31·5* cm	$V_t = 155$ ml

Sample applicator	Flow adaptor	Other bed surface
No	Upper	*None*

Eluant	Gradient
0·9% NaCl	*None*

Flow rate	*1·32* ml/min	Flow direction	Flow control
	16 ml/cm² h	*Downward*	*Hydrostatic Pressure*

Sample composition				Sample volume*
Component	I	*Blue dextran 2000*	*2* mg/ml	*2 and 50* ml
	II	*Vitamin B₁₂*	*0·3* mg/ml	
	III		mg/ml	
	IV		mg/ml	
	V		mg/ml	

Sample application			
Drained bed surface	*No*	Flow adaptor *Yes*	Under eluant *No*

Fractions	Time interval	Volume	Fraction collector
	5 min	*6·6* ml	*Automatic*

Monitor	Type	Paper speed
	Uvicord	*60 mm/h*

Detection
  Uvicord, visual, comparison of fractions with standard dilutions

Notes
  * *Elution curves for 2 and 50 ml samples should be obtained and plotted on the same diagram.*

Results and Calculations	Expt. No. *9*

Void vol.=Elution vol. of Blue Dextran 2000=*60·5* ml	$V_0 = 60 \cdot 5$ ml
	$V_t = 155$ ml
	$V_t - V_0 = 94 \cdot 5$ ml

Fraction No.	Component concentration		Elution volumes (ml)
9	<0·05 ⎤		I 60·5
10	0·2 ⎥		II 145
11	0·5 ⎬ Blue dextran 2000		
12	<0·05 ⎦		
22	<0·001 ⎤		
23	0·025 ⎥		
24	0·05 ⎬ Vitamin B$_{12}$		
25	0·025 ⎥		
26	<0·001 ⎦		

V_e (ml)	V_e–V_o (ml)	V_e–V_o/V_t–V_o	K_{av} values
I 60·5	60·5–60·5	0	I 0
II 145	145–60·5	84·5/94·5	II 0·9

Notes

Components were eluted as follows when a 50 ml sample was applied.
Blue dextran: fraction 9, 0·2 mg/ml; fractions 10–17, 2 mg/ml, fraction 18, 1 mg/ml.
Vitamin B$_{12}$: fraction 24, 0·001 mg/ml; fraction 25, 0·1 mg/ml, fractions 27–33,
0·3 mg/ml; fraction 34, 0·1 mg/ml.

From the present experiment it can be seen that it is possible to separate a considerably larger sample. The separation of a low molecular weight substance from a substance excluded from the gel is commonly known as desalting. In desalting operations the column is most efficient when a sample of at least 30% of V_t is used. On the other hand if substances are to be fractionated (e.g. serum fractionation, see Experiment 16) a sample volume of about 2% of V_t is more suitable.

EXPERIMENTS ILLUSTRATING DESALTING, FRACTIONATION AND
MOLECULAR WEIGHT DETERMINATION

EXPERIMENT 10

Calibration of a column for molecular weight determination.

Apparatus and chemicals

1. Chromatographic column, 2·5 cm i.d. × 45 cm.
2. Mariotte flask, 300 ml.
3. Pipette, 2 ml.

4. Sephadex G-200 Superfine, 7 g in 300 ml NaCl solution.

5. NaCl solution, 9 g/litre.

6. Sample solution, (i) 2 ml Blue dextran 2000 (2 mg/ml), (ii) 2 ml containing 5 mg/ml of each of the following proteins: ribonuclease A, trypsin, ovalbumin, bovine serum albumin.

7. Uvicord or other similar continuous recording instrument, otherwise a spectrophotometer.

Experimental details

Pack the column under a hydrostatic pressure of no more than 10–15 cm H_2O and allow equilibration to proceed overnight, with the column connected to the Uvicord. Flow rate should be 0·15–0·2 ml/min. Apply the Blue dextran solution noting the point of sample application and elute. After the void volume determination apply the mixture of proteins and elute overnight. If it is necessary to collect fractions to measure the proteins with a spectrophotometer collect fractions about every 30 min.

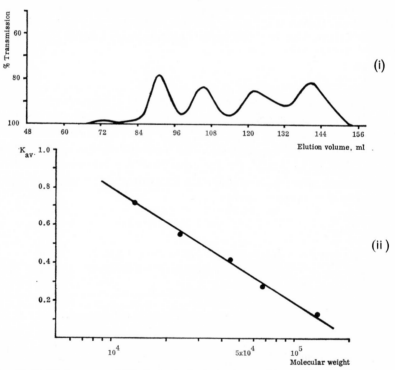

FIG. 18 (i). Elution curve (UV absorption) of proteins used for calibration: in order of elution—bovine serum albumin dimer, bovine serum albumin monomer, ovalbumin, trypsin, ribonuclease A.

FIG. 18 (ii). K_{av} values versus mol. wt. (logarithmic scale) for the calibration proteins.

TABLE XIV

Experimental data and results of Experiment 10

Title *Calibration of a Column for Molecular Weight Determination*			Expt. No. *10* Date *20.1.69* Name *J. M. Curling*

Gel type
  Sephadex G-200
   Superfine
	Lot No.
	6069
		Water regain
		$W_r = 20 \pm 2 \cdot 0$ ml/g
			Weight
			7 g

Column type *K 25/45*	Int. diameter *2·5* cm	Bed height *30* cm	Bed volume $V_t = 147$ ml

Sample applicator
  Yes
	Flow adaptor *None*
	    Upper
		
		Lower
			Other bed surface
			protection *None*

Eluant
  0·9% NaCl
	Gradient
	  None

Flow rate *0·17* ml/min
      2·1 ml/cm^2 h
	Flow direction
	  Downward
		Flow control
		  Hydrostatic
		  Pressure

Sample composition
Component   I   *Ribonuclease A*
         II *Trypsin*
        III *Ovalbumin*
        IV *Bovine serum albumin*
         V
	5 mg/ml
	5 mg/ml
	5 mg/ml
	5 mg/ml
	mg/ml
		Sample volume
		2 ml

Sample application Drained bed surface *Yes*	Flow adaptor *No*	Under eluant *No*

Fractions	Time interval *30* min	Volume *5·1* ml	Fraction collector *Automatic*

Monitor	Type *Uvicord*	Paper speed *20 mm/h*

Detection   *Uvicord only*

Notes

Results and Calculations	Expt. No. *10*

Void vol. = Elution vol. of Blue Dextran 2000 = *49·8* ml	$V_o =$ *49·8* ml $V_t = 147$ ml $V_t - V_o =$ *97·2* ml

Fraction No.	Component concentration		Elution volumes (ml)	
		Ribonuclease A	I	120·0
		Trypsin	II	103·5
		Ovalbumin	III	89·8
		BSA Monomer	IV	77·5
		BSA Dimer	V	61·7

	V_e (ml)	V_e-V_o (ml)	V_e-V_o/V_t-V_o	K_{av} values	
I	120·0	120·0–49·8	70·2/97·2	I	0·72
II	103·5	103·5–49·8	53·7/97·2	II	0·55
III	89·8	89·8–49·8	40·0/97·2	III	0·41
IV	77·5	77·5–49·8	27·7/97·2	IV	0·27
V	61·7	61·7–49·8	11·9/97·2	V	0·12

Notes

Molecular weights

Ribonuclease A	13 600
Trypsin	24 000
Ovalbumin	45 000
BSA Monomer	67 000
BSA Dimer	134 000

Results and calculations

From the Blue dextran run calculate the void volume of the column. Measure the elution volumes of the proteins. Observe that the serum albumin is eluted in two peaks corresponding to the dimer (mol. wt. = 134 000) and the monomer (mol. wt. = 67 000) .The other proteins have the following mol. wts: ovalbumin 45 000, trypsin 24 000, ribonuclease A 13 600. Calculate K_{av} values for the proteins and plot K_{av} (y-axis) against molecular weight on a logarithmic scale. Note that the curve obtained is a straight line and that all the proteins lie within the fractionation range of the gel. Sample results and calculations are in Fig. 18 (i), (ii) and Table XIV.

Conclusion

The column can be used for molecular weight determination within the molecular weight range 13 600 to 134 000.

EXPERIMENT 11

Molecular weight determination of egg albumin.

Apparatus and chemicals (see Experiment 10)

Sample solution: separate the white of an egg from the yolk. Dilute one volume of egg white with five volumes of the sodium chloride solution and filter.

Experimental details

Use the column prepared in Experiment 10 under exactly the same conditions. Apply a 2 ml sample of the egg white and elute. Collect 30 min fractions if necessary.

Results and calculations

Measure the elution volume of egg albumin and calculate its K_{av} value. Deduce the molecular weight of egg albumin from the graph.

Conclusion

Compare the molecular weight of the egg albumin with that of the commercial ovalbumin preparation.

EXPERIMENT 12

Molecular weight determination of horseradish peroxidase.

Apparatus and chemicals (see Experiment 10)

Sample solution: prepare the enzyme extract as follows.

Cut away the cortex from a small, fresh horseradish root: cut about 1 g of shavings from the root down as far as the woody central part. Grind the shavings in approximately 10 ml of sodium chloride solution (9 g/litre) and either centrifuge or filter to obtain a clear extract.

Experimental details

Use the column prepared in Experiment 10 under exactly the same conditions. Apply a 2 ml sample of the peroxidase extract and elute. Collect 30 min fractions. Determine the position of the enzyme activity and hence the elution volume of peroxidase with the reagent described below.

Prepare a pyrogallol-hydrogen peroxide reagent immediately before use as follows: weigh 0·25 g pyrogallol into a 100 ml graduated flask and dissolve in about 70ml 0·01M phosphate buffer, pH 7·0. Add 1 ml of 30% hydrogen peroxide and make up to 100 ml with buffer. Add a few drops to each fraction. Observe the colour reaction given by the enzyme within 5 min of the addition of the reagent.

Results and calculations

Deduce the molecular weight of peroxidase from the graph obtained in Experiment 10.

Conclusion

Compare the molecular weight of peroxidase obtained by gel filtration with values given in the literature.

EXPERIMENT 13

Desalting a protein solution.

Apparatus and chemicals

1. Chromatographic column, 2·5 cm i.d. × 45 cm.
2. Mariotte flask, 300 ml.
3. Pipette, 50 ml.
4. Sephadex G-25 Fine, 35 g in 300 ml NaCl solution.
5. NaCl solution, 9 g/litre.
6. Sample solution, 50 ml haemolysate containing 0·5 mg/ml potassium chromate.

Prepare the haemolysate as follows:
Ten ml citrated blood (or blood containing an anti-coagulant) is centrifuged for 50 min in a refrigerated centrifuge at 9000 revs/min. Plasma is discarded and the red blood cells washed 3 times with physiological saline, centrifuging at each step. Fifty ml distilled water is added after the last washing and the solution frozen overnight to complete cell lysis. The haemolysate is thawed and recentrifuged to obtain a clear solution. Filtration with "Celite analytical filter aid" may be necessary to obtain a perfectly clear solution.

Experimental details

Prepare the column as described in the Section "Packing the Column". Adjust the flow rate to about 2 ml/min and allow the bed to stabilize. The bed volume should be about 150 ml. Apply a sample equal in volume to at least one third of the bed volume.

Results

Observe that the haemoglobin is completely separated from the potassium chromate. Sample results are given in Table XV and Fig. 19.

Conclusion

This is a model system for desalting since the haemoglobin is eluted in the void volume ($K_{av} = 0$) and the potassium chromate has a K_{av} value = 1.

TABLE XV

Experimental data for Experiment 13

Title *Desalting a Protein Solution*	Expt. No. *13* Date *12.11.68* Name *J. M. Curling*

Gel type
    Sephadex G-25
	Lot No.
	    2300
		Water regain
		$W_r = 2 \cdot 5 \pm 0 \cdot 2$ ml/g
			Weight
			    35 g

Column type
    K 25/45
	Int. diameter
	    2·5 cm
		Bed height
		    30 cm
			Bed volume
			    $V_t = 147$ ml

Sample applicator
    None
	Flow adaptor *Yes*
	    Upper
		Other bed surface
		    protection *None*

Eluant
    0·9% NaCl
	Gradient
	    None

Flow rate   *1·8* ml/min
    21·6 ml/cm² h
	Flow direction
	    Downward
		Flow control
		    *Hydrostatic
		    Pressure*

Sample composition
Component   I   *Haemolysate containing
    0·5 mg/ml potassium
    chromate*
	Sample volume
	    50 ml

Sample application Drained bed surface *No*	Flow adaptor *Yes*	Under eluant *No*

Fractions
    None
	Time interval
	    min
		Volume
		    ml
			Fraction collector

Monitor	Type
	    Uvicord
		Paper speed
		    60 mm/h

Detection
    Uvicord and Visual

Notes
    N.B. Sample volume $\simeq V_{t/3}$. Results shown as Uvicord curve.

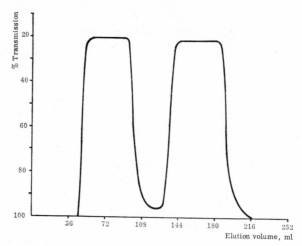

FIG. 19. Elution of haemoglobin (haemolysate) containing potassium chromate demonstrating optimum sample size for desalting.

EXPERIMENT 14

Separation of a monomer from a polymer on Sephadex G-25 Fine.

Apparatus and chemicals (see Experiment 13)

Sample solution, 3 ml containing 5 mg/ml starch and 5 mg/ml glucose.

Experimental details (see Experiment 13)

Collect fractions (approximately 10 ml) until a volume equal to the total volume of the column has been eluted. Divide each fraction into two parts. Test for the presence of starch in one series with iodine solution, 10 g/litre in KI (100 g/litre). Test for the presence of glucose with Fehling's solution in the other set of fractions.

Results and calculations

Calculate K_{av} for each component. Calculate the separation volume. Sample results are given in Table XVI.

Conclusion

The polyglucose, starch, which contains amylose (250–300 glucose units) and amylopectin (over 1000 glucose units) are well separated from each other on Sephadex G-25. The sample volume can be raised considerably, thus reducing the separation volume to a minimum.

TABLE XVI

Experimental data and results for Experiment 14

Title	*Separation of a Monomer from a Polymer on Sephadex G-25 Fine*		Expt. No. *14* Date *15.1.68* Name *J. M. Curling*

Gel type *Sephadex G-25 Fine*	Lot No. *2300*	Water regain $W_r = 2 \cdot 5 \pm 0 \cdot 2$ ml/g	Weight *35* g

Column type *K 25/45*	Int. diameter *2·5* cm	Bed height *30 cm*	Bed volume $V_t = 147$ ml

Sample applicator *Yes*	Flow adaptor *None* Upper	Lower	Other bed surface protection *None*

Eluant *0·9% NaCl s*		Gradient *None*	

Flow rate	1 ml/min *12·3* ml/cm² h	Flow direction *Downward*	Flow control *Hydrostatic Pressure*

Sample composition

Component	I	*Starch*	*5* mg/ml	Sample volume
	II	*Glucose*	*5* mg/ml	*2* ml
	III		mg/ml	
	IV		mg/ml	
	V		mg/ml	

Sample application Drained bed surface *Yes*	Flow adaptor *No*	Under eluant *No*

Fractions	Time interval *10* min	Volume *10* ml	Fraction collector *Automatic*

Monitor *None*	Type	Paper speed	

Detection
   Starch: *1% Iodine in 10% potassium iodide. Glucose: Fehling's solution or Clinistix®*

Notes
   Divide each fraction into two parts. Test one part for starch, the other for glucose.
   Starch found present in fractions 7 and 8 $(K_{av} = 0)$
   Glucose found present in fractions 14 and 15 $(K_{av} = 1)$

Desalting skim milk.

Milk contains both high and low molecular weight substances. The high molecular weight compounds, casein, lactalbumin, etc., can be separated from the low molecular weight salts and lactose on Sephadex.

Apparatus and chemicals (see Experiment 13)

Sample, skim milk, 50 ml.

Experimental details (see Experiments 13 and 14)

Test for the presence of lactose as described for glucose in Experiment 14. The casein fraction is easily seen. Test for chloride with $AgNO_3$ solution (10 g/litre).

Results

The yellow coloured fractions which follow the turbid casein fractions contain riboflavin. Salt and lactose are eluted together in the same fractions.

PREPARATION OF SERUM

Experiments 3, 16, 17, 21 require blood serum.

Allow 500 ml freshly collected blood (without added anti-coagulant) to stand at room temperature for 2–3 h and then overnight in a refrigerator. Carefully decant the serum and centrifuge if necessary to obtain a clear gold serum free from red blood cells. Keep the serum for Experiments 3, 16, 17, 21.

EXPERIMENT 16

Fractionation of bovine serum on Sephadex G-200 Superfine.

This experiment can be combined with immunoelectrophoresis or simply agarose gel electrophoresis for identification of separated serum proteins.

Apparatus, chemicals and some experimental details are given in Experiment 3. If the serum is to be labelled with fluorescein isothiocyanate adopt the following procedure.

Dilute 1 ml serum to 3 ml with physiological saline and adjust the pH to 9 with 0·5M (20 g/litre) NaOH. Add 20 mg fluorescein isothiocyanate and allow the reaction to proceed overnight with constant, gentle stirring.

If unlabelled serum is used, dilute the serum 1 : 1 with the NaCl solution.

Experimental details

Connect the column to a Uvicord, if available, and apply the sample. Collect approximately 10 ml fractions. If possible carry out electrophoresis on the fractions to identify the serum proteins.

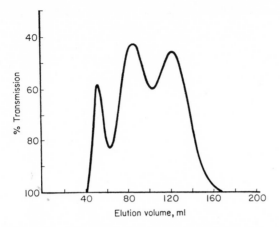

Fɪɢ. 20. Typical elution diagram of normal bovine serum albumin on Sephadex G-200

Results

The first peak contains macroglobulins (19S) the second γ-globulins (7S) and the third albumin.

A typical serum fractionation is shown in Fig. 20. Compare this curve with curves obtained using pathological sera (see, for instance Müller, H. E., 1968, *Med. Klin.*, **63**, 125–128).

EXPERIMENT 17*

Fractionation of bovine serum by thin-layer gel chromatography.

Apparatus and chemicals

The apparatus has been described in the Section "Apparatus for thin-layer gel chromatography" and consists simply of a thin-layer chamber, a glass plate, spreader, Whatman 3 MM filter paper (for wicks and replica). Sephadex G-200 Superfine, 1 g, is also required and sample solution, FITC labelled bovine serum. NaCl solution, 9 g/litre.

Any of the sample application techniques can be used but in this experiment it is probably better to use the microscope slide technique since it is easier to measure the migration distances of the separated zones (Fig. 21).

* This experiment can be combined with either Experiment 18 or 19 if FITC labelled serum is used since the coloured serum proteins can be used as markers in thin-layer gel chromatography.

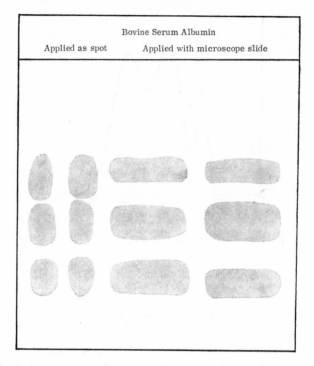

FIG. 21. Diagram showing positions of serum proteins on the thin-layer chromatogram.

Experimental details

These are given, in general, in the Section "Experimental technique in thin-layer gel chromatography". Having equilibrated the thin-layer plate apply two or three samples and start the elution. Stop the elution when three distinct zones are visible (3–4 h), otherwise stop the elution after 4 h. Take care to note the position of the starting line. Take a paper replica of the plate and stain as described in the Section "Identification of Proteins on the Chromatogram".

Calculations and results

Measure the distances from the starting line to the centre of each zone. Plot the inverse of the migration distances against the molecular weights of the proteins on a logarithmic scale. The mol. wts are: albumin = 67 000, γ-globulin = 169 000; macroglobulin is eluted in the "void volume"—i.e. with the "solvent front".

EXPERIMENT 18

Molecular weight determination of egg albumin (ovalbumin) by thin-layer gel chromatography.

Apparatus and chemicals (apparatus see Experiment 17)

   1. Sephadex G-150 Superfine, 1 g in NaCl solution (9 g/litre).

   2. Sample substances:

Fluorescein-labelled serum

Ribonuclease A (20 mg/ml) mol. wt. = 13 600

Soybean trypsin inhibitor (20 mg/ml) mol. wt. = 21 500

Bovine serum albumin (30 mg/ml) mol. wt. = 67 000 (monomer) 134 000 (dimer)

Ovalbumin (commercial preparation) (20 mg/ml) mol. wt. = 45 000

Egg white diluted 1 : 5 with NaCl solution—MW unknown.

Experimental details (see the Section "Apparatus for thin-layer gel chromatography" and Experiment 17)

Apply the samples as spots: volume should be about 5 μl. Start the elution and stop the experiment when the FITC-serum has separated into three zones. Prepare a paper replica of the chromatogram.

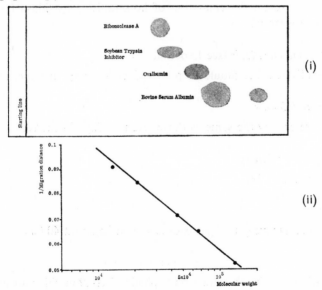

FIG. 22. Diagram showing a typical chromatogram of calibration proteins on Sephadex G-150 Superfine.

Results and calculations

Plot the inverse of the migration distances of the reference proteins against their molecular weights (logarithmic scale) and deduce the molecular weight of the main component of egg white from the graph. (Table XVII and Fig. 22.)

Conclusion

The molecular weight of ovalbumin should be about 45 000, i.e. in agreement with the value of the commercial preparation.

TABLE XVII

Experimental data and results of Experiment 18

Substance	Volume	Sample Con-centration	Migration distance (cm)	^{1}/Migration distance	Molecular weight
Ribonuclease A	5 μl	20 mg/ml	11·0	0·091	13 600
Soybean trypsin inhibitor	5 μl	20 mg/ml	11·8	0·085	21 500
Ovalbumin	5 μl	20 mg/ml	14·0	0·072	45 000
Bovine serum albumin	5 μl	40 mg/ml			
(Monomer)	—	—	15·4	0·065	67 000
(Dimer)	—	—	19·1	0·052	134 000

EXPERIMENT 19

Molecular weight determination of horseradish peroxidase by thin-layer gel chromatography.

Apparatus and chemicals (see Experiment 18)

Horseradish extract should be prepared as described in Experiment 12.

Experimental details

These are exactly the same as those given in Experiment 18.

Results and calculations

See Experiment 18.

Conclusion

The molecular weight of peroxidase should be about 40 000

EXPERIMENT 20

Separation of spinach extract on Sephadex LH-20 in chloroform.

Apparatus and chemicals

1. Chromatographic column 2·5 cm i.d. × 45 cm, solvent resistant, fitted with flow adaptors and P.T.F.E. capillary tubing.
2. 2 conical flasks, 300 ml.
3. 2 measuring cylinders, 5 ml.

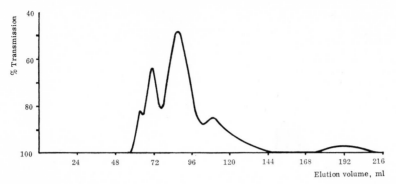

FIG. 23. Typical elution pattern of spinach extract (chloroform) run on Sephadex LH-20.

4. Sephadex LH-20, 35 g in 300 ml chloroform.
5. Chloroform, 1 litre.
6. Sample solution, chloroform extract of spinach leaves, 5 ml.

Experimental details

Pack the column as described in the Section "Packing Sephadex LH-20 in Chloroform" and allow the bed to stabilize under a flow rate of about 1 ml/min. Either upward or downward flow can be used. Apply the sample using the following technique. Close the column outlet and transfer the tubing from the chloroform reservoir to the measuring cylinder containing the sample. Open the column outlet and collect 3 ml of column effluent. Close the column outlet and transfer the tubing from the measuring cylinder back to the chloroform reservoir. Elute the sample.

Results

Observe that the spinach extract is fractionated into five components. Five coloured zones—light brown-green, emerald green, bright yellow, light yellow and light green—can be seen on the column. The components have not been identified with certainty but are no doubt chlorophyll a and b, xanthophyll and other carotenoids.

A typical separation (Uvicord diagram) is shown in Fig. 23.

EXPERIMENT 21

Ion-exchange chromatography: fractionation of serum proteins.

Apparatus and chemicals

1. Chromatographic column 1·5 cm i.d. × 30 cm.
2. Gradient apparatus* to hold 200 ml in each reservoir.

* The most simple arrangement is to use two 250 ml beakers connected by a piece of plastic tubing. The mixing reservoir can be stirred either magnetically or with a motor stirrer.

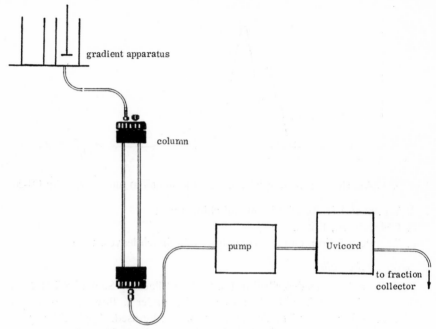

FIG. 24. Set-up for ion-exchange chromatography.

3. Peristaltic pump, flow adjusted to 0·2 ml/min.

4. QAE-Sephadex A-50, 0·8 g in Buffer A.

5. Sephadex G-25 Coarse, 0·2 g in Buffer A.

6. Buffer A: 0·1M Tris-HCl, pH 6·5, 500 ml.

7. Buffer B: Buffer A containing 1M NaCl, 250 ml. (0·1M Tris buffer contains 12·1 g/litre Tris).

8. Serum, diluted 1 : 1 with Buffer A, 3 ml.

9. Uvicord or similar.

10. Fraction collector, automatic (if fractions required).

11. Apparatus for agarose gel electrophoresis (optional) (example references are given at the end of this experiment).

Experimental details

Pack the ion-exchanger under an operating pressure of 30 cm water. When the ion-exchanger has packed completely, layer 0·5–1 cm of Sephadex G-25 Coarse on to the top of the bed to act as a bed surface protection. This is done most easily with eluant above the bed surface. Pipette the Sephadex G-25 on to the bed using a glass tube. Connect the top of column to a reservoir

TABLE XVIII

Experimental data and results of Experiment 21

Title	*Separation of Serum Proteins by Ion-exchange Chromatography*	Expt. No. *21* Date *15.5.69* Name *J. M. Curling*

Gel type *QAE-Sephadex A-50*		Weight *0·7* g

Column type *K 15/30*	Int. diameter *1·5* cm	Bed height *25·5→18·4* cm

Sample applicator *None*	Flow adaptor *None* Upper Lower	Other bed surface protection *Sephadex G-25 Coarse*

Eluant *0·1M Tris-HCl, pH 6·5, 0·1M Tris-HCl, pH 6·5+1M NoCl*	Gradient *NaCl, 0–0·5M*

Flow rate *0·2* ml/min *6·8* ml/cm² h	Flow direction *Downward*	Flow control *Pump*

Sample composition Component I *3% w/v Freeze dried serum* II *(Bovine)* III IV V	mg/ml mg/ml mg/ml mg/ml mg/ml	Sample volume *4* ml

Sample application Drained bed surface *Yes*	Flow adaptor *No*	Under eluant *No*

Fractions	Time interval *30* min	Volume *6* ml	Fraction collector *Automatic*

Monitor	Type *Uvicord*	Paper speed *20 mm/h*

Detection
Uvicord and agarose gel electrophoresis

Notes
Bed packed under 30 cm hydrostatic pressure.
Gradient elution carried out with 200 ml of each buffer in each reservoir. Only 200 ml needed for complete elution.

x

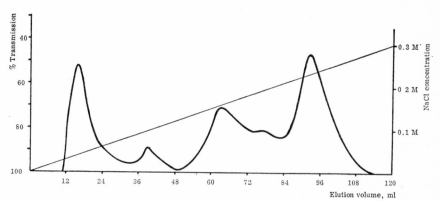

FIG. 25. Separation of serum proteins on QAE-Sephadex A-50 using a continuous ionic strength gradient.

containing Buffer A and the column outlet to a pump and then to a Uvicord (or similar). Allow the column to run overnight at a flow rate of 0·2 ml/min so that it becomes properly equilibrated. After equilibration connect the top of the column to a gradient apparatus as shown in Fig. 24. Apply the sample and elute. Collect approximately 10 ml fractions if further experiments are to be carried out on the separated proteins.

Results

At pH 6·5 (the pH of the buffer used) all the serum proteins except γ-globulin are bound to the ion-exchanger. γ-globulin is therefore eluted as soon as elution is started. The remaining serum proteins are eluted with increasing salt concentration in the same order as they appear in gel electrophoresis. Thus the next major peak contains β-lipoprotein, etc. and the last major peak contains albumin.

The proteins can be identified by agarose gel electrophoresis of the fractions. Fractions should first be concentrated (using for instance Sephadex G-25 Coarse). Sample results are given in Table XVIII and Fig. 25.

SAMPLE REFERENCES ON AGAROSE GEL ELECTROPHORESIS

Brishammar, S., Hjertén, S. and v. Hofsten, B. (1961). Immunological Precipitates in Agarose Gels. *Biochim. biophys. Acta*, **53**, 518.
Grabar, P. and Williams, Jr., C. A. (1953).*Biochim. biophys. Acta*, **10**, 193.
Wieme, R. J. (1959). "Studies on Agar Gel Electrophoresis." Arscia Uitgaren N.V., Brussels.

REFERENCES FOR FURTHER READING

METHODOLOGY OF GEL CHROMATOGRAPHY

Determann, H. (1968). "Gel Chromatography." Springer-Verlag, Berlin, Heidelberg, New York (English and German Editions available).
Fischer L. (1969). "An Introduction to Gel Chromatography." *In* "Laboratory Techniques in Biochemistry and Molecular Biology". (T. S. Work and E. Work eds). North-Holland Publishing Company, Amsterdam, London.

METHODOLOGY OF CHROMATOGRAPHY

Giddings, J. C. (1965) "Dynamics of Chromatography, Part 1 Principles and Theory." Marcel Dekker Inc., New York.
Heftmann, E. (ed.) (1967). "Chromatography." Reinhold Publishing Corporation, New York.
Stock, R. and Rice, C. B. F. (1967). "Chromatographic Methods." Chapman and Hall, London, England.

Data has also been taken from the special publications on gel chromatography of Pharmacia Fine Chemicals: a complete list is available on request. The very many references to the theory, methodology and applications of Sephadex have been selectively compiled and are available from Pharmacia Fine Chemicals as a "Literature Reference List 1959–1968" and Supplements.

ACKNOWLEDGEMENTS

I wish to thank Mr. A. Domicelj for his invaluable assistance in testing many of the experiments, Dr. G. Lüben for reading the manuscript and Mrs. M. Eriksson for patiently typing it.

APPENDIX

List of suppliers whose products were used in the preparation of this paper.

Chromatographic columns K 15/30, K 25/45, SR 25/45, Reservoirs R 25 and R 15, Sephadex G types, Sephadex LH-20, Sephadex Ion exchangers, and Dextran fractions were from Pharmacia Fine Chemicals AB, Uppsala, Sweden. These products are available from the Head Office in Uppsala or through any of the following subsidiaries or representatives:

ARGENTINA
Sanico S. A.
Casilla Correo No. 90
Sucursal 13
Buenos Aires

AUSTRALIA
Watson Victor Ltd.
95-99 Epping Road
North Ryde, N.S.W. 2113

AUSTRIA
Unilabor Ges. m.b.H.
Schliessfach 33
Rummelhardtgasse 6
A-1095 Wien IX

BELGIUM
N. V. Société Belge d'Optique
et d'Instruments de
Précision S. A.
Meersstraat, 108, Gent

BRAZIL
Intéc Ltda.
Av. 13 de Maio, 23–3°
Rio de Janeiro

CANADA
Pharmacia (Canada) Ltd.
110 Place Crémazie,
Suite 412
Montreal 351, Quebec

CHILE
Fred Muller S. A. C.
Agustinas 1350
P.O. Box 3894
Santiago

DENMARK
Meda A/S
H. C. Ørsteds Vej 22 C
1879 København V

EIRE
Moloney Bros. Ltd.
"Victoria House"
Beaumont Avenue
Churchtown
Dublin, 14

FINLAND
G. W. Berg & Co.
Fabiansgatan 14
Helsinki 13

FRANCE
Jarre-Jacquin
Recherches et Laboratoires
18, Rue Pierre Curie
75 Paris (V^e)

GERMANY
Deutsche Pharmacia
G.m.b.H.
6 Frankfurt am Main 50
Kurhessenstr. 95

GREAT BRITAIN
Pharmacia (G.B.) Ltd.
Paramount House
75 Uxbridge Road
Ealing, London W.5

GREECE
P. Bacacos S.A.
Omonia Square
Athens (101)

ITALY
Prodotti Gianni S.R.L.
Via Mecenate 30/14
I 20138 Milano

JAPAN
Kjellberg Kabushiki Kaisha
P.O. Box Central No. 12
Tokyo

MEXICO
Internacional Cientifica, S.A.
Angel del Campo 17-A
Mexico 8, D.F.

THE NETHERLANDS
Van Oortmerssen N.V.
De Ruyterstraat 48–50
Den Haag

NEW ZEALAND
Watson Victor Ltd.
4 Adelaide Road
Wellington

NORWAY
Nerliens Kemisk-Tekniske
A/S
Tollbugaten 32
Oslo 1

SOUTH AFRICA
Protea Physical and Nuclear
Instrumentation (Pty.) Ltd.
P.O. Box 7793
Johannesburg

SPAIN
Giralt S.A.
Capitan Haya, 76
Madrid 20

SWITZERLAND
Instrumenten-Gesellschaft
AG, Turbinenstrasse 31 a
8005 Zürich

TURKEY
Dr. Kimyager I. Yanço
Sadikiye Han No. 19
Bahçekapi-Istanbul

UNITED STATES
Pharmacia Fine Chemicals
Inc.
800 Centennial Avenue
Piscataway, N.J. 08854

U.V. Analyser: Uvicord I with Recorder 6520 A, LKB-Produkter, S-161 25 Bromma 1, Sweden.

Fraction Collector: Type FR3 and Peristaltic pump SP1, Stålprodukter, P.O. Box 12036, S-750 12 Uppsala, Sweden.

Proteins: Serva Entwicklungslabor, Heidelberg, Germany; Worthington Biochemical Corporation, Freehold, New Jersey, U.S.A.; Sigma Chemical Company, 3500 DeKalb St., St. Louis, Mo. 63118, U.S.A.

Fluorescein isothiocyanate, protein stains: Fluka AG, Chemische Fabrik, CH-9470 Buchs, Switzerland; BDH Chemicals Ltd., Poole, Dorset, England.

Author Index

Numbers in italics refer to pages in the References at the end of each article.

x§

Subject Index

A

Acetylcholine, 341
  bioassay, leech muscle, 344–50
Active transport, 89–90
Activities, phosphotransferases, measurement, 4–15
Aedes aegypti, trehalose, 376
Agria affinis, blood glucose, 376
Aldosterone, effect on toad bladder, 129–32
Alkaline phosphatase, multiple forms, 24
Alternating current, and insect cuticle, 199–203
Amino acids
  glycine in CNS, 31–8
  spinal cord, 47
Aminophylline, effect on frog skin, 104–11
Ampere, definition, 50
Amphibians, respiratory and circulatory systems, 233–93
  circulation, 255–85
  larvae and young, 285–6
  respiration, 234–55
  role of nervous system, 279–85
Amphotericin B, effect on toad bladder, 126–9
Anaerobiosis, turtle bladder, 147–9
Anaesthetics
  for amphibia, 233
  dialysis, 331
Analysis, base ratio, of RNA, 333–40
Annelida, phosphotransferases, 1, 3, 8
Anthrone spray, 390
Antidiuretic hormone, 124
Aphrodite aculeata, phosphotransferases, 8
Arachnida, phosphotransferases, 3
Arginine kinase, 1
Arginine phosphotransferase, 1, 2, 3, 5, 12, 14, 15, 20, 28, 29
Arthropoda, phosphotransferases, 3
Asterias rubens, phosphotransferases, 8
Asteroidea, phosphotransferases, 3

ATP/Magnesium sulphate solution, preparation, 6
ATPase activity
  assay, 12
  starch gel electrophoresis, 28
Axon, giant, membrane resting potential, 179

B

Base ratio analysis, small samples RNA, 333–40
Bioassay of acetylcholine, leech muscle, 344–50
Biuret reagent, 7, 10–11
Bladder, urinary, *see* toad, turtle
Blatta orientalis, phosphotransferases, 8
Blood
  carbohydrates, blowfly larva, 376–95, 401
  flow, amphibians, 263–9
    direct measurement, 267–9
    through heart, 263–7
  flowmeter, calibration, 288–93
    dynamic, 289–93
    static, 288–9
  gas and chemistry, dog, 329
  gas tensions and volumes, amphibians, 270–1
  glycine estimation, 31, 32
  pressure, amphibians, 256–62
    heart and central vessels, 260–1
    microcirculation, 262
    peripheral vessels, 261–2
  volume, amphibians, 271–9
    plasma, 272–6
    red cell, 276–9
Blowfly
  cuticle electrical measurements, 181
  glycogen changes, metamorphosis, 395–402
  lipid, fat body, 402–15
  maintaining a stock, 365–75
  non-glycogen carbohydrates, 376–95
Brain, glycine estimation, 32–8

Cumulative Contents